INTERNATIONAL ATOMIC WEIGHTS. 1955

NAME	SYM-BOL	ATOMIC NUMBER	ATOMIC WEIGHT*	NAME	SYM-BOL	ATOMIC NUMBER	ATOMIC WEIGHT*
Actinium	Ac	89	227	Mendelevium	Mv	101	[256]
Aluminum	Al	13	26.98	Mercury	Hg	80	200.61
Americium	Am	95	[243]	Molybdenum	Mo	42	95.95
Antimony	Sb	51	121.76	Neodymium	Nd	60	144.27
Argon	A	18	39.944	Neon	Ne	10	20.183
Arsenic	As	33	74.91	Neptunium	Np	93	[237]
Astatine	At	85	[210]	Nickel	Ni	28	58.71
Barium	Ba	56	137.36	Niobium	Nb	41	92.91
Berkelium	Bk	97	[249]	Nitrogen	N	7	14.008
Beryllium	Be	4	9.013	Osmium	Os	76	190.2
Bismuth	Bi	83	209.00	Oxygen	O	8	16.0000
Boron	B	5	10.82	Palladium	Pd	46	106.4
Bromine	Br	35	79.916	Phosphorus	P	15	30.975
Cadmium	Cd	48	112.41	Platinum	Pt	78	195.09
Calcium	Ca	20	40.08	Plutonium	Pu	94	[242]
Californium	Cf	98	[249]	Polonium	Po	84	210
Carbon	C	6	12.011	Potassium	K	19	39.100
Cerium	Ce	58	140.13	Praseodymium	Pr	59	140.92
Cesium	Cs	55	132.91	Promethium	Pm	61	[145]
Chlorine	Cl	17	35.457	Protactinium	Pa	91	231
Chromium	Cr	24	52.01	Radium	Ra	88	226.05
Cobalt	Co	27	58.94	Radon	Rn	86	222
Columbium: see Niobium †				Rhenium	Re	75	186.22
Copper	Cu	29	63.54	Rhodium	Rh	45	102.91
Curium	Cm	96	[245]	Rubidium	Rb	37	85.48
Dysprosium	Dy	66	162.51	Ruthenium	Ru	44	101.1
Einsteinium	E	99	[254]	Samarium	Sm	62	150.35
Erbium	Er	68	167.27	Scandium	Sc	21	44.96
Europium	Eu	63	152.0	Selenium	Se	34	78.96
Fermium	Fm	100	[255]	Silicon	Si	14	28.09
Fluorine	F	9	19.00	Silver	Ag	47	107.880
Francium	Fr	87	[223]	Sodium	Na	11	22.991
Gadolinium	Gd	64	157.26	Strontium	Sr	38	87.63
Gallium	Ga	31	69.72	Sulfur	S	16	32.066§
Germanium	Ge	32	72.60	Tantalum	Ta	73	180.95
Gold	Au	79	197.0	Technetium	Tc	43	[99]
Hafnium	Hf	72	178.50	Tellurium	Te	52	127.61
Helium	He	2	4.003	Terbium	Tb	65	158.93
Holmium	Ho	67	164.94	Thallium	Tl	81	204.39
Hydrogen	H	1	1.0080	Thorium	Th	90	232.05
Indium	In	49	114.82	Thulium	Tm	69	168.94
Iodine	I	53	126.91	Tin	Sn	50	118.70
Iridium	Ir	77	192.2	Titanium	Ti	22	47.90
Iron	Fe	26	55.85	Tungsten	W	74	183.86
Krypton	Kr	36	83.80	Uranium	U	92	238.07
Lanthanum	La	57	138.92	Vanadium	V	23	50.95
Lead	Pb	82	207.21	Xenon	Xe	54	131.30
Lithium	Li	3	6.940	Ytterbium	Yb	70	173.04
Lutetium	Lu	71	174.99	Yttrium	Y	39	88.92
Magnesium	Mg	12	24.32	Zinc	Zn	30	65.38
Manganese	Mn	25	54.94	Zirconium	Zr	40	91.22

* A value given in brackets is the mass number of the most stable known isotope.

† The English name of this element has been cha[...] [Inter-] national Union of Pure and Applied Chemistry.

§ Because of natural variations in the relative abund[...] weight of this element has a range of ±0.003.

COLLEGE CHEMISTRY

A Series of Chemistry Texts

LINUS PAULING, EDITOR

COLLEGE CHEMISTRY

An Introductory Textbook
of General Chemistry

SECOND EDITION

by LINUS PAULING

Professor of Chemistry in the California Institute of Technology

Illustrations by ROGER HAYWARD

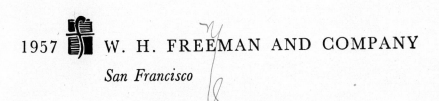
1957 W. H. FREEMAN AND COMPANY

San Francisco

Copyright © *1950, 1955, by Linus Pauling*   *C10*

Library of Congress Catalogue Card Number 55-5436
Printed in the United States of America

TO
DR. THOMAS ADDIS

who in applying science
to medicine
kept always uppermost
his deep sympathy
for mankind

Preface to the Second Edition

In the preparation of the second edition of this book an effort has been made to increase the clarity of the presentation of the subject. The first part of the book has been largely revised in such a way that the facts, concepts, and theories of chemistry are introduced more gradually and more systematically than in the first edition. Some new, rather simple illustrative exercises are given in the text, immediately following the sections that they illustrate. The exercises at the ends of the chapters have also been considerably revised, with elimination of some of the more difficult ones. Answers are given to many of the exercises that involve calculations.

The sequence of chapters has been changed to increase the systematization of the subject. The book has been divided into six parts, and, in order that the student may be helped to keep himself oriented during the year, each part is provided with an introduction, describing the chapters contained within this part and telling why the subjects in these chapters are being taken up at that place in the course.

Part I, which constitutes an introduction to the subject, deals with both descriptive chemistry and elementary chemical theory. Theoretical chemistry is taken up more thoroughly in Part II, Chapters 8 to 12, and Part IV, Chapters 17 to 23. In Part III, Chapters 13 to 16, there is given a discussion of the chemistry of a number of the non-metallic elements, as systematized by theoretical principles; and the nature of metals and alloys, metallurgy, and the chemistry of many metals are discussed in Part V, Chapters 24 to 29. Part VI consists of two chapters on chemical substances related to living organisms and one chapter on nuclear chemistry.

There has been a significant increase in the amount of organic chemistry in the book. In Chapter 7, on carbon and the compounds of carbon, there is a detailed discussion of the paraffin hydrocarbons, hydrocarbons containing double and triple bonds, organic isomers, the chloromethanes, alcohols, ethers, and organic acids, and a brief discussion of the chemical reactions of organic substances. Organic substances are also discussed, together with inorganic substances, in several other chapters of the book, in connection with the theories of chemistry. Chapter 30, Organic Chemistry, and Chapter 31, Biochemistry, deal exclusively with organic substances.

Chapter 3, The Electron and the Nuclei of Atoms, is a new chapter, designed to help the student to understand the electronic theory of molecular structure, upon which modern chemistry is based. In this chapter a non-mathematical account is given of some of the experiments carried out during the period of twenty years commencing about 1895 which led to the discovery of the electron and of the nuclei of atoms and the measurement of the properties of these fundamental particles. The electronic structure of atoms is then discussed in Chapter 5, in connection with the periodic table. Oxidation-reduction reactions and valence are introduced in a simple way in Chapter 6, preliminary to the more detailed discussion of these subjects and of the electronic theory of molecular structure given in Chapters 10, 11, and 12.

Many of my colleagues in the California Institute of Technology and many other teachers of chemistry have given advice during the preparation of this edition, and it is a pleasure for me to express my gratitude to them. I thank especially Professor F. J. Allen, of Purdue University, and Professor Ogden Baine, of Southern Methodist University, for their help.

LINUS PAULING

Pasadena, California
23 March 1955

Preface to the First Edition

The fundamental principles underlying the planning of the present book have been expressed in the preface of my earlier textbook, "General Chemistry, An Introduction to Descriptive Chemistry and Modern Chemical Theory," published three years ago. The first two paragraphs of the Preface of "General Chemistry" summarize these principles:

"Chemistry is a very large subject, which continues to grow, as new elements are discovered or made, new compounds are synthesized, and new principles are formulated. Nevertheless, despite its growth, the science can now be presented to the student more easily and effectively than ever before. In the past the course in general chemistry has necessarily tended to be a patch-work of descriptive chemistry and certain theoretical topics. The progress made in recent decades in the development of unifying theoretical concepts has been so great, however, that the presentation of general chemistry to the students of the present generation can be made in a more simple, straightforward, and logical way than formerly.

"For example, every boy now knows about atoms, and accepts them as part of his world—they are split in the atomic bomb and in the comic papers, they stare at him from advertisements. In this book I begin the teaching of chemistry by discussing the properties of substances in terms of atoms and molecules. The subject is then developed in as orderly a manner as has seemed possible at the present stage of chemical knowledge."

Although "General Chemistry" was written primarily for use by students planning to major in chemistry and related fields, it has been found useful also by students with primary interest in other subjects, including some who have not received instruction in chemistry in high school. Experience has shown, however, that there is need for a book based on the approach of "General Chemistry," but written in a more slowly paced, less mathematical form. The present book, "College

Chemistry," provides this more gradual introduction to modern chemistry. I propose, in the near future, to revise "General Chemistry" in such a way as to make it especially suited to use by first-year college students who plan to major in chemistry and by other well-prepared students with a special interest in the subject.

The present book does not present any change in point of view from the earlier one. Some of the chapters, especially those dealing with elementary theory, have been incorporated with little change. The effort has been made to introduce all new concepts gradually, with satisfactorily thorough discussion and precise definition. The treatment of the more advanced theoretical subjects has been simplified. Use is made of no mathematics but elementary algebra, and instruction is given in the ratio method of solving problems. The treatment of the gas laws has been completely revised, and the chapter devoted to gases has been moved forward. Descriptive chemistry has been introduced more gradually, with more thorough discussion of the chemistry of the common elements, especially hydrogen, oxygen, nitrogen, and carbon. A chapter on biochemistry, a discussion of color photography, and some other new features have been introduced.

In general, new technical words and terms are defined in the text. Use has also been made of some other words with which the student may not be familiar; it may occasionally be necessary for him to find the meaning of one of these words by looking it up in the dictionary. It is my hope that every student who reads the book will benefit by an increase in his general vocabulary as well as in his scientific vocabulary, and also by an increase in the precision and soundness of his thinking about non-scientific questions as well as about scientific questions.

I am indebted for assistance in various ways in the preparation of the book to Dr. Philip A. Shaffer, Jr., Prof. Norman Davidson, Prof. Ernest H. Swift, Prof. F. O. Koenig, Prof. Harper W. Frantz, Prof. Lloyd E. Malm, Mr. Linus Pauling, Jr., Mr. Peter J. Pauling, Dr. Eugene K. Maun, Miss Selina Weinbaum, and especially Mr. Roger Hayward, the illustrator. I also thank Dr. R. W. G. Wyckoff, Dr. D. S. Clark, Dr. S. Kyropoulos, Prof. C. E. Hall, Dr. J. A. Leermakers, the Malleable Founders' Society, and the Griffith Observatory for providing figures. I am further indebted to Prof. L. H. Farinholt, Prof. J. A. Timm, Prof. F. E. Blacet, Prof. J. F. Baxter, and many other teachers of chemistry who have made suggestions of ways in which my earlier book could be improved.

LINUS PAULING

February 28, 1950

Table of Contents

PART ONE

An Introduction to Modern Chemistry

Chemistry is a complex subject, and it is hard for a teacher to find a logical order in which to present it. Chemistry is the investigation and discussion of the properties of substances—of thousands of different substances. A part of chemistry, called *descriptive chemistry*, consists in the tabulation of the properties of substances as observed or as found by experiment. Another part, *theoretical chemistry*, consists in the formulation of principles that systematize and correlate the facts of descriptive chemistry.

Both theoretical chemistry and descriptive chemistry are presented in this book, in a sequence that has been designed to help you to understand the principles and to remember the facts of chemistry.

The book is divided into six parts. Part I, Chapters 1 to 7, constitutes an introduction to modern chemistry. In Chapter 1 some fundamental concepts and definitions relating to kinds of substances are presented. In Chapter 2, on the atomic structure of matter, there is a discussion of the way in which substances are built out of atoms, and the relation between the properties of substances and their atomic structure. The atoms themselves are known to be built of electrons and atomic nuclei; the nature of the electron and of the nuclei of atoms is presented in Chapter 3. The classification of substances into elements and compounds is discussed in Chapter 4. In Chapter 5, on the chemical elements and the periodic law, an important system of classification of the elements is described; and in the following two chapters this system is used as the basis for the discussion of the chemistry of some of the elements.

1

The background of knowledge of chemical facts provided by these chapters will then enable you to embark upon the study of some further aspects of theoretical chemistry, in Part II, Chapters 8 to 12. Part III, Chapters 13 to 16, presents a discussion of the chemistry of a number of additional elements, as systematized by theoretical principles. Part IV consists of seven chapters dealing mainly with theoretical subjects. The nature of metals and alloys and the chemistry of many metals are discussed in Part V, Chapters 24 to 29. Two chapters on the chemical substances related to living organisms and one chapter on nuclear chemistry constitute the concluding section, Part VI.

Chemistry is not something that exists only between the covers of a textbook. It is an important part of man's effort to understand the world in which we live, and to obtain a mastery of natural forces. I hope that, as you continue your study of chemistry, you will find pleasure in having a better understanding of the nature of the world and of the phenomena that take place about you, and that when you come to the end of this book and of your course in chemistry you will feel that the efforts that you have made to master the subject have been justified by the enlargement of your mental horizons.

Chapter 1

Chemistry and Matter

The rapid progress true Science now makes occasions my regretting sometimes that I was born so soon. It is impossible to imagine the heights to which may be carried, in a thousand years, the power of man over matter. O that moral Science were in as fair a way of improvement, that men would cease to be wolves to one another, and that human beings would at length learn what they now improperly call humanity.—

BENJAMIN FRANKLIN,
in a letter to the chemist Joseph Priestley, 8 February 1780.

Why study chemistry? An important reason is indicated in the foregoing statement by Benjamin Franklin—it is through chemistry and her sister sciences that the power of man, of mind, over matter is obtained. Nearly two hundred years ago Franklin said that science was making rapid progress. We know that the rate of progress of science has become continually greater, until now the nature of the world in which we live has been greatly changed, through scientific and technical progress, from that of Franklin's time.

Science plays such an important part in the modern world that no one can now feel that he understands the world in which he lives unless he has an understanding of science.

The science of chemistry deals with *substances*. At this point in the study of chemistry we shall not define the word substance in its scientific sense, but shall assume that you have a general idea of what the word means. Common examples of substances are water, sugar, salt, copper, iron, oxygen—you can think of many others.

A century and a half ago it was discovered by an English chemist, Sir Humphry Davy (1778–1829), that common salt can be separated, by passing electricity through it, into a soft, silvery metal, to which he gave the name sodium, and a greenish-yellow gas, which had been discovered some time earlier, and named chlorine. Chlorine is a corrosive gas, which attacks many metals, and irritates the mucous membranes of the nose and throat if it is inhaled. The discovery that salt is composed of a metal (sodium) and a corrosive gas (chlorine), and that the properties of salt are quite different from those of sodium or chlorine is one of the many surprising facts about the nature of substances that chemists have discovered.

A sodium wire will burn in chlorine, producing salt. The process of combination of sodium and chlorine to form salt is called a *chemical reaction*. Ordinary fire also involves a chemical reaction, the combination of the fuel with oxygen in the air to form the products of combustion. For example, gasoline contains compounds of carbon and hydrogen, and when a mixture of gasoline and air explodes (burns rapidly) in the cylinders of an automobile a chemical reaction takes place, in which the gasoline and the oxygen of the air react to form carbon dioxide and water vapor (plus a small amount of carbon monoxide), and at the same time to release the energy that moves the automobile. Carbon dioxide and carbon monoxide are compounds of carbon and oxygen, and water is a compound of hydrogen and oxygen.

Chemists study substances, in order to learn as much as they can about their properties (their characteristic qualities) and about the reactions that change them into other substances. Knowledge obtained in this way has been found to be extremely valuable. It not only satisfies man's curiosity about himself and about the world in which he lives, but it also can be applied to make the world a better place to live in, to make people happier, by raising their standards of living, ameliorating the suffering due to ill health, and enlarging the sphere of their activities.

Let us consider some of the ways in which a knowledge of chemistry has helped man in the past, and may help him in the future.

It was discovered centuries ago that preparations could be made from certain plants, such as poppies and coca, which, when taken by a human being, serve to deaden pain. From these plants chemists isolated pure substances, morphine and cocaine, which have the pain-deadening property. These substances have, however, an undesirable property, that of inducing a craving for them that sometimes leads to drug addiction. Chemists then investigated morphine and cocaine, to learn their chemical structure, and then made, in the laboratory, a great number of other substances, somewhat similar in structure, and tested these substances for their powers of deadening pain and of producing addiction. In this way some drugs that are far more valuable than the natural ones have been discovered; one example is procaine, a local anesthetic used in minor surgery.

A related story is that of the discovery of general anesthetics. A cen tury and a half ago Davy, as a young man just beginning his scientific career, tested many gases on himself by inhaling them. (He was lucky that he did not kill himself, because one of the gases he inhaled is very poisonous.) He discovered that one gas produced a state of hysteria when inhaled, and that people under the influence of this gas, which was given the name laughing gas, seemed not to suffer pain when they fell down or bumped into an object. It is surprising that this observation did not at once suggest to him that laughing gas might beneficially be used in surgical operations. No one seems to have had this idea, however, and the use of anesthetics was delayed for nearly half a century. Then an investigator in the United States noticed that the chemical substance ether, when inhaled, produces unconsciousness, and another noticed the same effect with chloroform. These substances were soon brought into general use for producing unconsciousness during surgical operations. The discovery of anesthesia was a great discovery, not only because it relieves pain, but also because it permits delicate surgical operations to be carried out that would be impossible if the patients remained conscious.

The rubber industry is one that may be mentioned as an example of a chemical industry. This industry began when it was discovered that raw rubber, a sticky material made from the sap of the rubber tree, could be converted into vulcanized rubber, which has superior properties (greatly increased strength, freedom from stickiness), by mixing it with sulfur and heating it. During recent years artificial materials similar to rubber (called synthetic rubber) have been made, which are in many ways better than natural rubber. The synthetic rubbers are made from petroleum.

The steel industry is another great chemical industry. Steel, which consists mainly of the metal iron, is our most important structural material. It is made from iron ore by a complex chemical process. In the United States the production of steel is carried on at the rate of more than 1000 lbs. per person per year.

Chemistry plays such an important part in the life of twentieth-century man that this age may properly be called the chemical age.

1–1. The Study of Chemistry

Chemistry has two main aspects: **descriptive chemistry**, *the discovery and tabulation of chemical facts;* and **theoretical chemistry**, *the formulation of theories that, upon verification, unify these facts and combine them into a system.**

* The broad field of chemistry may also be divided in other ways. An important division of chemistry is that into the branches *organic chemistry* and *inorganic chemistry*. Organic chemistry is the chemistry of the compounds of carbon, especially those that occur in plants and animals. Inorganic chemistry is the chemistry of the compounds of elements other than carbon. Each of these branches of chemistry is in part descriptive and in part theoretical. Many other

It is not possible to obtain a sound knowledge of chemistry simply by learning theoretical chemistry. Even if a student were to learn all the chemical theory that is known, he would not have a knowledge of the science, because a major part of chemistry (many of the special properties of individual substances) has not yet been well incorporated into chemical theory. It is accordingly necessary for the student to learn a number of the facts of descriptive chemistry simply by memorizing them. The number of these facts that might be memorized is enormous, and increases rapidly year by year, as new discoveries are made. In this book a selection from the more important facts is presented. You should learn some of these facts by studying them, and by frequently referring to them and renewing your knowledge of them. You should also learn as much about chemistry as possible from your own experience in the laboratory and from your observations of chemical substances and chemical reactions in everyday life.

A special effort has been made in this book to present the subject of chemistry in a logical and simple manner, and to correlate descriptive chemistry with the theories of chemistry. It is therefore necessary that the theoretical sections of the book be carefully studied and thoroughly understood. Read each chapter with care. Examine the arguments to be sure that you understand them.

At the beginning of many chapters there is a paragraph telling about the relation of the chapter to the other chapters and to the whole subject of chemistry. At the end, just preceding the problems, there is a list of concepts, facts, and technical terms that will serve as a guide in review of the chapter. Be sure that you understand the new concepts and terms before going on to the next chapter.

1–2. *Matter*

The universe is composed of **matter** *and* **radiant energy.**

The chemist is primarily interested in matter, but he must also study radiant energy—light, x-rays, radio waves—in its interaction with substances. For example, he may be interested in the color of substances, which is produced by their absorption of light.

Matter consists of all the materials around us—gases, liquids, solids. This statement is really not a definition. The dictionary states that matter is "that of which a physical object is composed; material." Then it defines material and physical object as matter, so that we are back where we started. The best course that we can follow is to say that no one really knows how to define matter, but that we agree to start out by using the

---

branches of chemistry, which in general are parts of organic chemistry and inorganic chemistry, have also been given names; for example, analytical chemistry, physical chemistry, biochemistry, nuclear chemistry, industrial chemistry. Their nature is indicated by their names.

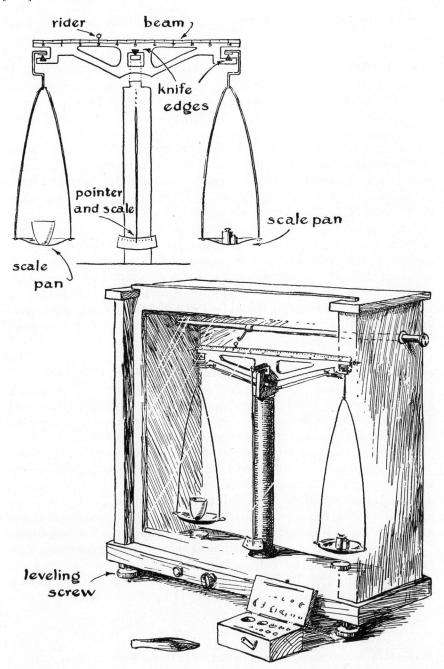

FIGURE 1-1 *A chemical balance.*

word. Often in science it is necessary to begin with some undefined words.

Mass and Weight. All matter has *mass*. Chemists are interested in the masses of materials, because they want to know how much material they need to use to prepare a certain amount of a product.

The **mass** *of an object is the quantity that measures its resistance to change in its state of rest or motion.*

The mass of an object also determines its *weight*. The weight of an object is only a measure of the *force* with which the object is attracted by the earth. This force depends upon the mass of the object, the mass of the earth, and the position of the object on the earth's surface, especially the distance of the object from the center of the earth. Since the earth is slightly flattened at its poles, the distance of its surface at the north pole or south pole from its center is less than that at the equator. In consequence the weight of an object as measured by a spring balance, which measures the force, is greater at the north or south pole than at the equator. For example, if your weight, measured by a spring balance, is 150.0 lbs. at the equator, it would be 150.8 lbs. at the north pole, measured on the same spring balance—nearly a pound more. Your mass, however, is the same.

The mass of an object remains the same at the north pole as at the equator, and it can easily be determined, at any place on the earth's surface, by comparison with a standard set of masses (standard "weights"). For small objects a *chemical balance*, such as shown in Figure 1-1, is used. Since the weights of two bodies of equal mass are the same at any place on the earth's surface, these bodies will balance one another when placed on the two pans of a balance with arms of equal length.

It is common practice to refer to the masses of objects as their weights. It might be thought that confusion would arise from the practice of using the word weight to refer both to the mass of an object and to the force with which the object is attracted by the earth. In general it does not, but if there is danger of confusion you should use the word mass.

The standard masses (standard weights) in the metric system are calibrated (checked) by comparison with the standard kilogram in Paris (Appendix 1).* The metric unit of mass is the *gram*. The abbreviation for gram is g, and for kilogram kg (1 kg = 1000 g).

1-3. *Kinds of Matter*

As we look about us we see material objects, such as a stone wall or a table, or one of the objects shown in Figure 1-2. The chemist is primarily

* There are many systems of weights and measures, which are ordinarily used in different countries. In order to avoid confusion, all scientists use the *metric system*, which is described in Appendix 1, in their scientific work. In general, we shall use the metric system in this book, but an occasional exercise or example may be given in the American system.

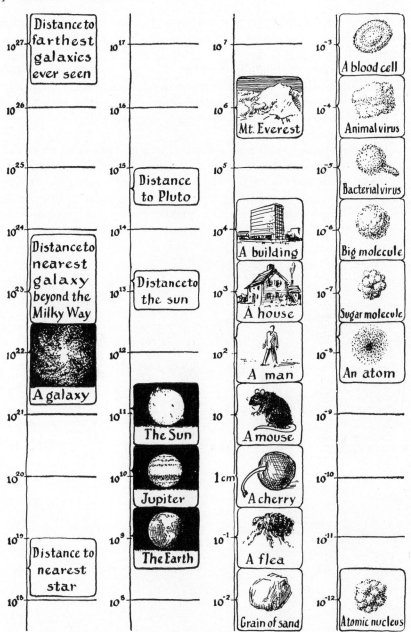

FIGURE 1-2   *A diagram showing dimensions of objects, from 10^{-12} cm (the nucleus of an atom) to 10^{27} cm (the radius of the known universe).*

interested not in the objects themselves, but in the kinds of matter of which they are composed. He is interested in wood, as a material, whether it is used for making a table or a chair. He is interested in granite, whether it is in a stone wall or in some other object. Indeed, his interest is primarily in those properties (characteristic qualities) of a material that are independent of the objects containing it.

The word **material** *is used in referring to any kind of matter, whether homogeneous or heterogeneous.*

A **homogeneous** *material is a material with the same properties throughout.*

A **heterogeneous** *material consists of parts with different properties.*

Wood, with soft and hard rings alternating, is obviously a heterogeneous material, as is also granite, in which grains of three different species of matter (the minerals* quartz, mica, and feldspar) can be seen (Figure 1-3).

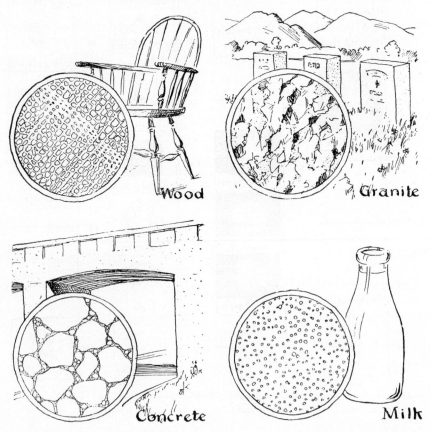

FIGURE 1-3   *Some heterogeneous materials.*

* A *mineral* is any homogeneous material occurring naturally as a product of inorganic processes (that is, not produced by a living organism).

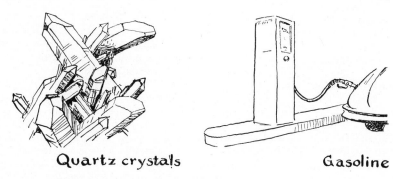

Quartz crystals   Gasoline

FIGURE 1-4   *Some homogeneous materials.*

Heterogeneous materials are mixtures of two or more homogeneous materials. For example, each of the three minerals quartz, mica, and feldspar that constitute the rock granite is a homogeneous material (Figure 1-4).

Let is now define the words *substance* and *solution*.

A **substance** *is a homogeneous species of matter with definite chemical composition.*

A **solution** *is a homogeneous material that does not have a definite composition.**

Pure salt, pure sugar, pure iron, pure copper, pure sulfur, pure water, pure oxygen, and pure hydrogen are representative substances. Quartz is also a substance (Figure 1-4).

On the other hand, a solution of sugar in water is not a substance according to this definition: it is, to be sure, homogeneous, but it does not satisfy the second part of the above definition, inasmuch as its composition is not definite, but is widely variable, being determined by the amount of sugar that happens to have been dissolved in a given amount of water. Gasoline is also not a pure substance; it is a solution (a homogeneous mixture) of several substances.

Sometimes the word substance is used in a broader sense, essentially as equivalent to material. Chemists usually restrict the use of the word in the way given by the definition above. The chemist's usage of the word substance may be indicated by using the phrase "pure substance."

Most materials that the chemist classifies as substances (pure substances) have definite chemical composition; for example, all samples of salt contain 39.4% sodium and 60.6% chlorine. Other compounds, however, show a small range of variation of chemical composition; an example is the iron sulfide that is made by heating iron and sulfur together. This homogeneous material when made in different ways shows a range in composition of from 35% to 39% sulfur.

---

* The word solution is commonly used for liquid solutions. Chemists also refer to gaseous solutions (mixtures of two or more pure gases) and to solid solutions.

Kinds of Definition. Definitions may be either precise or imprecise. The mathematician may define precisely the words that he uses; in his further discussion he then adheres rigorously to the defined meaning of each word. On the other hand, the words that are used in describing nature, which is itself complex, may not be capable of precise definition. In giving a definition for such a word the effort is made to describe the accepted usage.

For example, sometimes it is difficult to decide whether a material is homogeneous (a solution) or is heterogeneous (a mixture). A specimen of granite, in which grains of three different species of matter can be seen, is obviously a mixture. An emulsion of fat in water (a suspension of small droplets of fat in the water, as in milk, Figure 1-3) is also a mixture. The heterogeneity of a piece of granite is obvious to the eye. The heterogeneity of milk can be seen if a drop of milk is examined under a microscope. But if the droplets of fat in the emulsion were made smaller and smaller, it might become impossible to observe the heterogeneity of the material. In such a border-line case the material may be called either a solution or a mixture.

Substances are classified as *elementary substances* or *compounds*.

A substance that can be decomposed into two or more substances is a **compound.**

A substance that cannot be decomposed is an **elementary substance** (*or* **element**).*

Salt can be decomposed by an electric current into two substances, sodium and chlorine. Hence salt is a compound.

Water can be decomposed by an electric current into two substances, hydrogen and oxygen. Hence water is a compound.

Mercuric oxide can be decomposed by heat, to form mercury and oxygen. Hence mercuric oxide is a compound.

No one has ever succeeded in decomposing sodium, chlorine, hydrogen, oxygen, or mercury into other substances. Hence these five substances are accepted as elementary substances (elements).

At the present time (1955) exactly 100 elements are known. Several hundred thousand compounds of these 100 elements have been found in nature or made in the laboratory.

The process of decomposing a compound into two or more simpler substances is sometimes called *analysis*. The reverse process, of forming a substance by combining two or more substances, is called *synthesis*.

The composition of a compound can be determined by analysis. For example, a *qualitative analysis* of salt might be carried out by decomposing it with an electric current and identifying the products as sodium and chlorine; the chemist could then say that the salt is a compound of the two elements sodium and chlorine. To carry out a *quantitative analysis* he would have to weigh the substances; he could then report the composition as 39.4% sodium, 60.6% chlorine.

Our classification of matter is summarized in the following chart. You may find it worth while to examine this chart carefully. Can you define all of the words? Can you give two or three examples of each of the six

* The discovery of radioactivity made it necessary to change these definitions slightly (see the last section of Chapter 4).

kinds of materials that might constitute an object? Can you think of one or two materials that are hard to classify?

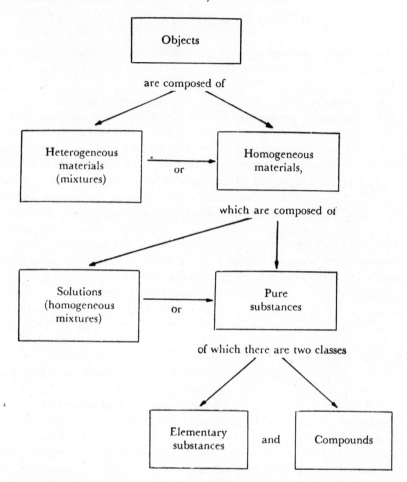

Illustrative Exercises

1-1. Is ice an elementary substance or a compound?

1-2. Is maple syrup (or corn syrup) a homogeneous material or a heterogeneous material? Is it a solution or a substance (pure substance)?

1-3. Sterling silver is a homogeneous material made by melting silver and copper together. In Great Britain its composition is 92.5% silver, 7.5% copper, and in the United States it is 90% silver, 10% copper (coinage silver). Any intermediate composition may be used, and will give a homogeneous material. Is sterling silver a compound, or is it a solid solution?

1-4. When the substance calcite is heated it forms lime and carbon dioxide. Is calcite an elementary substance or a compound? Can you say whether or not lime is an elementary substance or a compound?

1-5.   When diamond is heated in a vacuum (no other material present) it is converted
completely into graphite. Does this prove that diamond is a compound?

1–4. *The Physical Properties of Substances*

The study of the properties of substances constitutes an important
part of chemistry, because their properties determine the uses to which
they can be put.

The **properties** *of substances are their characteristic qualities.*

The **physical properties** *are those properties of a substance that can be
observed without changing the substance into other substances.*

Let us again use sodium chloride, common salt, as an example of a
substance. We have all seen this substance in what appear to be different
forms—table salt, in fine grains; salt in the form of crystals a quarter of
an inch in diameter, for use with ice for freezing ice cream; and natural
crystals of rock salt an inch or more across. Despite their obvious difference, all of these samples of salt have the same fundamental properties.
In each case the crystals, small or large, are naturally bounded by
square or rectangular *crystal faces* of different sizes, but with each face
always at right angles to each adjacent face. The *cleavage* of the different
crystals of salt is the same: when crushed, the crystals always break
(cleave) along planes parallel to the original faces, producing smaller
crystals similar to the larger ones. The different samples have the same
salty *taste*. Their *solubility* is the same: at room temperature 36 g of salt
can be dissolved in 100 g of water. The *density* of the salt is the same,
2.16 g/cm³. The density of a substance is the mass (weight) of a unit
volume (1 cubic centimeter) of the substance.

There are other properties besides density and solubility that can be
measured precisely and expressed in numbers. Such another property
is the *melting point*, the temperature at which a solid substance melts to
form a liquid. On the other hand, there are also interesting physical
properties of a substance that are not so simple in nature. One such
property is the *malleability* of a substance—the ease with which a substance can be hammered out into thin sheets. A related property is the
ductility—the ease with which the substance can be drawn into a wire.
Hardness is a similar property: we say that one substance is less hard
than the second substance when it is scratched by the second substance.
The *color* of a substance is an important physical property.

It is customary to say that under the same external conditions all
specimens of a particular substance have the same physical properties
(density, hardness, color, melting point, crystalline form, etc.). Sometimes, however, the word substance is used in referring to a material
without regard to its state. For example, ice, liquid water, and water
vapor may be referred to as the same substance. Moreover, a specimen
containing crystals of rock salt and crystals of table salt may be called

a mixture, even though the specimen may consist entirely of one substance, sodium chloride. This lack of definiteness in usage seems to cause no confusion in practice.

The concept "pure substance" is, of course, an idealization; all actual substances are more or less impure. It is a useful concept, however, because we have learned through experiment that the properties of various specimens of an impure substance with different impurities are nearly the same if the impurities are present in only small amounts. These properties are accepted as the properties of the ideal substance.

1–5. *The Chemical Properties of Substances*

The **chemical properties** *of a substance are those properties that relate to its participation in chemical reactions.*

Chemical reactions *are the processes that convert substances into other substances.*

Thus sodium chloride has the property of changing into a soft metal, sodium, and a greenish-yellow gas, chlorine, when it is decomposed by passage of an electric current through it. It also has the property, when it is dissolved in water, of producing a white precipitate when a solution of silver nitrate is added to it; and it has many other chemical properties.

Iron has the property of combining readily with the oxygen in moist air, to form iron rust; whereas an alloy* of iron with chromium and nickel (stainless steel) is found to resist this process of rusting. It is evident from this example that the chemical properties of materials are important in engineering.

Many chemical reactions take place in the kitchen. When biscuits are made with use of sour milk and baking soda there is a chemical reaction between the baking soda and a substance in the sour milk, lactic acid, to produce the gas carbon dioxide, which leavens the dough by forming small bubbles in it. And, of course, a great many chemical reactions take place in the human body. Foods that we eat are digested in the stomach and intestines. Oxygen in the inhaled air combines with a substance, hemoglobin, in the red cells of the blood, and then is released in the tissues, where it takes part in many different reactions. Many biochemists and physiologists are engaged in the study of the chemical reactions that take place in the human body.

Most substances have the power to enter into many chemical reactions. The study of these reactions constitutes a large part of the study of chemistry. Chemistry may be defined as *the science of substances—their structure, their properties, and the reactions that change them into other substances.*

---

* An *alloy* is a metallic material containing two or more elements. It may be either homogeneous or heterogeneous (a mixture of grains of two or more kinds). If homogeneous, it may be either a pure compound or a solid solution, or even a liquid solution—many alloys of mercury and other metals are liquid.

Illustrative Exercises

1-6. Which of the following processes would you class as chemical reactions?
   (a) The boiling of water.
   (b) The burning of paper.
   (c) The preparation of sugar syrup by adding sugar to hot water.
   (d) The formation of rust on iron.
   (e) The manufacture of salt by evaporation of sea water.

1-7. A kilogram of gold (2.2 lbs.) occupies the volume 51.5 cubic centimeters. What is the density of gold? (Ans. 19.4 g/cm³.)
   If the gold were in the form of a cube, what would be the length of its edge? Find the answer in centimeters, and also in inches.

1–6. Energy and Temperature

The concept of *energy* is as difficult to define as that of matter. Energy is involved in doing work, or in heating an object. A boulder at the top of a mountain has *potential energy*. As it rolls down the mountain side, its potential energy is changed into the *kinetic energy* of its motion. If it were to fall into a lake, and be slowed down by the friction of its motion through water, part of its kinetic energy would be changed by friction into *heat*, which then would raise the temperature of the boulder and of the water. In addition, part of its kinetic energy would be transferred to the water, and would evidence itself in waves radiating from the point of impact.

Another important kind of energy is *radiant energy*. Visible light, infrared radiation, ultraviolet radiation, x-rays, and radio waves are radiant energy. They are all closely similar in nature (see Section 28-5).

When a mixture of gasoline vapor and air is exploded, energy is liberated—energy which can do the work of propelling an automobile, and which in addition causes an increase in temperature of the engine and the exhaust gases. This energy is said to have been stored up in the gasoline and air as *chemical energy*.

The Law of Conservation of Energy. It has been found that *whenever energy of one form disappears an equivalent amount of energy of other forms is produced*. This principle is called the **law of conservation of energy**.

All chemical reactions are accompanied by either the liberation of energy or the absorption of energy. Usually this energy is in the form of heat. If some substances when mixed together in a flask undergo a chemical reaction with liberation of heat, the contents of the flask become warmer. If, on the other hand, they undergo a chemical reaction with absorption of heat, the contents of the flask become colder. These facts can be described by saying that every substance has a certain *heat content*, and that in general the heat contents of the products of a reaction differ from the heat contents of the reactants. In accordance with the law of conservation of energy, the *heat of the reaction* is the difference in heat contents of the products and the reactants. For example, a mixture of gasoline and oxygen has a greater total heat content than the products of their reaction, which are carbon dioxide and water. In consequence, some heat is liberated during the reaction.

Under some conditions chemical energy is liberated during a chemical reaction in forms other than heat. For example, the chemical energy stored up in an explosive may do work, in breaking a stone cliff into fragments. The chemical energy in the substances of an electric battery is converted into electric energy during the operation of the battery. Some of the chemical energy in a fuel may be converted into radiant energy as the fuel burns.

Temperature. If two objects are placed in contact with one another, heat may flow from one object to the other one. *Temperature* is the quality that determines the direction in which heat flows—it always flows from the object at higher temperature to the object at lower temperature.

Temperatures are ordinarily measured by means of a thermometer, such as the ordinary mercury thermometer, consisting of a quantity of mercury in a glass tube. The temperature scale used by scientists is the *centigrade scale* or *Celsius scale;* it was introduced by Anders Celsius, a Swedish professor of astronomy, in 1742. On this scale the temperature of freezing water is 0° C, and the temperature of boiling water is 100° C.

On the *Fahrenheit scale*, used in every-day life in English-speaking countries, the freezing point of water is 32° F, and the boiling point of water is 212° F. On this scale the

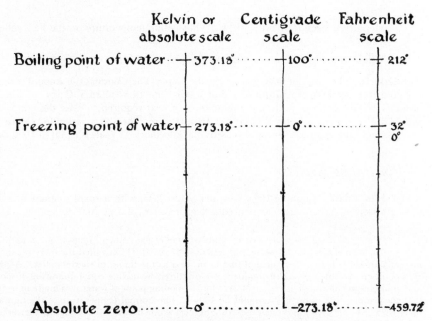

FIGURE 1-5 *Comparison of Kelvin, Centigrade, and Fahrenheit scales of temperature.*

freezing point and the boiling point differ by 180°, rather than the 100° of the centigrade scale.*

The relation between the centigrade scale and the Fahrenheit scale is indicated in Figure 1-5. To convert temperatures from one scale to another, you need only remember that the Fahrenheit degree is $\frac{100}{180}$ or $\frac{5}{9}$ of the centigrade degree, and that 0° C is the same temperature as 32° F.

Example 1. A school room may be kept at 68° F. What is this temperature on the centigrade scale?

    Solution. 68° F is 36° F (that is, 68° − 32°) above the freezing point of water. This number of Fahrenheit degrees is equal to $\frac{5}{9} \times 36 = 20°$ C. Since the freezing point of water is 0° C, the temperature of the room is 20° C.

The Absolute Temperature Scale. About one hundred fifty years ago it was noticed by scientists that a sample of gas that is cooled decreases in volume in a regular way, and it was seen that if the volume were to continue to decrease in the same way it would become zero at about −273° C. The concept was developed that this temperature, −273° C (more accurately, −273.16° C), is the minimum temperature, the *absolute zero*. A new temperature scale was then devised by Lord Kelvin, a great British physicist (1824–1907). It is called either the *absolute temperature scale* (A) or the *Kelvin scale* (K). The unit on this scale is the centigrade degree. † In order to convert a temperature from the centigrade scale to the absolute scale, it is only necessary to add 273.16°. Thus the freezing point of water, 0° C, is 273.16° K. The relation of the Kelvin scale to the centigrade scale and the Fahrenheit scale is also shown in Figure 1-5.

Illustrative Exercises

1-8.   The normal temperature of the human body is 98.6° F. What is it on the centigrade scale?

1-9.   Mercury freezes at about −40° C. What is this temperature on the Fahrenheit scale?

1-10.   What is the absolute zero on the Fahrenheit scale?

The Calorie. The unit of heat (energy) is the *calorie*. The calorie is the amount of heat required to raise the temperature of 1 g of water from 14.5° to 15.5° C; or, to within ordinary requirements of accuracy, the amount of heat required to raise the temperature of 1 g of liquid water by 1° C, at any temperature. The abbreviation for calorie is cal. A larger unit, the *kilocalorie*, is also used; one kilocalorie (1 kcal) is equal to 1000 cal.

Illustrative Exercise

1-11.   Into a flask containing 100 g of water at 20.0° C, with a small amount of acid dissolved in it, there was poured 100 g of water, also at 20.0° C, containing a

---

* The Fahrenheit scale was devised by Gabriel Daniel Fahrenheit (1686–1736), a natural philosopher who was born in Danzig and settled in Holland. He invented the mercury thermometer in 1714; before then alcohol had been used as the liquid in thermometers. As the zero point on his scale he took the temperature produced by mixing equal quantities of snow and ammonium chloride. His choice of 212° for the boiling point of water was made in order that the temperature of his body should be 100° F. The normal temperature of the human body is 98.6° F; perhaps Fahrenheit had a slight fever while he was calibrating his thermometer.

† Another absolute scale, the *Rankine scale*, is sometimes used in engineering work in the English-speaking countries. It uses the Fahrenheit degree, and has 0° R at the absolute zero.

small amount of sodium hydroxide. The temperature of the mixed solution increased to 24.5° C. Neglecting the effect of the substances dissolved in the water and the loss of heat to the flask, calculate how much heat (how many calories) was produced by the reaction of the acid and the sodium hydroxide.

1–7. *Pressure*

In chemical work it is often necessary to know not only the temperature at which an experiment is carried out, but also the *pressure*. For example, the large-scale industrial preparation of ammonia is carried out at high pressure, because the chemical reaction does not proceed satisfactorily at ordinary pressure.

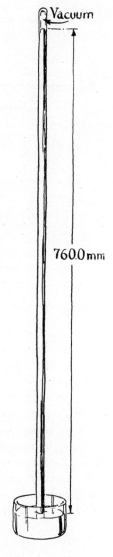

FIGURE 1-6

A simple mercury barometer.

Pressure is force per unit area. Pressure may be measured in grams per square centimeter, or in pounds per square inch, or in other units. The atmosphere of the earth exerts a pressure on all objects at the surface of the earth. The pressure of the atmosphere is 14.7 pounds per square inch.

Another unit of pressure that is often used is the *atmosphere* (abbreviation atm). The pressure 1 atm is the average pressure at the surface of the earth (at sea level) that is due to the weight of the air.

The pressure due to the atmosphere can be measured by means of a *barometer*. A simple barometer is shown in Figure 1-6. This barometer is made by filling a long glass tube, which is closed at one end, with mercury, being careful that no air remains entrapped, and then inverting the open end of the tube under the surface of some mercury in a cup. If the tube is longer than 760 millimeters (76 cm, about 29.9 inches) the surface of the mercury at the upper end of the tube drops, until the height of the mercury column, measured from the level of mercury in the cup, is just enough to balance the atmospheric pressure. This occurs when the weight of the column of mercury, per unit area, is equal to the pressure of the atmosphere.

Pressure is often reported as the height of the column of mercury required to balance it. For example, the pressure 1 atm is equal to 760 millimeters of mercury (abbreviated as mm of mercury, or mm Hg).

The units used to measure pressure are summarized in the following equation:

1 atm = 760 mm Hg = 14.7 pounds per square inch*

Illustrative Exercises

1 12.   Pressure can also be reported in grams per square centimeter. The density of mercury is 13.55 g/cm³. What is 1 atm pressure in g/cm²? (Remember that 1 atm = 76 cm Hg.)

1·13.   The density of water is about 1 g/cm³. At what depth would a diver have to descend under the surface of a lake in order that the pressure acting on him would be 2 atm, rather than the 1 atm that is due to the weight of the air? What is this depth in feet? (Remember that 1 inch equals 2.54 cm. You may want to use the answer to the preceding exercise to solve this one.)

1–8. *Solids, Liquids, and Gases*

Materials may exist as solids, liquids, or gases. A specimen of a solid, such as a piece of ice, has a definite volume and also has rigidity. It retains its shape, even when acted on by an outside force, provided that the force is not great enough to break or to deform the specimen. A liquid, such as a portion of water in a cup, has a definite volume, but adjusts its shape to the shape of the bottom part of its container. A gas, such as steam (water vapor) in the cylinder of a steam engine, has neither definite shape nor definite volume—it changes its shape and also its volume with change in the shape and volume of the container.

Ice, water, and water vapor represent the same chemical substance, water substance, in three different states. Ice is the *solid state* (*crystalline state*), water the *liquid state*, and water vapor the *gaseous state*.

* Engineers use the abbreviation psi for pounds per square inch.

Scientists usually distinguished between *crystalline solids* and *non-crystalline solids*.

A **crystal** *is a homogeneous material* (either a pure substance or a solution) *that, as a result of its regular internal structure, has spontaneously assumed the shape of a figure bounded by plane faces.*

For example, when a solution of salt evaporates small cubes of solid salt form. These cubes, which are bounded by plane square faces, are crystals.

Most solid substances are crystalline in nature. Sometimes the individual crystals, with plane faces and sharp edges and corners, are visible to the naked eye, and sometimes they can be seen only under a microscope.

Some solids, such as charcoal, do not show any crystalline character even when examined with a microscope of high power; these solids are called *amorphous solids* (the word amorphous means without shape).

Certain other materials, of which sealing wax is an example, are called *super-cooled liquids.* When a stick of sealing wax, which is hard and brittle at room temperature, is gradually warmed it begins to soften, and finally becomes a mobile liquid. As it is being cooled it shows a gradual change from a mobile liquid to a viscous liquid, and then to a solid. Even at room temperature it might be described as a liquid which is so viscous that it flows only extremely slowly.

1–9. *The Scientific Method*

During your study of chemistry you will also learn something about the *scientific method*.

Scientists do their work in many ways. A great scientific discovery is often the result of a great flight of the imagination—a brilliant new idea. If you have studied physics, you probably read that Archimedes is said to have been taking a bath when he had his brilliant idea, a "flash of genius," about the change in weight of a body immersed in a liquid (Archimedes' principle). Curiosity and an active imagination are great assets to a scientist.

No one knows the method for having brilliant new ideas, and this is not part of what is ordinarily called the scientific method. But scientists also work by applying common sense, reliable methods of reasoning, to the problems that they are attacking, and the procedure that they follow, which is called the scientific method, can be learned.

Part of the scientific method is the requirement that the investigator be willing to accept all of the facts. He must not be prejudiced; prejudice might keep him from giving proper consideration to some of the facts, or to some of the logical arguments involved in applying the scientific method, and in this way keep him from getting the right answer. If you

were to say "I have made up my mind—don't confuse me with a lot
of facts," you would not be applying the scientific method.

The remaining part of the scientific method consists of logical argument.

The first step in applying the scientific method is to obtain some facts,
by observation and experiment. The next step is to classify and correlate the facts by general statements. If a general statement is simple
in form it may be called a *law of nature*. If it is more complex it is called
a *theory*. Both laws of nature and theories are called *principles*.

The discussion of the scientific method will be continued in the first
section of the following chapter.

1–10. *How to Study Chemistry*

You may feel, now that you are just beginning your formal study of
chemistry, that you know nothing about this subject; *but in fact you
already know a great deal*—many things that the foremost scientists did
not know a century or two ago. From your general reading, from the
comic papers, the advertisements, and your contact with automobiles,
street signs, and other features of our modern world, you probably know
that not only oxygen, hydrogen, iron, and copper are elements, but
also that helium, neon, and argon are elements, and that they are gases;
that copper, zinc, tin, and lead are elements, and are metals; and that
sulfur, phosphorus, and bromine are elements that are non-metals. In
addition to knowing that water and sodium chloride are compounds,
you know that penicillin is a compound used for the treatment of infectious diseases. You know that substances are composed of atoms, and
that the atoms themselves consist of nuclei and electrons. You probably
even know, from reading the newspapers, that neutrons can cause the
nuclei of atoms of uranium 235 and plutonium 239 to split—to undergo
fission during the detonation of an atomic bomb; this is knowledge that
was possessed by nobody in the world a few years ago.

By studying chemistry you can make the understanding that you have
of the nature of the universe more precise, and you can add greatly to it.

It was mentioned in Section 1–1 that part of the study of chemistry
consists in memorizing some of the facts of descriptive chemistry. If you
are planning to become a chemist, or a scientist or professional man or
woman in a field in which chemistry is important, you should try to
learn a large number of the facts of descriptive chemistry. If your reason
for studying chemistry is not a professional one, you may not want to
learn so many of these facts, but only some of them, especially those
that are significant to everyday life.

In applying a theoretical principle in the solution of a problem, you
should make use of the following procedure. First, decide on the applicable principle and get it clearly in mind. Then apply it in a straight-

forward manner. *Do not guess:* if you are not sure of the proper step, think about the matter further, until you are sure.

In working problems you must be sure that you understand the theoretical principle that you are using before making the calculations. It is important to keep track of the physical units that are involved in the problem. One good way of doing this is to write the abbreviations for the units beside the numbers, and to cancel them when possible. For example, if you are told that 1.73 g of a substance occupies the volume 2.00 cm³, and are asked to calculate the density, you may write 1.73 g/2.00 cm³, and obtain immediately the answer 0.865 g/cm³. The fact that the answer is in units g/cm³ gives you a check on the correctness of the procedure that you have followed, inasmuch as you know that density is measured in units g/cm³.

Concepts and Terms Introduced in This Chapter

Chemistry—the study of substances, their structure, their properties, and their reactions.

Descriptive chemistry—the discovery and tabulation of chemical facts.

Theoretical chemistry—the formulation of theories that unify these facts and combine them into a system.

Matter—the gases, liquids, and solids that, with radiant energy, make up the universe.

Radiant energy—light, x-rays, radio waves.

Mass—the quantity that measures the resistance to change in state of motion of an object.

Weight—the force with which an object is attracted by the earth.

Material—any kind of matter.

Homogeneous material—material with the same properties throughout.

Heterogeneous material—material consisting of parts with different properties.

Mineral—any homogeneous material occurring naturally as a product of inorganic processes.

Substance—a homogeneous species of matter with definite chemical composition.

Solution—a homogeneous material that does not have a definite composition.

Compound—a substance that can be decomposed into two or more substances.

Elementary substance or element—a substance that cannot be decomposed.

Properties of substances—their characteristic qualities.

Physical properties—those properties not connected with participation in chemical reactions. Examples: formation of crystal faces, cleavage, taste, solubility, density, melting point, malleability, ductility, hardness, color.

Chemical properties—those properties that relate to participation of a substance in chemical reactions.

Chemical reactions—the processes that convert substances into other substances.

Alloy—a metallic material containing two or more elements.

Forms of energy—potential energy, kinetic energy, heat, radiant energy, chemical energy.

Law of conservation of energy—in all ordinary changes energy of one forms disappears at the same time that an equivalent amount of energy of other forms is produced.

Temperature—the quality that determines the direction in which heat flows.

Calorie—the unit of heat, the amount of heat required to raise the temperature of 1 g of water by 1° C.

Temperature scales—centigrade scale (Celsius scale); Fahrenheit scale; Kelvin scale (absolute temperature scale).

Pressure—force per unit area. Units of pressure: atm, mm Hg, pounds per square inch, g/cm^3.

Solids, liquids, gases. The crystalline state. Crystal—a homogeneous material that has spontaneously assumed the shape of a figure bounded by plane faces. Amorphous solids. Supercooled liquids.

The scientific method: willingness to accept all of the facts; freedom from prejudice; logical argument; classification and correlation of facts by use of general statements.

Exercises

1-14.   A cube of gold 2 cm on edge weighs 155.4 g. What is the density of gold?

1-15.   Classify the following materials as homogeneous or heterogeneous:

pure gold	air	glass
milk	ice	sugar
wood	gasoline	coffee

1-16.   Is the ice in a glacier to be classified, according to the definition of mineral, as a mineral?

1-17.   Classify the following homogeneous materials as substances or solutions:

rain water	ocean water	oxygen
air	gasoline	mercury
sterling silver	salt	honey

1-18.   What is the evidence proving that water is a compound, and not an element? What is the evidence indicating that oxygen is an element, and not a compound? Why is the word "proving" used in the first of the preceding sentences, and "indicating" in the second?

1-19.   How much heat is needed to raise the temperature of 200 g of water from 10° C to 50° C?

1-20.   The melting point of pure iron is 1535° C. What is this temperature on the Fahrenheit scale?

Reference Books

Further information about descriptive chemistry may be obtained from textbooks and treatises such as the following:

M. C. Sneed and J. L. Maynard, *General Inorganic Chemistry*, D. Van Nostrand Co., New York, 1942.

F. Ephraim, *Inorganic Chemistry*, Interscience Publishers, Inc., New York, 1954.

J. H. Hildebrand and R. E. Powell, *Principles of Chemistry*, The Macmillan Co., New York, 1952.

W. M. Latimer and J. H. Hildebrand, *Reference Book of Inorganic Chemistry*, The Macmillan Co., New York, **1951**.

Much useful information is tabulated in the following handbooks. It is suggested that the student majoring in chemistry obtain a copy of one of them:

Charles D. Hodgman (Editor-in-Chief), *Handbook of Chemistry and Physics*, Chemical Rubber Publishing Co., Cleveland, Ohio.

N. A. Lange, *Handbook of Chemistry*, Handbook Publishers, Sandusky, Ohio.

Detailed information about the elements and inorganic compounds may be found in comprehensive treatises; the greatest of these in English is

J. W. Mellor, *A Comprehensive Treatise on Inorganic and Theoretical Chemistry*, Longmans, Green and Co., New York, **1922–1937**.

You may read about the history of chemistry in the following books:

Alexander Findlay, *One Hundred Years of Chemistry*, The Macmillan Co., New York, **1948**.

Mary E. Weeks, *Discovery of the Elements*, Journal of Chemical Education, Easton, Pa., **1945**.

H. N. Smith, *Torchbearers of Chemistry*, Academic Press, New York, **1949**.

Bernard Jaffe, *Crucibles: The Story of Chemistry from Ancient Alchemy to Nuclear Fission*, Simon and Schuster, New York, **1948**.

F. J. Moore (revised by W. T. Hall), *A History of Chemistry*, McGraw-Hill Book Co., New York, **1939**.

James B. Conant, *On Understanding Science: An Historical Approach*, Yale University Press, New Haven, Conn., **1948**.

For the chemistry of stars, planets, comets, interstellar space, etc., see

R. H. Baker, *Astronomy*, D. Van Nostrand Co., New York, **1950**.

Many interesting articles may be found in the *Journal of Chemical Education* and in the *Scientific American*. The chemical articles in the *Encyclopaedia Britannica* are excellent.

Chapter 2

The Atomic
Structure of Matter

The properties of any kind of matter are most easily and clearly learned and understood when they are correlated with its structure, in terms of the molecules, atoms, and still smaller particles that compose it. This subject, the atomic theory of matter, will be taken up in this chapter.

The chapter begins with a brief discussion of hypotheses, theories, and laws (Section 2–1). The next section (2–2) describes the atomic theory of matter and presents the arguments advanced by Dalton in support of the theory a century and a half ago. A brief discussion of modern methods of studying atoms and molecules follows (Section 2–3). There are then described, as examples, a crystal of copper, built of atoms in a simple regular arrangement (Section 2–4), and a crystal of iodine, built of molecules (groups of atoms, Section 2–5). Some photographs of molecules made with the electron microscope are also shown in Section 2–5. Section 2–6 presents a brief description of the classification of crystals into systems. The nature of gases and liquids and the processes of evaporation and sublimation are treated in Sections 2–7 and 2–8, and the relation between temperature and the motion of molecules is discussed in Section 2–9. All of these aspects of atomic and molecular theory are important for the further study of chemistry.

2–1. *Hypotheses, Theories, and Laws*

When it is first found that an idea explains or correlates a number of facts, the idea is called a *hypothesis*. A hypothesis may be subjected to further tests and experimental checking of deductions that may be made from it. If it continues to agree with the results of experiment, the hypothesis is dignified by the name of *theory* or *law*.

A theory, such as the atomic theory, usually involves some idea about the nature of some part of the universe, whereas a law may represent a summarizing statement about observed experimental facts. For example, there is a law of the constancy of the angles between the faces of crystals. This law states that whenever the angles between corresponding faces of various crystals of a pure substance are measured, they are found to have the same value. The law simply expresses the fact that the angles between corresponding faces on a crystal of a pure substance are found to have the same value whether the crystal is a small one or a large one; it does not in any way explain this fact. An explanation of the fact is given by the atomic theory of crystals, the theory that in crystals the atoms are arranged in a regular order (as described later in this chapter).

It may be mentioned that chemists and other scientists use the word theory in two somewhat different senses. The first meaning of the word is that described above, namely, a hypothesis which has been verified. The second use of the word theory is to represent a systematic body of knowledge, compounded of facts, laws, theories in the limited sense described above, deductive arguments, etc. Thus by the atomic theory we mean not only the idea that substances are composed of atoms, but also all the facts about substances that can be explained and interpreted in terms of atoms, and the arguments that have been developed to explain the properties of substances in terms of their atomic structure.

2–2. *The Atomic Theory*

The most important of all chemical theories is the atomic theory. In 1805 the English chemist and physicist John Dalton (1766–1844), of Manchester, stated the hypothesis that *all substances consist of small particles of matter, of several different kinds, corresponding to the different elements.* He called these particles atoms, from the Greek word *atomos*, meaning indivisible. This hypothesis gave a simple explanation or picture of previously observed but unsatisfactorily explained relations among the weights of substances taking part in chemical reactions with one another. As it was verified by further work in chemistry and physics, Dalton's atomic hypothesis became the atomic theory. The existence of atoms is now accepted as a fact.

The rapid progress of our science during the current century is well illustrated by the increase in our knowledge about atoms. In a popular textbook of chemistry written in the early years of the twentieth century atoms were defined as the "imaginary units of which bodies are aggregates." Now, only half a century later, we have precise knowledge of many properties of atoms and molecules. Atoms and molecules can no longer be considered "imaginary."

Dalton's Arguments in Support of the Atomic Theory. The concept of atoms is very old. The Greek philosopher Democritus (about 460–370 B.C.), who had adopted some of his ideas from earlier philosophers, stated that the universe is composed of void (vacuum) and atoms. The atoms were considered to be everlasting and indivisible— absolutely small, so small that their size could not be diminished. He considered the atoms of different substances, such as water and iron, to be fundamentally the same, but to differ in some superficial way; atoms of water, being smooth and round, could roll over one another, whereas atoms of iron, being rough and jagged, would cling together to form a solid body.

The atomic theory of Democritus was pure speculation, and was much too general to be useful. Dalton's atomic theory, however, was a hypothesis which explained many facts in a simple and reasonable way.

In 1785 the French chemist Antoine Laurent Lavoisier (1743–1794) showed clearly that there is no change in mass during a chemical reaction—the mass of the products is equal to the mass of the reacting substances. This general statement is called the **law of conservation of mass.**

In 1799 another general law, the **law of constant proportions,** was enunciated by the French chemist Joseph Louis Proust (1754–1826). The law of constant proportions states that *different samples of a substance contain its elementary constituents (elements) in the same proportions.* For example, it was found by analysis that the two elements hydrogen and oxygen are present in any sample of water in the proportion by weight 1 : 8. One gram of hydrogen and 8 grams of oxygen combine to form 9 grams of water.

Dalton stated the hypothesis that elements consist of atoms, all of the atoms of one element being identical, and that compounds result from the combination of a certain number of atoms of one element with a certain number of atoms of another element (or, in general, from the combination of atoms of two or more elements, each in definite number). In this way he could give a simple explanation of the law of conservation of mass, and also of the law of constant proportions.

A **molecule** *is a group of atoms bonded to one another.* If a molecule of water is formed by the combination of two atoms of hydrogen with one atom of oxygen, the mass of the molecule would be the sum of the masses of two atoms of hydrogen and an atom of

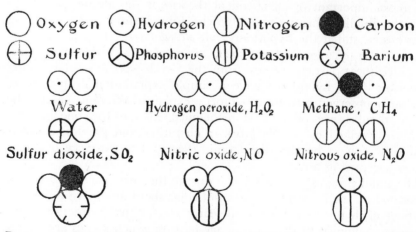

FIGURE 2-1 *Atomic symbols and molecular formulas used by John Dalton, about 1803.*

oxygen, in accordance with the law of conservation of mass. The definite composition of a compound is then explained by the definite ratio of atoms of different elements in the molecules of the compound.

Dalton also formulated another law, the **law of simple multiple proportions.*** This law states that *when two elements combine to form more than one compound, the weights of one element which combine with the same weight of the other are in the ratios of small integers.* It is found by experiment that, whereas water consists of hydrogen and oxygen in the weight ratio 1 : 8, hydrogen peroxide consists of hydrogen and oxygen in the ratio 1 : 16. The weights of oxygen combined with the same weight of hydrogen, one gram, in water and hydrogen peroxide are 8 g and 16 g; that is, they are in the ratio of the small integers 1 and 2. This ratio can be explained by assuming that twice as many atoms of oxygen combine with an atom of hydrogen in hydrogen peroxide as in water. This situation is illustrated in Figure 2-1, which shows the symbols used by Dalton to represent the atoms of some elements and the molecules of compounds.

Dalton had no way of determining the correct formulas of compounds, and he arbitrarily chose formulas to be as simple as possible: for example, he assumed that the molecule of water consisted of one atom of hydrogen and one atom of oxygen, as shown in the figure, whereas in fact it consists of two atoms of hydrogen and one of oxygen.

Illustrative Exercises

2-1. The molecule of sulfur dioxide contains one atom of sulfur and two atoms of oxygen. Sulfur dioxide is 50% sulfur and 50% oxygen by weight. What can you say about the relative weights of atoms of sulfur and oxygen?

2-2. Carbon monoxide is found on chemical analysis to contain 43% carbon and 57% oxygen. Carbon dioxide is found to contain 27% carbon and 73% oxygen. Show that these numbers are compatible with the law of simple multiple proportions.

2–3. Modern Methods of Studying Atoms and Molecules

During the second half of the nineteenth century chemists began to discuss the properties of substances in terms of assumed structures of the molecules—that is, of definite arrangements of the atoms relative to one another. Precise information about the atomic structure of molecules and crystals of many substances was finally obtained during the recent period, beginning about 1920. The physicists have developed many powerful methods of investigating the structure of matter. One of these methods is the interpretation of the *spectra* of substances (see Figure 28-1). A flame containing water vapor, for example, emits light that is characteristic of the water molecule; this is called the spectrum of water vapor. Measurements of the lines in the water spectrum have been made and interpreted, and it has been found that the two hydrogen atoms in the molecule are about 0.97 Å from the oxygen atom.† Moreover, it has been shown that the two hydrogen atoms are not on opposite sides of the oxygen atom, but that the molecule is bent, the angle formed by the three atoms being 106°. The distances between atoms and the angles formed by the atoms in many simple molecules have been determined by spectroscopic methods.

---

* The discovery of the law of simple multiple proportions was the first great success of Dalton's atomic theory. This law was not induced from experimental results, but was derived from the theory, and then tested by experiments.

† The Ångström (symbol Å), the unit of length used in describing atoms and molecules, is 1×10^{-8} cm. This very small unit of length is convenient because atoms are usually from 1 Å to 3 Å from neighboring atoms in a molecule or crystal, and it is easier to write 0.97 Å than 0.97×10^{-8} cm or 0.0000000097 cm. It was named in honor of a Swedish physicist, Anders Jonas Ångström (1814–1874).

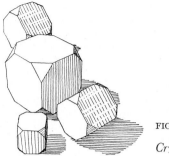

FIGURE 2-2

Crystals of native copper.

Also, the structures of many substances have been determined by the method of diffraction of electrons or diffraction of x-rays. These methods are too complex to be described in this book; you may be interested to read about them in one of the reference books or journals listed at the end of the chapter. In the following pages we shall describe many atomic structures that have been determined by these methods.

2–4. *The Arrangement of Atoms in a Crystal*

Most solid substances are crystalline in nature. Sometimes the particles of a sample of solid substance are themselves single crystals, such as the cubic crystals of sodium chloride in table salt. Sometimes these single crystals are very large; occasionally crystals of minerals several yards in diameter are found in nature.

In our discussion we shall use *copper* as an example. Crystals of copper as large as a centimeter on edge, as shown in Figure 2-2, are found in deposits of copper ore. An ordinary piece of the metal copper does not consist of a single crystal of copper, but of an aggregate of crystals. The crystal grains of a specimen of a metal can be made clearly visible by polishing the surface of the metal, and then etching the metal lightly with an acid. Often the grains are very small, and can be seen only with the aid of a microscope (Figure 2-3), but sometimes they are large, and can be easily seen with the naked eye, as in some brass doorknobs.

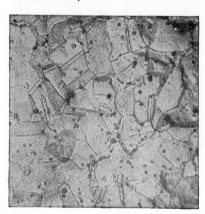

FIGURE 2-3

A polished and etched surface of a piece of cold-drawn copper bar, showing the small crystal grains which compose the ordinary metal. Magnification 200 × (200-fold linearly). The small round spots are gas bubbles. (From Dr. S. Kyropoulos.)

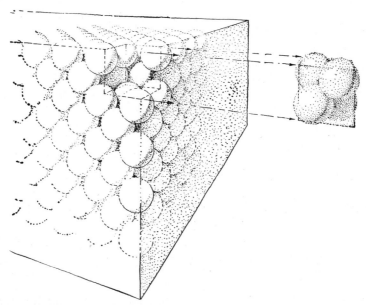

FIGURE 2-4   *The arrangement of atoms in a crystal of copper. The small cube, containing four copper atoms, is the unit of structure; by repeating it the entire crystal is obtained.*

It has been found by experiment* that *every crystal consists of atoms arranged in a three-dimensional pattern which repeats itself regularly.* In a crystal of copper all of the atoms are alike, and they are arranged in the way shown in Figures 2-4 and 2-5. This is a way in which spheres of uniform size may be packed together to occupy the smallest volume.

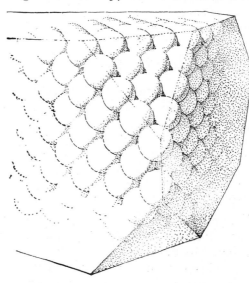

FIGURE 2-5

Another atomic view of a copper crystal, showing small octahedral faces and large cube faces.

* By x-ray diffraction.

You must remember while looking at Figures 2-4 and 2-5 that the atoms are shown greatly enlarged relative to the crystal. Even if the crystal were a small one, with edges only about 0.1 mm long, there would still be about 400,000 atoms in a row along each edge.

It is the **regularity of arrangement** *of the atoms in a crystal which gives to the crystal its characteristic properties, in particular the property of growing in the form of polyhedra.* (A polyhedron is a solid figure bounded by plane faces.) The faces of crystals are defined by surface layers of atoms, as shown in Figures 2-4 and 2-5. These faces lie at angles to one another which have definite characteristic values, the same for all specimens of the same substance. The sizes of the faces may vary from specimen to specimen, but the angles between them are always constant. The principal surface layers shown in Figures 2-4 and 2-5 for copper correspond to the faces of a cube (*cubic faces* or *cube faces*); these faces are always at right angles with one another. The smaller surface layer, obtained by cutting off a corner of a cube, is called an *octahedral face*. Native copper, found in deposits of copper ore, often is in the form of crystals with cubic and octahedral faces (Figure 2-2).

Atoms are not hard spheres, but are soft, so that by increased force they may be pushed more closely together (be compressed). This compression occurs, for example, when a copper crystal becomes somewhat smaller in volume under increased pressure. The sizes which are assigned to atoms correspond to the distance between the center of one atom and the center of a neighboring atom of the same kind in a crystal under ordinary circumstances. The distance from a copper atom to each of its twelve nearest neighbors in a copper crystal at room temperature and atmospheric pressure is 2.55 Å; this is called the *diameter* of the copper atom in metallic copper. The radius of the copper atom is half this value.

2–5. *The Molecular Structure of Matter*

Molecular Crystals. The crystal of copper, which we have been discussing as an example of a kind of matter, is built up of *atoms* arranged in a regular pattern. We shall now discuss crystals that contain *discrete groups of atoms* (distinct groups), which are called *molecules*. These crystals are called *molecular crystals*.

An example of a molecular crystal is shown in the upper left part of Figure 2-6, which is a drawing representing the structure of a crystal of the blackish-gray solid substance *iodine*. It is seen that the iodine atoms are grouped together in pairs, to form molecules containing two atoms each. Iodine is used as an example in this section and the following ones because its molecules are simple (containing only two atoms), and because it has been thoroughly studied by scientists.

The distance between the two atoms of iodine in the same molecule

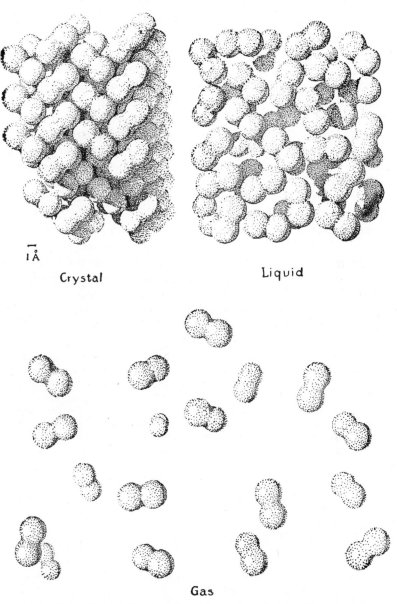

1 Å

Crystal   Liquid

Gas

FIGURE 2-6   *Crystal, liquid, and gaseous iodine, showing diatomic molecules* I_2.

of this molecular crystal is smaller than the distances between atoms in different molecules. The two iodine atoms in each molecule are only 2.70 Å apart, whereas the smallest distance between iodine atoms in different molecules is 3.54 Å.

The forces acting between atoms within a molecule are very strong, and those acting between molecules are weak. As a result of this, it is hard to cause the molecule to change its shape, whereas it is comparatively easy to roll the molecules around relative to one another. For example, under pressure a crystal of iodine decreases in size: the molecules can be pushed together until the distances between iodine atoms in different molecules have decreased by several percent; but the molecules themselves retain their original size, with no appreciable change in interatomic distance within the molecule. When a crystal of iodine at low temperature is heated it expands, so that each of the molecules occupies a larger space in the crystal; but the distance between the two iodine atoms in one molecule stays very close to the normal 2.70 Å.

The molecules of different chemical substances contain varying numbers of atoms, bonded tightly together. An example of a more complicated molecule is shown in Figure 2-7, which represents a portion of a crystal of *naphthalene*. The molecule of naphthalene contains ten carbon atoms, arranged in two hexagonal rings that have one edge in common, and eight hydrogen atoms. Naphthalene is a rather volatile substance, with a characteristic odor. In the form of moth balls, it is used as a moth repellent. The properties of naphthalene are determined by the structure of its molecules.

Photographs of Molecules Made with the Electron Microscope.   In the last few years it has finally become possible to see and to photograph molecules. They are too small to be seen with a microscope using ordinary visible light, which cannot permit objects much smaller in diameter than the wavelength of light, about 5000 Å, to be seen. A wonderful new instrument, the *electron microscope*, has now been developed, however, which permits objects a hundred times smaller in diameter to be seen. The electron microscope uses beams of electrons in place of beams of light. Its linear magnifying power is about 100,000, as compared with about 1000 for the ordinary microscope. It

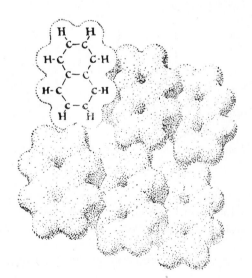

FIGURE 2-7

A portion of a crystal of naphthalene, showing molecules $C_{10}H_8$.

is accordingly possible to see objects as small as 50 Å in diameter with the electron microscope.

Two photographs made with the electron microscope are reproduced here, as Figures 2-8 and 2-9. They show molecules of viruses which cause disease in tomato plants.* Each "bushy stunt" virus molecule is about 230 Å in diameter. It is made of about 750,000 atoms. The "necrosis" virus molecules are somewhat smaller, about 195 Å in diameter. In each photograph the individual molecules can be clearly seen, and in the

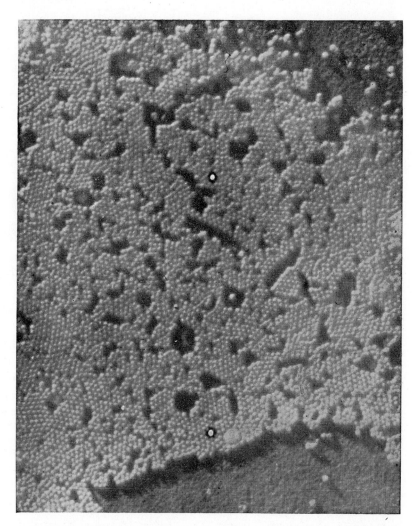

FIGURE 2-8   *Electron micrograph of a single layer of tomato bushy stunt virus molecules. The photograph was made to show added contrast by depositing a very thin layer of gold on the specimen at a small angle, giving the impression of shadows cast by the molecules. Linear magnification 55,000. (From Price, Williams, and Wyckoff, Arch. Biochem., 7, 175, 1946.)*

* A brief discussion of viruses is given in Chapter 31.

FIGURE 2-9   *Electron micrograph of crystals of necrosis virus protein, showing individual molecules in ordered arrangement. Linear magnification 65,000. (From R. W. G. Wyckoff.)*

photograph of necrosis-virus-protein molecules the regular way in which the molecules arrange themselves in the crystals is evident.

The magnifying power of the electron microscope is not yet great enough to permit ordinary molecules, such as those of naphthalene, to be seen and photographed, but scientists are working on methods of improving the instrument, and perhaps an electron micrograph of naphthalene will be available for inclusion in the third edition of this book.

The Six Crystal Systems.   Chemists often make use of the observed shapes of crystals to help in their identification. The description of the shapes of crystals is the subject of the science of *crystallography*. Every crystal can be classified in one of six crystal systems, called cubic (or isometric), hexagonal, tetragonal, orthorhombic, monoclinic, and triclinic. Characteristic shapes (forms) of crystals of these six systems are shown in Figures 2-10 and 2-11.

2–6. *Evaporation of Crystals. The Nature of a Gas*

At a very low temperature the molecules in a crystal of iodine lie rather quietly in their places in the crystal (Figure 2-6). As the temperature increases the molecules become more and more agitated; each one bounds back and forth more and more vigorously in the little space left for it by its neighbors, and each one strikes its neighbors more and more strongly as it rebounds from them.

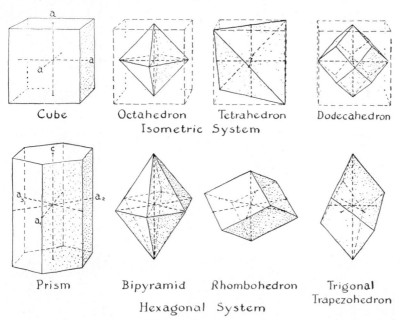

Cube   Octahedron   Tetrahedron   Dodecahedron
                   Isometric System

Prism   Bipyramid   Rhombohedron   Trigonal
                                                Trapezohedron
                   Hexagonal System

FIGURE 2-10   *Representative crystal forms of the cubic and hexagonal systems.*

A molecule on the surface of the crystal is held to the crystal by the forces of attraction that its neighboring molecules exert on it. Attractive forces of this kind, which are operative between all molecules when they are close together, are called *van der Waals attractive forces* (this name being used because it was the Dutch physicist J. D. van der Waals (1837–1923) who first gave a thorough discussion of intermolecular forces in relation to the nature of gases and liquids).

These attractive forces are quite weak, much weaker than the forces between the atoms in one molecule. Hence occasionally a certain molecule may become so agitated as to break loose from its neighbors, and to fly off into the surrounding space. If the crystal is in a vessel, there will soon be present in the space within the vessel through this process of evaporation a large number of these free molecules, each moving in a straight-line path, and occasionally colliding with another molecule or with the walls of the vessel to change the direction of its motion. These free molecules constitute *iodine vapor* or *iodine gas* (Figure 2-6). The gas molecules are very much like the molecules in the crystal, their interatomic distance being practically the same; it is the distances between molecules that are much larger in a gas than in a crystal.

It may seem surprising that molecules on the surface of a crystal should evaporate directly into a gas, instead of going first through the stage of being in a liquid layer; but in fact the process of slow evaporation of a crystalline substance is not uncommon. Solid pieces of camphor or of naphthalene (as used in moth balls, for example) left out in the

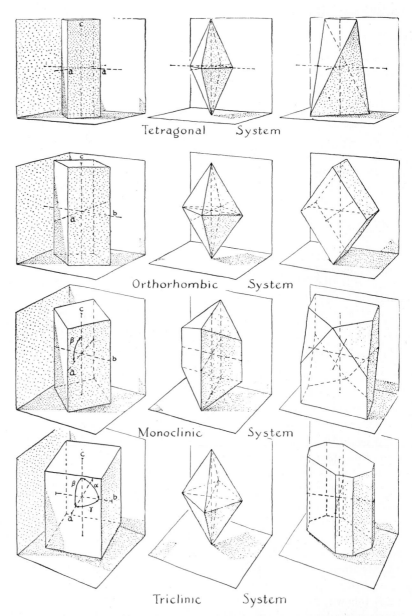

Tetragonal   System

Orthorhombic   System

Monoclinic   System

Triclinic   System

FIGURE 2-11   *Representative crystal forms of the tetragonal, orthorhombic, monoclinic, and triclinic crystal systems.*

air slowly decrease in size, because of the evaporation of molecules from the surface of the solid. Snow may disappear from the ground without melting, by evaporation of the ice crystals at a temperature below that of their melting point. Evaporation is accelerated if a wind is blowing, to take the water vapor away from the immediate neighborhood of the snow crystals, and to prevent the vapor from condensing again on the crystals.

The Nature of a Gas. The characteristic feature of a gas is that *its molecules are not held together, but are moving about freely, in a volume rather large compared with the volume of the molecules themselves.* The attractive forces between the molecules still operate whenever two molecules come close together, but usually these forces are negligibly small because the molecules are far apart.

Because of the freedom of motion of its molecules a specimen of gas does not have either definite shape or definite size. *A gas shapes itself to its container.*

Gases at ordinary pressure are very dilute—the molecules themselves constitute only about one one-thousandth of the total volume of the gas, the rest being empty space. Thus one gram of solid iodine has a volume of about 0.2 cm³ (its density* is 4.93 g/cm³), whereas one gram of iodine gas at 1 atmosphere pressure and at the temperature 184° C (its boiling point) has a volume of 148 cm³, over 700 times greater. The volume of all of the molecules in a gas is accordingly very small compared with the volume of the gas itself at ordinary pressure. On the other hand, the diameter of a gas molecule is not extremely small compared with the distance between molecules; in a gas at room temperature and 1 atmosphere pressure the average distance from a molecule to its nearest neighbors is about ten times its molecular diameter, as indicated in Figure 2-6†.

The Vapor Pressure of a Crystal. A crystal of iodine in an evacuated vessel will gradually change into iodine gas by the evaporation of molecules from its surface. Occasionally one of these free gas molecules will again strike the surface of the crystal, and it may stick to the surface, held by the van der Waals attraction of the other crystal molecules. This is called *condensation* of the gas molecules.

The rate at which molecules evaporate from a crystal surface is proportional to the area of the surface, but is essentially independent of the pressure of the surrounding gas, whereas the rate at which gas molecules strike the crystal surface is proportional to the area of the surface and also proportional to the concentration of molecules in the gas (the number of gas molecules in unit volume).

If some iodine crystals are put into a flask, which is then stoppered and allowed to stand at room temperature, it will soon be seen that the gas in the flask has become violet in color, showing that a quantity of iodine has evaporated. After a while it will be evident that the process of evaporation has apparently ceased, because the intensity of colora-

---

* It was mentioned in Section 1–4 that the density of a substance is the mass (weight) of a unit volume of the substance; in the metric system grams per cubic centimeter.

† You will remember that a cube 1 inch on edge has a diameter one tenth as great as that of a cube 10 inches on edge, an area one one-hundredth as great, and a volume one one-thousandth as great.

Iodine vapor, violet color

Iodine crystals

FIGURE 2-12

The evaporation of iodine crystals.

tion of the gas will no longer increase, but will remain constant (Figure 2-12). This steady state is reached when the concentration of gas molecules becomes so great that the rate at which gas molecules strike the crystal surface and stay there is just equal to the rate at which molecules leave the crystal surface. *The corresponding gas pressure is called the* **vapor pressure** *of the crystal.*

A steady state of such a sort is an example of *equilibrium*. It must be

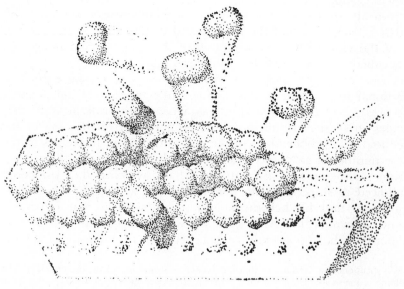

FIGURE 2-13   *Equilibrium between molecules evaporating from an iodine crystal and gas molecules depositing on the crystal.*

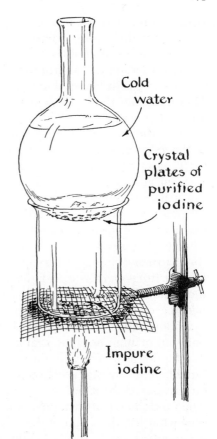

Cold water

Crystal plates of purified iodine

Impure iodine

FIGURE 2-14

The purification of iodine by sublimation.

recognized that equilibrium does not represent a situation in which nothing is happening, but rather a situation in which opposing reactions are taking place at the same rate, so as to result in no over-all change. This is indicated in Figure 2-13.

The vapor pressure of iodine increases with increase in temperature. The crystals of iodine which are heated to a temperature only a little below the melting point evaporate rapidly and the vapor may condense into crystals in a cooler part of the vessel. The complete process of evaporation of a crystal and recondensation of a gas directly as crystals, without apparently passing through the liquid state, is called *sublimation*. Sublimation is often a valuable method of purifying a substance; the way in which iodine can be purified by sublimation is shown in Figure 2-14.

2-7. *The Nature of a Liquid*

When iodine crystals are heated to 114° C they melt, forming liquid iodine. The temperature at which the crystals and the liquid are in equilibrium, that is, at which there is no tendency for the crystals to melt or for the liquid to freeze, is called the *melting point* of the crystals, and the *freezing point* of the liquid. This temperature is 114° C for iodine.

Liquid iodine differs from the solid (crystals) mainly in its *fluidity*. It is like the gas in being able to adjust itself to the shape of its container. However, like the solid, and unlike the gas, it has a definite volume, 1 g occupying about 0.2 cm³.

From the molecular viewpoint the process of melting can be described in the following way. As a crystal is heated its molecules become increasingly agitated, and move about more and more vigorously; but this thermal agitation does not carry any one molecule any significant distance away from the position fixed for it by the arrangement of its neighbors in the crystal. At the melting point the agitation finally becomes so great as to cause the molecules to slip by one another and to change somewhat their location relative to one another. They continue to stay close together, but do not continue to retain a regular fixed arrangement; instead the grouping of molecules around a given molecule changes continually, sometimes being much like the close packing of the crystal, in which each iodine molecule has twelve near neighbors, and sometimes considerably different, the molecule having only ten or nine or eight near neighbors, as shown in Figure 2-6. Thus in a liquid, as in a crystal, the molecules are piled rather closely together; but whereas a crystal is characterized by regularity of atomic or molecular arrangement, a liquid is characterized by randomness of structure. The randomness of structure usually causes the density of a liquid to be somewhat less than that of the corresponding crystal; that is, the volume occupied by the liquid is usually somewhat greater than that occupied by the crystal.

The Vapor Pressure and Boiling Point of a Liquid.   A liquid, like a crystal, is, at any temperature, in equilibrium with its own vapor when the vapor molecules are present in a certain concentration. The pressure corresponding to this concentration of gas molecules is called the *vapor pressure of the liquid* at the given temperature.

The vapor pressure of every liquid increases with increasing temperature. *The temperature at which the vapor pressure reaches a standard value (usually 1 atm) is called the* **boiling point** *of the liquid.* At this temperature it is possible for bubbles of the vapor to appear in the liquid and to escape to the surface.

The vapor pressure of liquid iodine reaches 1 atm at 184° C. Hence 184° C is the boiling point of iodine.

Other substances undergo similar changes when they are heated. When copper melts, at 1083° C, it forms liquid copper, in which the arrangement of the copper atoms shows the same sort of randomness as that of the molecules of liquid iodine. Under 1 atm pressure copper

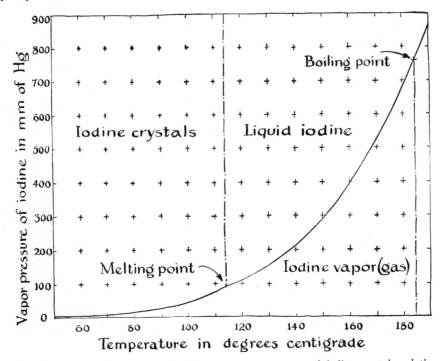

FIGURE 2-15   *A graph showing the vapor-pressure curve of iodine crystal and the vapor-pressure curve of liquid iodine. The melting point of the crystal is the temperature at which the crystal and the liquid have the same vapor pressure, and the boiling point of the liquid (at 1 atm pressure) is the temperature at which the vapor pressure of the liquid equals 1 atm.*

boils at 2310° C to form copper gas; the gas molecules are single copper atoms.

Note that it is customary to refer to the particles that move about in a gas as molecules even though each one may be only a single atom, as in the case of copper.

The Dependence of Vapor Pressure on Temperature.   It has been found by experiment that the vapor pressure of crystals and liquids increases as the temperature is raised. Curves showing the vapor pressure of iodine crystals and liquid iodine are shown in Figure 2-15.

2–8. *The Meaning of Temperature*

In the preceding discussion the assumption has been made that molecules move more rapidly and violently at any given temperature than at a lower one. This assumption is correct—the temperature of a system is a measure of the vigor of motion of all the atoms and molecules in the system.

With increase in temperature there occurs increase in violence of molecular motion of all kinds. Gas molecules rotate more rapidly, and the atoms within a molecule oscil-

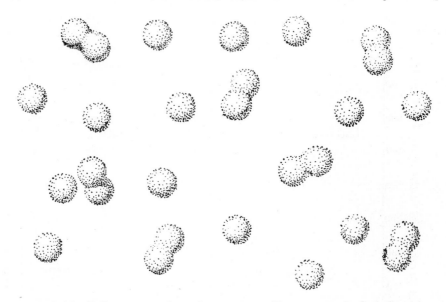

FIGURE 2-16   *Iodine vapor at elevated temperature; this vapor contains both diatomic molecules* (I_2) *and monatomic molecules* (I) *of iodine.*

late more rapidly relative to one another. The atoms and molecules in liquids and solids carry out more vigorous vibrational motions. This vigorous motion at high temperatures may result in chemical reaction, especially decomposition of substances. Thus when iodine gas is heated to about 1200° C at 1 atm pressure about one-half of the molecules dissociate (split) into separate iodine atoms (Figure 2-16).

You can get a better understanding of many of the phenomena of chemistry by remembering that the absolute temperature is a measure of the vigor of the motion of atoms and molecules.

Concepts and Terms Introduced in This Chapter

Tested hypotheses become theories or laws. The atomic theory—the most important of all chemical theories.

Atoms—small particles of different kinds, corresponding to the different elements.

Law of conservation of mass. Law of constant proportions. Law of simple multiple proportions.

Modern methods of studying atoms and molecules.

Crystalline copper. Regularity of atomic arrangement in crystals.

Molecule; molecular crystals. Iodine as an example. The six crystal systems.

Evaporation of crystals. Vapor pressure of crystals. Sublimation.

Van der Waals intermolecular forces.

The difference in nature of a crystal, a liquid, and a gas. Vapor pressure, freezing point, and boiling point of a liquid.

The meaning of temperature in relation to molecular motion.

Exercises

2-3.   In your own words, define atom, molecule, crystal, liquid, gas.

2-4.   Carbon dioxide (Dry Ice) consists of CO_2 molecules. These molecules are linear, with the carbon atom in the center. Make three drawings, representing your concepts of carbon dioxide gas, carbon dioxide liquid, and carbon dioxide crystal.

2-5.   Define vapor pressure of a crystal, and also vapor pressure of a liquid. Can you think of an argument showing that these two vapor pressures of a substance must be equal at the melting point?

2-6.   The vapor pressure of solid carbon dioxide at its melting point, $-56.5°$ C, is 5 atm. How do you explain the fact that solid carbon dioxide when used for packing ice cream does not melt to form liquid carbon dioxide? If you wanted to make some liquid carbon dioxide, what would you have to do?

2-7.   Give an example of a solid material that is crystalline and of one that is not crystalline.

2-8.   Classify the following statements as hypotheses, theories, laws, or facts:
       a. The moon is made of limestone.
       b. With a few exceptions, substances increase in volume on melting.
       c. The core of the earth is composed of a metallic form of hydrogen, which has not yet been prepared in the laboratory.
       d. Hydrogen, oxygen, nitrogen, and neon are all gases under ordinary conditions.
       e. All crystals are composed of atoms arranged in a regular way.

2-9.   Spectroscopic study of moonlight and sunlight has shown that the reflectivity of the moon (its power of reflecting light of different colors) is not the same as that of limestone. Does this single observed fact eliminate the hypothesis that the moon is composed of limestone? Would you change the name from hypothesis to theory if it had been found that the reflectivity of the moon was (to within experimental error) the same as that of limestone?

2-10. It is stated in the text that copper atoms are 2.55 Å in diameter.
       a. How many Ångströms are there in 1 inch?
       b. How many copper atoms side by side in contact would make a line 1 inch long?
       c. How many atoms of the same size in a simple square array would cover 1 sq. in. of surface?
       d. How many atoms of the same size in a simple cubic array would occupy 1 cu. in.?

2-11. There are about 0.9×10^{24} molecules of water in a cubic inch of water. If a cubic inch of water were poured into the ocean and thoroughly stirred, and a cubic inch of ocean water were then removed, about how many molecules from the original cubic inch would be found in it? Assume the volume of the ocean to correspond to an average depth of 1 mile over the entire surface of the earth.

2-12. If the molecules in a glass of water (say 10 cu. in.) were to be increased in diameter a millionfold, making each molecule the size of a small grain of sand, to what depth could the surface of the earth be covered uniformly with the enlarged molecules?

2-13. Arrange marbles, steel balls, or other spheres of the same size in a close-packed layer, such that each sphere is surrounded by six spheres in contact with it. Pack a similar layer on top of the first one, so that each sphere in the second layer is in the pocket formed by the three spheres in the lower layer. Note that a third layer could then be put directly above the first layer, or in another position; the second of these alternatives, repeated, leads to the structure of the copper crystal. Repeat this process to build a triangular pyramid. Note that this pyramid is a regular tetrahedron.

2-14. Describe qualitatively the structure of a crystal of iodine, of liquid iodine, of gaseous iodine at low temperature, and of gaseous iodine at high temperature.

2-15. What is the effect of increase in pressure on the boiling point of a liquid? Estimate the boiling point of liquid iodine at a pressure of $\frac{1}{2}$ atm (see Figure 2-15).

2-16. Camphor sublimes at 205° C. What is this temperature in °F? Can you suggest a way of extracting camphor from the leaves and wood of the camphor tree?

Reference Books

A somewhat more detailed discussion of the atomic structure of crystals than that given above can be found in Chapter 2 of L. Pauling, *General Chemistry*, 2nd Ed., W. H. Freeman and Company, San Francisco, **1953**.

A simple discussion of x-rays and the x-ray diffraction method of determining the structure of crystals is given in Chapter 3 of *General Chemistry*. For more detailed discussions see W. H. Bragg and W. L. Bragg, *X-Rays and Crystal Structure*, Harcourt, Brace and Co., New York, **1924,** or the article X-Rays and Crystal Structure in the Encyclopaedia Britannica, 14th Ed.

A simple account of the determination of the structure of gas molecules by the diffraction of electrons has been given by R. Spurr and L. Pauling, *Journal of Chemical Education,* **18**, 458 (1941).

Chapter 3

The Electron and
the Nuclei of Atoms

In the preceding chapter we have discussed the atomic theory, and have seen that some of the properties of substances can be explained by this theory. The two substances copper and iodine, which were used as the principal examples in the discussion, have different properties because their atoms are different.

Chemists of the nineteenth century asked whether it might be possible to understand the differences between atoms of different elements, such as copper and iodine, but they were not able to answer the question. About fifty years ago, however, it was discovered that atoms themselves are composed of still smaller particles. The discovery of the components of atoms and the investigation of the structure of atoms—the ways in which atoms of different kinds are built of the smaller particles—constitute one of the most interesting stories in the history of science. Moreover, knowledge about the structure of atoms has during recent years permitted the facts of chemistry to be systematized in a striking way, making the subject easier to understand and to remember. The student of chemistry can be helped greatly in mastering his subject by first obtaining a good understanding of atomic structure.

The particles that constitute atoms are *electrons* and *atomic nuclei*. Electrons and atomic nuclei carry electric charges, and these electric charges are in large part responsible for the properties of the particles and for the structure of atoms. We shall accordingly begin this chapter with a discussion of the nature of electricity.

3–1. *The Nature of Electricity*

The ancient Greeks knew that when a piece of amber is rubbed with wool or fur it achieves the power of attracting light objects, such as feathers or bits of straw. This phenomenon was studied by William Gilbert (1540–1603), Queen Elizabeth I's physician, who invented the adjective *electric* to describe the force of attraction, after the Greek word *elektron*, meaning amber. Gilbert and many other scientists, including Benjamin Franklin, investigated electric phenomena, and during the nineteenth century many discoveries about the nature of electricity, and of magnetism (which is closely related to electricity), were made.

It was found that if a rod of sealing wax, which behaves in the same way as amber, is rubbed with a woolen cloth, and a rod of glass is rubbed with a silken cloth, an electric spark will pass between the sealing-wax rod and the glass rod when they are brought near one another. More-over, it was found that a force of attraction operates between them. If the sealing-wax rod that has been electrically charged by rubbing with a woolen cloth is suspended from a thread, as shown in Figure 3-1, and the charged glass rod is brought near one end of it, this end will turn toward the glass rod. An electrified sealing-wax rod is repelled, however, by a similar sealing-wax rod, and also an electrified glass rod is repelled by a similar glass rod (Figure 3-1).

Through the experimental study of such phenomena, the ideas were developed that there are two kinds of electricity, which were called resinous electricity (that which is picked up by the sealing-wax rod) and vitreous electricity (that which is picked up by the glass rod), and that the two kinds of electricity attract one another, whereas each kind repels itself. Franklin simplified this picture of electricity somewhat, by assuming that only one kind of electricity can flow from an object to another object. He assumed that when a glass rod is rubbed with a silken cloth this electric "fluid" is transferred from the cloth to the glass rod, and he described the glass rod as *positively charged*, meaning that it had an excess of the electric fluid. He described the cloth as having a deficiency of the electric fluid, and being *negatively charged*. He pointed out that he did not really know whether the electric fluid had been

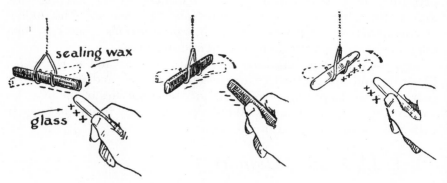

FIGURE 3-1   *Experiments showing the attraction of unlike charges of electricity and the repulsion of like charges.*

transferred from the silken cloth to the glass rod or from the glass rod to the silken cloth, and that accordingly the decision to describe vitreous electricity as positive (involving an excess of electric fluid) was an arbitrary one. We now know, in fact, that when the glass rod is rubbed with a silken cloth negatively charged particles, the electrons, are transferred from the glass rod to the silken cloth, and that Franklin thus made the wrong decision in his assumption.

Units of Electric Charge. The unit of electric charge in the metric system is called the *statcoulomb*. (The definition of this unit is given in textbooks of physics.) In practical work there is need for a larger unit of electric charge. The larger unit that has been adopted is the *coulomb*, which is closely equal to 3×10^9 statcoulombs:

1 coulomb $= 3 \times 10^9$ statcoulombs

3–2. *The Discovery of the Electron*

The idea that there are electric particles in substances was proposed, as a hypothesis, by G. Johnstone Stoney, an English scientist. Stoney knew that substances can be decomposed by an electric current—for example, water can be decomposed into hydrogen and oxygen in this way. He also knew that Michael Faraday had found that a definite amount of electricity is needed to liberate a certain amount of an element from one of its compounds. The experiment carried out by Faraday will be discussed in Chapter 10 of our book. In 1874, after thinking about these facts, Stoney stated that they indicate that *electricity exists in discrete units*, and that these units are associated with atoms. In 1891 he suggested the name *electron* for his postulated unit of electricity. The discovery of the electron by experiment was made in 1897 by Sir J. J. Thomson (1856–1940), in Cambridge University, England.*

The Properties of the Electron. The electron is a particle with a negative electric charge of magnitude -4.802×10^{-10} statcoulombs, or -1.601×10^{-19} coulombs.

The mass of the electron is 9.107×10^{-28} g, which is 1/1837 of the mass of the hydrogen atom.

The electron is very small. The radius of the electron cannot be determined exactly, but it is known to be about 1×10^{-12} cm. Since atoms have radii of about 1×10^{-8} cm, the electron is only about 1/10,000 as large as an atom.

* The experiments that led to the discovery of the electron are described in Section 3–7.

3–3. *The Flow of Electricity in a Metal*

Knowledge of the existence of electrons permits us to discuss some of the properties of electricity in a simple way.

In a metal or similar conductor of electricity there are electrons which have considerable freedom of motion, and which move along between the atoms of the metal when an electric potential difference is applied. A direct current of electricity passing along a copper wire is a *flow of electrons* along the wire.

Let us call to mind the analogy between the flow of electricity along a wire and the flow of water in a pipe. *Quantity* of water is measured in liters or cubic feet; quantity of electricity is usually measured either in *coulombs* or in *statcoulombs*. *Rate of flow*, or *current*, of water, the quantity passing a given point of the pipe in unit time, is measured in liters per second, or cubic feet per second; current of electricity is measured in *amperes* (coulombs per second). The rate of flow of water in a pipe depends on the *difference in the pressures* at the two ends of the pipe, with atmospheres or pounds per square inch as units. The current of electricity in a wire depends on the *electric potential difference* or *voltage drop* between its ends, which is usually measured in *volts*. The definitions of the unit of quantity of electricity (the coulomb) and the unit of electric potential (the volt) have been made by international agreement.

An electric generator is essentially an electron pump, which pumps electrons out of one wire and into another. A generator of direct current pumps electrons continually in the same direction, and one of alternating current reverses its pumping direction regularly, thus building up electron pressure first in one direction and then in the other. A 60-cycle generator reverses its pumping direction 120 times per second.

Illustrative Exercises

3-1. An ordinary electric light bulb is operated under conditions such that one ampere of current (one coulomb per second) is passing through the filament. How many electrons pass through the filament each second? (Remember that the charge of the electron is -1.60×10^{-19} coulombs.)

3-2. If a golf ball could be magnified 250,000,000 times, making it as big as the earth, each atom (3 or 4 Å in diameter) would become 3 or 4 inches in diameter. Would the electrons then look like peas, or birdshot, or fine grains of sand, or particles of dust?

3–4. *The Nuclei of Atoms*

In 1911 the British physicist Ernest Rutherford carried out some experiments* which showed that every atom contains, in addition to one or more electrons, another particle, called the *nucleus* of the atom. Every nucleus has a positive electric charge. It is very small, being only about as big as an electron (about 10^{-12} cm in diameter), and it is very heavy— the lightest nucleus is 1836 times as heavy as an electron.

There are many different kinds of nuclei; those of the atoms of one element are different from those of every other element. The nucleus of the hydrogen atom has the same electric charge as the electron, but

---

* These experiments are described in later sections of this chapter.

with opposite sign, positive instead of negative. The nuclei of other atoms have positive charges that are multiples of this fundamental charge.

3–5. *The Proton and the Neutron*

The *proton* is the simplest atomic nucleus. It is the nucleus of the most abundant kind of hydrogen atom, which is the lightest of all atoms.

The proton has an electric charge 4.802×10^{-10} statcoulomb or 1.601×10^{-19} coulomb. This charge is exactly the same as that of the electron, except that it is positive, whereas the charge of the electron is negative.

The mass of the proton is 1.672×10^{-24} g. This is 1836 times the mass of the electron.

The *neutron* was discovered by the English physicist James Chadwick in 1932. The mass of the neutron is 1.675×10^{-24} g, which is 1839 times the mass of the electron. The neutron has no electric charge.

It is customary for chemists to use an *atomic mass unit*, which is approximately the mass of the proton. Both the proton and the neutron have masses which are approximately one atomic mass unit.

3–6. *The Structure of Atomic Nuclei*

Several hundred different kinds of atomic nuclei are known to exist. Together with the electrons that surround them, they make up the atoms of the different chemical elements. At the present time physicists all over the world are working on the problem of the structure of atomic nuclei. They have not yet solved this problem, although they have learned a great deal about the properties of the nuclei, and the ways in which they can be made from other particles or converted into other particles. This phase of chemistry, which we call *nuclear chemistry*, is discussed in Chapter 32 of our book.

$_1H^1$ $_1H^2$ $_2He^4$
Proton Deuteron Alpha particle

FIGURE 3-2

Hypothetical structures of some atomic nuclei. We do not yet know just how these nuclei are constructed out of elementary particles, but it is known that nuclei are approximately 10^{-12} cm in diameter, and are, accordingly, very small even compared with atoms.

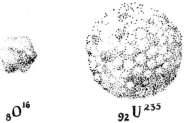

$_8O^{16}$ $_{92}U^{235}$

Although the detailed structures of nuclei are not known, physicists seem to be agreed in accepting the idea that they can all be described as being built up of protons and neutrons.

Let us first discuss, as an example, the *deuteron*. This is the nucleus of the *heavy hydrogen atom*, or *deuterium atom*. The deuteron has the same electric charge as the proton, but has about twice the mass of the proton. It is thought that the deuteron is made of one proton and one neutron, as indicated in Figure 3-2.

The nucleus of the helium atom, which is also called the *alpha particle*, has electric charge twice as great as that of the proton, and mass about four times as great as that of the proton. It is thought that the alpha particle is composed of two protons and two neutrons.

In Figure 3-2 there is also shown a drawing representing the nucleus of an oxygen atom, composed of eight protons and eight neutrons. The electric charge of this nucleus is eight times the electric charge of the proton. This electric charge would accordingly be neutralized by the negative charges of eight electrons. The mass of this oxygen nucleus is about 16 mass units.

There is also shown in the figure a hypothetical drawing of the nucleus of a uranium atom. This nucleus is composed of 92 protons and 143 neutrons. The electric charge of this nucleus is 92 times that of the proton; it would be neutralized by the negative charges of 92 electrons. The mass of this nucleus is about 235 times the mass of the proton.

In thinking about atoms and atomic nuclei, you must remember that the drawings of atomic nuclei in Figure 3-2 correspond to a magnification ten thousand times greater than the drawings of atoms and molecules that are shown elsewhere in this book. The nuclei are very small, even compared with atoms.

We shall continue the discussion of atomic nuclei of different kinds, and atoms of different kinds, in the following chapter.

3-7. *The Experiments That Led to the Discovery of the Electron*

Many interesting experiments involving electricity were carried out by physicists during the nineteenth century. These experiments ultimately led to the discovery of the electron. In order to understand them it is necessary to know something about the way in which the motion of an electrically charged particle is affected by other electric charges or by a magnet.

The Interaction of an Electric Charge with Other Electric Charges and with Magnets. An electric charge is said to be surrounded by an *electric field*, which exercises a force, either of attraction or of repulsion, on any other electric charge in its neighborhood. The strength of an electric field can be measured by determining the force that operates on a unit of electric charge.

In experimental work use is often made of an apparatus like that shown in Figure

FIGURE 3-3

The motion of an electrically charged particle in the uniform electric field between charged plates.

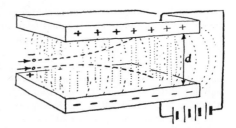

3-3, in which two large parallel plates of metal are held a small, constant distance from one another. By use of a battery or generator of electricity, one of these parallel plates is charged positively (that is, some electrons are taken away from it), and the other is charged negatively.

A wire or plate which has an excess of positive charge is called an *anode*. A wire or plate which has an excess of negative electric charge is called a *cathode*. In Figure 3-3 the upper plate is the anode and the lower plate is the cathode.

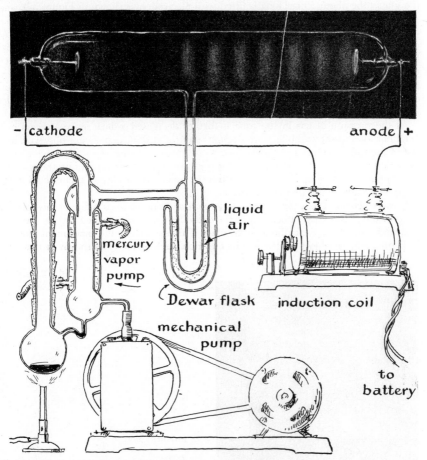

FIGURE 3-4 *Apparatus used to observe the discharge of electricity in a gas at low pressure. The dark space around the cathode is called the Crookes dark space; at still lower pressures the Crookes dark space fills the whole tube.*

A particle with negative electric charge placed between the plates would be attracted toward the upper plate and repelled from the lower plate. It would accordingly move in the direction of the upper plate. Similarly, a particle with positive electric charge placed between the plates would move toward the lower plate.

The force exerted on a positive charge by the electric field between the plates has the same effect as the force exerted on a mass by the gravitational field of the earth. Accordingly a positively charged particle shot into the region between the plates, as indicated in Figure 3-3, would fall to the bottom plate along the path indicated by the dashed line, in the same way that a rock thrown horizontally would fall toward the surface of the earth.

You know that a piece of iron or steel can be magnetized, to form a *magnet*, and that the magnet has the power of attracting other pieces of iron. A magnet also has the power of exerting a force on any electrically charged particle that shoots by it. A magnet can hence also be used to study charged particles.

The Discovery of the Electron.   During the nineteenth century many physicists carried out experiments on the conduction of electricity through gases. For example, if a glass tube about 50 cm long is fitted with electrodes, as shown in Figure 3-4, and a potential of about 10,000 volts is applied between the electrodes, no electricity is at first conducted between the electrodes. If, however, some of the air in the tube is pumped out, by use of pumps such as those indicated in the lower part of the figure, electricity begins to be conducted through the tube. While the electricity is being conducted through the tube light is emitted by the gas in the tube. You are familiar with this phenomenon, because you have seen many neon lamps in street signs. These neon lamps contain the gas neon, or some other gas, which is caused to emit light when electricity is conducted through the gas.

As the pressure of gas in the tube is further decreased a dark space appears in the neighborhood of the cathode, and alternate light and dark regions are observed in the rest of the tube, as shown in Figure 3-4. At still lower pressure the dark space increases in size until it fills the whole tube. At this pressure no light is given out by the gas which is still present in very small quantity within the tube, but the glass of the tube itself glows (*fluoresces*) with a faint greenish light.

It was discovered that the greenish light coming from the glass is due to the bombardment of the glass by rays liberated at the cathode. These rays, called *cathode rays*, travel in straight lines from the cathode to the glass. This is shown by the experiment illustrated in Figure 3-5: an object placed within the tube, such as the cross shown in this figure,

FIGURE 3-5

Experiment showing that cathode rays, starting from the cathode at the left, move through the Crookes tube in straight lines.

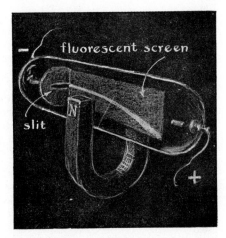

FIGURE 3-6

Experiment showing that the cathode rays have a negative charge.

casts a shadow on the glass—the glass fluoresces everywhere except in the region of this shadow.

It was shown by the French scientist Jean Perrin (1870–1942) in 1895 that these cathode rays consist of particles with a negative electric charge, rather than a positive charge. His experiment is illustrated in Figure 3-6. He introduced a shield with a slit in the tube, so as to form a beam of cathode rays. He also placed a fluorescent screen* in the tube, so that the path of the beam could be followed by the trace of the fluorescence. When a magnet was placed near the tube the beam was observed to be deflected in the direction corresponding to the presence of a negative charge on the particles.

J. J. Thomson then carried out some experiments that permitted him to make some quantitative statements about the particles that constitute the cathode rays. He used the apparatus shown in Figure 3-7, in which a beam of cathode rays can be affected by

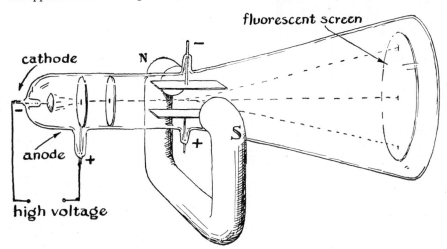

FIGURE 3-7   *The apparatus used by J. J. Thomson to determine the ratio of electric charge to mass of the cathode rays, through the simultaneous deflection of the rays by an electric field and a magnetic field.*

* A fluorescent screen is a sheet of paper or glass coated with a substance that shines when it is struck by electrons.

either a magnet that is brought up beside the tube, or by an electric field, produced by applying an electric potential to the two metal plates in the tube, or by both the magnet and the electric field. The effect on the beam of cathode rays was observed by use of a fluorescent screen. The results of his experiment convinced Thomson that the cathode-ray particles constitute a form of matter different from ordinary forms of matter. The particles were indicated by Thomson's experiments to be much lighter than atoms. Later and more accurate experiments showed that the mass of the cathode-ray particle is only 1/1837 times the mass of the hydrogen atom.

Although other investigators had carried out important experiments on cathode rays, the quantitative experiments by Thomson provided the first convincing evidence that these rays consist of particles (electrons) much lighter than atoms, and Thomson is hence given the credit for discovering the electron.

The Determination of the Charge of the Electron.   After the discovery of the electron by Thomson, many investigators worked on the problem of determining accurately the charge of the electron. The American physicist R. A. Millikan (1868–1953), who began his experiments in 1906, was the most successful of the earlier experimenters. By means of his oil-drop experiment he determined the value of the charge of the electron to within one percent in 1909.

The apparatus that he used is illustrated in Figure 3-8. Small drops of oil are formed by a sprayer, and some of them attach themselves to electrons that have been separated from molecules by action of a beam of x-rays. The experimenter watches one of these small oil drops through a microscope. He first measures the rate at which it falls in the earth's gravitational field. The small drops fall at a rate determined by their size, and measurement of the rate of fall of a drop permits the investigator to calculate the size.

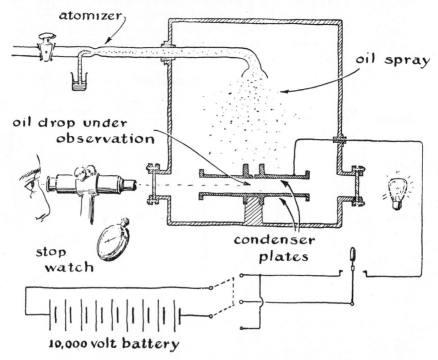

FIGURE 3-8   *A diagram of the apparatus used by R. A. Millikan in determining the charge of the electron by the oil-drop method.*

When the electric field is turned on, by charging the plates above and below the region where the oil drops are moving, some of the drops which carry no electric charge, continue to fall as before. Other drops, carrying electric charges, change their speed, and may rise, being pulled up by the attraction of the electric charge for the oppositely charged upper plate in the apparatus. The rate of a drop that has been watched falling is then observed. From these measurements, the magnitude of the electric charge on the drop can be calculated. In various experiments with different oil drops, values such as the following were obtained for the electric charge on the drop:

Charge $= 4.8 \times 10^{-10}$ statcoulombs

Charge $= 9.6 \times 10^{-10} = 2 \times 4.8 \times 10^{-10}$

Charge $= 4.8 \times 10^{-10}$

Charge $= 24.0 \times 10^{-10} = 5 \times 4.8 \times 10^{-10}$

All of these values have a common factor, 4.8×10^{-10} statcoulombs. Millikan accordingly concluded that this is the smallest electric charge that can occur under these conditions, and he identified it with the charge of the electron.

Since Millikan carried out his work, a number of other methods have been developed for determining the charge of the electron, and its value is now known to about 0.01 percent.

3–8. The Discovery of X-Rays and Radioactivity

Several great scientific discoveries were made in a period of a few years, beginning in 1895. These discoveries made great changes in chemistry as well as in physics. X-rays were discovered in 1895, radioactivity was discovered in 1896, the new radioactive elements polonium and radium were isolated in the same year, and the electron was discovered in 1897.

Wilhelm Konrad Röntgen (1845–1923), Professor of Physics in the University of Würzburg, Germany, reported in 1895 that he had discovered a new kind of rays, which he called x-rays. These rays are produced when electricity is passed through a tube such as that shown in Figure 3-4. The rays are outside of the tube; they radiate from the place where the cathode-ray electrons strike the glass. They have the power of passing through matter that is opaque to ordinary light, and of exposing a photographic plate. Within a few weeks after the announcement of this great discovery x-rays were being used by physicians for the investigation of patients with broken bones and other disorders.

Soon after the discovery of x-rays the French physicist Henri Becquerel (1852–1908) investigated some minerals containing uranium. He found that these minerals emit

FIGURE 3-9

A simple electroscope. When an electric charge is present on the gold foil and its support, the two leaves of the foil separate, because of the repulsion of like electric charges.

rays that, like x-rays, can pass through black paper and other opaque materials and expose a photographic plate. He also found that the radiation produced by the uranium minerals could, like x-rays, discharge an electroscope (Figure 3-9), by making the air conductive.

Marie Sklodowska Curie (1867–1934) then began a systematic investigation of "Bequerel radiation," using the electroscope as a test. She investigated many substances, to see if they were similar to uranium in producing rays. She found that natural pitchblend, an ore of uranium, is several times more active than purified uranium oxide.

With her husband, Professor Pierre Curie (1859–1906), she began to separate pitchblend into fractions and to determine their activity in discharging the electroscope. She isolated a fraction that was 400 times more active than uranium. This fraction consisted largely of bismuth sulfide. Since pure bismuth sulfide is not radioactive, she assumed that a new, strongly radioactive element, similar in chemical properties to bismuth, was present as a contaminant. This element, which she named *polonium*, was the first element discovered through its properties of radioactivity. In the same year, 1896, the Curies isolated another new radioactive element, which they named *radium*.

In 1899 Ernest Rutherford, working in the Cavendish Laboratory in Cambridge, England, under J. J. Thomson, reported that the radiation from uranium is of at least two distinct types, which he called alpha radiation and beta radiation. A French investigator, P. Villard, soon reported that a third kind of radiation, gamma radiation, is also emitted.

Alpha, Beta, and Gamma Rays.   The experiments showing the presence of three kinds of rays emitted by natural radioactive materials are illustrated by Figure 3-10. The rays, formed into a beam by passing along a narrow hole in a lead block, traverse a strong magnetic field. They are affected in three different ways, showing that the three kinds of rays have different electric charges. Alpha rays carry a positive electric charge. Beta rays carry a negative electric charge, and are deflected by a magnet in the opposite direction to the alpha rays. Gamma rays do not carry an electric charge, and are not deflected by the magnet.

Rutherford found that the alpha rays, after they are slowed down, produce the gas helium. Further studies made by him showed definitely that the *alpha rays are the positively charged parts of helium atoms*, moving at high speeds. The *beta rays are electrons*, also moving at high speeds—they are similar in nature to the cathode rays produced in an electric discharge tube. *Gamma rays are a form of radiant energy, similar to visible light.* They are identical with x-rays produced in an x-ray tube operated at very high voltage.

The identification of the positively charged alpha particles with helium atoms was made by Rutherford by an experiment in which he allowed alpha particles to be shot through a thin metal foil into a chamber, and later was able to show that helium

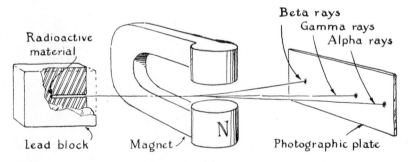

FIGURE 3-10   *The deflection of alpha rays and beta rays by a magnetic field.*

is present in the chamber. He could, moreover, correlate the amount of helium in the chamber with the number of alpha particles that had passed through the foil.

3–9. *The Discovery of the Nuclei of Atoms*

In 1911 Rutherford carried out the experiment that showed that most of the mass of atoms is concentrated in particles that are very small in size compared with the atoms themselves.

His experiment consisted in bombarding a film of some substance, a piece of metal foil, with a stream of fast-moving alpha particles, and observing the direction in which the alpha particles rebound from the atoms. The nature of the experiment is indicated by the drawing in Figure 3-11. A piece of radium emits alpha particles in all directions. A narrow hole in a lead block defines a beam of the alpha particles. This beam of alpha particles then passes through the metal foil, and the directions in which the alpha particles continue to move are observed. The direction in which an alpha particle moves can be detected by use of a screen coated with zinc sulfide. When an alpha particle strikes the screen a flash of light is sent out.

If the atoms bombarded with alpha particles were solid throughout their volume, we should expect all of the alpha particles in the beam to be deflected to some extent. Actually, however, Rutherford observed that most of the alpha particles passed through the metal foil without appreciable deflection: in one experiment, in which the alpha particles were sent through a gold foil 4000 Å thick, so that they penetrated about 1000 layers of atoms, only about one alpha particle in 100,000 was deflected. This one usually showed a great deflection, often through more than 90°, as indicated in the figure. When foil twice as thick was taken, it was found that about twice as many alpha particles showed deflection through large angles, with most of them still passing straight through.

These experimental results can be understood if the assumption is made that *most of the mass of the atom is concentrated into a very small particle*, which Rutherford called the atomic nucleus. If the alpha particle were also very small, then the chance of collision of these two very small particles as the alpha particle passed through the atom would be

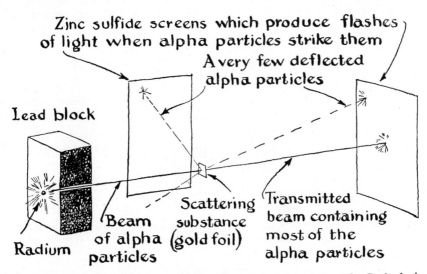

FIGURE 3-11   *A diagram representing the experiment carried out by Rutherford, which showed that atoms contain very small, heavy atomic nuclei.*

small. Most of the alpha particles could pass through the foil without striking any atomic nucleus, and these alpha particles would not then be deflected.

Since about one particle in 100,000 is deflected on passing through a foil consisting of 1000 atom layers, only about one particle in 100,000,000 would be deflected by a single layer of atoms. Rutherford concluded from this that the heavy nucleus has a cross-sectional area only 0.00000001 as great as the cross-sectional area of the atom, and hence that the diameter of the nucleus is only 1/10,000 as great as the diameter of the atom (the square root of 0.00000001 is 1/10,000).

Since atoms are a few Ångströms in diameter, the diameter of the nucleus is indicated to be approximately 10^{-4} Å or 10^{-12} cm. The atomic nucleus is hence about as big as an electron, which is about 10^{-12} cm in diameter.

The picture of the atom that has been developed from this experiment and similar experiments is indeed an extraordinary one. If we could magnify a piece of gold leaf by the linear factor 1,000,000,000—a billion fold—we would see it as an immense pile of atoms about two feet in diameter, each atom thus being about as big as a bushel basket. Practically the entire mass of each atom would, however, be concentrated in a single particle, the nucleus, about 0.001 inch in diameter, like an extremely small grain of sand. This nucleus would be surrounded by electrons, equally small, and moving very rapidly about. Rutherford's experiment would correspond to shooting through a pile of these bushel-basket atoms a stream of minute grains of sand, each of which would continue in a straight line unless it happened to collide with one of the minute grains of sand representing the nuclei of the atoms. It is obvious that the chance of such a collision would be very small. (The alpha particles are not deflected by the electrons in the atoms, because they are very much heavier than the electrons.)

Because of the new knowledge of the nature of atoms that it led to, Rutherford's experiment must be considered one of the most important experiments that any man has ever made.

Concepts and Terms Introduced in This Chapter

The nature of electricity. Repulsion of two electric charges with the same sign (both positive or both negative). Attraction of opposite electric charges (one positive and one negative).

Units of electric charge: statcoulomb, coulomb.

The electron. Its charge (negative) and mass (small).

The flow of electricity in a metal—a flow of electrons.

The nuclei of atoms. Proton, neutron. Heavier nuclei contain protons and neutrons.

The experiments that led to the discovery of the electron. Millikan's oil-drop experiment, giving the value of the charge of the electron.

Discovery of x-rays and radioactivity. Alpha, beta, and gamma rays. Rutherford's experiment.

Exercises

3-3. The helium nucleus is made of two protons and two neutrons. How many electrons must attach themselves to this nucleus to make a helium atom, which has no electric charge?

3-4 The uranium nucleus contains 92 protons. How many electrons are there in a uranium atom?

3-5. Describe the motion of a charged particle moving between two parallel metal plates, one of which is positively charged and one negatively charged.

3-6. Describe Perrin's experiment, which led him to conclude that cathode-ray particles (electrons) have a negative electric charge.

3-7. Describe the Rutherford experiment that led him to discover that atoms contain a very small, heavy nucleus.

3-8. What are alpha particles? Beta particles? Gamma rays?

Reference Books

R. F. Humphreys and R. Beringer, *First Principles of Atomic Physics*, Harper & Brothers, New York, **1950**.

H. E. White, *Classical and Modern Physics*, D. Van Nostrand Co., New York, **1950**.

S. Glasstone, *Sourcebook on Atomic Energy*, D. Van Nostrand Co., New York, **1950**.

Chapter 4

Elements, Elementary Substances, and Compounds

One of the most important parts of chemical theory is the division of substances into the two classes *elementary substances* and *compounds*. This division was achieved about a century and a half ago, principally through the efforts of the French chemist Lavoisier.

The arguments which Lavoisier and other early chemists used to decide whether a substance is an elementary substance or a compound have been briefly discussed in Chapter 1. During recent years more straightforward and definite methods have been found for identifying elementary substances. These methods, developed by physicists, involve the determination of the electric charge of the atomic nuclei (the number of unit electric charges). The power of the new methods has caused the definitions of the words element, elementary substance, and compound to be changed in recent years.

4–1. *The Chemical Elements*

A kind of matter consisting of atoms which all have nuclei with the same electric charge is called an **element.**

For example, all of the atoms which contain nuclei with the charge $+e$, each nucleus having one electron attached to it to neutralize its charge, comprise the element hydrogen, and all of the atoms which contain nuclei with the charge $+92e$ comprise the element uranium.

All pure substances can be divided into two classes: elementary substances, and compounds.

An **elementary substance** *is a substance that is composed of atoms of one element only.*

A **compound** *is a substance that is composed of atoms of two or more different elements.* These atoms of two or more different elements must be present in a definite numerical ration, since substances are defined as having a definite composition (Sections 1–3, 2–2).

Hydrogen, carbon, nitrogen, oxygen, sodium, iron, copper, zinc, lead, tin, silver, gold, chlorine, iodine, sulfur, and phosphorus are common elements; one hundred different elements in all are known at the present time.

Common salt, sugar, and baking soda are well-known compounds. Common salt contains atoms of two elements—atoms of sodium and atoms of chlorine. Sugar contains atoms of carbon, hydrogen, and oxygen, and baking soda contains atoms of sodium, hydrogen, carbon, and oxygen. Several hundred thousand different chemical compounds are now known, and many new ones are made every year.

Atomic Number. The electric charge of the nucleus of an atom, in units equal to the charge on the proton, is called the *atomic number* of the atom. It is usually given the symbol Z, the electric charge of a nucleus with atomic number Z being Z times e, with the charge of the proton equal to e, and the charge of the electron equal to $-e$. Thus the simplest atom, that of hydrogen, has atomic number 1; it consists of a nucleus with electric charge e, and an electron with electric charge $-e$. Uranium has atomic number 92.

The one hundred elements that have so far been discovered or made by scientists represent all the atomic numbers from 1 to 101.

The Assignment of Atomic Numbers to the Elements. Soon after the discovery of the electron as a constituent of matter it was recognized that elements might be assigned atomic numbers, representing the number of electrons in an atom of each element, but the way of doing this correctly was not known until 1913. In that year, H. G. J. Moseley (1887–1915), a young English physicist working in the University of Manchester, found that the atomic number of any element could be determined by the study of the x-rays emitted by an x-ray tube containing the element. By a few months of experimental work he was able to assign their correct atomic numbers to many elements.

A brief account of Moseley's experiment is given in Section 4–8, at the end of this Chapter.

Isotopes. It was mentioned in Chapter 3 that sometimes different atomic nuclei (with different mass) have the same electric charge. For example, the proton has electric charge $+e$, and the deuteron, which is built of a proton and a neutron, also has electric charge $+e$. The two nuclei differ in their mass, the deuteron having about twice the mass of the proton. When the proton combines with an electron a hydrogen atom is formed. Similarly, when a deuteron combines with an electron a hydrogen atom is formed, which differs from the light hydrogen atom in having a heavier nucleus. A third kind of hydrogen atom is also known. Its nucleus, called the *triton*, consists of a proton and two neutrons. Each of these three nuclei contains one proton, and hence has electric charge $+e$, and atomic number 1.

The *protium* atom, containing a proton as its nucleus, the *deuterium* atom, containing a deuteron as its nucleus, and the *tritium* atom, containing a triton as its nucleus, are three different kinds of hydrogen atoms, all equal in atomic number ($Z = 1$) and electric charge ($+e$) of their nuclei, but differing in mass. These three kinds of atoms are called the *isotopes* of hydrogen.*

The **isotopes** *of an element are atoms whose nuclei contain the same number of protons (equal to the atomic number of the element) but different numbers of neutrons.*

All known elements have two or more isotopes. In some cases (such as aluminum) only one isotope occurs naturally, the others being unstable. The maximum number of stable isotopes of any element is 10, possessed by tin.

The chemical properties of all the isotopes of an element are essentially the same. These properties are determined in the main by the atomic number of the nucleus, and not by its mass.

The Names and Symbols of the Elements.   The names of the elements are given in order of atomic number in Table 4-1. The chemical symbols of the elements, used as abbreviations for their names, are also given in the table. These symbols are usually the initial letters of the names, plus another letter when necessary. In some cases the initial letters of Latin names are used: Fe for iron (ferrum), Cu for copper (cuprum), Ag for silver (argentum), Au for gold (aurum), Hg for mercury (hydrargyrum). The system of chemical symbols was proposed by the great Swedish chemist Jöns Jakob Berzelius (1779–1848) in 1811.

The elements are shown in a special arrangement, the *periodic table*, at the front of the book and in Table 5-1, and are also given in alphabetical order in the front of the book and in Table 8-1, as well as in the order of their atomic numbers in Table 4-1.

You may find it useful to memorize, at this stage in your study of chemistry, the atomic numbers, names, and symbols of the first eighteen elements.

---

* The word isotope is from the Greek *isos*, the same, and *topos*, place; isotopes occupy the same place in the sequence of elements and in the periodic table (Chapter 5).

TABLE 4-1   *The Names, Atomic Numbers, and Symbols of the Elements*

ATOMIC NUMBER	SYM-BOL	ELEMENT	ATOMIC NUMBER	SYM-BOL	ELEMENT	ATOMIC NUMBER	SYM-BOL	ELEMENT
1	H	Hydrogen	35	Br	Bromine	69	Tm	Thulium
2	He	Helium	36	Kr	Krypton	70	Yb	Ytterbium
3	Li	Lithium	37	Rb	Rubidium	71	Lu	Lutetium
4	Be	Beryllium	38	Sr	Strontium	72	Hf	Hafnium
5	B	Boron	39	Y	Yttrium	73	Ta	Tantalum
6	C	Carbon	40	Zr	Zirconium	74	W	Tungsten
7	N	Nitrogen	41	Nb	Niobium	75	Re	Rhenium
8	O	Oxygen	42	Mo	Molybdenum	76	Os	Osmium
9	F	Fluorine	43	Tc	Technetium	77	Ir	Iridium
10	Ne	Neon	44	Ru	Ruthenium	78	Pt	Platinum
11	Na	Sodium	45	Rh	Rhodium	79	Au	Gold
12	Mg	Magnesium	46	Pd	Palladium	80	Hg	Mercury
13	Al	Aluminum	47	Ag	Silver	81	Tl	Thallium
14	Si	Silicon	48	Cd	Cadmium	82	Pb	Lead
15	P	Phosphorus	49	In	Indium	83	Bi	Bismuth
16	S	Sulfur	50	Sn	Tin	84	Po	Polonium
17	Cl	Chlorine	51	Sb	Antimony	85	At	Astatine
18	A	Argon	52	Te	Tellurium	86	Rn	Radon
19	K	Potassium	53	I	Iodine	87	Fr	Francium
20	Ca	Calcium	54	Xe	Xenon	88	Ra	Radium
21	Sc	Scandium	55	Cs	Cesium	89	Ac	Actinium
22	Ti	Titanium	56	Ba	Barium	90	Th	Thorium
23	V	Vanadium	57	La	Lanthanum	91	Pa	Protactinium
24	Cr	Chromium	58	Ce	Cerium	92	U	Uranium
25	Mn	Manganese	59	Pr	Praseodymium	93	Np	Neptunium
26	Fe	Iron	60	Nd	Neodymium	94	Pu	Plutonium
27	Co	Cobalt	61	Pm	Promethium	95	Am	Americium
28	Ni	Nickel	62	Sm	Samarium	96	Cm	Curium
29	Cu	Copper	63	Eu	Europium	97	Bk	Berkelium
30	Zn	Zinc	64	Gd	Gadolinium	98	Cf	Californium
31	Ga	Gallium	65	Tb	Terbium	99	E	Einsteinium
32	Ge	Germanium	66	Dy	Dysprosium	100	Fm	Fermium
33	As	Arsenic	67	Ho	Holmium	101	Mv	Mendelevium
34	Se	Selenium	68	Er	Erbium			

A symbol is used to represent an atom of an element, as well as the element itself. The symbol I represents the element iodine, and also may be used to mean the elementary substance. However, I_2 is the customary formula for the elementary substance, because it is known that elementary iodine consists of molecules containing two atoms in the solid and liquid states as well as in the gaseous state (except at very high temperature).

Illustrative Exercises

4-1.   The atomic number of oxygen is 8. What is the electric charge on the nucleus of the oxygen atom, in units e? In statcoulombs? How many electrons are there in the oxygen atom? Note that every electrically neutral atom must have a number of electrons around the nucleus equal to the atomic number of the atom; the negative charges of these electrons then exactly neutralize (balance) the total positive charge, $+Ze$, of the nucleus.

4-2. Write from memory the symbols and names of the elements with atomic numbers 1 to 18.

4-2. *The Distribution of the Elements*

You may be interested to know how the different elements are distributed throughout the earth and the universe.

The structure of the earth, as indicated by the analysis of evidence from records of earthquakes, study of rocks, and other observations, is shown in Figure 4-1. There is an outer crust, about 30 km thick, then an inner shell of denser rock, and a metallic core.

The estimated composition of the outer crust of the earth is shown in Figure 4-5 and the occurrence of the ten most common elements in it is given in Table 4-2.

TABLE 4-2   *The Estimated Composition by Weight of the Earth's Crust**

Oxygen	46.5%		Sodium	3.0%
Silicon	28.0%		Potassium	2.5%
Aluminum	8.1%		Magnesium	2.2%
Iron	5.1%		Titanium	0.5%
Calcium	3.5%		Hydrogen	0.2%

* This is the composition of the solid (rocky) crust of the earth, not including the ocean and the atmosphere. The ocean contains 85.79% oxygen, 10.67% hydrogen, 1.14% sodium, 2.07% chlorine, 0.14% magnesium, and 0.19% other elements.

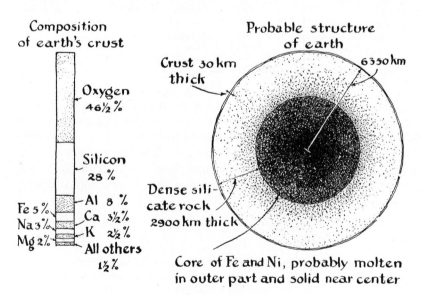

Composition of earth's crust

Oxygen 46½%
Silicon 28%
Fe 5%
Na 3%
Mg 2%
Al 8%
Ca 3½%
K 2½%
All others 1½%

Probable structure of earth

Crust 30 km thick
6350 km

Dense silicate rock 2900 km thick

Core of Fe and Ni, probably molten in outer part and solid near center

FIGURE 4-1   *The composition of the earth's crust.*

In some regions of the earth's surface there are denser rocks that are thought to be like the material in the shell under the earth's crust. On the assumption that the composition of these rocks is the same as the composition of this shell, and that the metallic core of the earth is an iron-nickel alloy resembling the metallic meteorites, the percentages given in Table 4-3 have been calculated for the distribution of elements in the whole earth.

TABLE 4-3   *The Estimated Composition by Weight of the Entire Earth*

Iron	39.8%	Calcium	2.5%
Oxygen	27.7%	Aluminum	1.8%
Silicon	14.5%	Sulfur	0.6%
Magnesium	8.7%	Sodium	0.4%
Nickel	3.2%	All others	0.8%

Astronomers have studied the light from the sun and stars, and have found that the same elements are present in these heavenly bodies as in the earth, but in different relative amounts. The sun and the stars contain great amounts of the two lightest elements, hydrogen and helium, which are relatively rare in the earth.

4–3. *The Formulas of Compounds*

Compounds are represented by formulas. These formulas are made up of the symbols of the elements contained in the compounds. For example, NaCl is the formula for sodium chloride, which consists of equal numbers of sodium and chlorine atoms. When the atoms of the different elements are not present in the compound in equal numbers, their ratios are indicated by the use of subscripts. Thus H_2O is the formula for water, each molecule of which contains two hydrogen atoms and one oxygen atom. (The subscript 1 is not usually written in formulas.)

If the true molecular structure of a substance is known, it is proper to indicate it in the formula. Hydrogen peroxide is a compound of hydrogen and oxygen which differs from water in that two hydrogen atoms and two oxygen atoms are contained in its molecule. The formula for hydrogen peroxide is H_2O_2, and not HO. Similarly the formula for naphthalene (Figure 2-8) is $C_{10}H_8$, and not C_5H_4, because each molecule contains ten carbon atoms and eight hydrogen atoms.

Sometimes parentheses are used in a formula, to indicate how the atoms are grouped together in the molecule or crystal. A subscript to a parenthesis applies to each symbol within the parentheses. For example, the formula $Ca(OH)_2$ means one calcium atom, two oxygen atoms, and two hydrogen atoms. Also, a number may appear in front of a group of symbols; it serves as a factor. For example, borax, $Na_2B_4O_7 \cdot 10H_2O$, consists of ten water molecules (twenty hydrogen atoms and ten oxygen

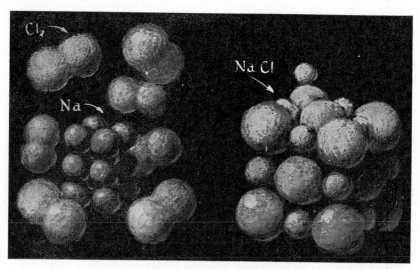

FIGURE 4-2   *At the left there are represented chlorine gas molecules (Cl_2) and metallic sodium, and at the right the same system after chemical reaction, with the formation of common salt, sodium chloride.*

atoms) in addition to two sodium atoms, four boron atoms, and seven oxygen atoms.

Atomic Ratios in Compounds.   In the crystal of sodium chloride there are atoms of two different kinds, arranged in the regular pattern shown at the right of Figure 4-2. The smaller atoms are those of sodium and the larger ones are those of chlorine. The surface layers shown, which are the cube faces of the sodium chloride crystal, contain both kinds of atoms in equal numbers, when the pattern is repeated a great number of times.

The numerical ratio of sodium and chlorine atoms in solid sodium chloride is fixed at 1:1 by the structure of the crystal, and that for sodium chloride gas is likewise fixed at 1:1 by the structure of the gas molecule, which contains one sodium atom and one chlorine atom. Similarly the numerical ratio of hydrogen atoms and oxygen atoms in water is fixed at 2:1 by the structure of the water molecule. *It is the definite structure of crystals and molecules that causes substances in general to contain elements in definite atomic ratios.*

Illustrative Exercises

4-3.   The formula of ethyl alcohol is C_2H_5OH. What elements are present in this compound? How many atoms of each element are there in one molecule of the compound?

4-4.   The front layer of atoms in the drawing of the crystal of sodium chloride, Figure 4-2, contains four sodium atoms and five chlorine atoms. Show that if this layer were very large (say 1000 atoms on edge) the ratio of the numbers of sodium and chlorine atoms would be very close to 1:1, and not 4:5. (Note that sodium atoms and chlorine atoms alternate in each row.)

4-5. Write the formula for the substance nitric acid; its molecule contains one hydrogen atom, one nitrogen atom, and three oxygen atoms.

4–4. *The Atomic and Molecular Nature of Chemical Reactions*

In Chapter 1 it was pointed out that a chemical reaction is a process in which certain substances, the reactants, are converted into other substances, the products. We shall now discuss chemical reactions in relation to the atomic theory.

During a **chemical reaction** *there occurs a* **rearrangement of atoms.**

For example, let us consider again the reaction of sodium and chlorine to form sodium chloride. The metal sodium consists of sodium atoms arranged in a regular structure which is similar to that described in Chapter 2 for copper, but is not identical with it. The gas chlorine consists of molecules, as shown in Figure 4-2. During the reaction of sodium and chlorine the sodium atoms in the metal separate from one another and the two chlorine atoms in the molecules of chlorine separate from one another. The atoms of sodium and chlorine then arrange themselves in a new structure, in which the atoms of the two kinds alternate, as shown at the right in Figure 4-2. This arrangement of sodium and chlorine atoms constitutes the new substance, sodium chloride, that has formed during the chemical reaction.

The gas hydrogen consists of molecules H_2. Oxygen also consists of

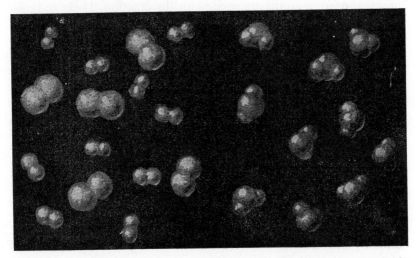

FIGURE 4-3   *At the left there is represented a gas containing hydrogen molecules* (H_2) *and oxygen molecules* (O_2), *and at the right the same system after chemical reaction, leading to the formation of water molecules,* H_2O.

molecules O_2. If two flasks, one containing hydrogen and one containing oxygen, are connected together, the two gases mix with each other quietly, to produce a gaseous mixture (left side of Figure 4-3). If, however, a flame is brought into contact with the gaseous mixture a violent explosion occurs, and afterward the presence of water can be shown. This explosion is the result of the combination of hydrogen and oxygen to form a new substance, water (right side of Figure 4-3), with the emission also of heat and light. During the explosion (which is a very rapid chemical reaction) the molecules of hydrogen and oxygen split into atoms, and two atoms of hydrogen attach themselves to each atom of oxygen, to form molecules of water, H_2O.

4–5. How to Balance the Equation for a Chemical Reaction

The chemical reaction of the formation of water from hydrogen and oxygen can be represented by an equation:

$$2H_2 + O_2 \longrightarrow 2H_2O$$

On the left side of this equation we have the formula H_2 for hydrogen and the formula O_2 for oxygen, and on the right side the formula H_2O for water. It would not, however, be correct to write this equation without the numerical prefixes that are indicated, because we use the formulas to indicate relative numbers of atoms, as well as to describe the reactants and the products of the chemical reaction. The water molecule contains twice as many hydrogen atoms as oxygen atoms, and accordingly the equation should show that twice as many hydrogen atoms as oxygen atoms are needed for the reaction. This can be achieved by introducing the coefficient (multiplier) 2 in front of the symbol for the hydrogen molecule. If four hydrogen atoms (two molecules) and two oxygen atoms (one molecule) react, two water molecules are formed. This is indicated by use of the coefficient 2 in front of the formula for water.

The coefficient 2 in the term $2H_2$ means that two molecules of hydrogen, four hydrogen atoms altogether, are involved in the reaction. The coefficient 2 in the term $2H_2O$ multiplies the entire formula H_2O; that is, $2H_2O$ means two molecules H_2O (four hydrogen atoms and two oxygen atoms).

Note that it is customary to use an arrow in a chemical equation, rather than the mathematical sign of equality.

The equation representing a chemical reaction can thus be written correctly by carrying out a process of **balancing the equation.** This is done by introducing numerical coefficients before the correct formulas of the reactants and products until there are exactly the same number of atoms of each element on the left side of the equation as on the right side of the equation.

The equation representing the reaction in which sodium chloride is formed from sodium and chlorine may be easily written. It is

$$2Na + Cl_2 \longrightarrow 2NaCl$$

It is a very good practice to check every chemical equation that you write, to be sure that it agrees with the **"law of the conservation of atoms of every element."**

Illustrative Exercises

4-6.   (a) How many atoms of hydrogen and how many atoms of oxygen are there in 100 molecules of water? (b) How many molecules of hydrogen and how many molecules of oxygen would be required to produce 100 molecules of water? (c) Write the equation for the reaction, with 100 H_2O as the product. (d) Reduce this equation to its simplest form, by dividing by the greatest common divisor of the coefficients of the three terms.

4-7.   Hydrogen peroxide, H_2O_2, easily decomposes into water and oxygen. Write a balanced equation for this reaction.

4-8.   Balance the following equations (the formulas are correct):

$$H_2 + Cl_2 \longrightarrow HCl$$

$$K + I_2 \longrightarrow KI$$

$$Fe + H_2SO_4 \longrightarrow FeSO_4 + H_2$$

$$C_{10}H_8 + O_2 \longrightarrow CO_2 + H_2O$$

$$C_6H_{14} + O_2 \longrightarrow CO_2 + H_2O$$

$$C_6H_{14} + O_2 \longrightarrow CO + H_2O$$

$$H_2O_2 \longrightarrow H_2O + O_2$$

$$C_2H_5OH + O_2 \longrightarrow CO_2 + H_2O$$

$$AgNO_3 + CaCl_2 \longrightarrow AgCl + Ca(NO_3)_2$$

$$Al + O_2 \longrightarrow Al_2O_3$$

4–6. The Difference in Chemical Properties
of Elements and Compounds

It is only recently that methods have become available for determining directly whether a substance contains atoms of only one kind or of two or more kinds. For two hundred years, since 1741, when M. V. Lomonosov (1711–1765), an imaginative Russian poet and chemist, published his new ideas about the nature of matter, and especially since 1789, when Lavoisier published such a clear discussion of the question as to convince nearly all of his fellow chemists, substances had undergone classification as elements or compounds on the basis of chemical reactions, as was briefly discussed in Chapter 1. Definite chemical evidence for the compound nature of a substance could be obtained, by decomposing it into two or more substances; if it was lacking, the substance was presumed to be an element.

There are two chemical tests for the compound nature of a substance.

First: if a substance can be decomposed (that is, if it can be made to undergo reaction in which it alone is destroyed) to form two or more product substances,* the original substance must be a compound. For example, molten salt can be decomposed completely into sodium and chlorine by passing an electric current through it; hence it is a compound. Similarly, mercuric oxide, HgO, can be decomposed into mercury and oxygen simply by heating it; hence it is a compound.

The second chemical test for the compound nature of a substance is the following: if two or more substances react to form a single product substance, that substance is a compound. Thus sodium and chlorine, in the proper relative amounts, will react completely to form common salt; hence common salt is a compound. Also hydrogen and oxygen mixed in the proper proportions will explode to form a single substance, water; hence water is a compound.

It is interesting to note that *until the new physical methods, especially the x-ray method* (Section 4–8), *were developed, there was no way of rigorously proving a substance to be an element.* In the early years of the science of chemistry a substance was accepted as an element so long as no reaction showing it to be a compound had been observed. At first some mistakes were made: lime (calcium oxide, CaO) was considered to be an element until the English chemist Sir Humphry Davy reduced it to calcium metal in 1808; and uranium dioxide, UO_2, was accepted as an element from 1789 to 1841. By 1900, however, all but about a score of the elements that are now known had been recognized and correctly identified as elements.

This chemical method of classifying substances is interesting as an example of logical argument. A *single experiment* in which a substance is decomposed into two or more other substances or is alone formed from them *proves* that it is a compound; this conclusion is inescapable. The *failure* of such an experiment, however, *does not prove* that the substance is an element. It is, indeed, not possible to prove that a substance is an element by tests of this kind, no matter how many are made. It may be convenient to assume it to be an element, in case that there is no evidence to the contrary; but if this is done it should not be forgotten that the assumption is not necessarily true.

It was not until the present century, when powerful methods of studying atoms were discovered, that scientists could be sure that the forms of matter which they called elements were all really elements, and that some were not compounds.

---

* Here it is assumed that the different products are essentially different, and do not contain the same atoms (as do oxygen and ozone, Chapter 6).

4–7. *Note on Radioactivity and the Transmutation of Elements*

For centuries, before the development of chemistry as a science, the alchemists strove to carry out the transmutation of elements, in particular to change mercury into gold with the aid of the "philosopher's stone." Then, as scientific chemistry developed and success in transmutation eluded the investigators, the opinion gained firm hold that the conversion of one element into another was impossible, and that atoms were immutable and indestructible. The definitions of element and elementary substance accepted during the nineteenth century were based upon this belief.

In 1896 there came the discovery of radioactivity by Henri Becquerel and the discovery of radium by Pierre and Marie Curie. Soon thereafter it was recognized that *radioactive changes involve the spontaneous conversion of atoms of one element into those of another*. It then became necessary to change the definition of element; this was done by saying that one element could not be converted into another *by artificial means*.

It has now become necessary to make another change in the definition. In 1919 Lord Rutherford and his collaborators at the Cavendish Laboratory in Cambridge, England, where active study of radioactive phenomena was under way, reported that they had succeeded in converting nitrogen atoms into oxygen atoms by bombarding nitrogen with high-speed alpha particles, which are given off by radium. The nitrogen nucleus, with charge $+7e$, and the alpha particle (helium nucleus), with charge $+2e$, react to produce an oxygen nucleus, with charge $+8e$, and a proton, with charge $+e$.

Since 1930 there has been very great progress in this field of artificial radioactivity, which now is the most actively prosecuted research field in physics. Nearly every element has now been rendered radioactive and converted into other elements by bombardment with particles moving at high speed, and a great body of information about the properties of atomic nuclei is being gathered.

These developments necessitate another change in the concept of element: it is now said that *an element cannot be transmuted into another element by ordinary chemical methods*. The discovery of these new phenomena might have led to confusion regarding the validity of the classification of substances as elementary substances and compounds were it not for the fact that our knowledge of the structure and properties of atoms has also increased rapidly in recent years.

4–8. *Moseley's Experiment*

It was mentioned in Section 4–1 that Moseley determined the atomic numbers of elements by the study of the x-rays emitted by an x-ray tube containing the element. The

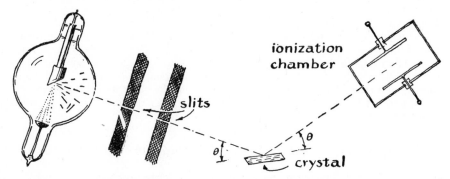

FIGURE 4-4   *The Bragg ionization-chamber technique of investigating the diffraction of x-rays by crystals.*

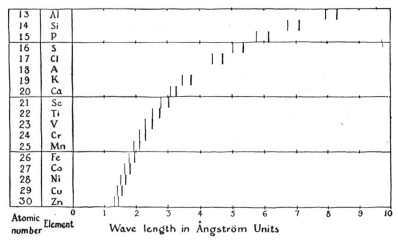

FIGURE 4-5   *Diagram showing regular change of wavelength of x-ray emission lines for a series of elements.*

apparatus that might be used to repeat Moseley's experiment is shown in Figure 4-4. The x-ray tube is drawn at the left side of this figure. Electrons that come from the cup near the bottom of the tube (as drawn) are speeded up by the electric potential (several thousand volts) applied to the two ends of the tube, and strike the target, which is near the center of the tube. The x-rays are emitted by the atoms of the target, when they are struck by the fast-moving electrons.

The element to be investigated is placed on the target of the x-ray tube, and the x-rays that it emits when bombarded by electrons are then analyzed by a technique developed in 1913 by Sir William Bragg (1862–1942) and his son, Sir Lawrence Bragg (born 1890). This consists in defining a beam of x-rays by a pair of slits, reflecting the beam of x-rays from the face of a crystal, as shown in Figure 4-4, and determining the position of the reflected beam either by use of an ionization chamber (a chamber in which the x-rays cause a gas to become a conductor of electricity), as indicated in the figure, or by use of a photographic plate.

It was found that the x-rays produced by an x-ray tube contain lines of definite wavelengths, characteristic of the material in the target of the x-ray tube. Moseley measured the wavelengths produced by a number of different elements, and found that they change in a regular way. The wavelengths of the two principal x-ray lines of the elements from aluminum to zinc (omitting the gas argon) are shown in Figure 4-5.

The regularity in the wavelengths can be shown more strikingly by plotting the square root of the reciprocals of the wavelengths of the two x-ray lines for the various elements arranged in the proper sequence, which is the sequence of the atomic numbers of the elements. In a graph of this sort, called a Moseley diagram, the points for a given x-ray line lie on a straight line. The Moseley diagram for the elements from aluminum to zinc is shown in Figure 4-6. It was easy for Moseley to assign the correct atomic numbers to the elements with use of a diagram of this sort.

Concepts and Technical Terms Introduced in This Chapter

Element—the kind of matter represented by atoms with the same atomic number.

Atomic number—the magnitude of the positive electric charge of the nucleus of an atom (in units equal to the charge of the electron).

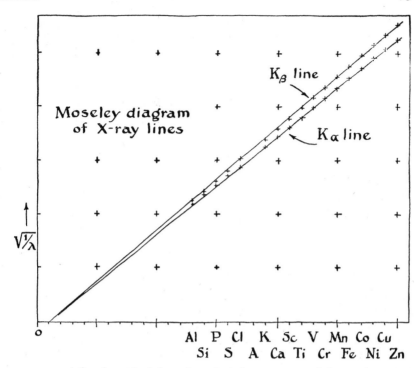

FIGURE 4-6   *A graph of the reciprocal of the square root of the wavelengths of x-ray lines, for the K_α line and the K_β line, of elements, plotted against the order of the elements in the periodic table. This graph, called the Moseley diagram, was used by Moseley in determining the atomic numbers of the elements.*

Elementary substance—a substance containing atoms of one kind only.

Compound—a substance containing two or more kinds of atoms in a definite ratio.

Isotopes.

The 101 elements, their names and symbols.

Distribution of elements.

Chemical formulas.

Chemical reactions, their atomic and molecular nature.

How to balance equations.

Difference in chemical properties of elements and compounds.

Radioactivity and the transmutation of elements.

Moseley's experiment, determining values of atomic numbers.

Exercises

4-9.   Define atomic number. Define elementary substance in terms of atoms.

4-10.   Describe a chemical experiment which would prove that water is not an element. Can you think of a chemical proof that iron is an element?

4-11. When sugar is strongly heated water vapor is driven off and a black residue, carbon, is left. Does this experiment prove rigorously that sugar is not an element?

4-12. Define chemical symbol and chemical formula. Explain the purpose of each letter or number in a formula.

4-13. Using your own words, give a definition of chemical reaction.

4-14. Balance the following equations of chemical reactions:

$$Fe + O_2 \longrightarrow Fe_2O_3$$

$$H_2 + N_2 \longrightarrow NH_3$$

$$HgO \longrightarrow Hg + O_2$$

$$CO + O_2 \longrightarrow CO_2$$

$$C_{12}H_{22}O_{11} + O_2 \longrightarrow CO_2 + H_2O$$

$$NaCl + H_2SO_4 \longrightarrow NaHSO_4 + HCl$$

$$KClO_3 \longrightarrow KCl + O_2$$

$$H_2 + O_2 \longrightarrow H_2O$$

$$Zn + H_2SO_4 \longrightarrow ZnSO_4 + H_2$$

4-15. How was the definition of element affected by the discovery of radioactivity in 1896?

4-16. What are the atomic number and approximate atomic weight of the element each of whose nuclei contains 79 protons and 118 neutrons? By reference to Table 4-1 identify this element.

4-17. How many protons and how many neutrons are in the nucleus of the isotope of chlorine with mass 35? Of the isotope of chlorine with mass 37? Of the isotope of plutonium with mass 239?

Reference Books

F. Sherwood Taylor, *The Alchemists*, Henry Schuman, 1948.

J. Newton Friend, *Man and the Chemical Elements*, Charles Griffin & Co., London, 1951.

Also the books listed at the end of Chapter 1, especially *Discovery of the Elements*, by Mary E. Weeks.

Chapter 5

The Chemical Elements, the Periodic Law, and the Electronic Structure of Atoms

The 101 known elements include some with which everyone is familiar and many which are rare. At room temperature some of the elementary substances are gases, some are liquids, and some are solids.* They show extremely great variety in their chemical properties and in the nature of the compounds that they form. In consequence the study of chemistry is not simple or easy; to obtain a reasonably broad knowledge of general chemistry it is necessary to learn a great many facts.

The facts of chemistry cannot be completely coordinated by a unifying theory. Nevertheless, the development of chemical theories has now proceeded far enough to be of great aid to the student, who can simplify his task of learning about the properties and reactions of substances by correlating this information with theories, such as the theory of atomic structure,† which has been discussed in the preceding chapters, and the *periodic law*, which we shall now consider.

---

* The elements that are gases at standard conditions (0°C and 1 atm) are hydrogen, helium, nitrogen, oxygen, fluorine, neon, chlorine, argon, krypton, xenon, and radon. The only elements that are liquids at standard conditions are bromine and mercury.

† Remember that atoms are built of particles of three kinds, protons, neutrons, and electrons. The nucleus of the atom is made of protons and neutrons; the number of protons determines its electric charge, and the total number of protons and neutrons its mass. The number of electrons around the nucleus equals the number of protons in it.

5–1. *The Periodic Law*

The periodic law states simply that *the properties of the chemical elements are not arbitrary, but depend upon the structure of the atom and vary with the atomic number in a systematic way.* The important point is that this dependence involves a crude periodicity which shows itself in the recurrence of characteristic properties.

For example, the elements with atomic numbers 2, 10, 18, 36, 54, and 86 are all chemically inert gases. Similarly the elements with atomic numbers one greater, namely, 3, 11, 19, 37, 55, and 87, are all light metals that are very reactive chemically. These six metals, lithium (3), sodium (11), potassium (19), rubidium (37), cesium (55), and francium (87), all react with chlorine to form colorless compounds that crystallize in cubes and show a cubic cleavage. The chemical formulas of these salts are similar: LiCl, NaCl, KCl, RbCl, CsCl, and FrCl. The composition and properties of other compounds of these six metals are correspondingly similar, and different from those of other elements.*

The comparison of the observed chemical and physical properties of elements and their compounds with the atomic numbers of the elements accordingly indicates that, after the first two elements, hydrogen and helium, which constitute the **very short period** (the word period is used for a sequence of elements), there are the **first short period** of eight elements (from helium, atomic number 2, to neon, 10), the **second short period** of eight elements (to argon, 18), the **first long period** of eighteen elements (to krypton, 36), the **second long period** of eighteen elements (to xenon, 54), and then the **very long period** of 32 elements (to radon, 86). In case that enough new elements of very large atomic number are made in the future it may well be found that there is another very long period of 32 elements, ending in another inert gas, with atomic number 118.

5–2. *The Periodic Table*

The periodic recurrence of properties of the elements with increasing atomic number may be effectively emphasized by arranging the elements in a table, called the *periodic table* or *periodic system* of the elements. Several alternative forms of the periodic table have been proposed and used. We shall base the discussion of the elements and their properties in this book on the simple table shown as Table 5-1 (it is also reproduced inside the front cover of the book).

---

* Actually very little is yet known about the sixth of these elements, francium, which has been only recently discovered; but there is little doubt that francium is closely similar to the other alkali metals in its properties. We say "little doubt" because *periodicity* has in the past consistently permitted chemists to make such predictions that have later been proved to be correct.

TABLE 5–1

Group O	
H 1	He 2

Periods 1–3:

I	II	III	IV	V	VI	VII	0
							He 2
H 1							Ne 10
							A 18
Li 3	Be 4	B 5	C 6	N 7	O 8	F 9	Ne 10
Na 11	Mg 12	Al 13	Si 14	P 15	S 16	Cl 17	A 18

Periods 4–7:

0	I	II	III	IVa	Va	VIa	VIIa	VIII			Ib	IIb	IIIb	IV	V	VI	VII	0
A 18	K 19	Ca 20	Sc 21	Ti 22	V 23	Cr 24	Mn 25	Fe 26	Co 27	Ni 28	Cu 29	Zn 30	Ga 31	Ge 32	As 33	Se 34	Br 35	Kr 36
Kr 36	Rb 37	Sr 38	Y 39	Zr 40	Nb 41	Mo 42	Tc 43	Ru 44	Rh 45	Pd 46	Ag 47	Cd 48	In 49	Sn 50	Sb 51	Te 52	I 53	Xe 54
Xe 54	Cs 55	Ba 56	La 57	Hf 72 ∗	Ta 73	W 74	Re 75	Os 76	Ir 77	Pt 78	Au 79	Hg 80	Tl 81	Pb 82	Bi 83	Po 84	At 85	Rn 86
Rn 86	Fr 87	Ra 88	Ac 89	Th 90 ◆	Pa 91	U 92	Np 93	Pu 94										

∗ Lanthanons:

Ce 58	Pr 59	Nd 60	Pm 61	Sm 62	Eu 63	Gd 64	Tb 65	Dy 66	Ho 67	Er 68	Tm 69	Yb 70	Lu 71

◆ Actinons:

Th 90	Pa 91	U 92	Np 93	Pu 94	Am 95	Cm 96	Bk 97	Cf 98	E 99	Fm 100	Mv 101

The Development of the Periodic Table.   The differentiation of chemical substances into two groups, elements and compounds, was achieved at the end of the eighteenth century. A long time was required for the recognition of the fact that the elements can be classified in the way now described by the periodic law. The first step was taken in 1817, when the German chemist J. W. Döbereiner (1780–1849) showed that the combining weight of strontium lies midway between the combining weights of the two related elements calcium and barium. Some years later he recognized the existence of other "triads" of similar elements (chlorine, bromine, and iodine; lithium, sodium, and potassium).

Other chemists then showed that the elements could be classified into groups consisting of more than three similar elements. Fluorine was added to the triad chlorine, bromine, and iodine, and magnesium to the triad calcium, strontium, and barium. Oxygen, sulfur, selenium, and tellurium had been classed as one group, and nitrogen, phosphorus, arsenic, antimony, and bismuth as another group of elements by 1854.

In 1862 the French chemist A. E. B. de Chancourtois arranged the elements in the order of atomic weights (the masses of their atoms). He noticed that elements differing by about 16 in atomic weight sometimes had similar properties, and suggested that "the properties of elements are the properties of numbers." The English chemist J. A. R. Newlands in 1863 proposed a system of classification of the elements in order of atomic weights, in which the elements were divided into seven groups of seven elements each. He termed his relation the *law of octaves*, by analogy with the seven intervals of the musical scale. His proposal was ridiculed, however, and he did not develop it further.

The most important step in the development of the periodic table was taken in 1869, when the Russian chemist Dmitri I. Mendelyeev (1834–1907) made a thorough study of the relation between the atomic weights of the elements and their physical and chemical properties. Mendelyeev proposed a periodic table containing seventeen columns, resembling in a general way the periodic Table 5-1 with the end columns (labeled 0) missing (these elements had not yet been discovered at that time). In 1871 Mendelyeev and the German chemist Lothar Meyer (1830–1895), who was working independently, proposed another table, with eight columns, obtained by splitting each of the long periods into a period of seven elements, an eighth group containing the three central elements (such as Fe, Co, Ni), and a second period of seven elements. The first and second periods of seven were later distinguished by use of the letters a and b attached to the group symbols, which were the Roman numerals. This nomenclature of the periods (Ia, IIa, IIIa, IVa, Va, VIa, VIIa, VIII, Ib, IIb, IIIb, IVb, Vb, VIb, VIIb) appears, slightly revised, in the present periodic table.

The periodic table in the second form proposed by Mendelyeev (the "short-period" form) remained popular for many years, but has now been largely replaced by the "long-period" form, used in this book, which is in better agreement with the new knowledge about the electronic structure of atoms.

The periodic law was accepted immediately after its proposal by Mendelyeev because of his success in making predictions with its use which were afterward verified by experiment. In 1871 Mendelyeev found that by changing seventeen elements from the positions indicated by the atomic weights which had then been assigned to them into new positions, their properties could be better correlated with the properties of the other elements. He pointed out that this change indicated the existence of small errors in the previously accepted atomic weights of several of the elements, and large errors for several others, to the compounds of which incorrect formulas had been assigned. Further experimental work verified that Mendelyeev's revisions were correct.

A very striking application of the periodic law was made by Mendelyeev. He was able to predict the existence of six elements that had not yet been discovered, corresponding to vacant places in his table. He named these elements eka-boron, eka-aluminum, eka-silicon, eka-manganese, dvi-manganese, and eka-tantalum (Sanskrit: *eka*, first; *dvi*, second).

Three of these elements were soon discovered (they were named scandium, gallium, and germanium by their discoverers), and it was found that their properties and the properties of their compounds are very close to those predicted by Mendelyeev for eka-boron, eka-aluminum, and eka-silicon, respectively. Since then the elements technetium, rhenium, and protactinium have been discovered or made artificially, and have been found to have properties similar to those predicted for eka-manganese, dvi-manganese, and eka-tantalum. A comparison of the properties predicted by Mendelyeev for eka-silicon and those determined experimentally for germanium is given below:

Mendelyeev's predictions for eka-silicon (1871):

Observed properties of germanium (discovered in 1886):

Atomic weight about 72.

Atomic weight 72.60.

Es will be obtained from EsO_2 or K_2EsF_6 by reaction with sodium.

Ge is obtained by reaction of K_2GeF_6 and sodium.

Es will be a dark gray metal, with high melting point and density 5.5.

Ge is gray, with melting point 958° C and density 5.36 g/cm³.

Es will be slightly attacked by acids, such as hydrochloric acid, HCl, and will resist alkalies, such as sodium hydroxide, NaOH.

Ge is not dissolved by HCl or NaOH, but is dissolved by concentrated nitric acid, HNO_3.

On heating Es, it will form the oxide EsO_2, with high melting point and density 4.7.

Ge reacts with oxygen to give GeO_2, m.p. 1100° C, density 4.70 g/cm³.

A hydrated EsO_2 soluble in acid and easily reprecipitated is expected.

$Ge(OH)_4$ dissolves in dilute acid and is reprecipitated on dilution or addition of base.

The sulfide, EsS_2, will be insoluble in water but soluble in ammonium sulfide.

GeS_2 is insoluble in water and dilute acids, but readily soluble in ammonium sulfide.

$EsCl_4$ will be a volatile liquid, with boiling point a little under 100° and density 1.9 g/cm³.

$GeCl_4$ is a volatile liquid, with b.p. 83° C and density 1.88 g/cm³.

5–3. Description of the Periodic Table

The **horizontal rows** *of the periodic table are called* **periods:** they consist of a very short period (containing hydrogen and helium, atomic numbers 1 and 2), two short periods of 8 elements each, two long periods of 18 elements each, a very long period of 32 elements, and an incomplete period.

The properties of elements change in a systematic way through a period: this is indicated in Figure 5-1, which shows the density of the elements, in the crystalline state, as a function of the atomic number. It is seen that there are five pronounced minima (low points) in the density curve. They occur for the elements sodium (11), potassium (19), rubidium (37), cesium (55), and francium (87). It was mentioned in Section 5–1 that these five elements together with lithium constitute a group of elements that are strikingly similar in their properties.

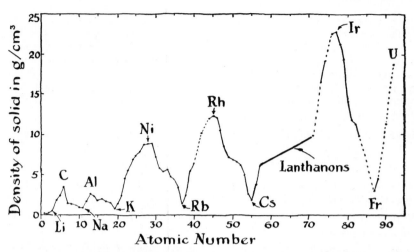

FIGURE 5-1   *The density of the elements in the solid state, in g/cm³. The symbols of the elements at high and low points of the jagged curve are shown.*

The **vertical columns** *of the periodic table,* with connections between the short and long periods as shown, *are the* **groups** *of chemical elements.* Elements in the same group may be called *congeners;* these elements have closely related physical and chemical properties.

The groups I, II, and III are considered to include the elements in corresponding places at the left side of all the periods in Table 5-1, and IV, V, VI, and VII the elements at the right side. The central elements of the long periods, called the *transition elements,* have properties differing from those of the elements of the short periods; these elements are discussed separately, as groups IVa, Va, VIa, VIIa, VIII (which, for historical reasons, include three elements in each long period), Ib, IIb, and IIIb.

The very long period is compressed into the table by removing fourteen elements, the *rare-earth metals* or *lanthanons* (elements resembling lanthanum, $Z = 57$), from $Z = 58$ to $Z = 71$, and representing them separately below. The elements from $Z = 90$ to $Z = 101$, called the *actinons** (elements resembling actinium, $Z = 89$), are listed below the lanthanons; those from $Z = 90$ to $Z = 94$ are also listed in the main body of the table.

The elements on the left side and in the center of the periodic table are **metals.** These elementary substances have the characteristic properties called *metallic properties*—high electric and thermal conductivity, metallic luster, the ability to be hammered into sheets (malleability) and to be drawn into wire (ductility). The elements on the right side

* There should be fourteen actinons ($Z = 90$ to $Z = 103$), but the last two have not yet been made.

of the periodic table are **non-metals,** the elementary substances not having metallic properties.

The metallic properties are most pronounced for elements in the lower left-hand corner of the periodic table, and the non-metallic properties are most pronounced for elements in the upper right-hand corner. The transition from metals to non-metals is marked by the *elements with intermediate properties*, which occupy a diagonal region extending from a point near the upper center to the lower right-hand corner. These elements, which are called **metalloids,** include boron, silicon, germanium, arsenic, antimony, tellurium, and polonium.

The groups of elements may be described briefly in the following way:

Group 0, the noble gases: The elements of this group, helium, neon, argon, krypton, xenon, and radon, are completely unreactive chemically; they do not form any chemical compounds. A discussion of the noble gases is given in the following sections of this chapter.

Group I, the alkali metals: the alkali metals, lithium, sodium, potassium, rubidium, cesium, and francium, are light metals which are very reactive chemically. Many of their compounds have important uses in industry and in life. The alkali metals and their compounds are discussed in Chapter 26. The word alkali is derived from an arabic word meaning ashes (compounds of these metals were obtained from wood ashes).

Group II, the alkaline-earth metals: These metals, beryllium, magnesium, calcium, strontium, barium, and radium, and their compounds are discussed in Chapter 26.

Group III, the boron or aluminum group: Boron is a metalloid, whereas aluminum and its other congeners are metals. The properties of boron and its congeners are discussed in Chapter 26.

Group IV, carbon and silicon: The chemistry of carbon is described in Chapter 7 and in greater detail in Chapters 30 and 31. The chemistry of silicon and the other elements of this group is described in Chapter 26.

Group V, the nitrogen or phosphorus group: Nitrogen and phosphorus are non-metals, their congeners arsenic and antimony are metalloids, and bismuth is usually classed as a metal. The chemistry of nitrogen is described in Chapter 15 and that of phosphorus and the other elements of the group in Chapter 16.

Group VI, the oxygen group: Oxygen and its congeners sulfur and selenium are non-metals, whereas tellurium and polonium are classed as metalloids. The chemistry of oxygen is discussed in Chapter 6, and that of sulfur and its congeners in Chapter 14.

Group VII, the halogen group: The halogens (fluorine, chlorine, bromine, iodine, and astatine) are the most strongly non-metallic elements. They are very reactive chemically, and form many compounds. Their chemistry is discussed in Chapter 13. The word halogen is from the Greek words *hals*, salt, and *genes*, producing.

Groups IVa, Va, VIa, VIIa, VIII, Ib, IIb, and IIIb, the transition elements: The elements in these groups are all metals. The groups themselves are usually given the name of the lightest metal; for example, VIa, including chromium, molybdenum, tungsten, and uranium, is called the chromium group. For historical reasons, however, the iron group is often considered to consist of three elements, iron, cobalt, and nickel, the congeners of these three elements being called the platinum group. These elements are discussed in later chapters of the book: iron, cobalt, nickel, and the platinum metals in Chapter 27; copper, zinc, gallium, and their congeners in Chapter 28; and chromium and manganese and related metals in Chapter 29.

You will avoid confusion in your further study if you fix firmly in your mind the usage of the word *period* to represent a *horizontal row* in the periodic table, and of the word *group* to represent a *vertical column* (with a jog between the short-period and the long-period part of the table). Also, you will find it helpful to remember the important sequence of numbers 2, 8, 8, 18, 18, 32, 32. These are the numbers of elements in the successive periods of the periodic table. (The last period, which is incomplete, will presumably be found, when more elements are made, to end with another noble gas with $Z = 118$.)

5–4. *The Noble Gases*

The first element in the periodic table, hydrogen, with atomic number 1, is a reactive substance that forms a great many compounds. The chemistry of hydrogen is discussed in the following chapter. Helium, the second element (atomic number 2), is much different; it is a gas with the very striking chemical property that *it forms no chemical compounds whatever*, but exists only in the free state. Its atoms will not even combine with one another to form polyatomic molecules, but remain as separate atoms in the gas, which is hence described as containing monatomic molecules. Because of its property of remaining aloof from other elements it is called a "noble" gas.

This lack of chemical reactivity is the result of an extraordinary stability of the electronic structure of the helium atom. This stability is characteristic of the presence of two electrons close to an atomic nucleus.

The other elements of the zero group—neon, argon, krypton, xenon, and radon—are also chemically inert. The failure of these inert elements to form chemical compounds is similarly due to the great stability of their electronic structures. These extremely stable electronic structures are formed by 2, 10, 18, 36, 54, and 86 electrons about a nucleus.

These six gases are called the *noble gases* (or sometimes the *rare gases* or *inert gases*). Their names, except radon, are from Greek roots: *helios*, sun; *neos*, new; *argos*, inert; *kryptos*, hidden; *xenos*, stranger. Radon is named after radium, from which it is formed by radioactive decomposition. The properties of the noble gases are given in Table 5-2. Note the regular dependence of melting point and boiling point on atomic number.

Helium.   Helium is present in very small quantities in the atmosphere. Its presence in the sun is shown by the occurrence of its spectral lines in sunlight. These lines were observed in 1868, long before the element was discovered on earth, and the lines were ascribed to a new element, which was named helium* by Sir Norman Lockyer (1836–1920).

TABLE 5-2   *Properties of the Noble Gases*

	SYMBOL	ATOMIC NUMBER	ATOMIC WEIGHT*	MELTING POINT	BOILING POINT
Helium	He	2	4.003	−272.2° C†	−268.9° C
Neon	Ne	10	20.183	−248.67°	−245.9°
Argon	A	18	39.944	−189.2°	−185.7°
Krypton	Kr	36	83.80	−157°	−152.9°
Xenon	Xe	54	131.30	−112°	−107.1°
Radon	Rn	86	222	−71°	−61.8°

* See Chapter 8.
† At 26 atm pressure. At smaller pressures helium remains liquid at still lower temperatures.

Helium occurs as a gas entrapped in some uranium minerals, from which it can be liberated by heating. It is also present in natural gas from some wells, especially in Texas and Canada; this is the principal source of the element.

Helium is used for filling balloons and dirigibles and for mixing with oxygen (in place of the nitrogen of the air) for breathing by divers, in order to avoid the "bends," which are caused by gas bubbles formed by release of the nitrogen of the atmosphere that had dissolved in the blood under increased pressure.

Neon.   The second noble gas, neon, occurs in the atmosphere to the extent of 0.002%. It is obtained, along with the other noble gases (except helium), by the distillation of liquid air (air that has been liquefied by cooling).

When an electric current is passed through a tube containing neon gas at low pressure, the atoms of neon are caused to emit light with their characteristic spectral lines. This produces a brilliant red light, used in advertising signs (neon signs). Other colors for signs are obtained by

---

* The ending "ium," which is otherwise used only for metallic elements, is due to Lockyer's incorrect surmise that the new element was a metal. "Helion" would be a better name, as its ending is consistent with those of the names of the other noble gases.

the use of helium, argon, and mercury, sometimes in mixtures with neon
or with one another.

Argon. Argon composes about 1% of the atmosphere. It is used in
incandescent light bulbs to permit the filament to be heated to a higher
temperature, and thus to produce a whiter light than would be practical
in a vacuum. The argon decreases the rate at which the metallic filament evaporates, by keeping vaporized metal atoms from diffusing
away from the filament, and permitting them to reattach themselves
to it.

Krypton, Xenon, and Radon. Krypton and xenon, which occur in
very small quantities in the air, have not found any significant use.
Radon, which is produced steadily by radium, is used in the treatment
of cancer. It has been found that the rays given off by radioactive substances are often effective in controlling this disease. A convenient way
of administering this radiation is to pump the radon that has been produced by a sample of radium into a small gold tube, which is then placed
in proximity to the tissues to be treated.*

The Discovery of the Noble Gases.   The story of the discovery of argon provides an
interesting illustration of the importance of attention to minor discrepancies in the
results of scientific investigations.

For over a hundred years it was thought that atmospheric air consisted, aside from
small variable amounts of water vapor and carbon dioxide, solely of oxygen (21%

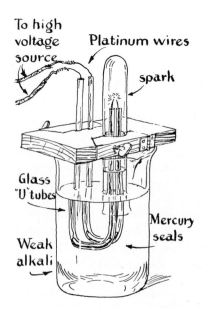

To high
voltage   **Platinum wires**
source

spark

Glass
"U" tubes

Mercury
seals
Weak
alkali

FIGURE 5-2

*The Cavendish apparatus, used in the inves-
tigation of the composition of air.*

* Radon is chemically unreactive, but its *nuclei* decompose; see Chapter 32.

by volume) and nitrogen (79%). In 1785 the English scientist Henry Cavendish (1731–1810) investigated the composition of the atmosphere. He mixed oxygen with air, and then passed an electric spark through the mixture, to form a compound of nitrogen and oxygen, which was dissolved in a solution in contact with the gas (Figure 5-2). The sparking was continued until there was no further decrease in volume, and the oxygen was then removed from the residual gas by treatment with another solution. He found that after this treatment only a small bubble of air remained unabsorbed, not more than $\frac{1}{120}$ of the original air. Although Lord Cavendish did not commit himself on the point, it seems to have been assumed by chemists that if the sparking had been continued for a longer time there would have been no residue, and Cavendish's experiment was accordingly interpreted as showing that only oxygen and nitrogen were present in the atmosphere.

Then in 1894, more than 100 years later, Lord Rayleigh began an investigation involving the careful determination of the densities of the gases hydrogen, oxygen, and nitrogen. To prepare nitrogen he mixed dried air with an excess of ammonia, NH_3, and passed the mixture over red-hot copper. Under these conditions the oxygen reacts with ammonia, according to the equation

$$4NH_3 + 3O_2 \longrightarrow 6H_2O + 2N_2$$

The excess ammonia is then removed by bubbling the gas through sulfuric acid. The remaining gas, after drying, should have been pure nitrogen, derived in part from the ammonia and in part from air. The density of this gas was determined. Another sample of nitrogen was made simply by passing air over red-hot copper, which removed the oxygen by combining with it to form copper oxide:

$$O_2 + 2Cu \longrightarrow 2CuO$$

When the density of this gas was determined it was found to be about 0.1% greater than that from the sample of ammonia and air. In order to investigate this discrepancy, a third sample of nitrogen was made, by use of a mixture of ammonia and pure oxygen. It was found that this sample of nitrogen had a density 0.5% less than that of the second sample.

Further investigations showed that nitrogen prepared entirely from air had a density 0.5% greater than nitrogen prepared completely from ammonia or in any other chemical way. Nitrogen obtained from air was found to have density 1.2572 g/l at 0° C and 1 atm, whereas nitrogen made by chemical methods had a density 1.2505 g/l. Rayleigh and Ramsay then repeated Cavendish's experiments, and showed by spectroscopic analysis that the residual gas was indeed not nitrogen but a new element. They then searched for the other noble gases and discovered them.

5–5. *The Electronic Structure of Atoms*

The noble gases are strange elements. They are different from all other elements—they do not form any compounds, whereas every other element forms many compounds.

This peculiarity of the noble gases is explained by the **electronic structure** of the noble-gas atoms—the way in which the electrons move about the atomic nuclei. This is the subject that we shall now consider, beginning with the electronic structure of the simplest element, hydrogen.

The knowledge about the structure of atoms that is presented in the following paragraphs has been obtained largely by physicists from the study of spectral lines, that is, study of the light waves with different wavelengths that are emitted by gases which are strongly heated or subjected to the action of an electric current. The understanding of atomic structure was obtained during the years between 1913 and 1925. It was in 1913 that Niels Bohr (born 1885), the great Danish physicist, developed his simple theory of the hydrogen atom, which during the following twelve years was expanded and refined into our present theory of atomic structure.

The detailed mathematical theory of quantum mechanics, the modern mathematical theory of the properties of electrons and other small particles, is not suited to study by the beginning student. However, the picture of the electronic structure of atoms that is provided by this theory is easy to understand and to learn. Knowledge of this electronic structure is important to the student of chemistry.

The Electronic Structure of the Hydrogen Atom. The smallest and lightest nucleus is the proton. The proton carries one unit of positive charge, and with one electron, which carries one unit of negative charge, it forms a hydrogen atom.

Soon after the development of the concept of the nuclear atom, some idea was gained as to the way in which a proton and an electron are combined to form a hydrogen atom. Because of the attraction of the oppositely charged electron and proton, the electron might be expected to revolve in an orbit about the much heavier proton in a way similar to that in which the earth revolves about the sun. Bohr suggested that the orbit of the electron in the normal hydrogen atom should be circular, with radius 0.530 Å. The electron was calculated to be going around this orbit with the constant speed 2.18×10^8 cm/sec, which is a little less than one percent of the speed of light (3×10^{10} cm/sec, about 186,000 miles per second).

As a result of studies made by many physicists, this picture is now known to be nearly but not quite right. The electron does not move in a definite orbit, but rather in a somewhat random way, so that it is sometimes very close to the nucleus and sometimes rather far away. Moreover, it moves mainly toward the nucleus or away from it, and it travels in all directions about the nucleus instead of staying in one plane. Although it does not stay just 0.530 Å from the nucleus, this is its most probable distance. Actually by moving around rapidly it effectively occupies all the space within a radius of about 1 Å of the nucleus, and so gives the hydrogen atom an effective diameter of about 2 Å. It is because of this motion of electrons that atoms, which are made of particles only 0.0001 Å in diameter, act as solid objects several Å in diameter. The speed of the electron in the hydrogen atom is not constant; but its average is the Bohr value 2.18×10^8 cm/sec.

Thus we can describe the free hydrogen atom as having a heavy nucleus at the center of a sphere defined by the space filled by the fast-moving electron in its motion about the nucleus. This sphere is about 2 Å in diameter.

The Electronic Structure of the Noble Gases. Electron Shells.   The distributions of electrons in atoms of the noble gases have been determined by physicists by methods that are too complex to be discussed here. The results obtained are shown in Figure 5-3. It is seen that *the electrons are not uniformly arranged about the atomic nuclei, but are instead arranged in concentric shells.*

The **helium atom** contains two electrons, each of which carries out motion about the helium nucleus similar to that of the one electron in the hydrogen atom. These two electrons are said to occupy the

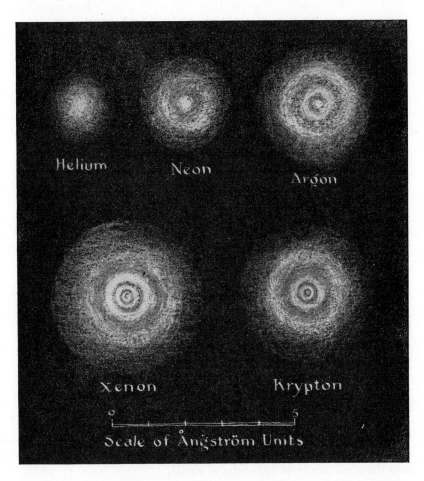

FIGURE 5-3   *Drawing of electron distributions in noble-gas atoms, showing successive electron shells.*

K shell. * This shell, of two electrons only, is the smallest of the concentric shells of electrons that any atom can have. Only two electrons can be put in the K shell. *All of the atoms heavier than hydrogen have two K electrons close to the nucleus.*

The **neon atom** consists of two K electrons close to the nucleus and an **outer shell of eight L electrons.** Thus the neon atom is more complicated than the helium atom, inasmuch as it has two shells instead of one.

The **argon atom** has in addition to the K shell of two electrons and the L shell of eight electrons another shell of eight electrons, the **M shell.**

Both neon and argon are hence built up from the preceding noble gas by increasing the nuclear charge by eight and by adding a new outer shell of eight electrons. This relation does not hold, however, with the noble gases heavier than the first three. **Krypton** has, it is true, a new outer shell of eight electrons, the **N shell,** but also the *next inner shell, the M shell,* has **expanded** *from eight to eighteen electrons.* Thus the electronic structure of krypton is obtained from that of argon by adding eighteen electrons, ten of which enter the shell which is outermost in the argon atom, the remaining eight forming a new outer shell.

At **xenon** there is added a new outer shell of electrons, the **O shell,** and again the next inner shell (the N shell) has expanded from eight to eighteen electrons.

Thus *each of the two short periods in the periodic table involves the addition of a new outer shell of eight electrons; and each of the two long periods involves the addition of a new outer shell of eight electrons and also the insertion of ten electrons into the next inner shell.*

The very long period of the periodic table, which is completed at **radon,** involves the addition of a new outer shell of eight electrons, the

TABLE 5-3   *Electron Shells of the Noble Gases*

ATOM	ATOMIC NUMBER	K	L	M	N	O	P
He	2	2					
Ne	10	2	8				
A	18	2	8	8			
Kr	36	2	8	18	8		
Xe	54	2	8	18	18	8	
Rn	86	2	8	18	32	18	8

P shell, the insertion of ten additional electrons into the next inner shell (the O shell), and also the insertion of fourteen additional electrons into the shell inside of that (the N shell).

* The use of the letter K for the innermost electron shell in an atom, and of L, M, $\cdots$ for other shells, is the result of historic accident. The letters are not abbreviations of words.

These successive shells K, L, M, N, O, P are also represented by the numbers 1, 2, 3, 4, 5, 6, which are the values of the *quantum number* that enters into the treatment of the electrons according to the quantum theory.

The electronic structures of the noble gases are summarized in Table 5-3.

The numbers 2, 8, 18, 32, which are the maximum numbers of electrons which can occupy the successive shells K, L, M, and N, are seen to be equal to $2n^2$, with $n = 1, 2, 3$, and 4, respectively.

Subshells of Electrons.   A given shell may be occupied by any number of electrons up to its maximum capacity. Atoms with 2, 8, 18, and 32 electrons in a shell are, however, especially stable. Thus the N shell contains 8 electrons in krypton, 18 in xenon, and 32 in radon.

The stability of these numbers results from the fact that each shell (except the K shell) consists of two or more subshells. The L shell contains a $2s$ subshell of 2 electrons and a $2p$ subshell of 6 electrons; for the other shells the subshells are as shown in Table 5-4.*

TABLE 5-4   *Subshells of Electrons*

	SUBSHELLS	NUMBER OF ELECTRONS			
K shell:	$1s$	2			
L shell:	$2s$	2	} 8		
	$2p$	6			
M shell:	$3s$	2	} 8	} 18	
	$3p$	6			
	$3d$	10			
N shell:	$4s$	2	} 8	} 18	} 32
	$4p$	6			
	$4d$	10			
	$4f$	14			

The Structure of Other Atoms.   Each of the elements from lithium to neon, in the first short period of the periodic system, has an inner K shell of 2 electrons and an outer L shell containing from one to eight electrons.

The electronic structure of atoms is often represented by *electron–dot symbols*, usually drawn by showing only the electrons of the outer shell. These symbols for the atoms lithium to neon are accordingly the following:

$$\text{Li·} \quad \text{Be·} \quad \text{B·} \quad \text{·C·} \quad \text{:N·} \quad \text{:O·} \quad \text{:F·} \quad \text{:Ne:}$$

---

* The letters s, p, d, f, etc., like the letters K, L, M, etc., were introduced by spectroscopists long ago, and do not have any deep meaning.

There are four *orbitals* (electron orbits) in the L shell, each of which can be unoccupied, or can be occupied by one electron, or be occupied by two electrons.

Two electrons in an orbital constitute an **electron pair.**

Thus carbon is shown with four unpaired electrons in its L shell; it has just one electron for each of the four orbitals. Neon, however, with eight L electrons, can fit them into the four L orbitals only as four electron pairs. The completed noble-gas outer shell of four electron pairs is called an **octet** of electrons. It is to be noted from Table 5-3 that each of the noble gases has such an outer shell.

The atoms in the second short period may be similarly represented:

$$Na\cdot \quad Mg\cdot \quad Al\cdot \quad \cdot \overset{\cdot}{Si}\cdot \quad \cdot \overset{\cdot}{P}\cdot \quad :\overset{\cdot}{S}\cdot \quad :\overset{\cdot}{Cl}\cdot \quad :\overset{\cdot\cdot}{A}:$$

The outer electrons in the atoms from sodium to argon occupy the M shell. At argon there are four electron pairs in this shell, occupying four orbitals. However, reference to Table 5-3 shows that the shell has the capacity of holding eighteen electrons, and hence that it consists of nine orbitals altogether, only four of which are occupied in argon.

The first few elements following argon in the periodic table have their outer electrons in the N shell:

$$K\cdot \quad Ca\cdot \quad Sc\cdot \quad \cdot \overset{\cdot}{Ti}\cdot$$

However, in the succeeding elements of the first long period of the periodic table the additional electrons are introduced into the unoccupied orbitals of the M shell. Since there are five orbitals in this shell in addition to the four which are occupied in argon, it is possible for ten electrons altogether to be introduced in this way. *The ten elements in the middle of the long period corresponding to these ten additional electrons introduced into the M shell are the iron transition elements.*

It is not customary to represent these M electrons, but only the electrons of the N shell in drawing the electronic structures of the nonmetallic elements of the first long period:

$$\cdot \overset{\cdot}{Ge}\cdot \quad :\overset{\cdot}{As}\cdot \quad :\overset{\cdot}{Se}\cdot \quad :\overset{\cdot\cdot}{Br}\cdot \quad :\overset{\cdot\cdot}{Kr}:$$

There is no accepted way to represent the electronic structures of the elements in the middle of the long period; sometimes all of the electrons in the M shell are indicated and sometimes only a part of them.

The electron-dot formulas for the elements of the second long period are just the same as for the corresponding elements of the first long period:

Rb·   Sr·   Ẏ·   ·Żr·

and   ·Sn·   :Sb·   :Te·   :Ï·   :Ẍe:

The very long period begins with the three elements cesium, barium, and lanthanum, the outer electrons of which are in the O shell:

Cs·   Ba·   La·

The fourteen elements following lanthanum are the lanthanons. They correspond to the introduction of fourteen additional electrons into the N shell, bringing its total number of electrons up to 32. The remaining elements are similar to those shown directly above them in the periodic table, and their electronic structures are similarly represented.

Illustrative Exercises

5-1.   (a) Without referring to the text, draw electron-dot symbols of atoms of the elements from lithium to neon, showing 1 to 8 electrons of the L shell. (b) What electrons in these atoms are not represented by dots in these symbols?

5-2.   The alkali metals, group I of the periodic table, are Li, Na, K, Rb, Cs, and Fr. Their atomic numbers are 3, 11, 19, 37, 55, and 87, respectively. (a) How do they differ in electronic structure from the noble gases that precede them in the periodic table? (b) Write electron-dot symbols for them.

5-3.   The halogens, group VII of the periodic table, are F, Cl, Br, I, and At, with atomic numbers 9, 17, 35, 53, and 85, respectively. Write electron-dot symbols for them, showing only electrons of the outermost shell.

5–6. Ionization Energies of the Elements

The chemical properties of elements are determined by the number of electrons in their atoms and also by the strength with which the electrons are held.

The helium atom contains two electrons, both of which are held tightly by the attraction of the nucleus. It is possible to remove one of these electrons, if a supply of energy is at hand.

The reaction we are considering is

$$He \longrightarrow He^+ + e^-$$

Here He^+ is the symbol for the *helium ion*, consisting of a helium nucleus, with charge $+2e$, and one electron, with charge $-e$; the helium ion thus has the residual charge $+e$ (represented in the symbol by the superscript $+$). The reaction is said to *ionize* the helium atom.

Ions are of great importance in chemistry, and we must now define the word ion:*

* The word ion is derived from the Greek word meaning to go, to move.

*An **ion** is an atom or group of atoms that is not electrically neutral, but instead carries a positive or negative electric charge.*

An atom (or group of atoms) is electrically neutral when the number of electrons surrounding the nucleus (or nuclei) is exactly equal to the atomic number (or sum of the atomic numbers). It is a positive ion if one or more electrons are missing, and it is a negative ion if it has one or more extra electrons.

Ionization is the process of producing ions from neutral atoms or molecules, by removing electrons or adding electrons.

The amount of energy required to remove an electron is called the *ionization energy* of the atom. It is customary to give values of this quantity in electron-volts (ev); one electron-volt is equal to 23,053 cal/mole.

The first ionization energy of helium (removing one electron) is 24.48 ev, and the second (removing the second electron) is 54.14 ev. Many values have also been determined by study of the spectra of the atoms.

Ionization energies of the elements from hydrogen to argon are given in Table 5-5, and values of the first ionization energy for the first sixty elements are plotted in Figure 5-4.

It is seen that there is a striking correlation of these values with the periodic table. The ionization-energy curve has sharp maxima at $Z = 2, 10, 18, 36$, and 54; that is, at the noble gases. These are immediately followed by deep minima, for the soft metals lithium, sodium, potassium, rubidium, and cesium, which were described in Section 5-1 as being closely similar to one another in properties.

We may well feel that the resistance that atoms of the noble gases offer to giving up any of their electrons is closely related to their striking chemical inertness. A further discussion of this question will be given in Chapter 10.

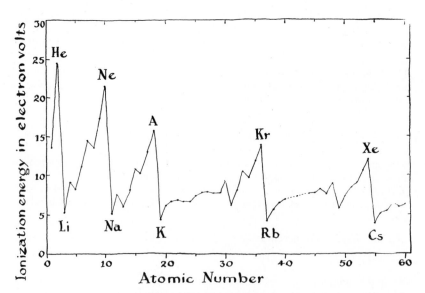

FIGURE 5-4   *The ionization energy, in electron-volts, of the first electron of atoms from hydrogen, atomic number 1, to neodymium, atomic number 60. Symbols of the elements with very high and very low ionization energy are shown in the figure.*

TABLE 5-5

Z	ELEMENT	NUMBERS OF ELECTRONS					IONIZATION ENERGIES, IN ELECTRON-VOLTS			
		1s	2s	2p	3s	3p	1st	2nd	3rd	4th
1	H	1					13.60			
2	He	2					24.58	54.40		
3	Li	2	1				5.39	75.62	122.42	
4	Be	2	2				9.32	18.21	153.85	217.66
5	B	2	2	1			8.30	25.15	37.92	259.30
6	C	2	2	2			11.26	24.38	47.86	64.48
7	N	2	2	3			14.54	29.61	47.43	77.45
8	O	2	2	4			13.61	35.15	54.93	77.39
9	F	2	2	5			17.42	34.98	62.65	87.23
10	Ne	2	2	6			21.56	41.07	64.	97.16
11	Na	2	2	6	1		5.14	47.29	71.65	98.88
12	Mg	2	2	6	2		7.64	15.03	80.12	109.29
13	Al	2	2	6	2	1	5.98	18.82	28.44	119.96
14	Si	2	2	6	2	2	8.15	16.34	33.46	45.13
15	P	2	2	6	2	3	11.0	19.65	30.16	51.35
16	S	2	2	6	2	4	10.36	23.4	35.0	47.29
17	Cl	2	2	6	2	5	13.01	23.80	39.90	53.5
18	A	2	2	6	2	6	15.76	27.62	40.90	59.79

Illustrative Exercises

5-4.   The first ionization energy of helium is 24.58ev, and the second is 54.40ev. In each case a $1s$ electron is removed. Can you explain why the second $1s$ electron is held so much more tightly than the first?

5-5.   What are the electron configurations of Li^+ and Be^+? Why does the second ionization energy have a much larger value for lithium than for beryllium?

5–7. An Energy-Level Diagram

A diagram representing the distribution of all electrons in all atoms is given in Figure 5-5.

Each orbital is represented by a square. The most stable orbital (its electrons being held most tightly by the nucleus) is the $1s$ orbital, at the bottom of the diagram. Energy is required to lift an electron from a stable orbital to a less stable one, above it in the diagram.

The electrons are shown being introduced in sequence: the first and second in the $1s$ orbital, the next two in the $2s$ orbital, the next six in the $2p$ orbitals, and so on. The sequence is indicated by arrows. The symbol and atomic number of each element are shown adjacent to the outermost electron (least tightly held electron) in the neutral atom.

The distribution of electrons among the orbitals is called the *electron configuration* of the atom. It is represented by the symbols of the subshells with the number of electrons in each subshell given above. Thus the electron configuration of helium is $1s^2$, and that of nitrogen is $1s^2\,2s^2\,2p^3$.

For the heavier atoms two or more electron configurations may have nearly the same energy, and there is some arbitrariness in the diagram shown in Figure 5-5. The con-

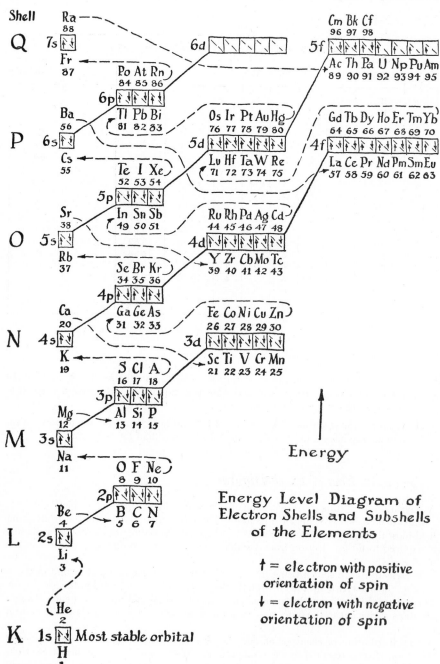

Energy

Energy Level Diagram of
Electron Shells and Subshells
of the Elements

↑ = electron with positive
orientation of spin

↓ = electron with negative
orientation of spin

FIGURE 5-5

figuration shown for each element is either that of the most stable state of the free atom (in a gas) or of a state close to the most stable state.

It was discovered in 1925 that *the electron has a spin*—it rotates about an axis, in the same way that the earth rotates about an axis through its north pole and south pole. An electron can orient its spin in either one of two ways. *Two electrons can occupy the same orbital only if their spins are opposed* (that is, oriented in opposite directions). The spins are represented by arrows in Figure 5-5.

The foregoing italicized sentence is a statement of the **Pauli exclusion principle.** W. Pauli (born 1900) was the first man to notice that an electron excludes another electron with the same orientation of its spin from the orbital it occupies. Hence only two electrons (one pair of electrons) can occupy one orbital, and they must have opposite spins.

Note that it is customary to write electron-dot formulas for some atoms in such a way as to show more unpaired electrons than are indicated in Figure 5-5. For example, in

Section 5-5 the electron-dot symbol $\cdot \overset{\cdot}{\underset{\cdot}{C}} \cdot$ was written for carbon. This symbol corre-

sponds to the configuration $1s^2\ 2s\ 2p\ 2p\ 2p$, with four unpaired electrons, whereas in Figure 5-5 it is shown as having the configuration $1s^2\ 2s^2\ 2p\ 2p$, with only two unpaired electrons. The former configuration is the more important one for chemical purposes. You may find it convenient to use electron-dot symbols that differ slightly from those indicated in Figure 5-5.

The Next Chapter. Having discussed the properties and electronic structure of the noble gases, which bear an especially simple relation to the periodic table, we shall now take up the other elements. Hydrogen, the first element, is discussed in the first part of the following chapter. Since we have dealt with helium ($Z = 2$) in the present chapter, it might be most logical to go on next to lithium ($Z = 3$) and its congeners. We shall, however, deviate from this order, and take up oxygen ($Z = 8$) immediately after hydrogen, because of the great importance of the compounds of oxygen.

Illustrative Exercises

5-6. (a) What is the electron configuration of fluorine? (Refer to Figure 5-5, and show all nine electrons. Remember that there are three $2p$ orbitals in the subshell.) (b) How many electron pairs are there in the atom? Which orbitals do they occupy? (c) How many unpaired electrons are there? Which orbital does it occupy?

5-7. (a) What are the electron configurations of beryllium and boron, as shown in Figure 5-5? (b) What electron-dot symbols do they correspond to? (c) What are the customary chemical electron-dot symbols for these atoms? (They show a larger number of unpaired electrons.)

5-8. Can you write the electron configuration for the element with $Z = 102$ (which has not yet been made), showing all 102 electrons? How many electrons are there in each shell (K, L, M, N, O, P, Q)?

Concepts and Terms Introduced in This Chapter

The periodic law; the periodic table.

Successive periods of 2, 8, 8, 18, 18, 32 elements.

Groups of elements; congeners. Metals; metalloids; non-metals.

Noble gases: helium, neon, argon, krypton, xenon, radon.

The electronic structure of the hydrogen atom.

The electronic structure of the noble gases. Electron shells.

Subshells. Orbitals. Electron pairs.

Ions, ionization, ionization energy. The energy-level diagram.

Electron configuration of atoms. The spin of the electron. The Pauli exclusion principle.

Exercises

5-9.   Without looking at the periodic table, but by remembering the number of elements in each row (2, 8, 8, 18, 18, 32), deduce what elements have atomic numbers 9, 10, 11, 17, 19, 35, 37, 54.

5-10. Sketch a plan of the periodic table, and fill in from memory the symbols of the first eighteen elements and the remaining alkali metals, halogens, and noble gases.

5-11. By extrapolation with use of the data given in Table 5-2, predict approximate values of the atomic weight, melting point, and boiling point of element 118. What would you expect its chemical properties to be?

5-12. Where was helium first detected? What is the principal source of this element at present?

5-13. List as many uses as you can for the various noble gases.

5-14. What predictions would you make about the formula, color, solubility, taste. and melting point of the compound that would be formed by reaction of chlorine and element 119?

5-15. What are the most important metallic properties? In what part of the periodic table are the elements with metallic properties?

5-16. Classify the following elements as metals, metalloids, or non-metals: potassium, arsenic, aluminum, xenon, bromine, silicon, phosphorus.

Reference Books

Mary Elvira Weeks, *Discovery of the Elements*, Journal of Chemical Education, Easton, **Pa.** Fourth edition, **1939.**

Many interesting articles about the periodic system of the elements have been published in recent years in the *Journal of Chemical Education.*

Chapter 6

Hydrogen and Oxygen

Hydrogen and oxygen form a great many compounds with other elements, and take part in a great number of chemical reactions. We shall begin our detailed study of descriptive chemistry in this chapter with the study of these two elements, and shall continue, in the following chapter, with another important element, carbon.

Hydrogen, with atomic number 1, is much different in its properties from all of the other elements, and it is therefore not usually classed in a group of the periodic table. Oxygen, with atomic number 8, is the first element of group VI.   *11 8568*

Both hydrogen and oxygen are gases at room temperature and atmospheric pressure. It is interesting that it was not until the early years of the seventeenth century that the word "gas" was used. This word was invented by a Belgian physician, J. B. van Helmont (1577–1644), to fill the need caused by the new idea that different kinds of "airs" exist. Van Helmont discovered that a gas (the gas that we now call carbon dioxide) is formed when limestone is treated with acid, and that this gas differs from air in that when respired it does not support life and that it is heavier than air. He also found that the same gas is produced by fermentation, and that it is present in the Grotto del Cane, a cave in Italy in which dogs were observed to become unconscious (carbon dioxide escaping from fissures in the floor displaces the air in the lower part of the cave).

During the seventeenth and eighteenth centuries other gases were discovered, including hydrogen, oxygen, and nitrogen, and many of their properties were investigated. However, it was not until nearly the end of the seventeenth century that these three gases were recognized as elements. When Lavoisier recognized that oxygen is an element, and that combustion is the process of combining with oxygen, the foundation of modern chemistry was laid.

In connection with the discussion of the chemical properties of hydrogen and oxygen in the following sections of this chapter, we shall have occasion to mention some of the principles of chemistry, using the properties of hydrogen and oxygen and their compounds as illustrations. In addition, a discussion will be given in this chapter of chemical nomenclature—the ways in which chemical compounds are named.

6–1. *Hydrogen*

Hydrogen, the first element in the periodic table, is unique: it has no congeners. It is a very widely distributed element. It is found in most of the substances which constitute living matter, and in many inorganic substances. There are more compounds of hydrogen known than of any other element, carbon being a close second. Its most important compound is water, H_2O.

Properties of Hydrogen.   Free hydrogen, H_2, is a colorless, odorless, and tasteless gas. It is the lightest of all gases, its density being about one fourteenth of that of air (Figure 6-1). Its melting point ($-259°$ C or $14°$ A) and boiling point ($-252.7°$ C) are very low, only those of helium being lower. Liquid hydrogen, with density 0.070 g/cm³, is, as might be expected, the lightest of all liquids. Crystalline hydrogen, with density 0.088 g/cm³, is also the lightest of all crystalline substances. Hydrogen is very slightly soluble in water; one liter of water at $0°$ C dissolves only 21.5 ml of hydrogen gas under 1 atm pressure. The solubility decreases with increasing temperature, and increases with increase in the pressure of the gas.

The Preparation of Hydrogen.   In the laboratory hydrogen may be easily made by the reaction of an acid such as sulfuric acid, H_2SO_4,

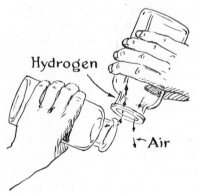

Hydrogen

Air

FIGURE 6-1

Pouring hydrogen from one bottle to another, with downward displacement of air.

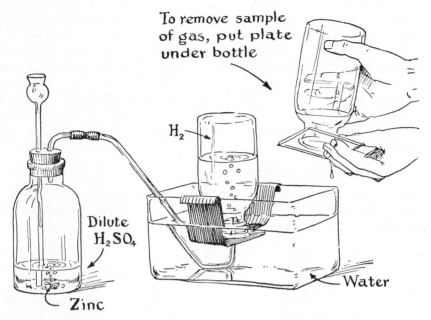

To remove sample
of gas, put plate
under bottle

H_2

Dilute
H_2SO_4

Zinc

Water

FIGURE 6-2   *The preparation of hydrogen in the laboratory.*

with a metal such as zinc. Figure 6-2 represents apparatus used for this purpose. The equation for the reaction is

$$H_2SO_4 + Zn \longrightarrow ZnSO_4 + H_2 \uparrow$$

The vertical arrow placed beside the formula of hydrogen in this equation is used to indicate that hydrogen is a gas, which escapes from the region of reaction.*

Hydrogen can also be prepared by the reaction of some metals with water or steam. Sodium and its congeners react very vigorously with water, so vigorously as to generate enough heat to ignite the liberated hydrogen. An alloy of lead and sodium, which reacts less vigorously, is sometimes used for the preparation of hydrogen. The equation for the reaction of sodium with water is the following:

$$2Na + 2H_2O \longrightarrow 2NaOH + H_2 \uparrow$$

The substance NaOH produced in this way is called *sodium hydroxide.*

Calcium also reacts with water, but with less vigor. The reaction of metallic calcium with cold water provides a simple and safe way of preparing hydrogen in the laboratory. The equation for this reaction is

$$Ca + 2H_2O \longrightarrow Ca(OH)_2 \downarrow + H_2 \uparrow$$

The substance $Ca(OH)_2$ is called *calcium hydroxide.* Calcium hydroxide

* A vertical arrow pointed *down* may be placed after a formula to indicate that the substance precipitates from solution.

is not very soluble in water, and in the course of the reaction of calcium with water a white precipitate of calcium hydroxide is formed.

It is to be seen from the equations above that each of the metals sodium and calcium liberates only half of the hydrogen contained in the water with which it reacts.

Much of the hydrogen that is used in industry is produced by the reaction of iron with steam. The steam from a boiler is passed over iron filings heated to a temperature of about 600° C. The reaction that occurs is

$$3Fe + 4H_2O \longrightarrow Fe_3O_4 + 4H_2$$

After a mass of iron has been used in this way for some time, it is largely converted into iron oxide, Fe_3O_4. The iron can then be regenerated by passing carbon monoxide, CO, over the heated oxide:

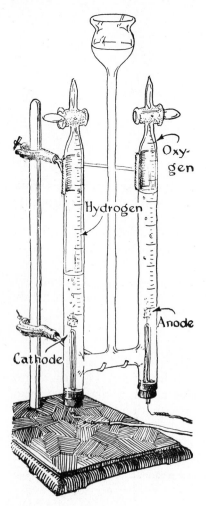

FIGURE 6-3

Apparatus for the electrolysis of water.

$$Fe_3O_4 + 4CO \longrightarrow 3Fe + 4CO_2$$

The carbon monoxide is changed by this reaction into CO_2, carbon dioxide. In this way the iron can be used over and over again.

Hydrogen can also be made by the reaction of a *metallic hydride* (a compound of a metal and hydrogen) with water. Thus calcium hydride, CaH_2, produces hydrogen according to the following reaction:

$$CaH_2 + 2H_2O \longrightarrow Ca(OH)_2 + 2H_2 \uparrow$$

Hydrogen (together with oxygen) can also be made by the *electrolysi.* of water. Pure water hardly conducts an electric current at all, but it becomes a good conductor if salt is dissolved in it. When two electrodes are introduced into such a solution and a suitable potential difference of electricity (voltage difference) is applied, hydrogen is liberated at one electrode (the cathode) and oxygen at the other electrode (the anode); this phenomenon of decomposition of a substance by an electric current is called electrolysis. The theory of this phenomenon will be discussed in a later chapter (Chapter 10). The over-all reaction that takes place is represented by the equation

$$2H_2O \longrightarrow 2H_2 \uparrow + O_2 \uparrow$$

Thus two molecules of hydrogen are formed for each molecule of oxygen.

History of the Discovery of Hydrogen.   It was discovered early in the sixteenth century that a combustible gas is formed when sulfuric acid acts upon steel filings or iron nails. Robert Boyle of Oxford observed that hydrogen would not burn in the rarefied atmosphere produced by his air pump. Henry Cavendish in 1781 showed that water is produced when hydrogen combines with oxygen. He did not, however, recognize that the hydrogen had originally been produced from water or acid, but thought that it had come from the metal that reacted with the acid. Cavendish's name for hydrogen was "inflammable air." Lavoisier named the element hydrogen (water-former, from Greek *hydor*, water, and *genon*, to form).

The Uses of Hydrogen in Industry.   Large amounts of hydrogen are used in industry in converting oils (liquid fats), such as cottonseed oil and whale oil, into solid fats, which are used as food or are converted into soap.* Because of its lightness hydrogen may be used to inflate balloons. Hydrogen has a higher conductivity of heat and a lower viscosity than other gases, such as air, and it is for these reasons sometimes used, in a closed system, as a cooling gas around the armatures in large electric generators.

6–2. *Oxygen*

Occurrence of Oxygen.   Oxygen is the most abundant element in the earth's crust. It constitutes by weight 89% of water, 23% of air

* This process is called the *hydrogenation* of oils.

(21% by volume), and nearly 50% of the common minerals (silicates). The average composition of the atmosphere is given in Table 6-1.

TABLE 6-1   *Composition of the Atmosphere*

SUBSTANCE	VOLUME PERCENT IN DRY AIR	SUBSTANCE	VOLUME PERCENT IN DRY AIR
Nitrogen	78.03	Neon	0.0018
Oxygen	20.99	Helium	0.0005
Argon	0.93	Krypton	0.0001
Carbon dioxide	0.03	Ozone	0.00006
Hydrogen	0.01	Xenon	0.000009

The Discovery of Oxygen.   Joseph Priestley (1733–1804), of Manchester, England, announced in 1774 the discovery of a gas with the ability to support combustion better than air. He had prepared the gas by heating some red mercuric oxide which was confined in a cylinder over mercury. K. W. Scheele of Sweden seems to have prepared and investigated oxygen before 1773, but an account of his work was not published until 1777.

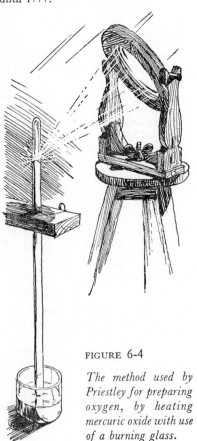

FIGURE 6-4

The method used by Priestley for preparing oxygen, by heating mercuric oxide with use of a burning glass.

FIGURE 6-5

Apparatus used by Lavoisier to show that when mercury is heated in contact with air one-fifth of the volume of the air combines with the mercury.

FIGURE 6-6 *Lavoisier's apparatus for analyzing water by passing steam over hot iron filings. The undecomposed steam is condensed into water in the cooled coil, and the hydrogen is collected over water in the bell jar.*

Red mercuric oxide, HgO, is made by heating mercuric nitrate, $Hg(NO_3)_2$, which itself is made by the action of nitric acid (HNO_3) on mercury. Priestley found that when mercuric oxide is heated to a high temperature it decomposes with the liberation of oxygen:

$$2HgO \longrightarrow 2Hg + O_2 \uparrow$$

In order to obtain the oxygen he introduced mercuric oxide into the top of a closed tube which had been filled with mercury, its open lower end being under the surface of a bath of mercury. He then heated the mercuric oxide by use of a burning glass (a large glass lens, Figure 6-4), and in this way collected the oxygen over mercury. He found that substances burned in the gas more vigorously than in air.

In 1775 Lavoisier, having learned about Priestley's work, reported his work on the nature of combustion and the oxidation of metals, and advanced his new theory of combustion. He showed that $\frac{1}{5}$ of the volume of air is removed by phosphorus or by mercury (when heated for a long time), and that by strongly heating the mercuric oxide formed in this way a gas with volume equal to the volume lost from the air could be recovered. He showed that this gas supported combustion vigorously, and could, when breathed, support life. The apparatus used by Lavoisier in his work is sketched in Figure 6-5. In 1783 Lavoisier analyzed water by passing steam over hot iron filings (Figure 6-6). Lavoisier named the new gas oxygen (Greek, *oxys*, acid, and *genon*, to form) because he thought, mistakenly, that it was a constituent of all acids.

Preparation and Properties. Ordinary oxygen consists of diatomic molecules, O_2. It is a colorless, odorless gas, which is slightly soluble in water—1 liter of water at 0° C dissolves 48.9 ml of oxygen gas at 1 atm pressure. Oxygen condenses to a pale blue liquid at its boiling point, $-183.0°$ C; and on further cooling freezes, at $-218.4°$ C, to a pale blue crystalline solid.

Oxygen may be easily prepared in the laboratory by heating potassium chlorate, $KClO_3$:

$$2KClO_3 \longrightarrow 2KCl + 3O_2 \uparrow$$

The reaction proceeds readily at a temperature just above the melting point of potassium chlorate if a small amount of manganese dioxide, MnO_2, is mixed with it. Although the manganese dioxide accelerates the rate of evolution of oxygen from the potassium chlorate, it itself is not changed.

A substance with this property of accelerating a chemical reaction without itself undergoing significant change is called a **catalyst,** *and is said to* **catalyze** *the reaction.*

Oxygen is made commercially mainly by the distillation of liquid air. Nitrogen is more volatile than oxygen, and tends to evaporate first from liquid air. By properly controlling the conditions of the evaporation nearly pure oxygen can be obtained. The oxygen is stored and shipped in steel cylinders, at pressures of 100 atm or more. Some oxygen is also made commercially, together with hydrogen, by the electrolysis of water.

The Uses of Oxygen. A considerable part of the energy liberated by an ordinary flame is required to heat the nitrogen of the air to the flame temperature, and hence much higher flame temperatures can be reached by using pure oxygen instead of air. An oxygen flame (oxygen and illuminating gas) is used for working glass of high softening point (such as Pyrex glass), and an oxy-hydrogen flame is used for working silica (Figure 6-7). The oxy-acetylene flame (acetylene is a compound of hydrogen and carbon, with formula C_2H_2) and the oxy-hydrogen flame are used for welding iron and steel, and for cutting iron and steel plates as much as several inches thick. The cutting operation is carried out by use of excess of oxygen, which oxidizes some of the iron, and carries it away.

The energy required to keep the human body warm and to carry on the chemical and physical processes involved in life is obtained from chemical reaction of oxygen with organic material derived from or contained in the food which we eat. The oxygen required for this process enters the lungs, is picked up by a protein, hemoglobin, in the red cells of the blood, and is carried by the blood to the tissues, where part of it is released. In case the lungs are damaged by noxious gases or by disease, such as pneumonia, and it becomes difficult for the oxygen of the air to be transferred to the blood at the proper rate, a patient may be aided by being placed in an oxygen-rich atmosphere (40 to 60% oxygen) either in an "oxygen tent" or by use of an oxygen mask. Aviators breathe

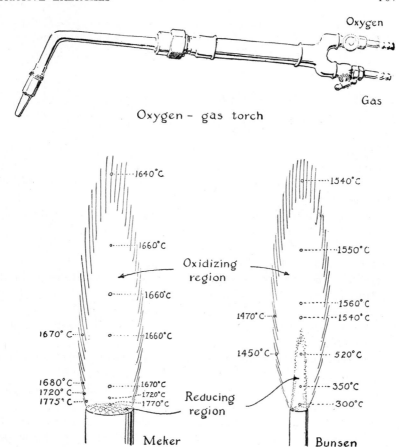

FIGURE 6-7   *Burners and torch.*

pure oxygen at high altitudes, where the pressure of oxygen in the air is insufficient for human needs, and oxygen tanks and helmets are used by rescue workers in gas-filled mines and buildings.

Illustrative Exercises

6-1. Write the chemical equation (balanced, of course) for one reaction that might be used to prepare hydrogen in the laboratory

6-2. Write the equation for a reaction that might be used to prepare oxygen.

6-3. Why is manganese dioxide mixed with potassium chlorate in the usual laboratory procedure for preparing oxygen?

6-4. What is a catalyst?

6-5. (a) Write the equation for the reaction of acetylene, C_2H_2, and oxygen, assuming that the products are water and carbon dioxide, CO_2. (b) Write the equation for the reaction of acetylene and oxygen with products water and carbon monoxide, CO. (c) Under what conditions would you expect the products to be water and carbon dioxide? Water and carbon monoxide?

6–3. Compounds of Hydrogen and Oxygen.
The Naming of Chemical Compounds

Compounds consisting of two elements are called *binary compounds*. For example, water, H_2O, is a binary compound of hydrogen and oxygen, and sodium chloride, NaCl, is a binary compound of sodium and chlorine.

The chemical name of a binary compound is obtained by stating the name of one of the elements, usually the more metallic of the two elements, and adding the name of the second element, with its ending changed to *ide*. The ending ide is characteristic of binary compounds.

Sodium chloride, for example, is a compound of sodium and chlorine. Sodium is a metal, and chlorine is a non-metal. It is accordingly the word chlorine that is modified by the use of the ending ide, so that it become chloride, and this word follows the word sodium in the name sodium chloride.

The symbols for the elements should be written in the same order in the formula, the symbol for the more metallic of the two elements coming first, and that for the less metallic second; for example, NaCl for sodium chloride.

It was mentioned in Chapter 5 that the most strongly metallic elements are those toward the bottom and the left side of the periodic table, and the most strongly non-metallic are those toward the top and the right. Hydrogen is to be considered about equivalent to boron or phosphorus. The chemical name for water is hydrogen oxide; binary compounds of oxygen are called *oxides*.

Sometimes the number of atoms in the formula of a compound is indicated by the use of a prefix. For example, the two oxides, SO_2 and SO_3, of sulfur are called sulfur dioxide and sulfur trioxide, respectively. The prefixes *mono, di, tri, tetra, penta, hexa, hepta,* and *octa* are used to indicate one atom, two atoms, and so on to eight atoms. For example, the molecule N_2O_3 is called dinitrogen trioxide; the prefixes di and tri indicate that the molecule contains two atoms of nitrogen and three atoms of oxygen.

Many metals form two oxides (some of them form more than two). It is customary in the case of metals to make use of a suffix to the name of the metal in order to distinguish between the oxides. The suffix *ous* is used for the compound containing the smaller amount of oxygen (or other non-metallic element), and the suffix *ic* is used for the compound containing the larger amount of oxygen (or other non-metallic element).

Often these suffixes are used with the Latin name of the element, rather than the English name. For example, the metal tin (Latin name *stannum*, symbol Sn) forms two oxides, SnO and SnO$_2$. These are named stannous oxide and stannic oxide, respectively.

The Compounds of Oxygen.   Oxides of all of the elements have been prepared, except the noble gases. Examples are sodium oxide, Na$_2$O; magnesium oxide, MgO; aluminum oxide, Al$_2$O$_3$; zinc oxide, ZnO; sulfur dioxide, SO$_2$. Most of the elementary substances combine so vigorously with oxygen that they will burn, either spontaneously (phosphorus) or after they have been ignited, by heating (sulfur, hydrogen, sodium, magnesium, iron, etc.). A few metals, such as copper and mercury, form oxides only slowly, even when heated; in some cases it is necessary to prepare oxides by indirect methods, rather than by direct reaction with oxygen. The properties of oxides are discussed in later sections of the book.

The Compounds of Hydrogen.   Hydrogen forms binary compounds with all of the metalloids and non-metals except the noble gases. It also combines with many of the metals.

The compounds of hydrogen with metals and metalloids are called *hydrides:* an example is lithium hydride, LiH.

Many of the compounds of hydrogen with non-metallic elements have special names; for example, CH$_4$, methane; NH$_3$, ammonia; H$_2$O, water; SiH$_4$, silane; PH$_3$, phosphine; and AsH$_3$, arsine.

Illustrative Exercises

6-6.   Assign names to the following binary compounds: MgO, NaH, KCl, CaH$_2$, Al$_2$O$_3$, SiO$_2$, CaS, Na$_2$O, Li$_3$N, AlF$_3$.

6-7.   The following pairs of elements form binary compounds in which the atoms of the two elements occur in equal numbers. Write formulas for them, and assign names to them: cesium and fluorine; nitrogen and boron; oxygen and beryllium; carbon and silicon; aluminum and phosphorus; chlorine and fluorine.

6-8.   Using prefixes to indicate the number of atoms of different kind, assign names to the following binary compounds: MgCl$_2$, BF$_3$, SiO$_2$, PCl$_5$, SF$_6$, CO, CO$_2$, SO$_2$, SO$_3$, SiCl$_4$.

6–4. *Oxidation and Reduction*

Hydrogen combines with oxygen with great vigor. A stream of hydrogen when ignited burns in oxygen or air with a very hot, almost colorless flame (Figure 6-8), and a mixture of hydrogen and oxygen when ignited explodes with great violence.

When hydrogen burns in air or oxygen, forming hydrogen oxide

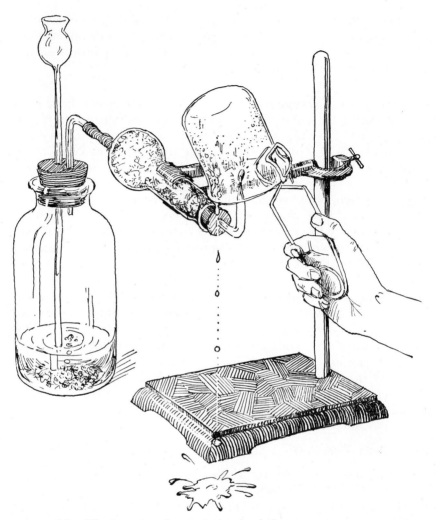

FIGURE 6-8   *The formation of water by burning hydrogen.*

(water), the hydrogen is said to have been *oxidized*. The process is called *oxidation*, and oxygen is called the *oxidizing agent*.

The tendency of hydrogen to combine with oxygen to form water is so great that the gas will even remove oxygen from many metallic oxides. Thus when a stream of hydrogen is passed over hot copper oxide, CuO, in a heated tube, the copper oxide is converted into metallic copper (Figure 6-9):

$$CuO + H_2 \longrightarrow Cu + H_2O$$

This reaction is described as the *reduction* of copper oxide by hydrogen. Hydrogen is called the *reducing agent* in the reaction. Copper oxide is said to have been *reduced* to metallic copper.

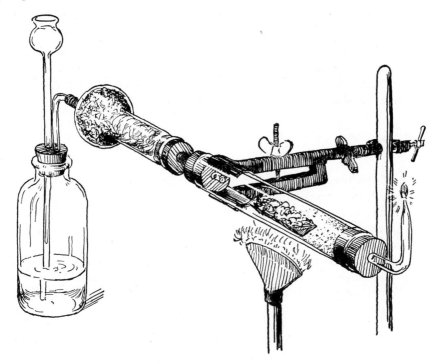

FIGURE 6-9   *The reduction of a metal oxide by hydrogen.*

In the reaction of hydrogen and copper oxide the copper oxide is the oxidizing agent. In every reaction of this sort there is a reducing agent which is oxidized and an oxidizing agent which is reduced.

Illustrative Exercises

6-9.   (a) In the reaction of acetylene and oxygen to form water and carbon dioxide, what is the reducing agent? (b) What is the oxidizing agent? (c) What substance has been oxidized?

6-10. Write the equation for the reaction of reduction of ferrous oxide, FeO, to iron by use of hydrogen as the reducing agent.

6–5. *Valence*

If there were no order in the way in which atoms of different elements combine to form the molecules and crystals of compounds, it would be necessary for us to memorize one by one the formulas of thousands of substances. Fortunately there is a great deal of order in the formulas of substances, resulting from the fact that some elements have a definite combining capacity, or *valence* (from Latin *valentia*, vigor or capacity), which determines the number of other atoms with which an atom of the element can combine. Other elements, more complex in their behavior, may exhibit any one of two or more combining capacities.

The simplest concept of valence is that *the* **valence** *of an element is the number of bonds that an atom of the element can form with other atoms.*

For example, we may assign to the water molecule, H_2O, the following **valence-bond structure:**

$$\begin{array}{c} H \qquad\quad H \\ \diagdown \quad\diagup \\ O \end{array}$$

Each of the two hydrogen atoms is attached to the oxygen atom by a **valence bond,** represented by the line connecting the symbols for the atoms. Hydrogen forms one valence bond: the valence of hydrogen is said to be 1. Oxygen forms two valence bonds; its valence is 2. These are the usual valences of hydrogen and oxygen.

The binary compound of hydrogen and chlorine is hydrogen chloride, HCl. Assuming that the hydrogen atom forms one bond, the valence-bond structure for this molecule is H—Cl. Accordingly, chlorine in this compound has the valence 1.

Sodium hydride has the formula NaH; hence we assign the valence 1 to sodium also. If sodium retains the valence 1 in other compounds, chlorine the valence 1, and oxygen the valence 2, we would predict for sodium chloride the formula Na—Cl, and for sodium oxide the formula Na—O—Na. Compounds with the formulas NaCl and Na_2O are known.

An element with valence 1 is said to be *univalent.* The Latin prefix uni is used rather than the Greek prefix mono, because the word valence has a Latin root. The adjectives *bivalent, tervalent, quadrivalent, quinquevalent, sexivalent, septivalent,* and *octavalent* are used to describe elements with valences from 2 to 8, respectively.[*]

Sometimes two or three lines are drawn between two atoms in a valence-bond formula. Two lines drawn between two atoms represent a *double bond,* corresponding to the use of two valences for each atom. Three lines are used to represent a *triple bond.*

The formula NH_3 for ammonia shows that nitrogen is tervalent in this compound, and the formula CH_4 for methane shows that carbon is quadrivalent. The valence-bond formulas for these molecules are the following:

$$\begin{array}{cc} \begin{array}{c} H \\ | \\ H-N-H \end{array} & \begin{array}{c} H \\ | \\ H-C-H \\ | \\ H \end{array} \end{array}$$

---

[*] Some chemists use the words monovalent, bivalent, trivalent, tetravalent, pentavalent, hexavalent, etc.

For carbon dioxide, CO_2, we write the valence-bond formula $O\!=\!C\!=\!O$. The carbon atom exercises its quadrivalence by forming two double bonds (four bonds altogether) with the two oxygen atoms, and each oxygen atom exercises its bivalence by forming one double bond.

Similarly, the molecule hydrogen cyanide, HCN, is assigned the valence-bond formula $H\!-\!C\!\equiv\!N$. Here hydrogen is univalent, carbon is quadrivalent (forming one single bond and one triple bond), and nitrogen is tervalent.

It is sometimes useful to think of the atom as having hooks attached to it, the number of hooks being equal to its valence; the molecule is then considered to be built up by fastening a hook from one atom into a hook of another atom.

There is a close relation between the valence of an element and the position of the element in the periodic table. The maximum valence that an element can have is given by its group number in the table. For example, in the second short period, from sodium, in group I, to chlorine, in group VII, the maximum valence increases from 1, for sodium, to 7, for chlorine. Oxides of the elements in the second short period have been found to have the following formulas:

	Na_2O	MgO	Al_2O_3	SiO_2	P_2O_5	SO_3	Cl_2O_7
Valence of element	1	2	3	4	5	6	7

Throughout the following chapters of our book the relation between the valences of elements and their position in the periodic table will be emphasized.

A more detailed discussion of valence will be presented in Chapters 10, 11, and 12.

Illustrative Exercises

6-11. The valence of chlorine in combination with metals is 1. Predict formulas for the chlorides of sodium, magnesium, aluminum, and silicon.

6-12. Titanium forms an oxide with formula TiO_2. What is the valence of titanium? What would you predict as the formula of a binary compound of titanium and chlorine?

6-13. Boron, in group III of the periodic table, has valence 3. What is the formula of the oxide of boron?

6–6. Ions

In Section 5–6 there was given a brief discussion of ions. We shall now return to this important subject, beginning with an account of their discovery.

Two hundred years ago, during the eighteenth century, scientists (they were then called natural philosophers) were making many discoveries about the nature and properties of electricity. An Italian physicist named Beccaria discovered that pure water is a very poor conductor of electricity. In 1771 the British scientist Henry Cavendish reported that he had found that salt dissolved in water causes the electric conductivity to increase very greatly. Many scientists then carried on investigations of the conductance of electricity by salt solutions, and of chemical reactions produced by electricity, but the discovery of the way in which salt solutions carry an electric current was not made for over one hundred years.

In 1884 a young Swedish scientist Svante Arrhenius (1859–1927), then twenty-five years old, published his doctor's dissertation, on measurements of the electric conductivity of salt solutions and his ideas as to their interpretation. These ideas were rather vague, but he later made them more precise, and then published a detailed paper on ionic dissociation in 1887.

The hypothesis made by Arrhenius is that a solution of salt, such as sodium chloride, contains electrically charged particles, which are called ions (Section 5–6). This hypothesis was not accepted at first, but before long chemists found that it explained so many of the facts of chemistry in a simple way that it was accepted, and it is now an important part of chemical theory.

The electron had not yet been discovered when Arrhenius proposed his theory, but we shall discuss the theory in terms of the electronic structure of ions.

Sodium has atomic number 11. The nucleus of a sodium atom has electric charge $+11e$, and the atom is electrically neutral when the nucleus is surrounded by 11 electrons. If an electron were to be removed from the sodium atom, leaving only 10 electrons around the nucleus, the resulting particle would have a positive charge, $+e$. This particle, composed of a sodium nucleus and 10 electrons, is called a *sodium ion*. Similarly, a chlorine atom, with 17 electrons surrounding a nucleus with charge $+17e$, is converted into a *chloride ion*, with negative charge $-e$, by the addition of an eighteenth electron. The transfer of an electron from a sodium atom to a chlorine atom produces a sodium ion, Na^+, and a chloride ion, Cl^-.

Arrhenius assumed that in a solution of sodium chloride in water there are present sodium ions, Na^+, and chloride ions, Cl^-. When electrodes are put into such a solution, the sodium ions are attracted toward the cathode, and move in that direction, and the chloride ions are attracted toward the anode, and move in the direction of the anode. The motion of these ions, in opposite directions, through the solution provides the mechanism of conduction of the current of electricity by the solution.

Positive ions, which are attracted toward the cathode, *are called* **cations.**
Negative ions, which are attracted toward the anode, *are called* **anions.**

It is now known that a crystal of sodium chloride is also composed of ions, sodium ions, Na^+, and chloride ions, Cl^-, arranged as shown in Figure 4-6; it is not composed of neutral atoms of sodium and chlorine.

6–7. *Acids, Bases, and Salts*

The Nature of Acids and Bases.   The alchemists observed that many different substances when dissolved in water give solutions with certain properties in common, such as acidic taste and the property of reacting with metals such as zinc with liberation of hydrogen. These substances were classed as *acids*. It is now known that the acidic properties of the solutions are due to the presence of *hydrogen ion*, H^+, in concentration greater than in pure water.

The usage of the word acid is variable. For many purposes it is convenient to say that an **acid** *is a hydrogen-containing substance which dissociates on solution in water to produce hydrogen ion.*

Examples of acids are

Hydrochloric acid, HCl (hydrogen chloride)
Hydrobromic acid, HBr (hydrogen bromide)
Hydrosulfuric acid, H_2S (hydrogen sulfide)
Sulfuric acid, H_2SO_4
Sulfurous acid, H_2SO_3
Phosphoric acid, H_3PO_4
Nitric acid, HNO_3
Perchloric acid, $HClO_4$
Chloric acid, $HClO_3$
Carbonic acid, H_2CO_3

A **base** *is a substance containing the hydroxide ion, OH^-, or the hydroxide group, OH, which can dissociate in aqueous solution as the hydroxide ion, OH^-.*
Basic solutions have a characteristic brackish taste.

Hydroxides of metals are compounds of metals with the hydroxide group, OH. The hydroxides of the metals are bases. The hydroxides LiOH, NaOH, KOH, RbOH, and CsOH are called *alkalies;* and those $Be(OH)_2$, $Mg(OH)_2$, $Ca(OH)_2$, $Sr(OH)_2$, and $Ba(OH)_2$ are called *alkaline earths.* A basic solution is also called an *alkaline solution.*

Acids and bases react to form compounds which are called **salts.** Thus the reaction of sodium hydroxide and hydrochloric acid produces the salt sodium chloride, NaCl, and water:

$$NaOH + HCl \longrightarrow NaCl + H_2O$$

Similarly the reaction of calcium hydroxide and phosphoric acid produces water and calcium phosphate, $Ca_3(PO_4)_2$:

$$3Ca(OH)_2 + 2H_3PO_4 \longrightarrow Ca_3(PO_4)_2 + 6H_2O$$

Hydrogen Ion (Hydronium Ion) and Hydroxide Ion. The hydrogen ion, H^+, has a very simple structure: it consists of a bare proton, without the electron that is attached to it in a hydrogen atom. The hydrogen ion has a positive electric charge of one unit. The bare proton, H^+, does not exist in appreciable concentration in aqueous solutions, but instead exists attached to a water molecule, forming the *hydronium ion*, H_3O^+.

Because of the additional complexity introduced into chemical equations by use of H_3O^+ in place of H^+, it is customary for the sake of convenience to write equations for reactions of acids in aqueous solution with use of the symbol H^+. It is to be understood that this is a shorthand device, and that the molecular species present is the hydronium ion, H_3O^+.

The hydroxide ion, which is present in basic solutions, carries a negative charge: its formula is OH^-.

Indicators. Acids and bases have the property of causing many organic substances to change in color. Thus if lemon juice is added to a cup of tea, the tea becomes lighter in color; a dark brown substance in the tea is converted into a light yellow substance. That this change is reversible may be shown by adding an alkaline substance, such as common baking soda (sodium hydrogen carbonate, $NaHCO_3$) to the tea; this will restore the original dark color. A substance that has this property of changing color when acid or base is added to it is called an *indicator*.

A very common indicator is *litmus*, a dye obtained from certain lichens. Litmus assumes a red color in acidic solution and a blue color in basic solution. A useful way of testing the acidity or basicity of a solution is by use of paper in which litmus has been absorbed, called *litmus paper*. A solution which gives litmus paper a color intermediate between blue and red is called a *neutral solution*. Such a solution contains hydrogen ions and hydroxide ions in equal (extremely small) concentrations.

Nomenclature of Acids, Bases, and Salts. Acids with 1, 2, and 3 replaceable hydrogen atoms are called *monoprotic, diprotic*, and *triprotic acids*, respectively, and bases with 1, 2, and 3 replaceable hydroxide groups are called *monohydroxic, dihydroxic*, and *trihydroxic bases*. For example, HCl is a monoprotic acid, H_2SO_4 a diprotic acid, and H_3PO_4 a triprotic acid. NaOH is a monohydroxic base, and $Ca(OH)_2$ a dihydroxic base.

Salts such as Na_2SO_4, which result from complete neutralization of an acid by a base, are called *normal salts;* those containing more acid are called *acid salts.*

The ways of naming salts are illustrated by the following examples; older names which are now not approved are given in parentheses:

Na_2SO_4: sodium sulfate, normal sodium sulfate

$NaHSO_4$: sodium hydrogen sulfate; sodium acid sulfate; (sodium bisulfate)

Na_3PO_4: normal sodium phosphate; trisodium phosphate

Na_2HPO_4: disodium monohydrogen phosphate; sodium monohydrogen phosphate

NaH_2PO_4: sodium dihydrogen phosphate

There are three kinds of names given in the list of acids at the beginning of this section. A name of one kind, illustrated by hydrochloric acid, has the prefix *hydro* and the suffix *ic* attached to the name of the element characteristic of the acid. The molecules of acids with names of this kind do not contain oxygen. The salts are named by omitting the prefix *hydro*, and replacing the suffix *ic* by the suffix *ide*. Thus the sodium salt of hydrochloric acid is sodium chloride.

The names of some other acids, such as sulfuric acid, have the same suffix, *ic*, but no prefix. The molecules of these acids contain oxygen atoms. The salts are named simply by changing the suffix to *ate*. Thus the normal sodium salt of sulfuric acid is sodium sulfate.

Sulfurous acid is a representative of another class of acids, the names of which have the suffix *ous*. In general these acids have fewer oxygen atoms in the molecule than the corresponding *ic* acids. The salts are named by changing the suffix *ous* to *ite*. Thus the normal sodium salt of sulfurous acid is sodium sulfite.

A few acids have names that do not fit into this classification, but they are not very important.

Acidic Oxides and Basic Oxides.   An oxide such as sulfur trioxide, SO_3, or diphosphorus pentoxide, P_2O_5, which does not contain hydrogen but which with water forms an acid, is called an *acidic oxide* or *acid anhydride*. The equations for the reactions of formation of the corresponding acids from these oxides are the following:

$$SO_3 + H_2O \longrightarrow H_2SO_4$$

$$P_2O_5 + 3H_2O \longrightarrow 2H_3PO_4$$

The oxides of most of the non-metallic elements are acidic oxides.

An oxide which with water forms a base is called a *basic oxide*. The oxides of the metals are basic oxides (even though some of them are very little affected by water). Thus sodium oxide, Na_2O, reacts with water to form a base, sodium hydroxide:

$$Na_2O + H_2O \longrightarrow 2NaOH$$

Acidic oxides and basic oxides may combine directly with one another to form salts:

$$Na_2O + SO_3 \longrightarrow Na_2SO_4$$

$$3CaO + P_2O_5 \longrightarrow Ca_3(PO_4)_2$$

Illustrative Exercises

6-14. Write the equation for the reaction of sodium hydroxide and perchloric acid, to form sodium perchlorate.

6-15. Write equations for three reactions of potassium hydroxide and phosphoric acid, to form three potassium salts of phosphoric acid, representing replacement of 1, 2, and 3 atoms of hydrogen by atoms of potassium. Write names for the three salts.

6-16. What is the formula of normal calcium sulfide?

6-17. Nitrous acid has the formula HNO_2. Write an equation for the reaction of formation of its sodium salt. What is the name of this salt?

6-18. Dichlorine heptoxide, Cl_2O_7, is the anhydride of perchloric acid. Write the equation for the reaction of the heptoxide with water to form the acid.

6-19. What is the anhydride of carbonic acid, H_2CO_3?

6–8. The Ionization of Acids, Bases, and Salts

Most salts, like sodium chloride, dissolve in water to form solutions with large electric conductivity. The conductivity of the solutions is so large as to show that the *salts are completely ionized* in aqueous solution.

For example, the substance sodium sulfate, Na_2SO_4, dissolves in water to form a solution containing sodium ions, Na^+, and sulfate ions, SO_4^{--}. An ion such as the sulfate ion, a group of two or more atoms with an electric charge, is called a *complex ion*.

Some acids and bases are also completely ionized in aqueous solution. For example, hydrochloric acid, a solution of hydrogen chloride, HCl, in water, contains hydrogen ion, H^+, and chloride ion, Cl^-, and only a few undissociated hydrogen chloride molecules, HCl. Similarly, a solution of sodium hydroxide, $NaOH$, contains the sodium ion, Na^+, and the hydroxide ion, OH^-.

Some acids and bases, and also a few salts, are, however, only partially ionized in solution. For example, acetic acid when dissolved in water produces a solution containing rather small amounts of hydrogen ion, H^+, and acetate ion, $C_2H_3O_2^-$, and a large amount of undissociated molecules of acetic acid, $HC_2H_3O_2$. The acids and bases that are completely ionized in aqueous solution are called *strong acids* and *strong bases*. Those that are only partially ionized are called *weak acids* and *weak bases*.

An example of a salt that is only partially ionized in aqueous solution

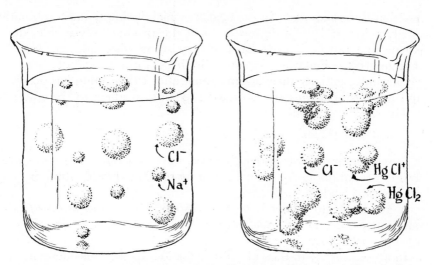

FIGURE 6-10   *A solution of a completely dissociated salt (at the left) and of a partially dissociated salt (at the right).*

is mercuric chloride, $HgCl_2$. A solution of mercuric chloride contains the molecular species* $HgCl_2$, $HgCl^+$, Hg^{++}, and Cl^-, all in appreciable concentrations. This substance is exceptional—most salts are completely ionized.

Acids, bases, and salts that are completely ionized are called *strong electrolytes;* those that are only partially ionized are called *weak electrolytes.* The difference between a solution of a strong electrolyte and a solution of a weak electrolyte is illustrated in Figure 6-10.

Writing Equations for Ionic Reactions.   In writing an equation for a chemical reaction between strong electrolytes in solution, *ions* should usually be written as reactants and products.† Thus the precipitation of silver chloride on the addition of a solution of hydrochloric acid to a solution of silver nitrate should be written

$$Ag^+ + Cl^- \longrightarrow AgCl \downarrow$$

and not

$$AgNO_3 + HCl \longrightarrow AgCl \downarrow + HNO_3$$

Silver nitrate, hydrochloric acid, and nitric acid are all strong electrolytes, and their solutions consist nearly entirely of the dissociated ions. The ionic equation written above accordingly represents the actual

---

* It is customary to use the term "molecular species" to refer to ions as well as neutral molecules.

† Sometimes the use of molecular formulas in equations is advantageous, in that it shows what reagents are to be used in an experiment.

reaction that takes place in the beaker, which is simply the combination of silver ion and chloride ion to form the product, silver chloride. It is true that nitrate ion was present in solution with the silver ion, and that hydrogen ion was present with the chloride ion; but these ions remain in essentially their original state after the reaction has occurred, and there is hence usually no reason to indicate them in the equation.

The same equation

$$Ag^+ + Cl^- \longrightarrow AgCl \downarrow$$

is, moreover, applicable also to the precipitation of, say, silver perchlorate solution (containing Ag^+ and ClO_4^-) by sodium chloride solution (containing Na^+ and Cl^-).

A good rule to follow is *to write the chemical equation to correspond as closely as possible to the actual reaction, showing the molecules or ions which actually react and are formed.*

In accordance with this rule, either the ions or the molecules might be shown for reactions involving weak electrolytes. If a substance is not ionized at all, the formula for its molecules should be used in the equation.

Illustrative Exercises

6-20.　(a) Hydrochloric acid, HCl, is a strong acid. What molecular species are present in a dilute aqueous solution of this acid? (b) Sodium hydroxide, NaOH, is a strong base. What molecular species are present in its solution? (c) Write an equation for the reaction that occurs when these two solutions are mixed.

6-21.　When a solution of silver nitrate, containing the ions Ag^+ and NO_3^- (nitrate ion), is added to a solution of sodium chloride a white precipitate of the insoluble substance silver chloride, AgCl, is formed. (a) Write the equation for this reaction. (b) What molecular species remain in the solution?

6–9. *Ozone. The Phenomenon of Allotropy*

Ozone is a blue gas which has a characteristic odor (its name is from the Greek *ozein*, to smell) and is a stronger oxidizing agent than ordinary oxygen. It is formed when an electric current is passed through oxygen (Figure 6-11).

Although its properties are different from those of ordinary oxygen, ozone is not a compound, but is elementary oxygen in a different form—a form with three atoms in the molecule (O_3) instead of two, as in ordinary oxygen (Figure 6-12).

The existence of an elementary substance in two or more forms is called **allotropy** (Greek *allotropia*, variety, from *allos*, other, and *tropos*, direction). Ordinary oxygen and ozone are the **allotropes** of oxygen. Allotropy is shown by many elements; it is due either to the existence of two of more kinds of molecules (containing different numbers of atoms) or to the

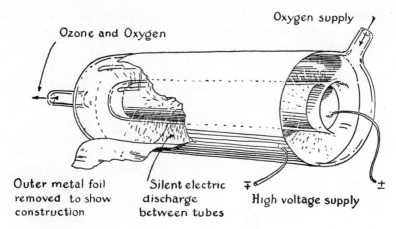

FIGURE 6-11 *An ozonizer, for converting oxygen to ozone by use of a silent electric discharge.*

existence of two or more different crystalline forms; that is, of different arrangements of the atoms or molecules in a crystalline array.

Ozone contains more energy than oxygen: the heat evolved when 48 g of ozone* decomposes to oxygen is 32,400 cal, and that amount of energy must have been given to the ozone molecule by the electric discharge when the ozone was formed. Because of its greater energy content, ozone is more reactive than oxygen. It converts mercury and silver into oxides, and it readily frees iodine from potassium iodide, whereas oxygen does not cause these reactions at room temperature.

The Uses of Ozone. Like some other oxidizing agents (such as chlorine), ozone has the power of converting many colored organic sub-

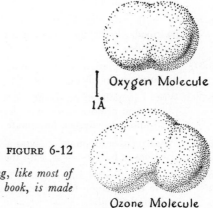

Oxygen Molecule

1 Å

FIGURE 6-12

Molecules of oxygen and ozone. This drawing, like most of the drawings of atoms and molecules in this book, is made with linear magnification about 60,000,000.

Ozone Molecule

* Note the convention in chemistry that "48 g of ozone" is singular in number; it means a quantity of ozone weighing 48 g, rather than forty-eight separate grams of ozone.

stances to colorless products; it accordingly finds use as a bleaching agent for oils, waxes, starch, and flour. It is also used instead of chlorine to sterilize drinking water, by destroying the bacteria in it.

Concepts, Facts, and Terms Introduced in This Chapter

Hydrogen, its physical properties, preparation, uses.

Oxygen, its occurrence, physical properties, preparation, uses.

Potassium chlorate as a source of oxygen; manganese dioxide, a catalyst.

The naming of chemical compounds. Oxides. Hydrides. Oxidation and reduction. Oxidizing agent. Reducing agent.

Valence. Valence bond. Double bond. Triple bond.

Ions. Arrhenius theory of ionization. Cation. Anion. Transfer of electrons between atoms.

Acid. Base. Salt. Hydrogen ion (hydronium ion). Hydroxide ion. Hydroxides of metals. Alkali. Alkaline earth. Indicator. Litmus paper. Nomenclature of acids, bases, and salts. Acidic oxide. Basic oxide.

Writing equations for ionic reactions.

Ozone. Allotropy.

Exercises

6-22. What are allotropes? What differences in properties and structure between oxygen and ozone can you mention?

6-23. Do you know any elements other than oxygen that exist in allotropic forms?

6-24. What is the lightest gas? The lightest liquid? The lightest crystalline substance?

6-25. Write an equation for the preparation of hydrogen by reaction of zinc and hydrochloric acid. (Hydrochloric acid is not so good as sulfuric acid for this preparation, because the hydrogen that is produced is apt to be impure, containing some hydrogen chloride.)

6-26. Write the equation for the neutralization of acetic acid, $HC_2H_3O_2$, by sodium hydroxide. Write the equation for the neutralization of this acid by calcium hydroxide.

6-27. Write an equation for the combustion of phosphorus in oxygen to produce diphosphorus pentoxide, P_2O_5.

6-28. Write equations to represent the formation from sodium hydroxide and phosphoric acid of normal sodium phosphate, disodium monohydrogen phosphate, and sodium dihydrogen phosphate.

6-29. What relative amounts of sodium hydroxide would be required for the three reactions of Exercise 6-28, with the same amount of phosphoric acid?

6-30. What are the acid anhydrides of nitric acid, sulfuric acid, and phosphoric acid? Write the equation for the reaction of the anhydride of nitric acid with water to form the acid.

6-31. When sulfur is burned in air it forms the gas sulfur dioxide, SO_2. What is the formula of the acid of which this gas is the anhydride?

6-32.   What uses of ozone are based upon its oxidizing power?

6-33.   Assign chemical names to the following compounds: CaH_2, $Ca(OH)_2$, $Mg_3(PO_4)_2$, Li_3N, HI, $KHSO_4$. Which of them are binary compounds?

6-34.   Why is the production of hydrogen from iron and steam commercially practical? Write the equation for the reaction.

6-35.   What property of hydrogen makes it less desirable than helium for inflating balloons and dirigibles?

6-36.   Write the equation for the reaction of citric acid, $H_3C_6H_5O_7$ (the acid present in citrus fruits), and potassium hydroxide to form water and potassium citrate, $K_3C_6H_5O_7$. Is citric acid a monoprotic acid, a diprotic acid, or a triprotic acid?

6-37.   Write equations for the neutralization of ammonium hydroxide, NH_4OH, with hydrochloric acid, sulfuric acid, and nitric acid.

Chapter 7

Carbon and Compounds of Carbon

Carbon is the first element of the fourth group of the periodic table, the others being silicon, germanium, tin, and lead (Chapter 26). Carbon forms a great many compounds, and its chemistry is especially interesting to us because most of the substances that make up a human body (and other living organisms) are compounds of carbon. Moreover, the compounds of carbon illustrate well the principles that have been discussed in the preceding chapters and others that need to be discussed. It is for these reasons that we now consider the chemistry of carbon.

Organic Chemistry and Biochemistry. The name *organic chemistry*, which was originally used to refer to the chemistry of substances that occur in living organisms (plants and animals), is now used for *the chemistry of the compounds of carbon*. The chemistry of the elements other than carbon is called *inorganic chemistry*.

Biochemistry may be considered to be a part of organic chemistry. It deals especially with the chemical reactions that take place in living organisms. The manufacture of the artificial fiber nylon, for example, is included in organic chemistry, but not in biochemistry; the structure, methods of synthesis, and general chemical properties of vitamin B_1 are a part of organic chemistry, and the special reactions of this substance in plants and animals are a part of biochemistry.

We shall consider some aspects of organic chemistry and biochemistry throughout this book, beginning in the following paragraphs. A more detailed discussion of organic chemistry will then be given in Chapter 30, and of biochemistry in Chapter 31.

7–1. Structural Formulas of Carbon Compounds

The chemistry of carbon was greatly advanced about a century ago through the development of a general *structure theory*, which we shall now discuss in order that the later sections of this chapter may be based on it. This theory is a chemical theory, induced from chemical facts. In recent years it has received added verification through the determination of exact structures of molecules and crystals by physical methods, especially x-ray diffraction, electron diffraction, and the analysis of the spectra of substances.

During the first half of the nineteenth century many organic compounds were obtained from plants and animals or were made in the laboratory. They were analyzed for their constituent elements, and their properties were carefully studied. Efforts were made to find some correlation between the chemical composition and the properties of the substances. These efforts led to the development of the concept of valence and the assignment of valence-bond structures to substances (Section 6–6).

In 1852 the statement was made by E. Frankland, in England, that atoms have a definite combining power, which determines the formulas of compounds. A few years later (1858) a Scottish chemist, Archibald S. Couper, introduced the idea of the valence bond, and drew the first structural formulas. During the same year August Kekulé in Germany showed that carbon is quadrivalent (can form four valence bonds) and that many compounds of carbon involve bonds between carbon atoms.

The structural formula of a carbon compound usually can easily be assigned from a knowledge of the composition of the compound and of some of its properties. Usually each carbon atom forms four valence bonds, each hydrogen atom one, each oxygen atom two, and each nitrogen atom three. (There are some exceptional compounds, which will be discussed later.)

For example, as was mentioned in Section 6–6, methane has the

structure $H\!-\!\overset{\displaystyle H}{\underset{\displaystyle H}{\overset{|}{\underset{|}{C}}}}\!-\!H$, involving four single bonds, and carbon dioxide has

the structure $O\!=\!C\!=\!O$, involving two double bonds. A more complex

molecule is ethyl alcohol, with the structural formula $H\!-\!\overset{\displaystyle H}{\underset{\displaystyle H}{\overset{|}{\underset{|}{C}}}}\!-\!\overset{\displaystyle H}{\underset{\displaystyle H}{\overset{|}{\underset{|}{C}}}}\!-\!O\!-\!H$.

The quadrivalence of the carbon atom is closely related to its electronic structure. The carbon atom has six electrons, two of which, in the K shell (Section 5–5), are very tightly held by the nucleus. The other four, in the L shell, are responsible for the four valence bonds that the carbon atom can form. The electronic structure of the valence bond will be discussed in Chapter 11.

We do not need to know the electronic structure of the valence bond in order to use the chemical structure theory. Indeed, the quadrivalence of carbon was known and structural formulas (valence-bond formulas) of compounds were written by chemists for forty years before the electron was discovered, and another thirty years had gone by before a clear picture had been obtained of the electronic structure of the valence bond. The development, a century ago, of the chemical structure theory as a correlating theory for the mass of information about the chemical properties of substances is one of the greatest of all feats of the human intellect.

7–2. Elementary Carbon

Carbon occurs in nature in its elementary state in two allotropic forms: **diamond,** the hardest substance known, which often forms beautiful transparent and highly refractive crystals, used as gems (Figure 7-1); and **graphite,** a soft, black crystalline substance, used as a lubricant and in the "lead" of lead pencils. *Bort* and *black diamond* are imperfectly crystalline forms of diamond, which do not show the cleavage characteristic of diamond crystals. Their density is slightly less than that of crystalline diamond, and they are tougher and somewhat harder. They are used in diamond drills and other grinding devices.

Charcoal, coke, and carbon black (lampblack) are microcrystalline or amorphous (non-crystalline) forms of carbon. The density of diamond is 3.51 g/cm³ and that of graphite is 2.26 g/cm³.

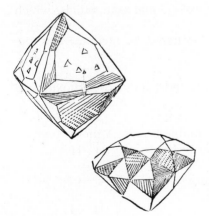

FIGURE 7-1

A natural crystal of diamond, with octahedral faces and smaller faces rounding the edges, and a brilliant-cut diamond.

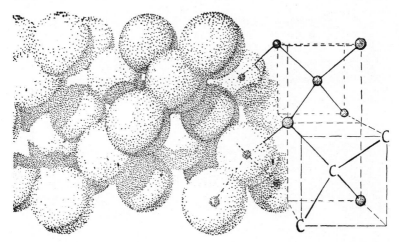

FIGURE 7-2 *The structure of diamond.*

The great hardness of diamond is explained by the structure of the diamond crystal, as determined by the x-ray diffraction method. In the diamond crystal (Figure 7-2) each carbon atom is surrounded by four other carbon atoms, which lie at the corners of a regular tetrahedron about it. A structural formula can be written for a small part of a diamond crystal:

Valence bonds connect each carbon atom with four others. Each of these four is bonded to three others (plus the original one), and so on throughout the crystal. The entire crystal is a giant molecule, held together by valence bonds. To break the crystal many of these valence bonds must be broken; this requires a large amount of energy, and hence the substance is very hard.

The structure of graphite is shown in Figure 7-3. It is a layer structure. Each atom forms two single bonds and one double bond with its three nearest neighbors, as shown in the lowest part of the drawing. The distance between layers is over twice the bond length in a layer (the distance between two bonded atoms). The crystal of graphite can be described as built of giant flat molecules, which are loosely held together in a pile. The layers can be easily separated; hence graphite is a soft substance, which is even used as a lubricant.

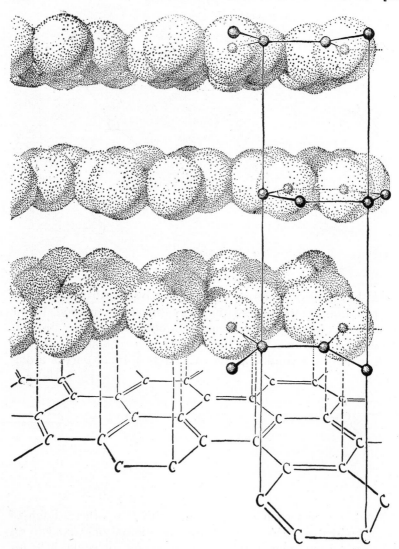

FIGURE 7-3   *The structure of graphite.*

Hardness. The property of hardness is not a simple one to define. It has probably evaded precise definition because the concept of hardness represents a composite of several properties (tensile strength, resistance to cleavage, etc.). Various scales of hardness and instruments for testing hardness have been proposed. One test consists of dropping a diamond-tipped weight on the specimen and measuring the height of rebound. In another test (the Brinell test) a hardened steel ball is pressed into the surface of the specimen, and the size of the produced indentation is measured.

A very simple test of hardness is the scratch test—a specimen that scratches another specimen and is not scratched by it is said to be harder than the second specimen. The scratch-test used by mineralogists is the *Mohs scale*, with reference points (the *Mohs hardness*) from 1 to 10, defined by the following ten minerals:

1. Talc, $Mg_3Si_4O_{10}(OH)_2$
2. Gypsum, $CaSO_4 \cdot 2H_2O$
3. Calcite, $CaCO_3$
4. Fluorite, CaF_2
5. Apatite, $Ca_5(PO_4)_3F$
6. Orthoclase, $KAlSi_3O_8$
7. Quartz, SiO_2
8. Topaz, $Al_2SiO_4F_2$
9. Corundum, Al_2O_3
10. Diamond, C

Diamond is indeed far harder than corundum, and recent modifications of the Mohs scale have been suggested which assign a much larger hardness number, such as 15, to diamond. The hardness of graphite is between 1 and 2.

7–3. Carbon Monoxide and Carbon Dioxide

Carbon burns to form the gases *carbon monoxide*, CO, and *carbon dioxide*, CO_2, the former being produced when there is a deficiency of oxygen or the flame temperature is very high.

Carbon Monoxide. Carbon monoxide is a colorless, odorless gas* with small solubility in water (35.4 ml per liter of water at $0°$ C and 1 atm). It is poisonous, because of its ability to combine with the hemoglobin in the blood in the same way that oxygen does, and thus to prevent the hemoglobin from combining with oxygen in the lungs and carrying it to the tissues. It causes death when about one-third of the hemoglobin in the blood has been converted into carbonmonoxyhemoglobin. The exhaust gas from automobile engines contains some carbon monoxide, and it is accordingly dangerous to be in a closed garage with an automobile whose engine is running. Carbon monoxide is a valuable industrial gas, for use as a fuel and as a reducing agent.

Carbon Dioxide. Carbon dioxide is a colorless, odorless gas with a weakly acid taste, due to the formation of some carbonic acid when it is dissolved in water. It is about 50% heavier than air. It is easily soluble in water, one liter of water at $0°$ C dissolving 1713 ml of the gas under 1 atm pressure. Its melting point (freezing point) is higher than the point of vaporization at 1 atm of the crystalline form. When crystalline carbon dioxide is heated from a very low temperature, its vapor pressure reaches 1 atm at $-79°$, at which temperature it vaporizes without melting. If the pressure is increased to 5.2 atm the crystalline substance melts to a liquid at $-56.6°$. Under ordinary pressure, then, the solid substance is changed directly to a gas. This property has made solid carbon dioxide (Dry Ice) popular as a refrigerating agent.

Carbon dioxide combines with water to form *carbonic acid*, H_2CO_3, a weak acid whose salts are the *carbonates*. The carbonates are important minerals (see calcium carbonate, Section 7–5).

---

* Until recently chemists were uncertain as to the structural formula of carbon monoxide. It will be described in Chapter 11.

Uses of Carbon Dioxide.   Carbon dioxide is used for the manufacture of *sodium carbonate*, $Na_2CO_3 \cdot 10H_2O$ (washing soda); *sodium hydrogen carbonate*, $NaHCO_3$ (baking soda), and *carbonated water*, for use as a beverage (soda water). Carbonated water is charged with carbon dioxide under a pressure of 3 or 4 atm.

Carbon dioxide can be used to extinguish fires by smothering them. One form of portable fire extinguisher is a cylinder of liquid carbon dioxide—the gas can be liquefied at ordinary temperatures under pressures of about 70 atm. Some commercial carbon dioxide (mainly

Manifold which conducts gases from the ovens to washers that remove ammonia and condensable vapors

Iron doors at the ends of the ovens permit the coke to be pushed out by a mechanical ram.

Inspection ports

Heating flues

Gas returned from the washers

Air valves

Brick checker-work alternately heats the incoming air and is heated by the burnt gases.

These passages alternately supply fresh air and conduct burnt gases to the chimney.

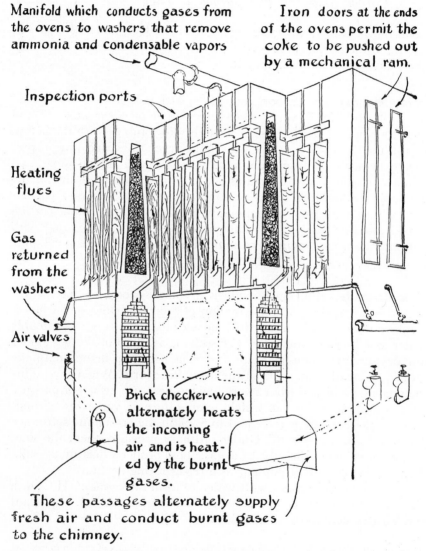

FIGURE 7-4   *A by-product coke oven.*

solid carbon dioxide) is made from the gas emitted in nearly pure state from gas wells in the western United States. Most of the carbon dioxide used commercially is a by-product of cement mills, lime-kilns, iron blast furnaces, and breweries.

7–4. Fuels

Carbon and hydrogen are the principal constituents of the solid fuels coal and wood. Coal has been formed in nature by the slow decomposition of vegetable matter, in the presence of water and absence of air. Most of it was formed during the Carboniferous Period of geologic time, about 250 million years ago (the method of measuring geologic times by use of radioactivity is described in Section 32–2). Coal consists of free carbon mixed with various carbon compounds and some mineral matter. *Anthracite coal* (hard coal) contains only a small amount of volatile matter, and burns with a nearly colorless flame; *bituminous coal* (soft coal) contains much volatile matter, and burns with a smoky flame.

Bituminous coal can be converted into *coke* by heating without access of air. When the heating is carried out in a by-product coke oven, such as that illustrated in Figure 7-4, many substances distill out, including gas for fuel, ammonia, and a complex mixture of liquid and solid organic compounds. The solid material remaining in the ovens, consisting mainly of carbon, is called coke. It burns with a nearly colorless flame, and is used in great amounts in metallurgical processes.

Petroleum is a very important liquid fuel. It is a complex mixture of compounds of carbon and hydrogen.

The gas obtained from a coke furnace (*coal gas*) consists of hydrogen (about 50%), methane, CH_4 (30%), carbon monoxide (10%), and minor components. This coal gas was the original illuminating gas.

Natural gas, from gas wells and oil wells, consists largely of methane.

Producer gas is made by passing a limited supply of air through hot coal or coke (Figure 7-5). The layer of coal or coke which first comes into contact with the stream of air is oxidized to carbon dioxide:

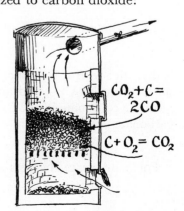

$$CO_2 + C = 2CO$$

$$C + O_2 = CO_2$$

FIGURE 7-5

A furnace for making producer gas.

$$C + O_2 \longrightarrow CO_2$$

As the carbon dioxide rises through the incandescent coke it is reduced to carbon monoxide, which, mixed with nitrogen of the air, escapes from the furnace:

$$CO_2 + C \longrightarrow 2CO$$

Producer gas contains about 25% of carbon monoxide by volume, the rest being nitrogen. Its fuel value is low.

Water gas is made by passing steam through incandescent coke:

$$C + H_2O \longrightarrow CO + H_2$$

This reaction absorbs heat, so that the coke becomes cool. An air blast is then substituted for the steam, until the fuel is heated to a temperature at which it is bright red, and then steam is blown in again. Sometimes a mixture of steam and air is used, instead of alternating the two gases. Water gas and producer gas are used in industrial processes and for domestic heating.

Illustrative Exercises

7-1. Write equations for the reaction of carbon with oxygen when there is a deficiency of oxygen and when there is an excess of oxygen, and for the reaction of carbon monoxide with oxygen. (The blue lambent flame seen over a charcoal fire is due to combustion of carbon monoxide.)

7-2. (a) What is the principal combustible substance in each of the following fuels: coal, coke, coal gas, natural gas, producer gas, water gas? (b) Write the equation for the burning of each of these substances.

7–5. Carbonic Acid and Carbonates

When carbon dioxide dissolves in water some of it reacts to form carbonic acid:

$$CO_2 + H_2O \longrightarrow H_2CO_3$$

The structural formula of carbonic acid is $O{=}C\begin{smallmatrix} \nearrow O{-}H \\ \searrow O{-}H \end{smallmatrix}$. The acid is diprotic; with a base such as sodium hydroxide it may form both a normal salt, Na_2CO_3, and an acid salt, $NaHCO_3$. The normal salt contains the carbonate ion, CO_3^{--}, and the acid salt contains the hydrogen carbonate ion, HCO_3^{-}

For many years chemists assigned the structural formula $O{=}C\begin{smallmatrix} \nearrow O^- \\ \searrow O^- \end{smallmatrix}$

to the carbonate ion. With this formula, one of the oxygen atoms is attached to the carbon atom by a double bond, and the other two are attached by single bonds. Then in 1914 W. L. Bragg carried out an x-ray diffraction study of calcite, $CaCO_3$, and found that the three bonds from the carbon atom to the three oxygen atoms in the carbonate ion in this crystal are identical. This new experimental fact required a change in the structural formula. The new structural formula was proposed in 1931, when the chemical *resonance theory* was developed. According to this theory a molecule may have a structure that is a

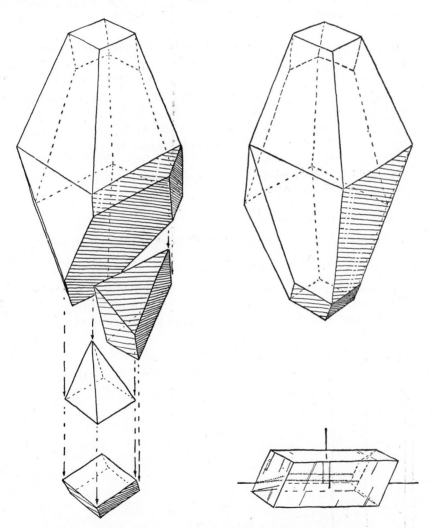

FIGURE 7-6 *Natural crystals of calcite, $CaCO_3$, showing planes of cleavage and how they produce the cleavage rhombohedron (left). The property of birefringence (double refraction) is possessed by calcite (lower right).*

hybrid of two or more valence-bond structures. For the carbonate ion the structure is a hybrid of three structures:

$$\left\{ \quad O=C \diagtriangleup{O^-}{O^-} \qquad {}^-O-C \diagtriangleup{O}{O^-} \qquad {}^-O-C \diagtriangleup{O^-}{O} \quad \right\}$$

Each oxygen atom is attached to the carbon atom by a bond that is a hybrid of a double bond (one-third) and a single bond (two-thirds). The three carbon-oxygen bonds are thus identical.

Calcium carbonate. The most important carbonate mineral is calcium carbonate, $CaCO_3$. This substance occurs in beautiful colorless crystals as the mineral *calcite* (Figure 7-6). *Marble* is a micro-crystalline form of calcium carbonate, and *limestone* is a rock composed mainly of this substance. Calcium carbonate is the principal constituent also of pearls, coral, and most sea shells. Calcium carbonate also occurs in a second crystalline form, as the mineral *aragonite* (Figure 7-7).

When calcium carbonate is heated (as in a lime-kiln, Figure 7-8, where limestone is mixed with fuel, which is burned) it decomposes, forming calcium oxide (*quicklime*):

$$CaCO_3 \longrightarrow CaO + CO_2 \uparrow$$

Quicklime is slaked by adding water, to form calcium hydroxide:

$$CaO + H_2O \longrightarrow Ca(OH)_2$$

Slaked lime prepared in this way is a white powder that can be mixed with water and sand to form *mortar*. The mortar hardens by forming crystals of calcium hydroxide, which cement the grains of sand together;

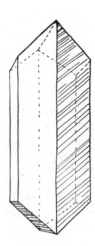

FIGURE 7-7

Natural crystal of aragonite, another form of calcium carbonate, $CaCO_3$.

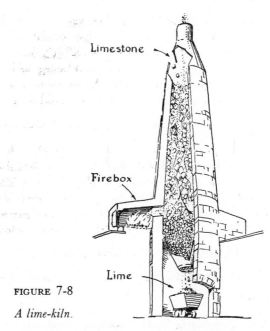

Limestone

Firebox

Lime

FIGURE 7-8

A lime-kiln.

then on exposure to air the mortar continues to get harder by taking up carbon dioxide and forming calcium carbonate:

$$Ca(OH)_2 + CO_2 \longrightarrow CaCO_3 + H_2O$$

Large amounts of limestone are used also in the manufacture of Portland cement, described in Chapter 26.

Sodium carbonate (*washing soda, sal soda*), $Na_2CO_3 \cdot 10H_2O$, is a white, crystalline substance used as a household alkali, for washing and cleaning, and as an industrial chemical. The crystals of the decahydrate lose water readily, forming the monohydrate, $Na_2CO_3 \cdot H_2O$. The monohydrate when heated to $100°$ changes to anhydrous sodium carbonate (*soda ash*), Na_2CO_3.

Sodium hydrogen carbonate (*baking soda, bicarbonate of soda*), $NaHCO_3$, is a white substance usually available as a powder. It is used in cooking, in medicine, and in the manufacture of *baking powder*.

Baking powder is a leavening agent used in making biscuits, cakes, and other food. Its purpose is to provide bubbles of gas, to make the dough "rise." The same foods can be made by use of sodium hydrogen carbonate and sour milk, instead of baking powder. In each case the reaction that occurs involves the action of an acid on sodium hydrogen carbonate, to form carbon dioxide. When sour milk is used the acid that reacts with the sodium hydrogen carbonate is lactic acid, $HC_3H_5O_3$, the equation for the reaction being

$$NaHCO_3 + HC_3H_5O_3 \longrightarrow NaC_3H_5O_3 + H_2O + CO_2 \uparrow$$

The product $NaC_3H_5O_3$ is sodium lactate, the sodium salt of lactic acid. Cream of tartar baking powder consists of sodium hydrogen carbonate, potassium hydrogen tartrate ($KHC_4H_4O_6$, commonly known as cream of tartar), and starch, the starch being added to keep water vapor in the air from causing the powder to form a solid cake. The reaction that occurs when water is added to a cream of tartar baking powder is

$$NaHCO_3 + KHC_4H_4O_6 \longrightarrow NaKC_4H_4O_6 + H_2O + CO_2 \uparrow$$

Baking powders are also made with calcium dihydrogen phosphate, $Ca(H_2PO_4)_2$, sodium dihydrogen phosphate, NaH_2PO_4, or sodium aluminum sulfate, $NaAl(SO_4)_2$, as the acidic constituent.

The leavening agent in ordinary bread dough is *yeast*, a microorganism. This microorganism produces an *enzyme* (an organic catalyst) that converts sugar into alcohol and carbon dioxide:

$$C_6H_{12}O_6 \longrightarrow 2C_2H_5OH + 2CO_2 \uparrow$$

The formula $C_6H_{12}O_6$ in this equation represents glucose, a simple sugar.

The Ammonia-Soda Process. Sodium carbonate is a very important chemical, over three million tons being made every year. About a quarter of the total amount is used in making glass, and another quarter in making soap, the rest being required in the textile and paper industries and many others. Nearly all of this great quantity of sodium carbonate is made from sodium chloride by a process called the *ammonia-soda process* or *Solvay process*.

This process depends upon the fact that sodium hydrogen carbonate is less soluble in water than are sodium chloride, ammonium hydrogen carbonate (NH_4HCO_3), and ammonium chloride.

The raw materials used in the process are sodium chloride and calcium carbonate (limestone), as well as coal to supply power and heat. The limestone is heated in a kiln, to produce carbon dioxide and lime (calcium oxide):

$$CaCO_3 \longrightarrow CaO + CO_2 \uparrow$$

The carbon dioxide is allowed to react with a solution of sodium chloride which has been saturated with ammonia; ammonium ion and hydrogen carbonate ion are formed in the solution:

$$NH_3 + H_2O + CO_2 \longrightarrow NH_4^+ + HCO_3^-$$

When a sufficiently large amount of carbon dioxide has dissolved in the solution, the solution becomes saturated with sodium hydrogen carbonate, which precipitates out:

$$Na^+ + HCO_3^- \longrightarrow NaHCO_3 \downarrow$$

The solid sodium hydrogen carbonate is filtered off, purified by re-crystallization, and dried. Most of it is converted into sodium carbonate, by heating it:

$$2NaHCO_3 \longrightarrow Na_2CO_3 + H_2O + CO_2 \uparrow$$

The carbon dioxide formed in this reaction is used along with that made from limestone to make more sodium hydrogen carbonate.

The low cost of sodium carbonate made by this process depends upon the fact that the ammonia can be practically completely recovered. At the end of the process, after the sodium hydrogen carbonate has precipitated out and has been filtered off, a solution of ammonium chloride remains. The calcium oxide obtained from the lime kiln is converted into calcium hydroxide by the addition of water, and the calcium hydroxide when added to the solution of ammonium chloride liberates ammonia:

$$CaO + H_2O \longrightarrow Ca(OH)_2$$
$$Ca(OH)_2 + 2NH_4Cl \longrightarrow CaCl_2 + 2H_2O + 2NH_3 \uparrow$$

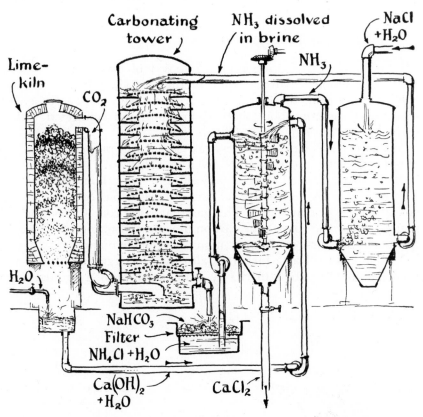

FIGURE 7-9 *Diagram of a chemical plant for making sodium carbonate by the ammonia-soda (Solvay) process.*

Hence the only substances used up in the process are limestone and common salt, and the only by-product (subsidiary substance produced in the process) is calcium chloride.

The large-scale apparatus used in this industrial process is illustrated in Figure 7-9.

Illustrative Exercises

7-3. A solution of carbon dioxide in water contains the following molecules and ions, in addition to H_2O and CO_2: H_2CO_3, H^+, HCO_3^-, CO_3^{--}. Write equations for the production of these substances. What are their names?

7-4. Write equations for two successive reactions of sodium hydroxide (solid) and carbon dioxide.

7-5. Write the structural formulas of carbonic acid and the carbonate ion.

7-6. Write equations for the preparation of quicklime from limestone and of slaked lime from quicklime.

7-7. Write equations for the two principal reactions that occur during the setting of mortar.

7–6. The Paraffin Hydrocarbons

The *hydrocarbons* are compounds composed of hydrogen and carbon alone. The simplest hydrocarbon is **methane, CH_4**. The methane molecule is tetrahedral, the four hydrogen atoms lying at the corners of a regular tetrahedron about the carbon atom, and connected with the carbon atom by single bonds (Figure 7-10).

Methane is a colorless, odorless gas. Some of its properties, and those of some other hydrocarbons, are given in Table 7-1.

Natural gas, from oil wells or gas wells, is usually about 85% methane. The gas made by destructive heating of coal or oil (Section 7–4) also consists largely of methane. The gas that rises from the bottom of a marsh is methane (plus some carbon dioxide and nitrogen), formed by the anaerobic (air-free) fermentation of vegetable matter.

Methane is used as a fuel. It is also used in large quantities for the manufacture of carbon black, by combustion with a limited supply of air:

$$CH_4 + O_2 \longrightarrow 2H_2O + C$$

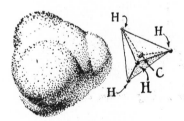

FIGURE 7-10

The structure of the methane molecule.

The methane burns to form water, and the carbon is deposited as very finely divided carbon, which finds extensive use as a filler for rubber for automobile tires.

Methane is the first member of a series of hydrocarbons called the *methane series* or *paraffin series*. Some of the compounds of this series are listed in Table 7-1.

The name paraffin means "having little affinity." The compounds of this series are not very reactive chemically. They occur in petroleum. The molecules heavier than ethane are characterized by containing carbon atoms attached to one another by single bonds. **Ethane** has the

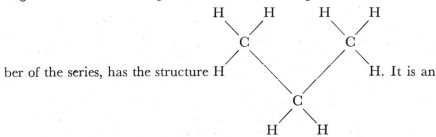

structure H—C—C—H It is a gas (Table 7-1), which occurs in large amounts in natural gas from some wells. **Propane,** the third member of the series, has the structure H ... H. It is an easily liquefied gas, and is used as a fuel.

In the structural formula for propane there is a *chain* of three carbon atoms bonded together. The next larger paraffin, **butane,** C₄H₁₀, can be obtained by replacing a hydrogen atom at one end of the chain by a

TABLE 7-1   *Some Physical Properties of Normal Paraffin Hydrocarbons*

SUBSTANCE	FORMULA	MELTING POINT	BOILING POINT	DENSITY OF LIQUID
Methane	CH_4	$-183°$ C	$-161°$ C	0.54 g/ml
Ethane	C_2H_6	-172	-88	.55
Propane	C_3H_8	-190	-45	.58
Butane	C_4H_{10}	-135	-1	.60
Pentane	C_5H_{12}	-130	36	.63
Hexane	C_6H_{14}	-95	69	.66
Heptane	C_7H_{16}	-91	98	.68
Octane	C_8H_{18}	-57	126	.70
Nonane	C_9H_{20}	-54	151	.72
Decane	$C_{10}H_{22}$	-30	174	.73
Pentadecane	$C_{15}H_{32}$	10	271	.77
Eicosane	$C_{20}H_{42}$	38		.78
Triacontane	$C_{30}H_{62}$	70		.79

methyl group, $-\overset{\displaystyle H}{\underset{\displaystyle H}{\mathrm{C}}}-$H. Its formula is obtained by adding CH_2 to that

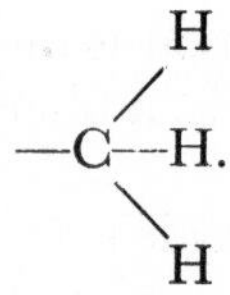

of propane. These hydrocarbons, with longer and longer chains of carbon atoms, are called the *normal paraffins*.

The lighter members of the paraffin series are gases, the intermediate members are liquids, and the heavier members are solid substances. The common name *petroleum ether* refers to the pentane-hexane-heptane mixture, used as a solvent and in dry cleaning. *Gasoline* is the heptane-to-nonane mixture (C_7H_{16} to C_9H_{20}), and *kerosene* the decane-to-hexadecane mixture ($C_{10}H_{22}$ to $C_{16}H_{34}$). *Heavy fuel oil* is a mixture of paraffins containing twenty or more carbon atoms per molecule. The *lubricating oils, petroleum jelly* ("vaseline"), and *solid paraffin* are mixtures of still larger paraffin molecules.

Isomerism.   The phenomenon of *isomerism* is shown first in the paraffin series by butane, C_4H_{10}. **Isomerism** *is the existence of two or more compound substances having the same composition but different properties.* (It is analogous to the allotropy of elementary substances, Section 6–10.) The difference in properties is usually the result of difference in the structure of the molecule, that is, in the way that the atoms are bonded together. There are two isomers of butane, called *normal butane* (*n*-butane) and *isobutane*. These substances have the structure shown below and in Figure 7-11; normal butane is a "straight chain" (actually the carbon chain is a zigzag chain, because of the tetrahedral nature of the carbon atom), and the isobutane molecule contains a branched chain:

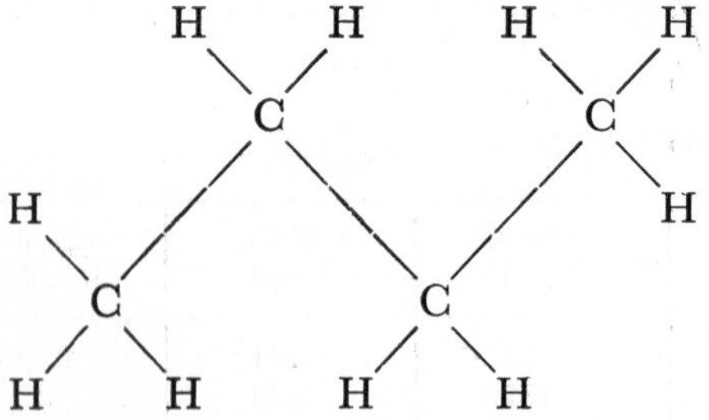

n-butane

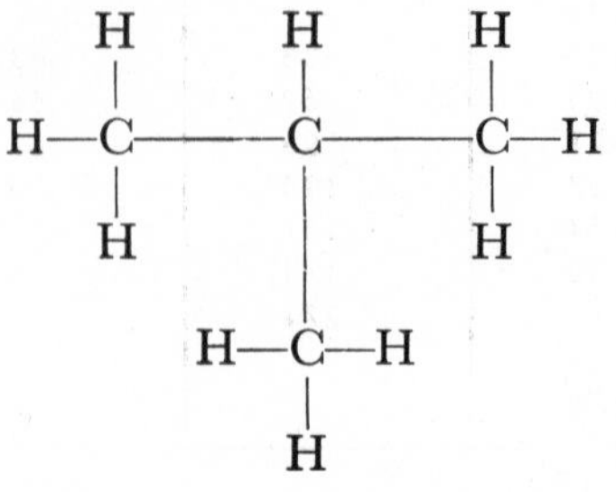

isobutane

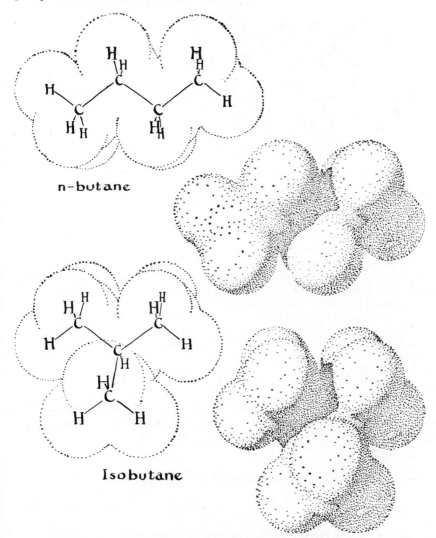

FIGURE 7-11   *The structure of the isomers normal butane and isobutane.*

In general, the properties of these isomers are rather similar; for example, their melting points are $-135°$ C and $-145°$ C, respectively.

The normal (straight-chain) hydrocarbons "knock" badly when burned in a high-compression gasoline engine, whereas the highly branched hydrocarbons, which burn more slowly, do not knock. The "Octane number" (the antiknock rating) of a gasoline is measured by comparing it with a mixture of *n*-heptane and a highly branched octane, with name 2,2,4-trimethylpentane and structural formula

The octane number is the percentage of this octane in the mixture with the same knocking properties as the gasoline being tested.

The substance *tetraethyl lead*, $Pb(C_2H_5)_4$, is widely used in gasoline as an antiknock agent. Gasoline containing it is called *ethyl gas*.

Names of Organic Compounds. Chemists have developed a rather complicated system of names for organic compounds. The student of general chemistry needs to know only a small part of this system.

The simpler substances usually have special names; for example, methane, ethane, propane, butane. From pentane on (Table 7-1) the names of the paraffins give the number of carbon atoms, with use of the Greek prefixes for the numbers.

The group obtained by removing a hydrogen atom from a paraffin has the name of the paraffin with the ending *ane* changed to *yl.* Thus the methyl group is $-CH_3$, the ethyl group is $-C_2H_5$ (as in lead tetraethyl, above), and so on.

A branched hydrocarbon is given a name, according to the system of nomenclature, that is based on the longest chain of carbon atoms in it. The carbon atoms are numbered from one end (1,2,3, · · ·), and groups attached to them, in place of hydrogen atoms, are indicated. For example, the substance called isobutane above (in the discussion of isomerism) may be called 2-methylpropane. Another example is 2,2,4-trimethylpentane, the structural formula of which is given above in the discussion of knocking of gasoline engines.

7–7. Hydrocarbons Containing Double Bonds and Triple Bonds

The substance **ethylene,** C_2H_4, consists of molecules

, in which there is a double bond between the two carbon atoms. This double bond confers upon the molecule the property of much greater chemical reactivity than is possessed by the paraffins. For example, whereas chlorine, bromine, and iodine do not readily attack the paraffin hydrocarbons, they easily react with ethylene; a mixture of chlorine and ethylene reacts readily at room temperature in the dark, and with explosive violence in light, to form the substance *dichloroethane*, $C_2H_4Cl_2$:

$$C_2H_4 + Cl_2 \longrightarrow C_2H_4Cl_2$$

or

$$\begin{matrix} H & & H \\ & \diagdown \diagup & \\ & C{=}C & \\ \diagup & & \diagdown \\ H & & H \end{matrix} \quad + \text{ Cl—Cl} \rightarrow \begin{matrix} Cl & & H \\ & \diagdown \diagup & \\ H{-}C{-}{-}C{-}H \\ \diagup & & \diagdown \\ H & & Cl \end{matrix}$$

In the course of this reaction the double bond between the two carbon atoms has become a single bond, and the single bond between the two chlorine atoms has been broken. Two new bonds, single bonds between a chlorine atom and a carbon atom, have been formed.

A reaction of this sort is called an *addition reaction*. An **addition reaction** *is a reaction in which a molecule adds to a molecule containing a double bond, converting the double bond into a single bond.*

Because of this property of readily combining with other substances such as the halogens, ethylene and related hydrocarbons are said to be *unsaturated*. Ethylene is the first member of a homologous series of hydrocarbons, called the *ethylene series*.

Ethylene is a colorless gas (b.p. $-104°$ C) with a sweetish odor. It can be made in the laboratory by heating ethyl alcohol, C_2H_5OH, with concentrated sulfuric acid, preferably in the presence of a catalyst (such as silica). Concentrated sulfuric acid is a strong dehydrating agent, which removes water from the alcohol molecule:

$$C_2H_5OH \xrightarrow{\;H_2SO_4\;} C_2H_4 + H_2O$$

The formula H_2SO_4 is written above the arrow in this equation to show that sulfuric acid is needed to cause the reaction to take place.

Ethylene is made commercially simply by passing alcohol vapor over a catalyst (aluminum oxide) at about $400°$ C. The reaction is *endothermic;*[*] a small amount of heat if absorbed when it takes place:

$$C_2H_5OH \longrightarrow C_2H_4 + H_2O$$

Endothermic chemical reactions are in general favored by heating the reactants.

Ethylene has the interesting property of causing green fruit to ripen, and it is used commercially for this purpose. It is also used as an anesthetic.

Acetylene, which has the structural formula $H{-}C{\equiv}C{-}H$, is the first member of a homologous series of hydrocarbons containing triple bonds. Aside from acetylene, these substances have not found wide use, except for the manufacture of other chemicals.

Acetylene is a colorless gas (b.p. $-84°$ C), with a characteristic garlic-like odor. It is liable to explode when compressed in the pure state, and is usually kept in solution under pressure in acetone. It is used as a fuel, in the oxy-acetylene torch and the acetylene lamp, and is also used as the starting material for making other chemicals.

[*] Reactions that emit heat are called *exothermic*.

Acetylene is most easily made from **calcium carbide** (calcium acetylide, CaC_2). Calcium carbide is made by heating lime (calcium oxide, CaO) and coke in an electric furnace:

$$CaO + 3C \longrightarrow CaC_2 + CO \uparrow$$

Calcium carbide is a gray solid that reacts vigorously with water to produce calcium hydroxide and acetylene:

$$CaC_2 + 2H_2O \longrightarrow Ca(OH)_2 + C_2H_2 \uparrow$$

The existence of calcium carbide and other carbides with similar formulas and properties shows that acetylene is an acid, with two replaceable hydrogens. It is an extremely weak acid, however, and its solution in water does not taste acidic. The calcium carbide crystal is ionic; its structure resembles that of sodium chloride (Figure 4-6), with calcium ions, Ca^{++}, in place of the sodium ions, and acetylide ions, C_2^{--}, in place of the chloride ions.

Acetylene and other substances containing a carbon-carbon triple bond are very reactive. They readily undergo addition reactions with chlorine and other reagents, and they are classed as unsaturated substances.

7–8. Some Other Organic Compounds

The Chloromethanes. Methane and other paraffins will react with chlorine and bromine when exposed to sunlight or when heated to a high temperature. When a mixture of methane and chlorine is passed through a tube containing a catalyst (aluminum chloride, $AlCl_3$, mixed with clay) heated to about $300°$ C, the following reactions occur:*

$$CH_4 + Cl_2 \longrightarrow CH_3Cl + HCl$$

$$CH_3Cl + Cl_2 \longrightarrow CH_2Cl_2 + HCl$$

$$CH_2Cl_2 + Cl_2 \longrightarrow CHCl_3 + HCl$$

$$CH_3Cl + Cl_2 \longrightarrow CCl_4 + HCl$$

In each of these reactions a chlorine molecule, with structural formula Cl—Cl, is split into two chlorine atoms; one chlorine atom takes the place of a hydrogen atom bonded to carbon, and the other combines with the displaced hydrogen atom, to form a molecule of hydrogen chloride, H—Cl. Using structural formulas, we rewrite the first reaction:†

* The relative amounts of the four products may be varied somewhat by changing the ratio of methane and chlorine in the gas mixture used.

† It does not matter whether [structural formula of methane shown] or H—C—H is written for methane.

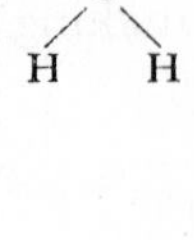

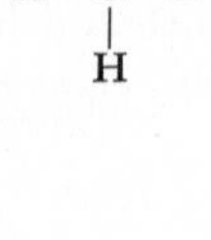

$$
\begin{array}{ccc}
\overset{\displaystyle H \quad\ H}{\underset{\displaystyle H \quad\ H}{\diagdown\!\diagup}\!\underset{}{C}\!\diagup\!\diagdown}
& + \; Cl\!-\!Cl \longrightarrow &
\overset{\displaystyle H \quad\ Cl}{\underset{\displaystyle H \quad\ H}{\diagdown\!\diagup}\!\underset{}{C}\!\diagup\!\diagdown}
& + \; H\!-\!Cl
\end{array}
$$

The four chlorine derivatives of methane, which are called the *chloro-methanes*, have the following individual names:

H Cl	H Cl	H Cl	Cl Cl
\\ /	\\ /	\\ /	\\ /
C	C	C	C
/ \\	/ \\	/ \\	/ \\
H H	H Cl	Cl Cl	Cl Cl
Monochloromethane or methyl chloride	Dichloromethane or methylene chloride	Trichloro-methane or chloroform	Tetrachloro-methane or carbon tetrachloride

Chemical reactions such as these four are called *substitution reactions. A* **substitution reaction** *is the replacement of one atom or group of atoms in a molecule by another atom or group of atoms.* The four chloromethanes are *substitution products* of methane. Substitution reactions and addition reactions (Section 7–7) are extensively used in practical organic chemistry.

Some physical properties of the chloromethanes are given in Table 7-2. All four are colorless, with characteristic odors, and with low boiling points, increasing with the number of chlorine atoms in the molecule. The chloromethanes do not ionize in water.

Chloroform and carbon tetrachloride are used as solvents; carbon tetrachloride is an important dry-cleaning agent. Chloroform is also used as a general anesthetic.

Care must be taken in the use of carbon tetrachloride that no large amount of its vapor is inhaled, because it damages the liver.

TABLE 7-2   *Some Physical Properties of the Chloromethanes*

SUBSTANCE	FORMULA	MELTING POINT	BOILING POINT	DENSITY OF LIQUID
Methyl chloride	CH_3Cl	$-98°$ C	$-24°$ C	0.92 g/ml
Dichloromethane	CH_2Cl_2	-97	40	1.34
Chloroform	$CHCl_3$	-64	61	1.49
Carbon tetrachloride	CCl_4	-23	77	1.60

Methyl Alcohol and Ethyl Alcohol.   An *alcohol* is obtained from a hydrocarbon by replacing one hydrogen atom by a hydroxyl group, —OH. Thus methane, CH_4, gives *methyl alcohol*, CH_3OH, and ethane, C_2H_6, gives *ethyl alcohol*, C_2H_5OH. The names of the alcohols are often written by using the ending *ol;* methyl alcohol is called *methanol*, and ethyl alcohol *ethanol*. They have the following structural formulas:

$$H-\underset{\underset{\displaystyle H}{|}}{\overset{\overset{\displaystyle H}{|}}{C}}-O-H \qquad H-\underset{\underset{\displaystyle H}{|}}{\overset{\overset{\displaystyle H}{|}}{C}}-\underset{\underset{\displaystyle H}{|}}{\overset{\overset{\displaystyle H}{|}}{C}}-O-H$$

Methyl alcohol   Ethyl alcohol

To make methyl alcohol from methane the methane may be converted to methyl chloride by treatment with chlorine, as described above, and the methyl chloride then converted to methyl alcohol by treatment with sodium hydroxide:

$$CH_3Cl + NaOH \longrightarrow CH_3OH + NaCl$$

Methyl alcohol is made by the destructive distillation of wood; it is sometimes called wood alcohol. It is a poisonous substance which on ingestion causes blindness and death. It is used as a solvent, and for the preparation of other organic compounds.

The most important method of making ethyl alcohol is by the fermentation of sugars with yeast. Grains and molasses are the usual raw materials for this purpose. Yeast produces an enzyme that catalyzes the fermentation reaction. In the following equation the formula $C_6H_{12}O_6$ is that of a sugar, glucose (also called dextrose and grape sugar, Chapter 30):

$$C_6H_{12}O_6 \longrightarrow 2CO_2 \uparrow + 2C_2H_5OH$$

Ethyl alcohol is a colorless liquid (m.p. $-117°$ C, b.p. $79°$ C) with a characteristic odor. It is used as a fuel, as a solvent, and as the starting material for preparing other compounds. Beer contains 3 to 5% alcohol, wine usually 10 to 12%, and distilled liquors such as whiskey, brandy, and gin 40 to 50%.

The *ethers* are compounds obtained by reaction of two alcohol molecules, with elimination of water. The most important ether is **diethyl ether** (ordinary ether), $(C_2H_5)_2O$. It is made by treating ethyl alcohol with concentrated sulfuric acid, which serves as a dehydrating agent:

$$2C_2H_5OH \longrightarrow C_2H_5OC_2H_5 + H_2O$$

It is used as a general anesthetic, and as a solvent.

The Organic Acids.   Ethyl alcohol can be oxidized by oxygen of the air to **acetic acid,** $HC_2H_3O_2$ or CH_3COOH:

$$C_2H_5OH + O_2 \longrightarrow CH_3COOH + H_2O$$

This reaction occurs easily in nature. If wine, containing ethyl alcohol, is allowed to stand in an open container, it undergoes the acetic-acid fermentation, and changes into vinegar, by the above reaction. The change is brought about by micro-organisms ("mother of vinegar"), which produce enzymes that catalyze the reaction.

Acetic acid has the following structural formula:

It contains the group

, which is called the *carboxyl group*. It

is this group that gives acidic properties to the organic acids.

Acetic acid melts at 17° C and boils at 118° C. It is soluble in water and alcohol. The molecule contains one hydrogen atom that ionizes from it in water, producing the *acetate ion*, $C_2H_3O_2^-$. The acid reacts with bases to form salts. An example is sodium acetate, $NaC_2H_3O_2$, a white solid:

$$HC_2H_3O_2 + NaOH \longrightarrow NaC_2H_3O_2 + H_2O$$

Chemical Reactions of Organic Substances. In the above paragraphs we have discussed derivatives of methane and ethane in which a hydrogen atom is replaced by a chlorine atom, —Cl, a hydroxyl group, —OH, or a carboxyl group, —COOH. There are many other groups that can replace a hydrogen atom, to form other substances.

In general, the chemical reactions that can be used to convert methane into its derivatives can be applied also to the other hydrocarbons. By chemical analysis and the study of the chemical reactions of a new substance the chemist can determine its formula. For example, if a substance contains only carbon, hydrogen, and oxygen, and has acidic properties like those of acetic acid (its solution in water turns blue litmus red, it reacts with sodium hydroxide to form a salt), the chemist assumes that it contains a carboxyl group, —COOH. An important part of organic chemistry is the use of special reactions that identify different groups in a molecule.

Illustrative Exercises

7-8. Write the equation for the reaction of ethane and chlorine to form monochloroethane (C_2H_5Cl, also called ethyl chloride, a colorless gas, b.p. 12° C). What is its structural formula? Is there more than one isomer of C_2H_5Cl? (Answer: no)

7-9. Write the equation for the reaction of monochloroethane to form dichloroethane. How many isomers of dichloroethane do you predict? (Answer: two) What are their structural formulas?

7-10. What would you expect to be formed by the reaction of monochloroethane and sodium hydroxide? Write the equation for the reaction.

7-11. Write the equation for the reaction of addition of chlorine to ethylene, showing the structural formulas. How many isomers of the product are obtained?

7-12. Write the structural formulas of methane, ethane, propane, n-butane, and isobutane. Write equations for the burning (with oxygen of the air) of each of these substances.

7-13. What is the structural formula of dimethyl ether? Write the equation for its preparation from methyl alcohol and concentrated sulfuric acid.

7-14. What is the structural formula of the compound C_3H_8O that has the name methyl ethyl ether?

7-15. The name 1,2-dichloroethane is applied to the dichloroethane isomer in which the two chlorine atoms are bonded to different carbon atoms (the numbers 1,2, $\cdots$ are used to designate successive carbon atoms in a chain). Write the equation for the reaction of this substance with a large amount (an excess) of a strong solution of sodium hydroxide. (The product, called *ethylene glycol*, is used as an antifreeze agent in automobile radiators.)

7-16. Formic acid, HCOOH, is the first member in the series of carboxylic acids. (It can be obtained by distilling ants, and its name is from the Latin word for ant.) Write the equation for the preparation of formic acid by oxidation of methyl alcohol.

7–9. *The Carbon Cycle in Nature*

The atmosphere contains about 0.03% carbon dioxide. Additional carbon dioxide is being poured into the atmosphere all of the time—all animals exhale carbon dioxide, which has been produced by the oxidation of carbon compounds in their tissues, and carbon dioxide is also produced by the burning of wood and coal and the slow decay of plant and animal remains. If there were not some mechanism for removing carbon dioxide from the atmosphere, the composition of the atmosphere would in the course of time change enough to make the earth unsatisfactory for life in its present form.

There is a mechanism for the removal of carbon dioxide from the atmosphere: this mechanism is the utilization of atmospheric carbon dioxide by plants. The amount of plant life on the earth is such that a steady state has been reached, in which the content of carbon dioxide in the atmosphere has remained nearly constant for tens of millions of years. Through the cooperation of plants and animals there has been achieved a *carbon cycle* in nature.

Carbon dioxide is taken from the air by the plants, and broken down into carbon (in the form of *carbohydrates*, compounds of carbon with hydrogen and oxygen in the ratio H_2O), and free oxygen, which is liberated into the air. Some of the plants are burned or are oxidized during the process of decay, their carbon being returned to the atmosphere as carbon dioxide. Others are eaten by animals, and the carbon in the plant tissues is changed into carbon in the animal tissues. Ultimately the compounds of carbon in the animal tissues are oxidized, and the carbon is returned to the atmosphere as carbon dioxide in the exhaled breath of the animals, or the animal dies, and the carbon is ultimately returned to the atmosphere through oxidation to carbon dioxide during decay.

The carbon cycle in the form that is of most interest to man involves three steps: carbon dioxide in the atmosphere is converted into carbon compounds in the tissues of plants; the plants (or animals that have eaten the plants) are eaten by man, and the carbon compounds are converted into carbon compounds in the tissues of man; the carbon compounds are oxidized in the tissues by oxygen which has been inhaled, and the carbon dioxide that is produced is exhaled into the atmosphere.

Energy is required to convert carbon dioxide and water into carbohydrates (cellulose, starch, sugars) and free oxygen. This energy is obtained by the plant from sunlight. The process of using the energy of sunlight to carry out the reaction is called *photosynthesis:*

$$CO_2 + H_2O + \text{energy from sunlight} \longrightarrow (CH_2O) + O_2$$

The formula (CH_2O) is used to indicate that there are many units with composition CH_2O in the molecules of carbohydrates produced; a simple sugar such as glucose has the formula $C_6H_{12}O_6$. The reaction of photosynthesis that is carried out by plants is one of the most important of all chemical reactions.

It has not been found possible to carry out the reaction of photosynthesis in the laboratory. Early in the history of the world, however, nature found a way, by developing a special catalyst which is highly effective. This catalyst, called *chlorophyll*, is a complex substance containing magnesium ion. It is the green substance that gives the green color to the leaves of plants. Chlorophyll is green because it absorbs the light in the red-orange region of the spectrum (Section 28–6), and allows the green light to pass through or to be reflected. The energy of the absorbed light is used for the chemical reaction which is catalyzed by the chlorophyll.* This process of photosynthesis is one of the important ways in which man obtains energy from the sun.

There are great amounts of carbon dioxide, in combined form, in the sea and in rocks. Sea water contains about 0.15% of its weight in carbon dioxide, mainly as hydrogen carbonate ion, HCO_3^-. The total amount of carbon dioxide contained in sea water is about one thousand times as much as that in the atmosphere. Also, very large quantities of carbon dioxide are bound in carbonate rocks, especially limestone. We can understand that if the climatic conditions were to change somewhat large amounts of carbon dioxide might be released from the oceans and from rocks, and the concentration in the air might increase. It is probable that there were much larger amounts of carbon dioxide in the atmosphere during the Carboniferous Period that at the present time, and

* Chlorophyll has been found not to be active after it has been extracted from the plants.

that for this reason plant life flourished, permitting the great coal beds to be laid down.

Facts, Concepts, and Terms Introduced in This Chapter

Organic chemistry and biochemistry.

The structure theory of organic chemistry. Structural formulas (valence-bond formulas).

Diamond, graphite, charcoal, coke, carbon black. Structural formulas of diamond and graphite. Hardness; Mohs scale.

Carbon monoxide. Its action as a poison—carbonmonoxyhemoglobin. Uses.

Carbon dioxide. Its uses.

Fuels: anthracite coal, bituminous coal, coke, petroleum, coal gas, natural gas, producer gas, water gas.

Carbonic acid and the carbonates. Structure of carbonate ion—resonance theory. Calcium carbonate: calcite, marble, limestone, aragonite. Quicklime, slaked lime, mortar. Sodium carbonate (washing soda, sal soda, soda ash). Sodium hydrogen carbonate (baking soda, bicarbonate of soda). Baking powder. Yeast. Enzyme, an organic catalyst. The ammonia-soda process for making sodium carbonate.

The paraffin hydrocarbons. Methane, ethane, propane, butane, · · ·, a homologous series of organic compounds. Petroleum ether, gasoline, kerosene, heavy fuel oil, lubricating oil, petroleum jelly, solid paraffin.

Isomerism. n-Butane and isobutane. Knocking of internal combustion engines; octane number of fuel. Tetraethyl lead; ethyl gas.

Hydrocarbons containing double bonds and triple bonds. Ethylene; its preparation, properties, and uses. Unsaturated compounds; addition reactions with chlorine and other reagents. Acetylene. Calcium carbide.

Other organic compounds. Substitution reactions of paraffins. Methyl chloride, dichloromethane, chloroform, carbon tetrachloride. Methyl alcohol, ethyl alcohol. Fermentation; conversion of sugar into ethyl alcohol. Acetic acid, vinegar. Other organic acids —carboxylic acids. The carboxyl group. Reactions of organic substances.

The carbon cycle in nature. Photosynthesis, chlorophyll.

Exercises

7-17. Compare diamond and graphite as to composition, hardness, density, structure, and principal uses.

7-18. Compare carbon monoxide and carbon dioxide as to color, odor, solubility in water, physiological activity, and combustibility.

7-19. Why is solid carbon dioxide popular as a refrigerating agent?

7-20. Write the equation for the reaction of sodium hydrogen carbonate with hydrochloric acid. Do you think that baking soda and dilute hydrochloric acid (added separately to the dough) could be used in cooking in place of baking powder?

7-21. Outline the successive steps in the ammonia-soda process for making sodium carbonate, and write equations for the reactions. What are the raw materials used, and what are the products?

7-22. What is an addition reaction? A substitution reaction? Write an equation to illustrate each, using bromine, Br_2, as one of the reactants.

7-23. What are the principal substances in gasoline?

7-24. How many isomers do you predict for pentane, C_5H_{12}? Draw their structural formulas.

7-25. Propylene, C_3H_6, follows ethylene in the ethylene series. What is its structural formula? Write the equation, using structural formulas, for its addition reaction with chlorine.

7-26. What product would you expect to get if ethylene were allowed to react with chlorine at room temperature in the dark? At high temperature, with an excess of chlorine? Write equations.

7-27. Draw a structural formula for tetraethyl lead.

7-28. What are the principal uses of ethylene and acetylene?

7-29. Write equations for the preparation of calcium carbide from lime and coke and of acetylene from calcium carbide and water.

7-30. Write equations for the preparation of ethyl alcohol from ethane by use of chlorine and sodium hydroxide as reagents.

7-31. Write the equation for the fermentation reaction of glucose, $C_6H_{12}O_6$.

7-32. Ethylene glycol, mentioned in Exercise 7-15, can be oxidized to oxalic acid, $H_2C_2O_4$. Oxalic acid contains two carboxyl groups. What is its structural formula? It is a poisonous substance, which occurs in small quantities in some plants, such as rhubarb.

7-33. Write the equation for the acetic fermentation reaction, which converts wine into vinegar.

7-34. Make a diagram to illustrate the carbon cycle in nature.

References: Books on Organic Chemistry

J. B. Conant and A. N. Blatt, *Fundamentals of Organic Chemistry*, The Macmillan Co., New York, **1950**.

L. F. and M. Fieser, *Textbook of Organic Chemistry*, D. C. Heath Co., Boston, **1950**.

R. C. Fuson and H. R. Snyder, *Organic Chemistry*, John Wiley and Sons, New York, **1954**.

H. J. Lucas, *Organic Chemistry*, American Book Co., New York, **1953**.

Roger J. Williams and Lewis F. Hatch, *An Introduction to Organic Chemistry*, D. Van Nostrand Company, Inc., New York, **1948**.

Many other good books on organic chemistry have been published.

PART TWO

Some Aspects of
Chemical Theory

In Chapter 1 we discussed different kinds of matter—homogeneous materials and heterogeneous materials, mixtures, solutions, and pure substances. In Chapter 2 a beginning was made on the correlation of the properties of substances and their structure, especially in relation to the atomic theory. We have seen that the characteristic properties of crystals are a consequence of their regular structure. A crystal of copper, which was discussed as an example, contains atoms of copper packed closely together in a regular three-dimensional arrangement, and a crystal of iodine, discussed as an example of a molecular crystal, contains molecules, each made of two iodine atoms, packed closely together in another regular arrangement. In a liquid the atoms or molecules are packed together, but not in a regular arrangement, and they are able to move around one another, permitting the liquid to flow, and to adjust its shape to its container. In a gas the atoms or molecules are free to move away from one another, permitting the gas to expand to fill the volume of its container.

In Chapter 3 the study of structure was carried one step further, to the structure of the atom itself. An account was given of the experiments that led to the discovery that the atom is not a fundamental particle of matter, incapable of subdivision, but is itself composed of simpler particles: each atom contains one nucleus, which has a positive electric charge, and one or more electrons, which have negative electric charges. Atoms are known in which the nucleus has a single unit of positive electric charge (hydrogen), two units of positive electric charge (helium), and so on, without a gap, to 100 units of positive electric charge (centurium). The number of electric charges on the nucleus is called the atomic number of the atom. The structure of the nucleus itself was also discussed: every nucleus can be described as composed of protons and neutrons (except the simplest one, the proton itself). The number of protons in the nucleus is equal to the atomic number of the atom. All of the atoms with a given atomic number constitute an element; 100 elements are known.

A substance composed only of atoms of one element is called an elementary substance, and a substance composed of atoms of two or more elements, in definite proportions, is called a compound; a discussion of the nature of elements and compounds was presented in Chapter 4.

The 100 elements differ greatly from one another in their properties, and the task of learning and remembering many of the important facts about them would be an appalling one if it could not be systematized. It is fortunate that the properties of the elements depend upon their atomic numbers in a systematic way, as expressed in the periodic law. In Chapters 5, 6, and 7 we have described the arrangement of the elements, the periodic table, that corresponds to the periodic law, and have discussed the properties of a number of the commoner elements, and their compounds, in correlation with the periodic table. An important concept, the concept of valence, which determines the composition of compounds, has also been briefly discussed. The dependence of the valence of an element on the position of the element in the periodic table provides a striking illustration of the value of the periodic law in systematizing the facts of chemistry.

We are now ready to embark upon a further study of chemical theory, which is presented in the following five chapters. We have learned, in the earlier chapters, that compounds are formed of atoms of different elements, in definite proportions: water, for example, consists of molecules containing two atoms of hydrogen and one atom of oxygen. We see that if we knew the relative weights of the atoms we could calculate the weights of hydrogen and oxygen in water— that is, the composition of water. Chapter 8 is devoted to this quantitative aspect of chemistry—weight relations in chemical reactions. The quantitative discussion of chemical reactions and of the properties of substances is then continued in Chapter 9, on the properties of gases.

The concept of valence is amplified in Chapters 10, 11, and 12. It has been found that the power of atoms to combine with one another is determined by their electronic structure. In some chemical reactions there is a transfer of electrons from one atom to another; some of these reactions are discussed in Chapter 10, which deals with ions, ionic valence, and electrolysis. The structure of molecules and crystals in which electrons are shared between two atoms is treated in Chapter 11, on covalence and electronic structure. A general discussion of chemical reactions involving electron transfer is presented in Chapter 12, on oxidation-reduction reactions.

When you have completed the study of Part II of this book, and have gained an understanding of these more quantitative and precise aspects of chemical theory, you will be in a position to proceed more effectively than before with the study of the properties and reactions of chemical substances.

Chapter 8

Weight Relations in Chemical Reactions

In every branch of chemistry it is necessary to make calculations about the weights of substances involved in chemical reactions; and sometimes calculations of this sort are of interest in every-day life.

These calculations can always be carried out by considering the atoms involved and using their atomic weights. No new principles are needed —the applications of arithmetic and algebra closely resemble those of the problems of every-day life. The only difficulty that the student might have is that of getting accustomed to dealing with such small objects as atoms and molecules.

Analyze each problem that you meet; do not memorize rules for solving these problems. When you have a problem to solve, think about it until you are sure that you understand it; in particular, consider the behavior of the atoms involved. Then formulate an equation containing the unknown quantities, making use of atomic weights, and solve it. It is often helpful to solve a problem in steps.

8–1. *The Atomic Weights of the Elements*

All of the weight relations in chemical reactions depend upon the weights of the atoms of the elements. These weights (or masses), called *atomic weights*, are very important in the study and practice of chemistry.

The Meaning of Atomic Weights. The fact that many elements consist of a mixture of stable isotopes complicates the discussion of atomic weights.

The chemical atomic weights of elements are the average relative weights (masses) of atoms of the elements, the average being for the usual isotopic composition of each element.

The base of atomic weights is the element oxygen, with its atomic weight arbitrarily taken as 16.00000. Oxygen was chosen as the base by general agreement of chemists for the reason that it combines with most of the elements, whose atomic weights can then be evaluated by the experimental determination of the weight relations involved in the oxygen compounds. The choice of 16.00000 is due to the facts that with this standard an astonishingly large number of elements have nearly integral atomic weights (carbon, C, 12.011; nitrogen, N, 14.008; sodium, Na, 22.997; etc.) and that none has atomic weight less than one unit (hydrogen, H, 1.0080; helium, He, 4.003; lithium, Li, 6.940). The atomic mass unit (atomic weight unit) is defined as exactly 1/16 of the mass of an average oxygen atom. The atomic weight of an element is the average mass of an atom of the element measured in this unit.

Ordinary hydrogen contains about one deuterium atom (mass 2.0143 units) to every 5000 light hydrogen atoms (mass 1.0078 units). We see that the extra mass, approximately one unit, of one deuterium atom to every 5000 light atoms would cause an increase in the average mass of 1/5000, or 0.0002 units, and that accordingly the average mass, or chemical atomic weight, of ordinary hydrogen is 1.0078 + 0.0002 = 1.0080.

The chemical atomic weight defined in this way, as the average for the usual isotopic composition of the element, would not be very useful unless the isotopic composition were constant. It is in fact found that the isotopic composition of most elements (the proportion of different isotopes) is the same for all natural occurrences of the element, to within the precision of experimental determination of atomic weights. An exception is lead, which is found in certain minerals (where it was formed by radioactive decomposition of thorium) with atomic weight 205 96 and in others (where it was formed from uranium) with atomic weight 208.0. The atomic weight of ordinary lead, from the common mineral galena, PbS, is 207.21. Since galena is the source of almost all the lead that is used, this is the value given in the table of atomic weights.

The History of the Atomic Weight Scale. John Dalton, who in 1803 made the old atomic hypothesis into a useful scientific theory by developing the concept of atomic weights, chose as the base the value 1 for hydrogen. Later Berzelius, who made many atomic-weight determinations, used 100 for oxygen as the base; this was not accepted, and the Belgian chemist J. S. Stas in his careful work from 1850 on used the value 16 for oxygen, considering this equivalent to 1 for hydrogen. By 1905 it was recognized that the ratio of atomic weights for hydrogen and oxygen, as determined by measuring experimentally the ratio of weights of hydrogen and of oxygen that combine with one another to form water, differs from 1 :16 by nearly 1 percent. Most of the experimental values of atomic-weight ratios had been determined relative to oxygen, for which 16

TABLE 8-1   *International Atomic Weights 1955*

NAME	SYM-BOL	ATOMIC NUMBER	ATOMIC WEIGHT*	NAME	SYM-BOL	ATOMIC NUMBER	ATOMIC WEIGHT*
Actinium	Ac	89	227	Mendelevium	Mv	101	[256]
Aluminum	Al	13	26.98	Mercury	Hg	80	200.61
Americium	Am	95	[243]	Molybdenum	Mo	42	95.95
Antimony	Sb	51	121.76	Neodymium	Nd	60	144.27
Argon	A	18	39.944	Neon	Ne	10	20.183
Arsenic	As	33	74.91	Neptunium	Np	93	[237]
Astatine	At	85	[210]	Nickel	Ni	28	58.71
Barium	Ba	56	137.36	Niobium	Nb	41	92.91
Berkelium	Bk	97	[249]	Nitrogen	N	7	14.008
Beryllium	Be	4	9.013	Osmium	Os	76	190.2
Bismuth	Bi	83	209.00	Oxygen	O	8	16.0000
Boron	B	5	10.82	Palladium	Pd	46	106.4
Bromine	Br	35	79.916	Phosphorus	P	15	30.975
Cadmium	Cd	48	112.41	Platinum	Pt	78	195.09
Calcium	Ca	20	40.08	Plutonium	Pu	94	[242]
Californium	Cf	98	[249]	Polonium	Po	84	210
Carbon	C	6	12.011	Potassium	K	19	39.100
Cerium	Ce	58	140.13	Praseodymium	Pr	59	140.92
Cesium	Cs	55	132.91	Promethium	Pm	61	[145]
Chlorine	Cl	17	35.457	Protactinium	Pa	91	231
Chromium	Cr	24	52.01	Radium	Ra	88	226.05
Cobalt	Co	27	58.94	Radon	Rn	86	222
Columbium: see Niobium†				Rhenium	Re	75	186.22
Copper	Cu	29	63.54	Rhodium	Rh	45	102.91
Curium	Cm	96	[245]	Rubidium	Rb	37	85.48
Dysprosium	Dy	66	162.51	Ruthenium	Ru	44	101.1
Einsteinium	E	99	[254]	Samarium	Sm	62	150.35
Erbium	Er	68	167.27	Scandium	Sc	21	44.96
Europium	Eu	63	152.0	Selenium	Se	34	78.96
Fermium	Fm	100	[255]	Silicon	Si	14	28.09
Fluorine	F	9	19.00	Silver	Ag	47	107.880
Francium	Fr	87	[223]	Sodium	Na	11	22.991
Gadolinium	Gd	64	157.26	Strontium	Sr	38	87.63
Gallium	Ga	31	69.72	Sulfur	S	16	32.066§
Germanium	Ge	32	72.60	Tantalum	Ta	73	180.95
Gold	Au	79	197.0	Technetium	Tc	43	[99]
Hafnium	Hf	72	178.50	Tellurium	Te	52	127.61
Helium	He	2	4.003	Terbium	Tb	65	158.93
Holmium	Ho	67	164.94	Thallium	Tl	81	204.39
Hydrogen	H	1	1.0080	Thorium	Th	90	232.05
Indium	In	49	114.82	Thulium	Tm	69	168.94
Iodine	I	53	126.91	Tin	Sn	50	118.70
Iridium	Ir	77	192.2	Titanium	Ti	22	47.90
Iron	Fe	26	55.85	Tungsten	W	74	183.86
Krypton	Kr	36	83.80	Uranium	U	92	238.07
Lanthanum	La	57	138.92	Vanadium	V	23	50.95
Lead	Pb	82	207.21	Xenon	Xe	54	131.30
Lithium	Li	3	6.940	Ytterbium	Yb	70	173.04
Lutetium	Lu	71	174.99	Yttrium	Y	39	88.92
Magnesium	Mg	12	24.32	Zinc	Zn	30	65.38
Manganese	Mn	25	54.94	Zirconium	Zr	40	91.22

* A value given in brackets is the mass number of the most stable known isotope.

† The English name of this element has been changed recently, by action of the International Union of Pure and Applied Chemistry.

§ Because of the natural variations in the relative abundance of the isotopes of sulfur the atomic weight of this element has a range of ±0.003.

had been used: by accepting 16.00000 for oxygen as base, no change in the older tables was needed, except for hydrogen.

It is good that the decision to accept oxygen as the base was reached, since only a few years ago (1938) the ratio of atomic weights H : O was revised from 1.0078 : 16 to 1.0080 : 16 as the result of more precise experimental work. If hydrogen were being used as the base of atomic weights this change would have required changes of almost all atomic weights by 0.02%, instead of only that of hydrogen, because most atomic weights had been determined by comparison with oxygen.

Prout's Hypothesis.   An imaginative physician and chemist, William Prout of Edinburgh and London, in 1816 suggested that all atoms are built of hydrogen, with all atomic weights multiples of that of hydrogen. At that time the available rough values of atomic weights showed in general no disagreement with this hypothesis, and Prout rejected as erroneous those few that did. As more accurate values were obtained, however, it became clear that Prout's simple hypothesis was contradicted by the facts; chlorine, for example, has the atomic weight 35.46, and boron 10.82.

Prout's hypothesis was revived by the discovery of isotopes; thus chlorine consists of two natural isotopes with mass numbers 35 and 37, and boron of two isotopes with mass numbers 10 and 11, in each case with nearly integral atomic weights and present in such relative amounts as to give the chemical atomic weight. It is now seen that Prout's idea contained a large element of truth.

The Einstein Equation and the Masses of Nuclei.   A striking property of nuclei is that *the mass of a heavy nucleus is slightly less than the sum of the masses of the protons and neutrons that combine to form it.* The reason for this is that during combination of the protons and neutrons a large amount of energy is released in the form of radiation. In consequence of the relativistic relation (the *Einstein equation*) between mass and energy, which is $E = mc^2$ (E = energy, m = mass, c = velocity of light), this release of radiation leads to a corresponding decrease in mass by about 1 percent (see Chapter 32). The change in mass that accompanies ordinary chemical reactions as a result of the emission or absorption of heat is too small to be detected.

The Values of the Atomic Weights. The 1955 atomic weights of the elements, as announced by the International Committee on Atomic Weights,* are given in Table 8-1.

8–2. *The Quantitative Meaning of Chemical Symbols and Formulas*

A symbol such as Cu is used to indicate the element copper, either in the elementary substance or in compounds. It also means a definite amount of copper—one atom or one atomic weight (63.54) in any weight unit (such as 63.54 g or 63.54 pounds). In particular, however, it is often used to mean one *gram-atom* of copper, 63.54 g.

Similarly a formula such as $CuSO_4 \cdot 5H_2O$ represents the compound copper sulfate pentahydrate, which contains the four elements whose symbols are involved in the atomic ratios indicated by the formula.

* Report of the Commission on Atomic Weights of the International Union of Pure and Applied Chemistry. This report is discussed in the *Journal of the American Chemical Society*, July 20, 1956.

These ratios are 1Cu : 1S : 9O : 10H. The formula also means one formula weight (in arbitrary units) of the substance. In particular, the formula is often used to mean one *gram-formula weight*, 249.69 g, and hence to mean 1 gram-atom of copper, plus 1 gram-atom of sulfur, 9 gram-atoms of oxygen, and 10 gram-atoms of hydrogen.

The *molecular weight* of a substance is the average weight* in atomic weight units of a molecule of a substance. If the molecular formula of the substance is known, the molecular weight is calculated by adding the atomic weights of the elements as given in the formula of the substance. Inasmuch as the true formula of a substance may not be known, it is often convenient to use the *formula weight*, the sum of the atomic weights of the atoms in an assumed formula for a substance, which may not be the correct molecular formula (an example: HO for hydrogen peroxide instead of H_2O_2). A gram-formula weight is then the amount of the substance with weight equal to the formula weight in grams, as indicated above for copper sulfate pentahydrate.

A *mole* (or *gram-molecular weight*) of any substance is the amount of the substance with weight equal to the molecular weight in grams. When it is known that the formula written for a substance is its correct molecular formula, the molecular weight and the formula weight are of course the same, and the mole equals the gram formula weight.

Often the state of aggregation of a substance is represented by appended letters: $Cu(s)$ refers to crystalline copper (s standing for solid), $Cu(l)$ to liquid copper, and $Cu(g)$ to gaseous copper. Sometimes a substance is indicated as solid or crystalline by a line drawn under its formula (both $\underline{AgCl}$ and $AgCl(s)$ mean solid silver chloride). A substance in solution is sometimes represented by its formula followed by *aq* (for aqueous solution).

8–3. *Examples of Weight-Relation Calculations*

The way to work a weight-relation problem is by thinking about the problem, in terms of atoms and molecules, and then deciding how to carry out the calculations. You should not memorize any rule about these problems—such rules are apt to confuse you, and to cause you to make mistakes.

The kind of arguments usually carried out in working these problems is best indicated by the detailed solution of some examples.

In general, chemical problems may be solved by using a slide rule for the numerical work. This gives about three reliable figures in the answer, which is often all that is justified by the accuracy of the data. Sometimes the data are more reliable, and logarithms or long-hand calculations might be used to obtain the answer with the accuracy

---

* The expression "average weight" is used here because of the existence of stable isotopes of most of the elements.

called for. Unless the problem requires unusual accuracy, you may round values of atomic weights off to the first decimal point; for example, you may use 32.1 for sulfur, instead of 32.066.

Example 1. What is the percentage of lead in galena, PbS? Calculate to 0.1%.

    Solution. The formula weight of PbS is obtained by adding the atomic weights of lead and sulfur, which we obtain from Table 8-1:

Atomic weight of lead	207.2
Atomic weight of sulfur	32.1
Formula weight of PbS	239.3

    Hence 239.3 g of PbS contains 207.2 g of lead. We see that 100.0 g of PbS would contain

$$\frac{207.2 \text{ g Pb}}{239.3 \text{ g PbS}} \times 100.0 \text{ g PbS} = 86.6 \text{ g Pb}$$

    Hence the percentage of lead in PbS is 86.6%.

    You may prefer to work examples of this sort by use of *proportion.* It is good practice in using this method to write the definition of the unknown quantity, usually represented by the letter x.

    Let x = percentage of lead in galena; that is, x = grams of lead in 100 g of PbS.

    We may now write two ratios (two fractions), each being the ratio of the weight of lead to the weight of PbS containing it; these ratios must be equal, because of the constancy of composition of the compound lead sulfide:

$$\frac{207.2}{239.3} = \frac{x}{100.0 \text{ g}}$$

The ratio on the left is the ratio of the atomic weight of lead to the formula weight of PbS. That on the right is the ratio of the weight of lead in 100.0 g of PbS to the weight of the PbS. On solving this equation we obtain the answer given above.

Example 2. A propellant for rockets can be made by mixing powdered potassium perchlorate, $KClO_4$, and powdered carbon (carbon black), C, with a little adhesive to bind the powdered materials together. What weight of carbon should be mixed with 1000 g of potassium perchlorate, in order that the products of the reaction be KCl and CO?

    Solution. Taking the equation for the reaction as

$$KClO_4 + 4C \longrightarrow KCl + 4CO$$

we first calculate the formula weight of $KClO_4$:

$$
\begin{array}{ccc}
\text{K} & & 39.1 \\
\text{Cl} & & 35.5 \\
40 = 4 \times 16.0 & & \underline{64.0} \\
& & 138.6
\end{array}
$$

The atomic weight of carbon is 12.0; the weight 4C is 48.0. Hence the weight of carbon required is $\dfrac{48.0}{138.6}$ times the weight of potassium perchlorate:

$$
\frac{48.0 \text{ atomic mass units C}}{138.6 \text{ atomic mass units KClO}_4} \times 1000 \text{ g KClO}_4 = 346 \text{ g C}
$$

Hence about **346 g** of carbon is required for 1000 g of potassium perchlorate.

Example 3.   How much iron can be obtained by the reduction of one ton of hematite iron ore, assuming it to be pure Fe_2O_3?

Solution.   We assume that all the iron atoms in ferric oxide (hematite) can be converted into elementary iron by reduction; and we write the corresponding equation:

$$
Fe_2O_3 + \text{reducing agent} \longrightarrow 2Fe + \text{product}
$$

From this equation we see that one formula Fe_2O_3 of hematite gives on reduction two atoms of iron. The formula weight of Fe_2O_3 is 159.7, as is found in the following way:

Weight of 2Fe = 2×55.85 = 111.7
Weight of 3O = 3×16.0 = $\underline{48.0}$
Formula weight of Fe_2O_3 159.7

It is evident that the ratio of the weight of iron that can be obtained from hematite to the weight of hematite is 111.7/159.7. Accordingly if we multiply the weight of hematite, 1 ton, by this quantity we obtain the weight in tons of iron that could be produced from the hematite:

$$
\frac{111.7 \text{ units iron}}{159.7 \text{ units } Fe_2O_3} \times 1 \text{ ton } Fe_2O_3 = \mathbf{0.699 \text{ ton}} \text{ Fe or}
$$
$$
\mathbf{1398 \text{ pounds}} \text{ of iron}
$$

Example 4.   An oxide of europium contains 86.4% of europium. What is its simplest formula?

Solution.   In 100 g of this oxide of europium there are contained, according to the reported analysis, 86.4 g of europium and 13.6 g of oxygen. If we divide 86.4 g by the gram-atomic weight of europium, 152.0 g, we obtain 0.568 as the number of gram-atoms of europium. Similarly, by dividing 13.6 g by the gram-atomic weight of oxygen, 16 g, we obtain 0.850 as the number of gram-atoms of oxygen in 100 g of this oxide of europium. Hence the relative numbers of atoms of europium and oxygen in the compound are in the ratio 0.568 to 0.850. If we set this ratio, 0.568/0.850, on the slide rule, we see that it is very close to 2/3, being 2/2.994. Hence the simplest formula is **Eu_2O_3.**

We say that this is the simplest formula in order not to rule out the possibility that the substance contains more complex molecules, such as Eu_4O_6, in which case it would be proper to indicate in the formula the larger numbers of atoms per molecule.

Example 5. A substance is found by qualitative tests to consist of only carbon and hydrogen (it is a hydrocarbon). A quantitative analysis is made of the substance by putting a weighed amount, 0.2822 g, in a tube which can be strongly heated from outside, and then burning it in a stream of dry air. The air containing the products of combustion is passed first through a weighed tube containing calcium chloride, which absorbs the water vapor, and then through another weighed tube containing a mixture of sodium hydroxide and calcium oxide, which absorbs the carbon dioxide. When the first tube is weighed, after the combustion is completed, it is found to have increased in weight by 0.1598 g, this being accordingly the weight of water produced by the combustion of the sample. The second tube is found to have increased in weight by 0.9768 g. What is the simplest formula of the substance?

Solution. It is convenient to solve this problem in steps. Let us first find out how many moles of water were produced. The number of moles of water produced is found by dividing 0.1598 g by 18.02 g, the weight of a mole of water; it is 0.00887. Each mole of water vapor contains two gram-atoms of hydrogen; hence the number of gram-atoms of hydrogen in the original sample is twice this number, or 0.01774.

Similarly the number of moles of carbon dioxide in the products of combustion is obtained by dividing the weight of carbon dioxide, 0.9768 g, by the molar weight of the substance, 44.01 g. It is 0.02219, which is also the number of gram-atoms of carbon in the sample of substance, because each molecule of carbon dioxide contains one atom of carbon.

The original substance accordingly contained carbon atoms and hydrogen atoms in the ratio 0.02219 to 0.01774. This ratio is found on calculation to be 1.251, which is equal to $\frac{5}{4}$, to within the accuracy of the analysis. Accordingly the simplest formula for the substance is **C_5H_4.**

If the analyst had smelled the substance, and noticed an odor resembling moth balls, he would have identified the substance as naphthalene, $C_{10}H_8$.

8-5. The Deter
by Use of ¿

In 1907 J. J. Thomson ¿
of an ionized atom (or io:
the ionized atoms in elect
graph. It has become usefu
uses have been for the di
The importance of these ¿
works.

Let us consider, as an
also in Chapter 2. Iodine
I₂. As the temperature is r
thermal agitation by beir
gas into atoms can also be
through the gas. A fast-m
molecule of iodine so vigc

$$I_2 \longrightarrow 2I$$

In such an electric disc:
be struck such a blow as
electrons; that is, the mole
electron, and one cation,

$$I_2 \xrightarrow{\text{collision}} I^- + I^+$$

A cation I⁺ might suffer a
converting it into a doubl

$$I^+ \xrightarrow{\text{collision}} I^{++} + e^-$$

All atoms, even such st
gaseous cations in an elec
form stable singly charged
under these circumstanc
gaseous molecular ions s
such as H⁺, C⁺, C⁺⁺, C⁺

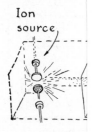

Ion
source,

Det
ve

FIGURE 8-1   I

Illustrative Exercises

8-1.   Calculate, to 0.1%, the percentage composition of water.

8-2.   The atomic weight of calcium is 40.0 and that of carbon is 12.0; what is the formula weight of calcium carbonate, $CaCO_3$? What is the percentage of calcium in it? How much lime, CaO, could be made by heating 100 tons of limestone in a lime kiln?

8-3.   How many grams of hydrogen can be liberated by the reaction of 20.0 g of zinc with sulfuric acid?

8-4.   An oxide of mercury contains 7.4% oxygen and 92.6% mercury. What is its formula?

8-5.   What is the weight of chloroform that might be made by reaction of 1000 g of methane with chlorine?

8-6.   What relative weights of oxygen and acetylene would be burned in an oxyacetylene torch to produce water and carbon monoxide? Water and carbon dioxide?

8-7.   What weight of ethyl alcohol might be obtained by fermentation of 1000 g of glucose?

8-4. Determination of Atomic Weights by the Chemical Method

It is hard to over-estimate the importance of the table of atomic weights. Almost every activity of a chemist involves the use of atomic weights in some way. During the past 150 years successive generations of chemists have carried out experiments in the effort to provide more and more accurate values of the atomic weights, in order that chemical calculations could be carried out with greater accuracy.

Until recently almost all atomic weight determinations were made by the chemical method. This method consists in determining the amount of the element that will combine with one gram-atom of oxygen or of another element with known atomic weight. The method is illustrated by the following examples.

Example 6.   During the period 1882 to 1895 Professor E. W. Morley (1838–1923) of Western Reserve University carried out the first experiments that showed definitely that the ratio of atomic weights of hydrogen and oxygen is not exactly 1 : 16. In one such experiment he found that 1.8467 g of hydrogen combines with 14.656 g of oxygen to form water. What is the atomic weight of hydrogen, calculated from the result of this experiment?

Solution.   Water has the formula H_2O. Hence the observed weights of the two gases are the relative weights of two atoms of hydrogen and one atom of oxygen. If the weight of oxygen, 14.656, is multiplied by the fraction 16.000/14.656 it becomes 16.000, which is the atomic weight of oxygen. Accordingly if the weight

of hyd
would

1.

This
16.000
is one-l
gen as

Example 7
1928), whc
Prize (it wa
with great
atomic weig
0.26496 g o
weighing th
of chlorine
assuming cl
Solutic
by the
atoms

Grai

The fo:
as of c

Grai

The w

Wei
Wei
Wei

This is
numbe

Gra
per

Hence
is **70.0**

The Principle of the Mass Spectrograph. The principle of the mass spectrograph can be illustrated by the simple apparatus shown in Figure 8-1.

At the left is a chamber in which positive ions are formed by an electric discharge, and then accelerated toward the right by an electric potential. The ions passing through the first pin-hole have different velocities; in the second part of the apparatus a beam of ions with approximately a certain velocity is selected, and allowed to pass through the second pin-hole, the ions with other velocities being stopped. (We shall not attempt to describe the construction of the velocity selector.) The ions passing through the second pin-hole then move on between two metal plates, one of which has a positive electric charge and the other a negative charge. The ions accordingly undergo an acceleration toward the negative plate, and are deflected from the straight path A that they would pursue if the plates were not charged.

The force acting on an ion between these plates is proportional to $+ne$, its electric charge (n being the number of missing electrons), and its inertia is proportional to its mass M. The amount of deflection is hence determined by ne/M, the ratio of the charge of the ion to its mass.

Of two ions with the same charge, the lighter one will be deflected in this apparatus by the greater amount. The beam C might accordingly represent the ion C^+, with charge $+e$ and mass 12 atomic weight units (the atomic weight of carbon), and the beam B the heavier ion O^+, with the same charge but with mass 16.

Of two ions with the same mass, the one with the greater charge will be deflected by the greater amount. Beams B and C might represent O^{++} and O^{+++}, respectively.

By measuring the deflection of the beams, relative values of ne/M for different ions can be determined. Since e is constant, relative values of ne/M for different ions are also inverse relative values of M/n: therefore this method permits the direct experimental determination of the relative masses of atoms, and hence of their atomic weights. By this method Thomson discovered the first known non-radioactive isotopes, those of neon, in 1913.

The value of the integer n, the degree of ionization of the ions, can usually be fixed from knowledge of the substances present in the discharge tube; thus neon gives ions with $M/n = 20$ and 22 ($n = 1$), 10 and 11 ($n = 2$), etc.

Instead of the mass spectrograph described above, others of different design, using both an electric field and a magnetic field, are usually used. These instruments are

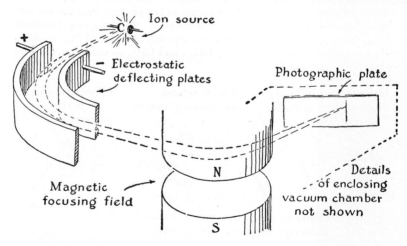

FIGURE 8-2   *A focusing mass spectrograph, using both electrostatic and magnetic deflection of the beam of ions.*

designed so that they focus the beam of ions with a given value of M/n into a sharp line on a photographic plate. An instrument of this sort, using both an electric field, with curved plates, and a magnetic field, is sketched in Figure 8-2.

Modern types of mass spectrographs (Figure 8-2) have an accuracy of about one part in 100,000 and a resolving power of 10,000 or more (that is, they are able to separate ion beams with values of M/n differing by only one part in 10,000). The great accuracy of modern mass spectrographs makes the mass-spectrographic method of determining atomic weights more useful and important at present than the chemical method.

Mass-spectrographic comparisons with O^{16} are made in the following way. An ion source which produces ions both of oxygen and of the element to be investigated is used; the lines of oxygen and of the element in such states of ionization that their ne/M values are nearly the same are then obtained—thus for S^{32}, S^{33}, and S^{34} the lines for the doubly ionized atoms would lie near the line for singly ionized oxygen. Accurate relative measurements of these lines can then be made.

The Physicists' Atomic-Weight Scale.   Atomic masses obtained with the mass spectrograph are usually reported relative to $O^{16} = 16.00000$. These atomic masses are called the *atomic weights on the physicists' scale.* Since ordinary oxygen contains 0.2% of O^{18} and 0.04% of O^{17}, these mass values must be corrected by division by a suitable divisor to give the values on the chemists' atomic-weight scale, based on the average weight 16.00000 for ordinary oxygen. The value of this conversion divisor is 1.000275.

The Determination of Atomic Weights with the Mass Spectrograph.   For a simple element, with only one isotope, the value of the atomic mass of that isotope is the atomic weight of the element. Thus for gold, which consists entirely of one stable isotope, Au^{197}, the mass-spectrographic mass (relative to $O^{16} = 16.00000$) is reported to be 197.039. This is the atomic weight of gold on the physicists' scale. In order to find the atomic weight of gold on the chemists' scale this number must be divided by 1.000275. It is then changed into 196.985, which is the atomic weight of gold on the chemists' scale as determined by the mass spectrograph. In 1953 this value, rounded off to 197.0, was accepted by the International Committee, in place of the old value 197.2, which had been determined by the chemical method.

Concepts and Terms Introduced in This Chapter

Atomic weights. The table of international atomic weights.

Gram-atom; gram formula weight; mole (gram molecular weight).

Weight-relation calculations.

Determination of atomic weights by chemical methods; by use of the mass spectrograph.

The physicists' atomic-weight scale.

Exercises

Note: Slide-rule accuracy is usually sufficient for chemical problems. This is not so for atomic-weight problems, which contain data given to five or six significant figures; for these problems five-place or seven-place logarithms or some equivalent method of calculation must be used, and the atomic weights should be calculated to five or six significant figures.

8-8.   How much sulfuric acid, H_2SO_4, could be obtained from 100 lbs. of sulfur? (Answer: 306 lbs.)

8-9. The density of oxygen at 20° C and 1 atm is 1.33 g/l. What weight of mercuric oxide, HgO, would have to be decomposed to produce 5 l of oxygen at this temperature and pressure?

8-10. Calculate the elementary composition of sugar (sucrose), $C_{12}H_{22}O_{11}$; that is, calculate the percentage of each element in this substance. (Ans. 42.1% C, 6.5% H, 51.4% O)

8-11. What is the elementary composition of alum, $KAl(SO_4)_2 \cdot 12H_2O$?

8-12. Kernite, $NaB_4O_7 \cdot 4H_2O$, can be shipped to its destination and there treated with water to form borax, $Na_2B_4O_7 \cdot 10H_2O$. What saving in freight cost results from doing this, instead of converting it to borax before shipping? (Ans. 28.4%)

8-13. What volume of oxygen gas, at 20° C and 1 atm, could be obtained by the complete decomposition of 10 g of potassium chlorate, $KClO_3$? (See Exercise 8-9)

8-14. How much baking soda should be mixed with 1 level teaspoonful (4 g) of cream of tartar to make baking powder? Cream of tartar is potassium hydrogen tartrate, $KHC_4H_4O_6$, and baking soda is sodium hydrogen carbonate, $NaHCO_3$. The reaction that takes place in rising dough made with baking powder is

$$KHC_4H_4O_6 + NaHCO_3 \longrightarrow KNaC_4H_4O_6 + H_2O + CO_2$$

8-15. Platinum forms two chlorides, one of which contains 26.7% chlorine and the other 42.1% chlorine. What are the formulas of the two substances? (Ans. $PtCl_2$, $PtCl_4$)

8-16. What is the percentage of oxygen in water, H_2O? In heavy water, D_2O (deuterium oxide)?

8-17. On combustion of hydrocarbon (a substance containing only hydrogen and carbon) 0.02998 g gave 0.01587 g H_2O and 0.10335 g CO_2. What are possible formulas of the substance?

8-18. A sample of goat cheese weighing 0.1103 g was ignited (heated strongly in a crucible until the organic matter has been burned off), and the ash was dissolved in water and precipitated with silver nitrate, forming 0.00283 g AgCl. Assuming the chloride in the cheese to be sodium chloride, calculate the percentage of sodium chloride in the cheese. (Ans. 1.05%)

8-19. Chemical analyses of the samples of the mineral lepidolite from different places have given values of the lithium content between 2.0% and 2.8%. How well do these values agree with the formula $K_2Li_3Al_5Si_6O_{20}F_4$, given in Section 7-1?

8-20. A known fluoride of silver contains 85.1% silver. What is its simplest formula?

8-21. Two chlorides of a metal were found on analysis to contain 50.91% and 46.37%, respectively, of the metal. What are the possible values of the atomic weight of the metal? What is the metal? (Refer to the atomic-weight table.)

8-22. An oxychloride of vanadium is found on analysis to have the elementary composition V 60.17%, O 18.89%, Cl 20.94%. What is the simplest formula which can be assigned to it? (Ans. V_2O_2Cl)

8-23. Potassium and cadmium form an intermetallic compound containing 2.61% potassium. What is its simplest formula?

8-24. By dissolving aluminum in hydrochloric acid, precipitating $Al(OH)_3$ with sodium hydroxide, and heating the collected precipitate to convert it to the oxide, the ratio of aluminum to oxygen in the oxide was found to be 1.124015. Calculate from this experimental value the atomic weight of aluminum. (Ans. 26.976)

8-25. On complete combustion 6.06324 g of anthracene, $C_{14}H_{10}$, gave 20.96070 g of carbon dioxide. Calculate the atomic weight of carbon, using 1.0080 for hydrogen. (Ans. 12.011)

8-26. Calculate the percentages of the various elements in the drug Chloromycetin, $C_{11}H_{12}N_2O_5Cl_2$.

8-27. A certain substance containing carbon, hydrogen, and oxygen gave 0.6179 g of carbon dioxide and 0.1264 g of water on combustion of a sample weighing 0.2200 g. What is the empirical formula of the substance? The amount of oxygen is to be obtained by difference.

8-28. A monohydroxic base and a diprotic acid react completely to give a salt containing 44.9% K, 18.4% S, and 36.7% O. What is the formula of the salt? Name the acid and base, and write the equation for their reaction to produce this salt.

8-29. The appearance of a rock indicates that it is a mixture of magnesite (magnesium carbonate, $MgCO_3$), and quartz (SiO_2). It is found that 1.00 g of the rock yields 0.430 g of carbon dioxide, on treatment with hydrochloric acid. Write the equation for the reaction, and calculate the percentage of magnesite and the percentage of quartz in the rock.

References

W. M. MacNevin, "Berzelius—Pioneer Atomic Weight Chemist" (historical), *J. Chem. Ed.*, **31,** 207 (1954).

"Positive Rays," *Encyclopaedia Britannica*, 14th Edition—a good description of the mass spectrograph.

Chapter 9

The Properties
of Gases

9–1. *The Nature of the Gas Laws*

Gases differ remarkably from liquids and solids in that the volume of a sample of gas depends in a striking way on the temperature of the gas and the applied pressure. The volume of a sample of liquid water, say 1 kg of water, remains essentially the same when the temperature and pressure are changed somewhat. Increasing the pressure from 1 atm to 2 atm causes the volume of a sample of liquid water to decrease by less than 0.01% and increasing the temperature from 0° C to 100° C causes the volume to increase by only 2%. On the other hand, the volume of a sample of air is cut in half when the pressure is increased from 1 atm to 2 atm, and it increases by 36.6% when the temperature is changed from 0° C to 100° C.

We can understand why these interesting phenomena attracted the attention of scientists during the early years of development of modern chemistry through the application of quantitative experimental methods of investigation of nature, and why many physicists and chemists during the past century have devoted themselves to the problem of developing a sound theory to explain the behavior of gases.

In addition to our desire to understand this part of the physical world, there is another reason, a practical one, for studying the gas laws. This reason is concerned with the *measurement of gases*. The most convenient way to determine the amount of material in a sample of a solid is to weigh it on a balance. This can also be done conveniently for liquids; or we may measure the volume of a sample of a liquid, and, if we want to know its weight, multiply the volume by its density, as found by a previous experiment. The method of weighing is usually not conveniently used for gases, because their densities are very small; volume

170

measurements can be made much more accurately and easily by the use of containers of known volume. But the volume of a sample of gas depends greatly on both the pressure and the temperature, and to calculate the weight of gas in a measured volume the law of this dependence must be known. It is partly for this reason that study of the pressure-volume-temperature properties of gases is a part of chemistry.

Another very important reason for studying the gas laws is that the *density* of a dilute gas is related in a simple way to its *molecular weight*, whereas there is no similar simple relation for liquids and solids. This relation for gases (*Avogadro's law*) was of great value in the original decision as to the correct atomic weights of the elements, and it is still of great practical significance, permitting the direct calculation of the approximate density of a gas of known molecular composition, or the experimental determination of the effective (average) molecular weight of a gas of unknown molecular composition by the measurement of its density. These uses are discussed in detail in the following sections.

It has been found by experiment that **all ordinary gases behave in nearly the same way.** The nature of this behavior is described by the *perfect-gas laws* (often referred to briefly as the *gas laws*).

It is found experimentally that, to within the reliability of the gas laws (better than 1% under ordinary conditions) the volume of a sample of any gas is determined by only three quantities: the *pressure* of the gas, the *temperature* of the gas, and the *number of molecules* in the sample of the gas. The law describing the dependence of the volume of the gas on the pressure is called *Boyle's law;* that describing the dependence of the volume on the temperature is called the *law of Charles and Gay-Lussac;* and that describing the dependence of the volume on the number of molecules in the sample of gas is called *Avogadro's law.*

In the following sections of this chapter these three laws are formulated and applied in the solution of some problems. It is also shown that they can be combined into a single equation, which is called the *perfect-gas equation.*

9–2. *The Dependence of Gas Volume on Pressure. Boyle's Law*

An investigation of the dependence of the volume of a sample of gas on the applied pressure can be made by use of an automobile tire pump; the investigator can in this way measure the volume of the gas in the cylinder of the pump by measuring the position of the piston, as a function of the weight applied to the handle of the pump. A more precise investigation can be carried out with the simple apparatus shown at the left side of Figure 9-1, a long glass tube, with one end turned up. A sample of air is trapped in the upturned closed end by means of mercury. When the level of the mercury in the two arms of the tube is

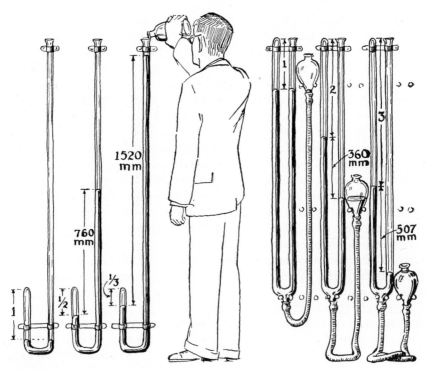

FIGURE 9-1   *A simple apparatus for demonstrating Boyle's law of the dependence of volume of a gas on the applied pressure.*

the same, as shown at the far left of the figure, the sample of gas is under a pressure of 1 atm.

It has been pointed out in Chapter 1 that the standard atmospheric pressure is just equal to the pressure exerted by a column of mercury 760 mm high. Accordingly if mercury is poured into the open end of our tube until the mercury levels in the two arms differ by 760 mm, the pressure exerted on the gas will be equal to 2 atm, 1 atm being due to the weight of the column of mercury and 1 atm to the pressure of the atmosphere on the top of this column. It is found that under this pressure the volume of the sample of air is reduced to one half of its original volume. If more mercury is poured in the tube, until the difference in level of the two columns of mercury is 1520 mm, or 2 atm, the total pressure exerted on the sample of air is then 3 atm, and the volume of the enclosed air is found to be one-third of the original volume.

Experiments such as this one have shown that **for nearly all gases, the volume of a sample of gas at constant temperature is inversely proportional to the pressure;** that is, the product of pressure and volume under these conditions is constant:

$$pV = \text{constant (temperature constant, moles of gas constant)}$$

This equation expresses Boyle's law. The law was inferred from experimental data by the English natural scientist Robert Boyle (1627–1691) in 1662.

Boyle's law describes the behavior of gases under reduced pressure as well as under increased pressure. An investigation of the behavior of a sample of gas under reduced pressure can be carried out with an apparatus such as that shown at the right side of Figure 9-1. This apparatus closely resembles that shown at the left side, the attached rubber tube with the glass reservoir serving as a convenient means of removing some of the mercury.

If the volume of a sample of gas enclosed in the tube is measured at 1 atm (when the mercury levels in the two arms of tube are the same, as shown in the diagram at the left of the figure), and then mercury is removed, permitting the level of mercury in the open arm to fall below that in the closed arm of the tube, it is found that the volume of the sample of gas becomes just equal to twice its original value when the level of the mercury in the open arm lies 380 mm below that in the closed arm. The pressure due to 380 mm of mercury is $\frac{1}{2}$ atm; it is seen that this pressure, due to the mercury, is opposing the atmospheric pressure, so that the pressure acting on the enclosed sample of gas is the difference between 1 atm and $\frac{1}{2}$ atm, or $\frac{1}{2}$ atm. Accordingly under these conditions also there is an inverse proportionality of volume and pressure, the product of pressure and volume remaining constant.

If more mercury is removed from the system, so that the difference in level of mercury in the two arms becomes 507 mm, the volume of the sample of gas will become just 3 times its original value. The column of mercury 507 mm high exerts a pressure of $\frac{2}{3}$ atm, which opposes in part the pressure of the atmosphere, leaving $\frac{1}{3}$ atm as the pressure acting on the sample of the gas. Again the product of pressure and volume is equal to the original value.

The practical use of Boyle's law may be illustrated by some examples.

Example 1. A sample of gas is found by measurement to have the volume 1000 ml at the pressure 730 mm of mercury. What would be its volume at normal atmospheric pressure, 760 mm of mercury?

Solution. Let p_1 and V_1 be the initial pressure, 730 mm Hg, and volume, 1000 ml, respectively. Let p_2 be the changed pressure, 760 mm Hg, and V_2 be the changed volume, which we wish to determine. From Boyle's law, Equation 1, we know that the product pv remains constant; hence we write

$$p_1 V_1 = p_2 V_2$$

or 730 mm Hg $\times$ 1000 ml = 760 mm Hg $\times$ V_2
Solving for V_2, we obtain

$$V_2 = \frac{730 \text{ mm Hg}}{760 \text{ mm Hg}} \times 1000 \text{ ml} = \textbf{960 ml}$$

There is another way of solving the problem that involves more thinking, and that may help to prevent errors. We know that Boyle's law is of such a form that the volume changes by a factor equal to the ratio of the two pressures. We can hence obtain the final volume by multiplying the initial volume by the ratio $\frac{730}{760}$. (We know that the ratio $\frac{760}{730}$ is not the correct one to multiply by, because *increase* in pressure always causes a *decrease* in volume, and the factor must accordingly be *less* than 1.) Thus we obtain as the desired volume

$$\frac{730}{760} \times 1000 \text{ ml} = \textbf{960 ml}$$

It is good practice to *work every problem in your head*, in a rough numerical way, in order to verify that the answer that you have obtained by your calculation is a reasonable one. In the present problem we note that the pressure is increased by 30 mm of Hg, which is about 4%. Hence the volume must decrease by about 4%. Since 4% of 1000 ml is 40 ml, the answer should be about 960 ml.

In the second calculation above there occurs the fraction $\frac{730}{760}$, without the units mm Hg after either of the two numbers. When a ratio of two quantities measured in the same units occurs in an expression, as in this case, it is not necessary to show the units. Thus when a ratio of two temperatures or of two pressures occurs in the solution of later problems only the ratio of the numbers will in general be written.

Example 2. What is the weight of oxygen that can be put in an oxygen tank with volume 2 cu. ft. under pressure of 1500 lbs. per sq. in.? The density of oxygen at 1 atm pressure and room temperature (18° C) is 1.34 g/l.

Solution. Let us convert the volume of the tank to liters and the pressure to atmospheres. The number of liters in 1 cu. ft. can be found by remembering that 2.54 cm = 1 inch. The number of cm³ in 1 cu. ft. is accordingly $(12 \times 2.54)^3 = 30.48^3 = 28316$ cm³. Hence 1 cu. ft. = 28.32 l, and 2 cu. ft., the volume of the tank, is 56.6 l. We also remember, from Chapter 1, that 1 atm pressure is equal to 14.7 lbs. per sq. in. Hence the pressure in the tank in atmospheres is 1500/14.7 = 102 atm. By application of Boyle's law we see that a volume of 56.6 l of gas at 102 atm will become much larger, by the factor 102, when the pressure is decreased to 1 atm; the volume at 1 atm is accordingly

$$\frac{102}{1} \times 56.6\ 1 = 5773\ 1$$

The weight of this volume of oxygen in grams is the product of the volume by the density, 1.34 g/l, which is 7730 g or, dividing by 454, the number of grams in a pound, 17.0 lb. The weight of oxygen that the tank will hold under this pressure is accordingly **17.0 lbs.**

Illustrative Exercises

9-1.   If the pressure on a sample of gas (held at constant temperature) were to be doubled, how would its volume change? If the volume were doubled, how would the pressure change?

9-2.   A sample of gas in a glass apparatus being used by a chemist was found to have volume 2000 ml at pressure 0.1000 mm of mercury. What would its volume be when the pressure is increased to 1 atm?

The Partial Pressures of Components of a Gas Mixture.   It is found by experiment (Dalton, 1801) that when two samples of gas at the same pressure are mixed there is no change in volume. If the two samples of gas were originally present in containers of the same size, at a pressure of 1 atm, each container after the mixing was completed would contain a mixture of gas molecules, half of them of one kind and half the other. It is reasonable to assume that each gas in this mixture exerts the pressure of $\frac{1}{2}$ atm, as it would if the other gas were not present. Dalton's **law of partial pressures** states that *in a gas mixture the molecules of gas of each kind exert the same pressure as they would if present alone*, and that *the total pressure is the sum of the partial pressures exerted by the different gases in the mixture.*

Correction for the Vapor Pressure of Water.   When a sample of gas is collected over water (Figure 9-2), the pressure of the gas is due in part to the water vapor in it. The pressure due to the water vapor in the gas in equilibrium with liquid water is equal to the vapor pressure of water. Values of the vapor pressure at different temperatures are given in Appendix 3.

The way in which a correction for the vapor pressure of water can be made is illustrated in the following example.

Example 3.   An experiment is made to find out how much oxygen is liberated from a given amount of potassium chlorate, $KClO_3$. The quantity 2.00 g of this salt is weighed out, mixed with some manganese dioxide, to serve as catalyst, and introduced into a test tube, which is provided with a cork and delivery tube leading to a bottle filled with water and inverted in a pneumatic trough. The test tube is heated, and

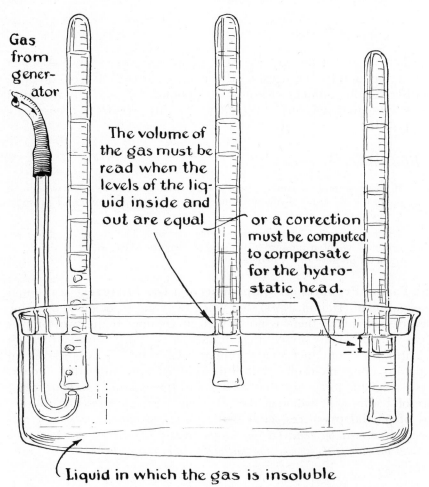

Gas from gener-ator

The volume of the gas must be read when the levels of the liquid inside and out are equal

or a correction must be computed to compensate for the hydro-static head.

Liquid in which the gas is insoluble

FIGURE 9-2 *Diagram illustrating the measurement of volume of a gas collected over water.*

the heating is continued until the evolution of gas ceases. The volume of the liberated gas was determined to be 59 ml. The temperature was 18° C, and the pressure was 748.3 mm Hg. What was the weight of oxygen liberated? How does this compare with the theoretical yield?

Solution. The atmospheric pressure, 748.3 mm Hg, is balanced in part by the pressure of the oxygen collected in the bottle, and in part by the pressure of the water vapor dissolved by the oxygen as it bubbles through the water. By reference to Appendix 3 we see that the vapor pressure of water at 18° C is 15.5 mm Hg. Accordingly the pressure due to the oxygen in the bottle is less than 748.3 mm by this amount, and is equal to 748.3 − 15.5 = 732.8 mm Hg.

Let us now find what volume the liberated oxygen would occupy at standard pressure, 760 mm Hg. The volume at the pressure 732.8 mm Hg is 591 ml. We know that gases become smaller in volume when they are compressed; the volume at the higher pressure, 760 mm, will hence be less than 591, and we see that the volume 591 must be multiplied by the fraction $\dfrac{732.8}{760}$:

$$\text{Volume of oxygen at 760 mm Hg} = \frac{732.8}{760} \times 591 \text{ ml} = 570 \text{ ml}$$

In the preceding example (Example 2) the density of oxygen at 1 atm pressure and 18° C was given as 1.34 g/l; that is, 1.34 g per 1000 ml. The weight of 570 ml of oxygen under these conditions is easily calculated; this is the answer to the first question in our example.

$$\text{Weight of oxygen liberated} = \frac{570}{1000} \times 1.34 \text{ g} = \mathbf{0.764 \text{ g}}$$

Note how simple the means are by which the weight of liberated oxygen was found, to 1 mg accuracy—only rough volume measurements (to 1 ml) needed to be made.

To answer the second question let us calculate the theoretical yield of oxygen from 2.00 g of potassium chlorate. The equation for the decomposition of potassium chlorate is

$$KClO_3 \longrightarrow KCl + \tfrac{3}{2}O_2$$

(Note that it is sometimes convenient to represent a fractional number of molecules in an equation.) We see that 1 gram formula weight of $KClO_3$, 122.5 g, should liberate 3 gram-atoms of oxygen, 48.0 g. Hence the amount of oxygen that should be liberated from 2.00 g of potassium chlorate is $\dfrac{48.0}{122.5} \times 2.00 \text{ g} = 0.786 \text{ g}$.

The observed amount of oxygen liberated is seen to be less than the theoretical amount by 0.022 g, or **2.8%**.

In applying Boyle's law in the solution of a problem you should always check your calculations by deciding whether the change in pressure given in the problem should cause the volume to increase or to decrease, and then verifying that your answer agrees with your decision on this point.

Illustrative Exercise

9-3. (a) A volume of gas was collected over water at 25° C. The measured pressure was 750.0 mm Hg. How much of this pressure was due to water vapor, and how much to the gas? (b) What would be the pressure of the gas if the water vapor were to be removed by use of a drying agent, the volume and temperature being kept the same?

9–3. *Dependence of Gas Volume on Temperature.*
The Law of Charles and Gay-Lussac

After the discovery of Boyle's law, it was more than one hundred years before the dependence of the volume of a gas on the temperature was investigated. Then in 1787 the French physicist Jacques Alexandre Charles (1746–1823) reported that different gases expand by the same fractional amount for the same rise in temperature. Dalton in England continued these studies in 1801, and in 1802 Joseph Louis Gay-Lussac (1778–1850) extended the work, and determined the amount of expansion per degree Centigrade. He found that all gases expand by $\frac{1}{273}$ of their volume at 0° C for each degree Centigrade that they are heated above this temperature. Thus a sample of gas with volume 273 ml at 0° C has the volume 274 ml at 1° C and the same pressure, 275 ml at 2° C, 373 ml at 100° C, etc.

We now state the law of the dependence of the volume of a gas on temperature, the **law of Charles and Gay-Lussac,** in the following way. **If the pressure and the number of moles of a sample of gas remain constant, the volume of the sample of gas is proportional to the absolute temperature:**

$$V = \text{constant} \times T \text{ (pressure constant, number of moles constant)}$$

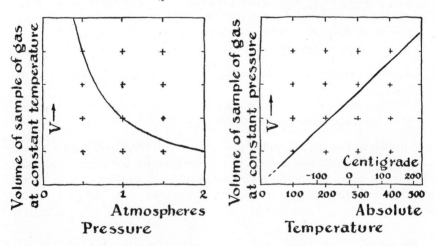

FIGURE 9-3   *Curves showing, at the left, the dependence of the volume of a sample of gas at constant temperature and containing a constant number of molecules on the pressure, and, at the right, the dependence of the volume of a sample of gas at constant pressure and containing a constant number of molecules on the temperature.*

You will note that the dependence of volume on the absolute temperature is a direct proportionality, whereas the volume is inversely proportional to the pressure. The nature of these two relations is illustrated in Figure 9-3.

The use of the law of Charles and Gay-Lussac in working problems is illustrated by the example given below.

Standard Conditions. It is customary to refer the volumes of gases to 0° C and a pressure of 1 atm. This temperature and pressure are called **standard conditions**. A sample of gas is said to be *reduced to standard conditions* when its volume is calculated at this temperature and pressure.

Example 4. One gram of methane has a volume of 1513 ml at 25° C. and 1 atm. What is its volume at standard conditions?

    Solution. Our problem is to find the volume of a sample of gas at 0° C which has the volume 1513 ml at 25° C; or, changing to the absolute temperature scale, to find the volume of a sample of gas at 273° K which has volume 1513 ml at 298° K.

    Cooling a gas causes its volume to decrease. Accordingly we know that we must multiply the volume at the higher temperature by $\frac{273}{298}$, rather than by the reciprocal of this fraction. Thus we have

$$\text{Volume of gas at standard conditions} = \frac{273}{298} \times 1513 \text{ ml} = \textbf{1386 ml}$$

Correction of the Volume of a Gas for Change in Both Pressure and Temperature. Boyle's law and the law of Charles and Gay-Lussac can be applied in a straightforward manner to calculate the change in volume of a sample of gas from one pressure and temperature to another pressure and temperature, as is illustrated by the following example:

Example 5. A sample of gas has volume 1200 ml at 100° C and 800 mm pressure. Reduce to standard conditions.

    Solution. We may solve this problem by multiplying the original volume by a ratio of pressures, to correct for the change in pressure, and by a ratio of temperatures to correct for the change in temperature. We must decide for each ratio whether the correction is greater or less than one.

    In this case the sample is initially at a greater pressure than 1 atm (760 mm) and hence it will expand when the pressure is reduced to 1 atm. Accordingly the pressure factor must be $\frac{800}{760}$, and not $\frac{760}{800}$. Also the sample will contract (decrease in volume) when it is cooled, and hence the temperature factor must be $\frac{273}{373}$, and not $\frac{373}{273}$. Therefore we write

$$V = \frac{800}{760} \times \frac{273}{373} \times 1200 \text{ ml} = \mathbf{925 \text{ ml}}$$

This method is to be used in solving any pressure-volume-temperature problem for a sample of gas, provided that the number of molecules in the sample remains constant.

The Absolute Temperature Scale.   The idea of the absolute zero of temperature was developed as a result of the discovery of the law of Charles and Gay-Lussac; the absolute zero would be the temperature at which an ideal gas would have zero volume. For some years (until 1848) the absolute temperature scale was defined in terms of a gas thermometer; the absolute temperature was taken as proportional to the volume of a sample of gas at constant pressure. An absolute temperature scale based on the laws of thermodynamics was formulated by Lord Kelvin. This is the absolute temperature scale which is now accepted, and which was discussed in Chapter 1. The hydrogen gas thermometer agrees very closely with the Kelvin scale except at very low temperatures, and is widely used in practice.

By the usual methods of reaching low temperatures (the compression and expansion of gases) every gas has been liquefied. Helium, the gas with the lowest boiling point, boils at 4.2° K. By boiling liquid helium under low pressure a temperature of about 0.82° K was reached in 1923 by H. Kamerlingh Onnes (1853–1926), working in Leiden, Holland. This seemed to be close to the limit that could be achieved in the effort to reach extremely low temperatures; but in 1927 an American physical chemist, William F. Giauque (born 1895), suggested and put into practice a novel method of reaching extremely low temperatures. This consists in the demagnetization of a paramagnetic substance* previously cooled with liquid helium; in this way temperatures of about 0.001° K have been reached.

Illustrative Exercises

9-4.   To what temperature would a sample of gas, held at constant pressure, have to be heated in order to have double the volume that it has at 0° C?

9-5.   A sample of carbon dioxide is found to have volume 450 ml at 21° C and 780 mm of mercury. What would be its volume at standard conditions?

9-6.   (a) A balloon contains 10,000 m³ (cubic meters) of hot air, at temperature 200° C and pressure 1 atm. What volume would it have at 18° C and 1 atm? (b) How much does this amount of air weigh? The density of air is 1.21 g/l at 18° C and 1 atm. (c) How much does 10,000 m³ of air at 18° C and 1 atm weigh? (This is the amount of air displaced by the balloon; the difference of the two weights is the lifting power of the balloon.)

9–4. Avogadro's Law

In 1805 Gay-Lussac began a series of experiments to find the volume percentage of oxygen in air. In the course of this work he made a very important discovery. The experiments were carried out by mixing a certain volume of hydrogen with air and exploding the mixture, and

---

* A *paramagnetic* substance is a substance that tends to move into a strong magnetic field, such as that between the poles of a magnet. A *diamagnetic* substance tends to move out of the field.

then testing the remaining gas to see whether oxygen or hydrogen had been present in excess. He was surprised to find a very simple relation: 1000 ml of oxygen required just 2000 ml of hydrogen, to form water. Continuing the study of the volumes of gases that react with one another, he found that 1000 ml of hydrogen chloride combines exactly with 1000 ml of ammonia, and that 1000 ml of carbon monoxide combines with 500 ml of oxygen to form 1000 ml of carbon dioxide. On the basis of these observations he formulated the **law of combining volumes:** *the volumes of gases that react with one another or are produced in a chemical reaction are in the ratios of small integers.*

Such a simple empirical law as this called for a simple theoretical interpretation, and in 1811 Amadeo Avogadro (1776–1856), Professor of Physics in the University of Turin, Italy, proposed a hypothesis to explain the law. Avogadro's hypothesis was that **equal numbers of**

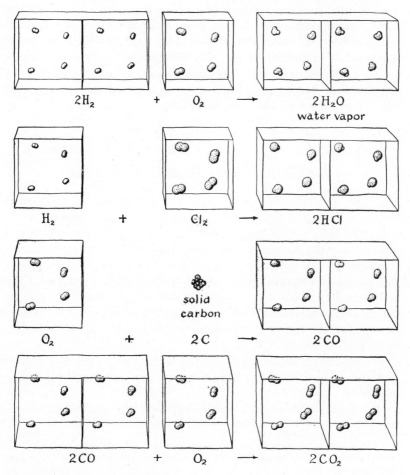

FIGURE 9-4 *The relative volumes of gases involved in chemical reactions.*

molecules are contained in equal volumes of all gases under the same conditions. This hypothesis has been thoroughly verified to within the accuracy of approximation of real gases to ideal behavior, and it is now called a law—**Avogadro's law.***

During the last century Avogadro's law provided the most satisfactory and the only reliable way of determining which multiples of the equivalent weights of the elements should be accepted as their atomic weights; the arguments involved are discussed in the following sections. But the value of this law remained unrecognized by chemists from 1811 until 1858. In this year Stanislao Cannizzaro (1826–1910), an Italian chemist working in Geneva, showed how to apply the law systematically, and immediately the uncertainty regarding the correct atomic weights of the elements and the correct formulas of compounds disappeared. Before 1858 many chemists used the formula HO for water and accepted 8 as the atomic weight of oxygen; since that year H_2O has been accepted as the formula for water by everyone.†

Avogadro's Law and the Law of Combining Volumes. Avogadro's law requires that the volumes of gaseous reactants and products (under the same conditions) be approximately in the ratios of small integers; the numbers of molecules of reactants and products in a chemical reaction are in integral ratios, and the same ratios represent the relative gas volumes. Some simple diagrams illustrating this for several reactions are given in Figure 9-4. Each cube in these diagrams represents the volume occupied by four gas molecules.

9–5. *The Use of Avogadro's Law in the Determination of the Correct Atomic Weights of Elements*

The way in which Avogadro's law was applied by Cannizzaro in 1858 for the selection of the correct approximate atomic weights of elements was essentially the following. Let us accept as the molecular weight of a substance the weight in grams of 22.4 liters of the gaseous substance reduced to standard conditions. (Any other volume could be used— this would correspond to the selection of a different base for the atomic weight scale.) *Then it is probable that of a large number of compounds of a particular element at least one compound will have only one atom of the element per molecule; the weight of the element in the standard gas volume of this compound is its atomic weight.*

For gaseous compounds of hydrogen the weight per standard volume and the weight of the contained hydrogen per standard volume are as follows:

* Dalton had considered and rejected the hypothesis that equal volumes of gases contain equal numbers of atoms; the idea that elementary substances might exist as polyatomic molecules (H_2, O_2) did not occur to him.

† The failure of chemists to accept Avogadro's law during the period from 1811 to 1858 seems to have been due to a feeling that molecules were too "theoretical" to deserve serious consideration.

	WEIGHT OF GAS, IN GRAMS	WEIGHT OF CONTAINED HYDROGEN, IN GRAMS
Hydrogen (H_2)	2	2
Methane (CH_4)	16	4
Ethane (C_2H_6)	30	6
Water (H_2O)	18	2
Hydrogen sulfide (H_2S)	34	2
Hydrogen cyanide (HCN)	27	1
Hydrogen chloride (HCl)	36	1
Ammonia (NH_3)	17	3
Pyridine (C_5H_5N)	79	5

In these and all other compounds of hydrogen the minimum weight of hydrogen in the standard gas volume is found to be 1 g, and the weight is always an integral multiple of the minimum weight; hence 1 can be accepted as the atomic weight of hydrogen. The elementary substance hydrogen then is seen to consist of diatomic molecules H_2, and water is seen to have the formula H_2O_x, with x still to be determined.

For oxygen compounds the following similar table of experimental data can be set up:

	WEIGHT OF GAS, IN GRAMS	WEIGHT OF CONTAINED OXYGEN, IN GRAMS
Oxygen (O_2)	32	32
Water (H_2O)	18	16
Carbon monoxide (CO)	28	16
Carbon dioxide (CO_2)	44	32
Nitrous oxide (N_2O)	44	16
Nitric oxide (NO)	30	16
Sulfur dioxide (SO_2)	64	32
Sulfur trioxide (SO_3)	80	48

From the comparison of oxygen and water in this table it can be concluded rigorously that the oxygen molecule contains two atoms or a multiple of two atoms; we see that the standard volume of oxygen contains twice as much oxygen (32 g) as is contained by the standard volume of water vapor (16 g of oxygen). The data for the other compounds provide no evidence that the atomic weight of oxygen is less than 16; hence this value may be adopted. Water thus is given the formula H_2O.

Note that this application of Avogadro's law provided rigorously only a maximum value of the atomic weight of an element. The possibility was not eliminated that the true atomic weight was a sub-multiple of this value.

Illustrative Exercises

9-7.   A sample of gas with volume 22.4 l weighs 17.0 g at standard conditions. What is the molecular weight of the gas?

9-8.   Ammonia, NH_3, can be made from nitrogen and hydrogen with use of a catalyst. What volume of hydrogen would combine with 1 l of nitrogen?

9-9.   Tellurium hexafluoride, TeF_6, is a gas at $0°$ C and 1 atm. Calculate its density.

9-10. A fluoride of an element is a gas containing 84.0% fluorine and 16.0% of the element, and with density 3.03 g/l at standard conditions. What is the largest possible value of the atomic weight of the element?

9–6. Other Methods of Determining Correct Atomic Weights

1. At the present time there is one completely reliable method of determining which multiple of the equivalent weight of an element is its atomic weight. This method is to determine the atomic number of the element from its x-ray spectrum. The atomic weight is then twice its atomic number (for light elements) or a little more (up to 25% more for heavy elements). This reliable method was not available at the time of discovery of most of the elements.

2. The kinetic theory of gases requires that the molal heat capacity of a gas at constant pressure be approximately 5 cal per degree for a monatomic gas and 7 or 8 cal per degree for other gases. The heat capacity is the amount of energy required to raise the temperature of a substance by one degree; the molal heat capacity refers to one mole of substance. This method was used in 1876 to show that mercury vapor consists of monatomic molecules, and hence that its atomic weight is equal to its molecular weight as determined by the density of the vapor. It was also applied to the noble gases (which are monatomic) on their discovery.

3. It was pointed out in 1819 by Dulong and Petit in France that for the heavier solid elementary substances (with atomic weights above 35) the product of the heat capacity per gram and the atomic weight is approximately constant, with value about 6.2 cal per degree. This is called the **rule of Dulong and Petit**. The rule can be used to get a rough value of the atomic weight of a solid element by dividing 6.2 by the measured heat capacity of the solid elementary substance in cal/g. For example, the heat capacity of bismuth is 0.0294 cal/g. By dividing this into 6.2 we obtain 211 as the rough value of the atomic weight of bismuth given by the rule of Dulong and Petit; the actual atomic weight of bismuth is 209.

4. In the same year (1819) the German chemist Eilhard Mitscherlich (1794–1863) discovered the phenomenon of **isomorphism,** *the existence of different crystalline substances with essentially the same crystal form,* and suggested his **rule of isomorphism,** which states that *isomorphous crystals have similar chemical formulas.*

As an example of isomorphism, we may consider the minerals rhodochrosite, $MnCO_3$, and calcite, $CaCO_3$. Crystals of these two substances resemble one another very closely, as shown in Figure 9-5. The crystals have the same structure, as shown by x-ray diffraction; in rhodochrosite manganous ions, Mn^{++}, occupy the positions that are occupied by calcium ions, Ca^{++}, in calcite.

An illustration of the use of the rule of isomorphism is given by the work of the English chemist Henry E. Roscoe in determining the correct atomic weight of vanadium. Berzelius had attributed the atomic weight 68.5 to vanadium in 1831. In 1867 Roscoe noticed that the corresponding formula for the mineral vanadinite was not analogous to the formulas of other minerals isomorphous with it:

FIGURE 9-5

Isomorphous crystals of rhodochrosite and calcite (hexagonal system).

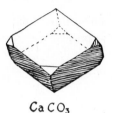

Apatite,	$Ca_5(PO_4)_3F$
Pyromorphite,	$Pb_5(PO_4)_3Cl$
Mimetite,	$Pb_5(AsO_4)_3Cl$
Vanadinite,	$Pb_5(VO_3)_3Cl$ (wrong)

The formula for vanadinite analogous to the other formulas is $Pb_5(VO_4)_3Cl$. On re-investigating the compounds of vanadium Roscoe found that this latter formula is indeed the correct one, and that Berzelius had accepted the oxide VO, vanadium monoxide, as the elementary substance. The atomic weight of vanadium now accepted is 50.95.

5. The method of chemical analogy—based on the assumption that substances with similar chemical properties usually have similar formulas—was of considerable use in the early period.

Illustrative Exercises

9-11.   It is found that a mineral isomorphous with calcite contains the metal zinc instead of calcium. What is the formula of the mineral?

9-12.   (a) It is found that 15 cal is required to raise the temperature of a sample of metal weighing 100 g by 1° C. What is the approximate atomic weight of the metal?

(b) The oxide of this metal contains 28.5% oxygen. Calculate a more exact value of the atomic weight.

9–7. The Complete Perfect-Gas Equation

Boyle's law, the law of Charles and Gay-Lussac, and Avogadro's law can be combined into a single equation,

$$pV = nRT$$

In this equation p is the pressure acting on a given sample of gas, V is the volume occupied by the sample of gas, n is the number of moles of gas in the sample, R is a quantity called the *gas constant*, and T is the absolute temperature.

The gas constant R has a numerical value depending on the units in which it is measured (that is, the units used for p, V, n and T). If p is measured in atmospheres, V in liters, n in moles, and T in degrees Kelvin the value of R is **0.0820 liter atmospheres per mole degree.**

If the number of moles in a sample of gas, n, remains constant and the temperature T remains constant, the perfect-gas equation simplifies to

$$pV = \text{constant}$$

The value of the constant in this equation is nRT. This equation is seen to be just the equation expressing Boyle's law.

Similarly, if the pressure p is constant and the number of moles in the sample of gas is constant, the perfect-gas equation simplifies to

$$V = \frac{nR}{p} T = \text{constant} \times T$$

This is the expression of the law of Charles and Gay-Lussac.

The perfect-gas equation can also be written in the form

$$n = \frac{pV}{RT}$$

This equation states that the number of moles of any gas is equal to a product of quantities independent of the nature of the gas, but depending only on the pressure, volume, and temperature; accordingly equal volumes of all gases under the same condition are stated by this equation to contain the same number of moles (molecules). This equation accordingly expresses Avogadro's law.

The value of the gas constant R is found experimentally by determining the volume occupied by 1 mole of a perfect gas at standard conditions. One mole of oxygen weighs exactly 32 g, and the density of oxygen gas at standard conditions is found by experiment to be 1.429 g/l. The quotient $32/1.429 = 22.4$ l is accordingly the volume occupied by 1 mole of gas at standard conditions.

The volume 22.4 liters is the volume of one mole of gas at standard conditions (0° C, 1 atm).

More accurate determinations, involving the measurement of the density of oxygen at low pressure, where it approaches a perfect gas more closely, have led to the value **22.4140 l** for the molal gas volume.

The volume occupied by one mole of gas at standard conditions is seen from the perfect-gas equation to be just the product of R and the temperature 0° C on the absolute scale. The value of R can hence be found by dividing 22.4 by 273:

$$R = \frac{1 \text{ atm} \times 22.4 \text{ l}}{1 \text{ mole} \times 273 \text{ deg}} = \textbf{0.0820 l atm/mole deg}$$

Avogadro's Number.   *Avogadro's number* N is defined as *the number of oxygen atoms in a gram-atom of oxygen.* It is, of course, also the number of atoms of any element in a gram-atom of that element, and the number of molecules in a mole of any substance. The volume 22.4 liters of any gas at standard conditions contains Avogadro's number of molecules.

The value of Avogadro's number was known to within an accuracy of about 30 percent in 1875. It was then determined to within 1 percent by Millikan in 1909, and then more accurately (to within 0.01 percent) in the period between 1930 and 1940 through the work of several experimental physicists. It is*

$$N = 0.6023 \times 10^{24}$$

It is difficult to imagine such a large number as Avogadro's number. Some idea of its magnitude is given by the following calculation. Let us suppose that the entire state of Texas, with area 262,000 square miles, were covered with a layer of fine sand 50 feet thick, each grain of sand being 1/100 of an inch in diameter. There would then be Avogadro's number of grains of sand in this immense sandpile. There is the same number of molecules of water in one mole of water—18 g, 1/25 of a pint.

9–8. *Calculations Based on the Perfect-Gas Equation*

Some of the ways in which the perfect-gas equation can be used in the solution of chemical problems are discussed in the following paragraphs.

The Calculation of the Density of a Gas or the Weight of a Sample of Gas from Its Molecular Formula.   If the molecular formula of a gaseous substance is known, an approximate value of its density can be calculated. This calculation can also be carried out for a mixture of known composition of gases of known molecular formulas. The method to be used is illustrated in the following examples.

Example 6.   What is the density of carbon dioxide at standard conditions?

* It may be pointed out that Avogadro's number as written above, 0.6023×10^{24}, differs from the usual convention about writing large numbers, according to which one integer is introduced before the decimal point. With this convention Avogadro's number would be expressed as 6.023×10^{23}—this is, in fact, the usual way of writing the number. However, there is a great convenience in learning Avogadro's number as 0.6023×10^{24}. An important use of this number involves the conversion of the volume of a gram-atom of an element into the volume per atom. The first volume is expressed in cm³, and the second in Å³. The relation between cm³ and Å³ involves the factor 10^{24}; indeed, 1 cm³ $= 10^{24}$ Å³. Accordingly, in case that Avogadro's number has been taken as 0.6023×10^{24} there is no trouble whatever in deciding on the position of the decimal point, whereas if 6.023×10^{23} is used for Avogadro's number it is always necessary to decide whether the decimal point should be moved one place to the right or one place to the left.

Solution. The molecular weight of carbon dioxide, CO_2, is 44. The volume occupied by 1 mole, 44 g, of carbon dioxide at standard conditions is 22.4 l. The density is the weight per unit volume; that is,

$$\text{Density of carbon dioxide} = \frac{44 \text{ g/mole}}{22.4 \text{ l/mole}} = \textbf{1.96 g/l}$$

Example 7. What is the approximate value of the density of air at 25° C?

Solution. Air is a mixture of oxygen and nitrogen, being mainly (about 80%) nitrogen. The molecular weight of oxygen is 32, and that of nitrogen is 28; we see that the average molecular weight of the mixture is approximately 29. The weight of 1 liter of air at standard conditions is accordingly 29/22.4 = 1.29 g/l.

When air is heated from 0° C (273° K) to 25° C (298° K) it increases in volume, and accordingly decreases in density. The fraction by which the density at 0° C must be multiplied to obtain the density at 25° C is seen to be 273/298; hence

$$\text{Density of air at } 25° \text{ C} = \frac{273}{298} \times 1.29 \text{ g/l} = \textbf{1.17 g/l}$$

The Determination of the Molecular Weight of a Gas. In the investigation of a new substance, one of the first things that a chemist does is to determine its molecular weight. If the substance can be vaporized without decomposing it, the density of its vapor provides a value of the molecular weight, and this method is usually used for volatile substances.

The density of a substance that is a gas under ordinary conditions is usually determined by the simple method of weighing a flask of known volume filled with the gas under known pressure, and then weighing the flask after it has been evacuated with a vacuum pump. In ordinary work the second weighing may be replaced by a weighing of the flask filled with air, oxygen, or other gas of known density. The volume of the flask is determined by weighing it filled with water.

Various refinements of technique are needed for accurate work. It is customary to counterbalance the flask by a similar sealed flask placed on the other pan of the balance. In very accurate work a correction must be made for the contraction of the evacuated flask resulting from the outside pressure. In ordinary work flasks with volumes of one or two liters are used, weighed on a balance with an accuracy of 0.1 mg. In determining the molecular weight of radon in 1911 the English chemists Ramsay and Gray had available only about 0.1 mm³ of the gas, weighing about 0.001 mg; the weight of this sample was determined to within 0.2% by use of a very sensitive microbalance.

Example 8. Determination of the Molecular Weight of a Substance by the Hofmann Method. A chemist isolated a substance in the

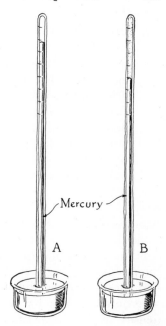

FIGURE 9-6

The Hofmann method for determining density of a vapor.

form of a yellow oil. He found on analysis that the oil contained only hydrogen and sulfur, and the amount of water obtained when a sample of the substance was burned showed that it consisted of about 3% hydrogen and 97% sulfur. To determine the molecular weight he prepared a very small glass bulb, weighed the glass bulb, filled it with the oil, and weighed it again; the difference in the two weighings, which is the weight of the oil, was 0.0302 g. He then introduced the filled bulb into the space above the mercury column in a tube, as shown in Figure 9-6. The level of the mercury dropped to 118 mm below its original level, after the oil had been completely vaporized. The temperature of the tube was 30° C. The volume of the gas phase above the mercury at the end of the experiment was 73.2 ml. Find the molecular weight and formula of the substance.

Solution. The vapor of the substance is stated to occupy the volume 73.2 ml at temperature 30° C and pressure 118 mm Hg. Its volume corrected to standard conditions is seen to be

$$73.2 \text{ ml} \times \frac{273}{303} \times \frac{118}{760} = 10.24 \text{ ml}$$

One mole of gas at standard conditions occupies 22,400 ml; hence the number of moles in the sample of the substance is 10.24/22,400 = 0.000457. The weight of this fraction of a mole is stated to be 0.0302 g; hence the weight of one mole is this weight divided by the number of moles:

$$\text{Molar weight of substance} = \frac{0.0302 \text{ g}}{0.000457 \text{ mole}} = \mathbf{66.0 \ g/mole}$$

The substance was found by analysis to contain 3% hydrogen and 97% sulfur. If we had 100 g of the oil, it would contain 3 g of hydrogen, which is 3 gram-atoms, and 97 g of sulfur, which is also 3 gram-atoms (the atomic weight of sulfur is 32). Hence the molecule contains equal numbers of hydrogen atoms and sulfur atoms. If its formula were HS its molecular weight would be the sum of the atomic weights of hydrogen and sulfur, 33. It is evident from the observed molecular weight that the formula is $\mathbf{H_2S_2}$, the molecular weight of which is 66.15.

Atomic-Weight Determinations by the Gas-Density Method. If a sufficiently careful measurement of the density of a gas is made, under conditions such that the gas obeys the perfect-gas law, a good value for the molecular weight of the gas can be obtained, which can be used to find the atomic weight of one of the elements in the gas. The way to determine this ideal value of the density of a gas is to determine the density of the gas at smaller and smaller pressures, and to extrapolate to zero pressure—all gases approach the perfect-gas law in their behavior as the pressure becomes very low.

For example, it has been found that the observed densities of sulfur dioxide at very low pressures correspond to an ideal density of 2.85796 g/l at standard conditions. The product of this value of the density and the precise value of the molar volume, 22.41401 per mole, is 64.058, which is the gas-density value of the molecular weight of sulfur dioxide. The sulfur dioxide molecule contains two oxygen atoms, which weigh exactly 32 g, and one sulfur atom. The weight of the sulfur atom, in atomic weight units, is hence seen to be 32.058, from these measurements; this agrees well with the accepted value of the atomic weight of sulfur, 32.066.

The gas-density method has provided many of the best values of modern atomic weights.

Illustrative Exercises

9-13.   Calculate the density of uranium hexafluoride gas, UF_6, at 100° C and 500 mm Hg.

9-14.   (a) The vapor density of a metal at 819° C and 76.0 mm Hg is measured, and found to be 0.1483 g/l. What is the molecular weight of the metal. (b) The heat capacity of the solid metal is 0.047 cal/g. Calculate a rough value of the atomic weight of the metal, and an accurate value.

9-9. *The Kinetic Theory of Gases*

During the nineteenth century the concepts that atoms and molecules are in continual motion and that the temperature of a body is a measure of the intensity of this motion were developed. The idea that the behavior of gases could be accounted for by considering the motion of the gas molecules had occurred to several people (Daniel Bernoulli in 1738, J. P. Joule in 1851, A. Kronig in 1856), and in the years following 1858 this idea was developed into a detailed kinetic theory of gases by Clausius, Maxwell, Boltzmann, and many later investigators. The subject is discussed in courses in physics and physical chemistry, and it forms an imporant part of the branch of theoretical science called statistical mechanics.

In a gas at temperature T the molecules are moving about, different molecules having at a given time different speeds v and different kinetic energies of translational motion $\frac{1}{2}mv^2$ (m being the mass of a molecule). It has been found that *the average kinetic energy per molecule, $\frac{1}{2} m[v^2]_{average}$, is the same for all gases at the same temperature, and that its va ue increases with the temperature, being directly proportional to T.*

The average (root-mean-square*) velocity of hydrogen molecules at $0°$ C is 1.84×10^5 cm/sec—over a mile per second. At higher temperatures the average velocity is greater; it reaches twice as great a value, 3.68×10^5 cm/sec, for hydrogen molecules at $820°$ C, corresponding to an absolute temperature four times as great.

Since the average kinetic energy, $\frac{1}{2} m[v^2]_{average}$, is equal for different molecules, the average value of the square of the velocity is seen to be inversely proportional to the mass of the molecule, and hence the average velocity (root-mean-square average) is inversely proportional to the square root of the molecular weight. The molecular weight of oxygen is just 16 times that of hydrogen; accordingly molecules of oxygen move with a speed just one quarter as great as molecules of hydrogen at the same temperature. The average speed of oxygen molecules at $0°$ C is 0.46×10^5 cm/sec.

The explanation of Boyle's law given by the kinetic theory is simple. A molecule on striking the wall of the container of the gas rebounds, and contributes momentum to the wall; in this way the collisions of the molecules of the gas with the wall produce the gas pressure which balances the external pressure applied to the gas. If the volume is decreased by 50% molecules strike a unit area of the wall twice as often, and hence the pressure is doubled. The explanation of the law of Charles and Gay-Lussac is equally simple. If the absolute temperature is doubled, the speed of the molecules is increased by the factor $\sqrt{2}$. This causes the molecules to make $\sqrt{2}$ times as many collisions as before, and each collision is increased in force by $\sqrt{2}$, so that the pressure itself is doubled by doubling the absolute temperature. Avogadro's law is also explained by the fact that the average kinetic energy is the same at a given temperature for all gases.

The Effusion and Diffusion of Gases. The Mean Free Paths of Molecules. There is an interesting dependence of the *rate of effusion* of a gas through a small hole on the molecular weight of the gas. The speeds of motion of different molecules are inversely proportional to the square roots of their molecular weights. If a small hole is made in the wall of a gas container, the gas molecules will pass through the hole into an evacuated region outside at a rate determined by the speed at which they are moving (these speeds determine the probability that a molecule will strike the hole). Accordingly the kinetic theory requires that the rate of effusion of a gas through a small hole be inversely proportional to the square root of its molecular weight. This law was discovered experimentally before the development of the kinetic theory—it was observed that hydrogen effuses through a porous plate four times as rapidly as oxygen.

---

* The root-mean-square average of a quantity is the square root of the average value of the square of the quantity.

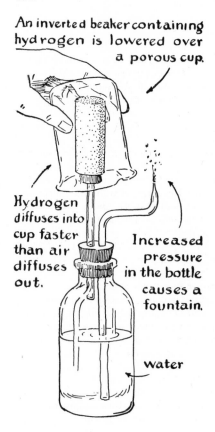

An inverted beaker containing
hydrogen is lowered over
                    a porous cup.

Hydrogen
diffuses into
cup faster
than air   Increased
diffuses   pressure
out.   in the bottle
                    causes a
                    fountain.

                    water

FIGURE 9-7

*Experiment illustrating the greater rate of
effusion of hydrogen than of air.*

An interesting experiment can be carried out which illustrates this effect. If a porous
cup filled with air is attached to a bottle of water provided with a fine nozzle, as shown
in Figure 9-7, and an inverted beaker filled with hydrogen is lowered over the porous
cup, water will be vigorously forced out of the nozzle. The explanation of this phenomenon is that the rate of effusion of hydrogen from the outside through the pores of the
porous cup to the inside of the cup is nearly four times as great as the rate of effusion
of air (oxygen and nitrogen) from the inside of the cup to the outside. Hence more gas
will enter the cup than leave the cup, and the pressure inside the system will temporarily
become correspondingly greater, causing the water to be forced out of the nozzle.

In the foregoing discussions we have ignored the appreciable sizes of gas molecules,
which cause the molecules to collide often with one another. In an ordinary gas, such
as air at standard conditions, a molecule moves only about 500 Å on the average between
collisions—that is, its *mean free path* under these conditions is only about two hundred
times its own diameter.

The value of the mean free path is significant for phenomena that depend on molecular collisions, such as the viscosity and the thermal conductivity of gases. Another such
phenomenon is the *diffusion* of one gas through another or through itself (such as of
radioactive molecules of a gas through the non-radioactive gas). In the early days of
kinetic theory it was pointed out by skeptics that it takes minutes or hours for a gas to
diffuse from one side of a quiet room to the other, even though the molecules are attributed velocities of about a mile per second. The explanation of the slow diffusion rate is
that a molecule diffusing through a gas is not able to move directly from one point to

another a long distance away, but instead is forced by collisions with other molecules to follow a tortuous path, making only slow progress in its resultant motion. Only when diffusing into a high vacuum can the gas diffuse with the speed of molecular motion.

9–10. *Deviations of Real Gases from Ideal Behavior*

Real gases differ in their behavior from that represented by the perfect-gas equation for two reasons. First, the molecules have a definite size, so that each molecule prevents others from making use of a part of the volume of the gas container. This causes the volume of a gas to be larger than that calculated for ideal behavior. Second, the molecules even when some distance apart do not move independently of one another, but attract one another slightly. This tends to cause the volume of a gas to be smaller than the calculated volume.

The amounts of the deviation for some gases are shown in Figure 9-8. It is seen that for hydrogen at $0°$ C the deviation is positive at all pressures—it is due essentially to the volume of the molecules, the effect of their attraction at this high temperature (relative to the boiling point, $-252.8°$ C) being extremely small.

At pressures below 120 atmospheres nitrogen (at $0°$ C) shows negative deviations from ideal behavior, intermolecular attraction having a greater effect than the finite size of the molecules.

The deviation of hydrogen and nitrogen at $0°$ C from ideal behavior is seen to be less than 10% at pressures less than 300 atmospheres. Oxygen, helium, and other gases with low boiling points also show small deviations from the perfect-gas law. For these gases the perfect-gas law holds to within 1% at room temperature or higher temperatures and at pressures below 10 atm.

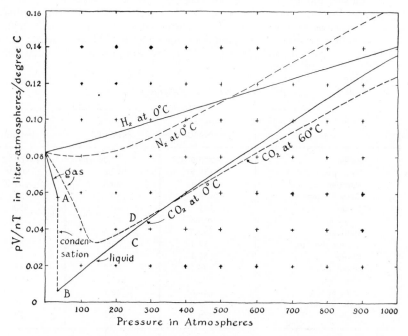

FIGURE 9-8   *The value of the product pV/nT for some gases, showing deviation from the perfect-gas law at high pressures.*

Larger deviations are shown by gases with higher boiling points—in general, the deviations from ideal behavior become large as the gas approaches condensation. It is seen from the figure that for carbon dioxide at 60° C the volume of the gas is only about 30% as great at 120 atm pressure as the volume calculated by the perfect-gas equation.

If the temperature is low the deviations are shown in a pronounced way by the condensation of the gas to a liquid (see the curve for carbon dioxide at 0° C). After carbon dioxide has been compressed to about 40 atmospheres at 0° C the effect of the attraction of the molecules for one another becomes so great that they cling together, forming a liquid, the system then consisting of two phases, the gaseous phase and the liquid phase. On further compression the volume decreases without change in pressure (region A of the figure) until all of the gas is condensed (point B). From point B on the volume of the liquid decreases much less rapidly with increase in pressure than would that of a gas, because the molecules of the liquid are effectively in contact; hence the curve rises (region C).

An extraordinary phenomenon, the **continuity of the liquid and gaseous states,** was discovered about eighty years ago by Thomas Andrews (1813–1885). He found that above a temperature characteristic of the gas, called the **critical temperature,** the transition from the gaseous state to the liquid state occurs without a sharp change in volume on increasing the pressure.

The critical temperature of carbon dioxide is 31.1° C. Above this temperature (at 60° C, for example, corresponding to the curve shown in the figure), all of the properties of the substance change continuously, showing no signs that the gas has condensed to a liquid. Nevertheless, when the pressure becomes greater than about 200 atm the substance behaves like carbon dioxide liquid, rather than like a gas (region D of Figure 9-8). It is, indeed, possible to change from the gas at 0° C and 1 atm pressure to the liquid at 0° C and 50 atm either by the ordinary process of condensing the gas to the liquid, passing through the two-phase stage, or, without condensation or any discontinuity, by heating to 60°, increasing the pressure to about 200 atm, cooling to 0°, and then reducing the pressure to 50 atm. The liquid could then be made to boil, simply by reducing the pressure and keeping the temperature at 0° C; and then, by repeating the cycle, it could be brought back to 0° C and 50 atm pressure without condensation, and be made to boil again.

TABLE 9-1   *Critical Constants of Some Substances*

GAS	CRITICAL TEMPERATURE	CRITICAL PRESSURE	DENSITY
Helium	−267.9° C	2.26 atm	0.0693 g/cm³
Hydrogen	−239.9	12.8	.031
Nitrogen	−147.1	33.5	.31
Carbon monoxide	−139	35	.31
Argon	−122	48	.53
Oxygen	−118.8	49.7	.43
Methane	−82.5	45.8	.16
Carbon dioxide	31.1	73.0	.46
Ethane	32.1	48.8	.21
Nitrous oxide	36.5	71.7	.45
Ammonia	132.4	111.5	.24
Chlorine	144.0	76.1	.57
Sulfur dioxide	157.2	77.7	.52
Water	374.2	218.4	.33

Values of the critical temperature, critical pressure, and critical density of some substances are given in Table 9-1.

Gases whose critical temperatures lie below room temperature were named *permanent gases* a century ago, when it was found impossible to liquefy them by increased pressure alone.

The possibility of continuous transition from the gaseous to the liquid state is understandable in view of the mutual characteristic of randomness of structure of these phases, as discussed in Chapter 2. It is, on the other hand, difficult to imagine the possibility of a gradual transition from a disordered state (liquid) to a completely ordered state (crystal); and correspondingly it has not been found possible to crystallize substances or to melt crystals without passing through a discontinuity at the melting point—there is no critical temperature for melting a crystal.

Concepts, Facts, and Laws Introduced in This Chapter

The properties of gases. Boyle's law. The law of Charles and Gay-Lussac. Avogadro's law. Standard conditions.

Perfect-gas law, $pV = nRT$.

The use of Avogadro's law for determining correct values of atomic weights. The determination of molecular weights.

Other methods of determining atomic weights: x-ray method; heat capacity of gases; heat capacity of solids; isomorphism; chemical analogy.

Atomic weights by the gas-density method. Kinetic theory; effusion, diffusion, mean free path. Deviation of gases from ideal behavior; continuity of liquid and gaseous states; critical temperature, pressure, density.

Exercises

9-15. The volume of a sample of gas is 750 ml at 250° C. What is its volume at 125° C under the same pressure? (Ans. 571 ml)

9-16. Calculate the volume occupied at 20° C and 1 atm pressure by the gas evolved from 1 cm³ of solid carbon dioxide (density 1.53 g/cm³).

9-17. The density of helium at 0° C and 1 atm is 0.1785 g/l. Calculate its density at 100° C and 200 atm. (Ans. 26.1 g/l)

9-18. A vessel is filled with hydrogen at a pressure of one atmosphere at 25° C. What pressure is there in the vessel at 21° K? What is the density of the gas at the beginning and at the end of this experiment?

9-19. What is the volume in cubic feet at standard conditions of one ounce-molecular-weight of a gas?* (Ans. 22.4)

9-20. The density of hydrogen cyanide at standard conditions is 1.29 g/l. Calculate the apparent molecular weight of hydrogen cyanide vapor.

9-21. What is the weight in ounces of 22.4 cu. ft. of carbon dioxide at standard conditions? (Ans. 44)

9-22. The volume of an ordinary hand-operated bicycle pump is about 0.01 cu. ft., and the volume of a bicycle tire is about 0.06 cu. ft. At what point in the stroke of the pump does air start to enter a tire which is at a gage pressure of 47 lbs. per sq. in.? Does the pressure in the tire change more per stroke when the tire is at gage pressure of 50 lbs./sq. in. than at 20 lbs./sq. in.?

* It is interesting in this connection that the master craftsmen of Lubeck defined the ounce as one one-thousandth of the weight of one cubic foot of ice-cold water.

9-23. The heat capacity of an element (a metalloid) is 0.0483 calories per gram. Calculate a rough value of the atomic weight of the element. The hydride of this element is found to contain 1.555% hydrogen. What are possible values of the exact atomic weight of the element? From the two experimental data, determine the exact atomic weight. (Ans. 128, 63.8 n, 127.6)

9-24. A gas was observed to have a density 5.37 g/l at 25° C and 1 atm. What is the molecular weight of the gas? Its heat capacity was found on measurement to be 0.039 cal/g. How many atoms are there in the molecule of the gas? Can you identify this gas? (Ans. 131.3, one, Xe)

9-25. The density of ethylene at very low pressure corresponds to the ideal density 1.251223 g/l at standard conditions. The formula of ethylene is C_2H_4. Calculate from this information a precise value of the molecular weight of ethylene. Assuming the atomic weight of hydrogen to be 1.0080, calculate the atomic weight of carbon.

9-26. The density of phosphorus trioxide, with elementary composition P_2O_3, was found to be 2.35 g/l at 800° C and 1 atm. What is the correct formula of the vapor? (Ans. P_4O_6)

9-27. What is the atomic weight of an element which has the two following properties: (a) 1 g of the element combines with 0.3425 g of chlorine; (b) the heat capacity of the solid element at 20° C is 0.031 cal/g?

9-28. Would deuterium (atomic weight 2.0147) effuse through a porous plate more rapidly or less rapidly than hydrogen? Calculate the relative rates of effusion of the two molecules. What would be the relative rate of effusion of a molecule made of one light hydrogen atom and one deuterium atom? (Less, 0.707, 0.816)

9-29. A piece of metal weighing 1.038 g was treated with acid, and was found to liberate 229 ml of hydrogen, measured over water. The temperature was 18° C, and the barometric pressure was 745.5 mm. What are possible values of the atomic weight of the element? The heat capacity of the solid element was found to be 0.0552 cal/g. Which of the possible values of the atomic weight is the correct one?

9-30. Why is diffusion normally such a slow process, despite the rapid movement of gas molecules? Under what conditions does diffusion take place with the speed of molecular motion?

9-31. An organic compound was analyzed by combustion, and it was found that a sample weighing 0.200 g produced 0.389 g of carbon dioxide and 0.277 g of water. Another sample, weighing 0.150 g, was found on combustion to produce 37.3 ml of nitrogen at standard conditions. What is the empirical formula of the compound?

9-32. A sample of gas weighing 0.1100 g was found to occupy 24.16 ml at 25° C and 740.3 mm. Calculate the molecular weight of the substance. (Ans. 114.3)

9-33. A sample of gas with volume 191 ml at 20° C and 743 mm was found to weigh 0.132 g. What is the molecular weight of the gas? What do you think the gas is?

9-34. (a) What volume of oxygen would be required for the complete combustion of 200 ml of acetylene, C_2H_2, and what volume of CO_2 would be produced? (b) Sulfur dioxide, SO_2, and hydrogen sulfide, H_2S, can be made to react to form free sulfur and water. What volume of sulfur dioxide would react in this way with 25 ml of hydrogen sulfide? (Ans. 500 ml, 400 ml, 12.5 ml)

9-35. Calculate the volume of sulfur dioxide, at standard conditions, that would be formed by the complete combustion of 8.00 g of sulfur.

9-36. A sample of a certain hydrocarbon was found to contain 7.75% hydrogen and 92.25% carbon. The density of the vaporized hydrocarbon at 100° C and 1 atm was found to be 2.47 times as great as that of oxygen under the same conditions. What is the molecular weight of the hydrocarbon, and what is its formula?

9-37. A sample of gas collected over water at 25° C was found to have volume 543.0 ml, the atmospheric pressure being 730 mm of Hg. What is the volume of the dry gas at standard conditions?

9-38. If 100 l of hydrogen at 0° C was compressed under 100 atm pressure, the temperature remaining 0° C, would the volume be more or less than 1000 ml? (See Figure 9-8.) What is the answer for nitrogen? Can you explain the difference in behavior of the two gases?

Chapter 10

Ionic Valence and Electrolysis

In Chapter 6 it was pointed out that the formulas of compounds can be systematized by assigning certain combining powers, valences, to the elements. The valence of an element was described as the number of valence bonds formed by an atom of the element with other atoms.

The effort to obtain a clear understanding of the nature of valence and of chemical combination in general has led in recent years to the dissociation of the concept of valence into several new concepts—especially *ionic valence*, *covalence*, and *oxidation number*. We shall examine these concepts in this chapter and the two following ones. *Metallic valence* will be discussed in Chapter 24.

In addition to ionic valence, there is given in the following sections of this chapter a discussion of electrolysis and electrochemical processes.

10–1. *Ions and Ionic Valence*

The Existence of Stable Ions. In the discussion of ionization potentials in Chapter 5 and of the mass spectrograph in Chapter 8 it was mentioned that atoms in a gas have the power to lose an electron, forming a positive ion such as I^+, or to gain an electron, forming a negative ion such as I^-. This ability to lose electrons or affinity for electrons is so great for many elements as to cause their cations or anions to be very stable, and to be present in most of the compounds of these elements.

Of the various ions which the iodine atom can form, only the singly charged negative ion, I^-, is stable in the compounds of iodine. This ion, called the *iodide ion*, is present in the iodides of the stronger metals.

The other halogens also form singly charged anions: the *fluoride ion*, F^-, the *chloride ion*, Cl^-, and the *bromide ion*, Br^-.

Neutral atoms of the alkali metals have no affinity for additional electrons, but instead each of these atoms holds one of its electrons only loosely—so loosely that in the presence of a halogen, which can take up the electron, it loses an electron, forming a singly charged positive ion. These cations, which are present in nearly all of the compounds of the alkali metals, are called the *lithium ion*, Li^+, the *sodium ion*, Na^+, the *potassium ion*, K^+, the *rubidium ion*, Rb^+, and the *cesium ion*, Cs^+.

The Structure of an Ionic Crystal. When metallic sodium and gaseous chlorine react each sodium atom transfers an electron to a chlorine atom:

$$2Na + Cl_2 \longrightarrow 2Na^+ + 2Cl^-$$

There occurs a strong electrostatic attraction between each sodium ion and every chloride ion in its neighborhood. There also occurs repulsion between ions of like sign. In consequence of these forces and the repulsive forces which operate between all ions or molecules when they get so close to one another that their electronic structures are in contact, the ions pile up together in a regular way, each sodium ion surrounding itself with six chloride ions as nearest neighbors, and keeping all other sodium ions somewhat farther away. The structure of the sodium chloride crystal is represented in Figure 4-6.

The Ionic Bond; Ionic Valence. The strong electrostatic forces acting between anions and cations are called *ionic bonds*. The magnitude of the electric charge on an ion (in units e) is called its *ionic valence*. Thus sodium has ionic valence $+1$ in sodium chloride and is said to be *unipositive*, chlorine has ionic valence -1 and is said to be *uninegative*.

Any specimen of matter big enough to be seen by the eye must be essentially electrically neutral. It might have an excess of either positive or negative ions, and thus be charged positively or negatively, but the amount of charge, measured in units e, is always small compared with the number of atoms. Hence a crystal of sodium chloride must contain substantially as many Na^+ ions as Cl^- ions, and its formula must be Na^+Cl^-. The composition of the crystal and the formula of the compound are thus determined by the ionic valences of the constituent elements: these ionic valences must add up to zero.

Ionic Valence and the Periodic Table. It is a striking fact that *every alkali ion and every halogenide ion contains the same number of electrons as one of the noble gases.* The stability of these ions and the lack of chemical reactivity of the noble gases can thus be attributed to the same cause—

the extraordinary stability of configurations of 2, 10, 18, 36, 54, and 86 electrons about an atomic nucleus.

The alkali metals (in group I of the periodic table) are unipositive because their atoms contain one more electron than a noble-gas atom, and this electron is easily lost, to produce the corresponding cation, Li^+, Na^+, K^+, Rb^+, and Cs^+. The ease with which the outermost electron is lost by an atom of an alkali metal, compared with other atoms, is shown by the values of the first ionization potentials given in Table 5-5 and Figure 5-4. The values of the first ionization potentials of the alkali metals are less than those for any other elements. Less energy is required to ionize these atoms than any others. The amount of energy, in kcal/mole, required to ionize gas atoms of the alkali metals is given in Table 10-1.

The halogens (in group VII of the periodic table) are uninegative because each of their atoms contains one less electron than a noble-gas atom, and readily gains an electron, producing the corresponding anion, F^-, Cl^-, Br^-, and I^-. The energy that is liberated when an extra electron is attached to an atom to form an anion is called the *electron affinity* of the atom. Values of electron affinities of the halogens, given in Table 10-1, are larger than those of any other atoms.

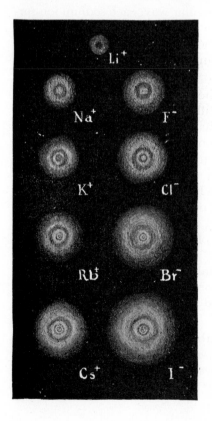

FIGURE 10-1

The electron distribution in alkali ions and halide ions.

TABLE 10-1   *Ionization Energies of the Alkali Metals and Electron Affinities of the Halogens*

ALKALI METAL	IONIZATION ENERGY IN KCAL/MOLE	HALOGEN	ELECTRON AFFINITY IN KCAL/MOLE
Lithium	124.3		
Sodium	118.5	Fluorine	90
Potassium	100.1	Chlorine	92
Rubidium	95.9	Bromine	89
Cesium	89.2	Iodine	79

The electron distributions in alkali ions and halogenide ions are shown in Figure 10-1. It is seen that these ions are closely similar to the corresponding noble gases, which are shown, on a somewhat larger scale, in Figure 5-3. With increase in nuclear charge from $+9e$ for fluoride ion to $+11e$ for sodium ion the electron shells are drawn closer to the nucleus, so that the sodium ion is about 30% smaller than the fluoride ion. The neon atom is intermediate in size.

Values of ionic radii have been determined, such that addition of

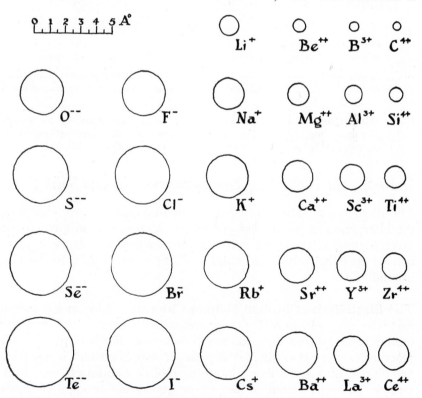

FIGURE 10-2   *A drawing representing the ionic radii of ions.*

two radii gives the expected contact distance between ions in a crystal. These values are shown in Figure 10-2.

The atoms of group II of the periodic table, by losing two electrons, can also produce ions with the noble-gas structures: these ions are Be^{++}, Mg^{++}, Ca^{++}, Sr^{++}, and Ba^{++}. The alkaline-earth elements are hence bipositive in valence. The elements of group III are terpositive, those of group VI are binegative, etc.

The formulas of binary salts of these elements can thus be written from knowledge of the positions of the elements in the periodic table:

$$Na^+F^- \quad Na^+Br^- \quad K^+I^- \quad Ca^{++}(F^-)_2 \quad Ba^{++}(Cl^-)_2$$

$$Al^{+++}(Cl^-)_3 \quad (Na^+)_2O^{--} \quad Ca^{++}O^{--} \quad (Al^{+++})_2(O^{--})_3$$

Ionic compounds are formed between the strong metals in groups I and II and the strong non-metals in the upper right-hand corner of the periodic table. In addition ionic compounds are formed containing the cations of the strong metals and the anions of acids, especially of the oxygen acids.

Illustrative Exercises

10-1. What ions can atoms of magnesium and oxygen form, by assuming the configuration of the nearest noble gas (neon)? What are the ionic valences of magnesium and oxygen? What is the predicted composition of magnesium oxide?

10-2. Assign ionic valences to the atoms in the following compounds: Na_2O, $MgCl_2$, Al_2O_3, CsF, SiO_2, PF_5. For each ion, state what noble-gas configuration has been assumed.

10-3. What is the electron configuration of the aluminum atom? Of the tripositive aluminum ion, Al^{+++}? From what orbitals were the three valence electrons removed? Why are there no compounds containing the ion Al^{++++}?

10–2. The Electrolytic Decomposition of Molten Salts

The discovery of ions resulted from the experimental investigations of the interaction of an electric current with chemical substances. These investigations were begun early in the nineteenth century, and were carried on effectively by Michael Faraday (1791–1867), in the period around 1830.

The Electrolysis of Molten Sodium Chloride.   Molten sodium chloride (the salt melts at 801° C) conducts an electric current, as do other molten salts. During the process of conducting the current a chemical reaction occurs—the salt is *decomposed*. If two electrodes (carbon rods) are dipped into a crucible containing molten sodium chloride and an electric potential (from a battery or generator) is applied, metallic sodium is produced at the negative electrode—the cathode—and chlo-

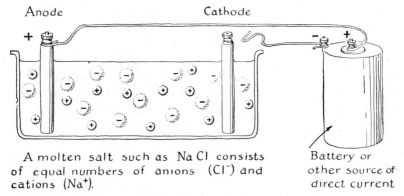

Anode   Cathode

A molten salt such as Na Cl consists
of equal numbers of anions (Cl⁻) and
cations (Na⁺).

Battery or
other source of
direct current

When the circuit is closed electrons flow as through a tube.

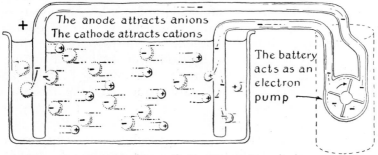

The anode attracts anions
The cathode attracts cations

The battery
acts as an
electron
pump

Anions give up their extra
electrons to the anode and
become neutral atoms.

Cations receive electrons
from the cathode and also
become neutral atoms.

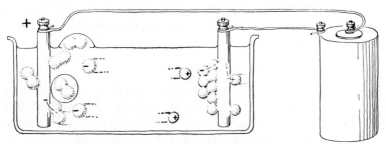

Neutral atoms of chlorine
unite to form bubbles
of chlorine gas (Cl_2).

Neutral sodium atoms
form a layer of
metallic sodium

FIGURE 10-3   *Electrolysis of molten sodium chloride.*

rine gas at the positive electrode—the anode. Such electric decomposition of a substance is called *electrolysis*

The Mechanism of Ionic Conduction.

Molten sodium chloride, like the crystalline substance, consists of equal numbers of sodium ions and chloride ions. These ions are very stable, and do not gain electrons or lose electrons easily. Whereas the ions in the crystal are firmly held in place by their neighbors, those in the molten salt move about with considerable freedom.

An electric generator or battery forces electrons into the cathode and pumps them away from the anode—electrons move freely in a metal or a semi-metallic conductor such as graphite. But electrons cannot ordinarily get into a substance such as salt; the crystalline substance is an insulator, and the electric conductivity shown by the molten salt is not electronic conductivity (metallic conductivity), but is conductivity of a different kind, called *ionic conductivity* or *electrolytic conductivity*. This sort of conductivity results from the motion of the ions in the liquid; the cations, Na^+, are attracted by the negatively charged cathode and move toward it, and the anions, Cl^-, are attracted by the anode and move toward it (Figure 10-3).

The Electrode Reactions.

The preceding statement describes the mechanism of the conduction of the current through the liquid. We must now consider the way in which the current passes between the electrodes and the liquid; that is, we consider the *electrode reactions*.

The process which occurs at the cathode is this: sodium ions, attracted to the cathode, combine with the electrons carried by the cathode to form sodium atoms; that is, to form sodium metal. The *cathode reaction* accordingly is

$$Na^+ + e^- \longrightarrow Na \tag{1}$$

The symbol e^- represents an electron, which in this case comes from the cathode. Similarly at the anode chloride ions give up their extra electrons to the anode, and become chlorine atoms, which are combined as the molecules of chlorine gas. The *anode reaction* is

$$2Cl^- \longrightarrow Cl_2 \uparrow + 2e^- \tag{2}$$

The Over-all Reaction.

The whole process of electric conduction in this system thus occurs in the following steps:

1. An electron is pumped into the cathode.
2. The electron jumps out of the cathode onto an adjacent sodium ion, converting it into an atom of sodium metal.
3. The charge of the electron is conducted across the liquid by the motion of the ions.

4. A chloride ion gives its extra electron to the anode, and becomes half of a molecule of chlorine gas.
5. The electron moves out of the anode toward the generator or battery.

The student should note that there is nothing mysterious about this complex phenomenon, after it is separated into its parts and the individual processes are analyzed. If the phenomenon seems mysterious, he should study it further, and if necessary ask the instructor to explain it.

The over-all reaction for the electrolytic decomposition is the sum of the two electrode reactions. Since two electrons are shown on their way around the circuit in Equation 2, we must double 1:

$$2Na^+ + 2e^- \longrightarrow 2Na$$
$$\underline{2Cl^- \longrightarrow Cl_2 \uparrow + 2e^-}$$
$$2Na^+ + 2Cl^- \xrightarrow[\text{electr.}]{} 2Na + Cl_2 \uparrow \tag{3}$$

or

$$2NaCl \xrightarrow[\text{electr.}]{} 2Na + Cl_2 \uparrow \tag{4}$$

The Equations 3 and 4 are equivalent; they both represent the decomposition of sodium chloride into its elementary constituents. The abbreviation "electr." (for electrolysis) is written beneath the arrow to indicate that the reaction occurs on the passage of an electric current.

Illustrative Exercise

10-4.   Molten magnesium chloride, $MgCl_2$, can be electrolyzed, forming magnesium and chlorine. Write equations for the cathode reaction, the anode reaction, and the over-all reaction.

10–3. The Electrolysis of an Aqueous Salt Solution

Although pure water does not conduct electricity in any significant amount, a solution of salt (or acid or base) is a good conductor. During electrolysis chemical reactions take place at the electrodes; often these reactions lead to the production of gaseous hydrogen and oxygen, as described in Chapter 6.

The phenomena that occur when a current of electricity is passed through such a solution are analogous to those described in the preceding section for molten salt. The five steps are the following:

1. Electrons are pumped into the cathode.
2. Electrons jump from the cathode to adjacent ions or molecules, producing the cathode reaction.
3. The current is conducted across the liquid by the motion of the dissolved ions.

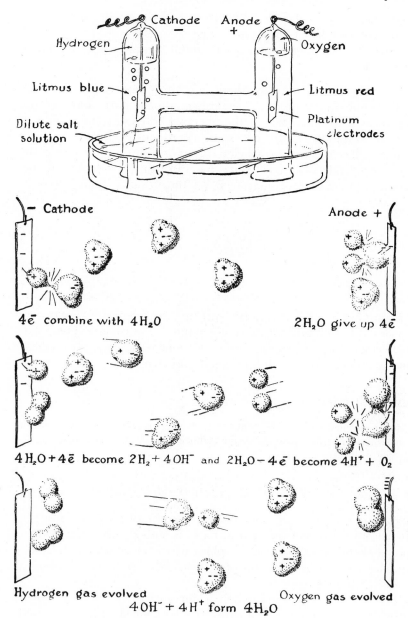

Cathode
–
Anode
+
Hydrogen
Oxygen
Litmus blue
Litmus red
Dilute salt solution
Platinum electrodes

– Cathode
Anode +

$4\bar{e}$ combine with $4H_2O$
$2H_2O$ give up $4\bar{e}$

$4H_2O + 4\bar{e}$ become $2H_2 + 4OH^-$ and $2H_2O - 4\bar{e}$ become $4H^+ + O_2$

Hydrogen gas evolved
Oxygen gas evolved
$4OH^- + 4H^+$ form $4H_2O$

FIGURE 10-4   *Electrolysis of dilute aqueous salt solution.*

4. Electrons jump from ions or molecules in the solution to the anode, producing the anode reaction.
5. The electrons move out of the anode toward the generator or battery.

Let us consider a dilute solution of sodium chloride (Figure 10-4). The process of conduction through this solution (step 3) is closely similar to that for molten sodium chloride. Here it is the dissolved sodium ions which move toward the cathode and the dissolved chloride ions which move toward the anode. By the motion of the ions in this way negative electric charge is carried toward the anode and away from the cathode.

But the electrode reactions for dilute salt solutions are entirely different from those for molten salts. Electrolysis of dilute salt solution produces hydrogen at the cathode and oxygen at the anode, whereas electrolysis of molten salt produces sodium and chlorine.

The *cathode reaction* for a dilute salt solution is

$$2e^- + 2H_2O \longrightarrow H_2 \uparrow + 2OH^- \tag{5}$$

Two electrons from the cathode react with two water molecules to produce a molecule of hydrogen and two hydroxide ions. The molecular hydrogen bubbles off as hydrogen gas (after the solution near the cathode has become saturated with hydrogen) and the hydroxide ions stay in the solution. The *anode reaction* is

$$2H_2O \longrightarrow O_2 \uparrow + 4H^+ + 4e^- \tag{6}$$

Four electrons enter the anode from two water molecules, which decompose to form an oxygen molecule and four hydrogen ions.

These electrode reactions, like other chemical reactions, may occur in steps; the description given in the preceding sentence of the course of the anode reaction is not to be interpreted as giving the necessary sequence of events.

The *over-all reaction* is obtained by multiplying Equation 5 by 2 and adding Equation 6: it is

$$6H_2O \xrightarrow[\text{electr.}]{} \underset{\text{cathode}}{2H_2 \uparrow} + \underset{\text{anode}}{O_2 \uparrow} + \underset{\text{anode}}{4H^+} + \underset{\text{cathode}}{4OH^-} \tag{7}$$

The reason that Equation 5 must be multiplied by 2 before it is added to Equation 6 is that when a current of electricity is conducted through the system the same number of electrons must pass from the cathode to the solution as from the solution to the anode; Equation 5 as written above involves two electrons, and Equation 6 involves four: hence Equation 5 must be doubled.

It is seen that in the electrolysis of the salt solution the solution around the anode becomes acidic, because of the production of hydrogen ions, and that around the cathode becomes basic, because of the production of hydroxide ions. This reaction could accordingly be used for the manufacture of acids such as hydrochloric acid and bases such as sodium hydroxide.

In the course of time, if the system were allowed to stand, the hydrogen ions produced near the anode and the hydroxide ions produced near the cathode would diffuse together and combine to form water:

$$H^+ + OH^- \longrightarrow H_2O$$

This reaction would, in particular, occur if the solution of electrolytes were to be stirred during the electrolysis. If this reaction of neutralization of hydrogen ion by hydroxide ion occurs completely the over-all electrolysis reaction is

$$2H_2O \underset{\underset{\text{cathode}}{\text{electr.}}}{\longrightarrow} 2H_2 \uparrow + \underset{\text{anode}}{O_2} \uparrow \tag{8}$$

In discussing the electrode reactions we have made little use of the fact that the electrolyte is sodium chloride. Indeed, *the electrode reactions are the same for almost all dilute aqueous electrolytic solutions*, and even for pure water as well. When electrodes are placed in pure water and an electric potential is applied the electrode reactions 5 and 6 begin to take place. Very soon, however, a large enough concentration of hydroxide ions is built up near the cathode and of hydrogen ions near the anode to produce a back electric potential that tends to stop the reactions. Even in pure water there are a few ions (hydrogen ions and hydroxide ions); these ions move slowly toward the electrodes, and neutralize the ions (OH^- and H^+, respectively) formed by the electrode reactions. It is the smallness of the current which the very few ions that are present in pure water can carry through the region between the electrodes that causes the electrolysis of pure water to proceed only very slowly.

Equations 5 and 6 above show water molecules undergoing decomposition at the electrodes. These equations probably represent the usual molecular reactions in neutral salt solutions. However, in acidic solutions, in which there is a high concentration of hydrogen ions, the cathode reaction may well be simply the reaction

$$2H^+ + 2e^- \longrightarrow H_2 \uparrow$$

and in basic solutions, in which there is a high concentration of hydroxide ions, the anode reaction may be

$$4OH^- \longrightarrow O_2 \uparrow + 2H_2O + 4e^-$$

The ions in an electrolytic solution can carry a larger current between the electrodes than can the very few ions in pure water. In a sodium chloride solution undergoing electrolysis sodium ions move to the cathode region, where their positive electric charges compensate the negative charges of the hydroxide ions that have been formed by the cathode reaction. Similarly the chloride ions that move toward the anode compensate electrically the hydrogen ions that have been formed by the acid reaction.

Production of hydroxide ions at the cathode and of hydrogen ions at the anode during the electrolysis can be demonstrated by means of litmus or a similar indicator.

The electrolysis of dilute aqueous solutions of other electrolytes is closely similar to that of sodium chloride, producing hydrogen and oxygen gases at the electrodes. Concentrated electrolytic solutions may behave differently; concentrated brine (sodium chloride solution) on electrolysis produces chlorine at the anode, as well as oxygen. We may understand this fact by remembering that in concentrated brine there are a great many chloride ions near the anode, and some of these give up electrons to the anode, and form chlorine molecules.

10–4. *Faraday's Laws of Electrolysis*

In 1832 and 1833 Michael Faraday, a great English chemist and physicist, reported his discovery by experiment of the fundamental laws of electrolysis:

1. **The weight of a substance produced by a cathode or anode reaction in electrolysis is directly proportional to the quantity of electricity passed through the cell.**

2. **The weights of different substances produced by the same quantity of electricity are proportional to the equivalent weights of the substances.**

These laws are now known to be the result of the fact that electricity is composed of individual particles, the electrons. Quantity of electricity can be expressed as number of electrons. The *equivalent weight* mentioned in the second of Faraday's laws is the formula weight or atomic weight of the substance divided by the number of electrons occurring with one formula of the substance in the electrode reaction. For example, in the electrolysis of a solution containing cupric ion copper is deposited at the cathode; the electrode reaction is

$$Cu^{++} + 2e^- \longrightarrow Cu$$

Since two electrons occur in this equation with one formula Cu, the equivalent weight of copper for this reaction is the atomic weight divided by 2.

The magnitude of the charge of one mole of electrons (Avogadro's number of electrons) *is 96,500 coulombs of electricity.* This is called a **faraday.**

1 faraday = 96,500 coulombs = 96,500 ampere seconds

Note that the charge of an electron (Chapter 3) is -1.602×10^{-19} coulombs, as determined by the Millikan oil-drop experiment and other methods. Avogadro's number is 0.6023×10^{24}. The product of these numbers is $-96,500$ coulombs of electricity. This is accordingly the electric charge, the quantity of electricity, on Avogadro's number of electrons, 1 mole of electrons. It is customary to define the faraday as this quantity of positive electricity, rather than of negative electricity.*

It is not difficult to make calculations involving weights of chemical substances and the amount of electricity passing through an electrolytic cell, if you keep clearly in mind what the relation between the number of atoms and the number of electrons is. You must remember that the *current* of electricity, measured in amperes, is the *rate* at which electricity is flowing through the cell. To find the *amount* of electricity the current must be multiplied by the *time* measured in seconds. *One ampere flowing for one second is the quantity 1 coulomb of electricity.*

The quantitative treatment of electrochemical reactions is made in the same way as the calculation of weight relations in ordinary chemical reactions, with use of the faraday to represent one mole of electrons.

It will be noted by the student that the voltage at which the cell operates does not affect the weights of different substances reacting in the cell. The weights of substances involved in electrode reactions are determined solely by the quantity of electricity that passes through the cell. If the voltage applied to the cell is too low, current will not flow through the cell; but if the voltage is large enough to produce a current through the cell the amount of reaction produced in a given time is determined only by the current, and not by the voltage.†

Example 1.   For how long a time would a current of 20 amperes have to be passed through a cell containing fused sodium chloride to produce 23 g of metallic sodium at the cathode? How much chlorine would be produced at the anode?
   Solution.   The cathode reaction is

$$Na^+ + e^- \longrightarrow Na$$

Hence 1 mole of electrons passing through the cell would produce 1 mole of sodium atoms. One mole of electrons is 1 faraday, and 1 mole of sodium atoms is a gram-atom of sodium, 23.00 g. Hence the amount of electricity required is 96,500 coulombs, 1 faraday. One coulomb is 1 ampere second. Hence 96,500 coulombs of electricity passes through the cell if 1 ampere flows for 96,500 seconds, or 20 amperes for $96,500/20 = \textbf{4825 sec.}$, or 1 hour 20 min. 25 sec.

---

* The value of the faraday may be determined by measuring the amount of electricity needed to deposit one gram-atom of silver from a solution containing silver ion, Ag^+. After Millikan had determined the value of the charge of the electron by his oil-drop experiment, he calculated the value of Avogadro's number by dividing this value into the faraday.

† It is assumed in making this statement that the nature of the chemical reaction that takes place in the cell is not changed by a change in the voltage.

The anode reaction is

$$2Cl^- \longrightarrow Cl_2 + 2e^-$$

To produce 1 mole of molecular chlorine, Cl_2, 2 faradays must pass through the cell. One faraday would hence produce 1 gram-atom of chlorine, which is **35.46 g.**

Example 2.   Two cells are set up in series, and a current is passed through them. (Cells are said to be set up in series when all of the electrons that flow along the wire from the generator or battery must pass first through the first cell, from the negative electrode to the positive electrode, and then through the second cell, from its negative electrode to the positive electrode, and so on.) Cell A contains an aqueous solution of silver sulfate, Ag_2SO_4, which forms silver ions, Ag^+, and sulfate ions, SO_4^{--}, in the solution. This cell has platinum electrodes, which are unreactive. Cell B contains a copper sulfate solution, $CuSO_4$, and has copper electrodes. The current is passed through until 1.600 g of oxygen has been liberated at the anode of cell A. What has occurred at the other electrodes? (See Figure 10-5.)

   Solution.   At the anode of cell A the reaction is

$$2H_2O \longrightarrow O_2 \uparrow + 4H^+ + 4e^-$$

Hence 4 faradays of electricity would liberate 32 g of oxygen. The amount of oxygen liberated, 1.600 g, is seen to be $\frac{1}{20}$ of 32 g;

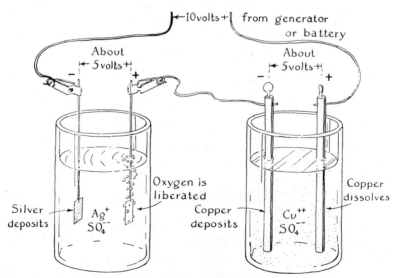

Cell A, Platinum electrodes   Cell B, Copper electrodes

FIGURE 10-5   *Two electrolytic cells in series.*

accordingly the amount of electricity that passed through the cell is $\frac{1}{20}$ of 4 faradays or 0.2 faradays. This amount of electricity must have taken part in the electrode reaction at each of the other three electrodes.

Let us now consider the reaction at the cathode of cell A. At this electrode metallic silver is deposited. The cathode reaction is accordingly

$$Ag^+ + e^- \longrightarrow Ag$$

One gram-atom of silver, 107.880 g, would be deposited by 1 faraday, and the passage of 0.200 faraday through the cell would accordingly deposit $0.2 \times 107.880 = $ **21.576 g** of silver on the platinum cathode.

At the cathode in cell B the reaction is

$$Cu^{++} + 2e^- \longrightarrow Cu$$

One gram-atom of copper, 63.57 g, would be deposited on the cathode by 2 faradays of electricity, and **6.357 g** by 0.200 faraday.

At the anode of this cell copper dissolves from the copper electrode, to form Cu^{++} ions in solution. The same number of electrons flows through the anode as through the cathode. Hence the same amount of copper, **6.357 g,** is dissolved from the anode as is deposited on the cathode. The anode reaction is

$$Cu \longrightarrow Cu^{++} + 2e^-$$

It may be mentioned that the total voltage difference supplied by the generator or battery (shown in the figure as 10 volts) is divided between the two cells coupled in series. The division need not be equal, as indicated, but is determined by the properties of the two cells.

Illustrative Exercise

10-5.   How many grams of magnesium and how many grams of chlorine would be liberated by passing one faraday of electricity through molten magnesium chloride, $MgCl_2$?

10–5. Electrolytic Production of Elements

Many metals and some non-metals are made by electrolytic methods. Hydrogen and oxygen are produced by the electrolysis of water containing an electrolyte. The alkali metals, alkaline-earth metals, magnesium, aluminum, and many other metals are manufactured either entirely or for special uses by electrochemical reduction of their compounds.

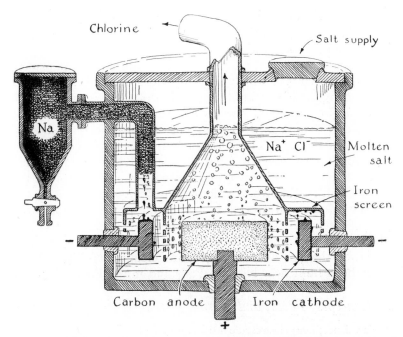

FIGURE 10-6 *A cell used for making sodium and chlorine by electrolysis of fused sodium chloride.*

The Production of Sodium and Chlorine. Many electrochemical processes depend for their success on ingenious devices for securing the purity of the product. As an illustration we may consider a cell used for making metallic sodium and elementary chlorine from sodium chloride.

The molten sodium chloride (usually with some sodium carbonate added to reduce its melting point) is in a vessel containing a carbon anode and iron cathode, separated by an iron screen which leads to pipes, as indicated in Figure 10-6. The gaseous chlorine is led off through one pipe, and the molten sodium, which is lighter than the electrolyte, rises and is drawn off into a storage tank.

Only about 8% of the chlorine used in the United States is produced in this way. Most of it is produced in connection with the production of sodium hydroxide and hydrogen by electrolysis of brine.

The Cost of Electrochemical Processes. Faraday's laws do not tell us enough to determine the cost of the electric energy required to carry out an electrochemical process. The cost of electricity is determined by the electric energy used, the energy being the product of the quantity of electricity, in coulombs, and the potential difference, in volts. The unit of electric energy is the watt-second (1 watt sec = 1 coulomb volt = 1 ampere volt second), or more customarily, the kilowatt hour. Calculations such as those given above determine the quantity of electricity required to produce a given amount of substance electrolytically, but not the voltage at which it must be supplied. The principles determining the voltage which a cell provides or needs for its operation are more complicated; a brief description of them is given in Chapter 23.

In any commercial process a considerable fraction of the required voltage is that needed to overcome the electric resistance of the electrolyte in the cell. The corresponding energy is converted into heat, and sometimes serves to keep the electrolyte molten. If the operating voltage of a cell is known, and the cost of electric power, per kilowatt hour (kwh), is known, a calculation of the electric cost can be made. In some industrial processes, such as the production of aluminum, the cost of electricity is such a large factor in the total cost of operation that the industrial plants are located near the sources of hydroelectric power. It is for this reason that important electrochemical industrial plants have been built near Niagara Falls and in the Pacific Northwest.

Concepts, Facts, and Terms Introduced in This Chapter

Ionic valence; ions; electrostatic attraction; ionic bonds.

Unipositive, bipositive, etc.; uninegative, binegative, etc.

Ionic valence and the periodic table.

Relation of ionic valence to noble-gas electronic structures. Ionization energies and electron affinities. Ionic radii.

Molten salts; ionic (electrolytic) conductivity; electrolysis; cathode reaction; anode reaction; over-all reaction.

Writing equations for electrode reactions and over-all reactions.

Electrolysis of aqueous solutions; ionic conduction; cathode reaction; anode reaction.

Faraday's law of electrolysis.

The faraday: Avogadro's number of electrons, 96,500 coulombs. Calculations involving quantity of electricity.

Electrolytic production of sodium and chlorine. The cost of electrochemical processes.

Exercises

10-6. Assuming that their atoms can lose enough electrons to reach the electronic structure of neon, what would be the charges on the positive ions with this configuration of the elements sodium to chlorine inclusive? Write the formulas of the corresponding oxides of these elements.

10-7. Assign ionic valences to the elements in the following compounds, by writing the corresponding number of plus signs or minus signs as a superscript to the symbol for the element:

LiF	LiI	Na_2O	$FeCl_3$	CaH_2	HCl
$CaCl_2$	$MgCl_2$	$FeCl_2$	TiO_2	BaO	SiF_4
B_2O_3	KBr	Na_2S	$RaCl_2$	CaS	LiH

By reference to the periodic table find which ions in these compounds do not have a noble-gas structure. and underline them in the formulas.

10-8. What forces hold a sodium chloride crystal together?

10-9. Magnesium oxide and sodium fluoride have the same crystal structure as sodium chloride (shown in Figure 4-6). Magnesium oxide is very much harder than sodium fluoride. Can you explain why the two substances differ so much in hardness? Can you also explain why the melting point of magnesium oxide (2800° C) is much higher than that of sodium fluoride (992° C)? Note that the ions in the two substances have the same electronic structure.

10-10. How is electric current conducted along a metallic wire? How is the current conducted from an inert cathode, such as the carbon cathode, through molten sodium chloride? From molten sodium chloride into an inert anode?

10-11. Why does molten sodium chloride conduct a current much better than does solid sodium chloride?

10-12. What substance would be formed at each electrode on electrolysis of molten lithium hydride, Li^+H^-, with inert electrodes? What is the electronic structure of the H^- ion?

10-13. Outline the complete mechanism of conduction of electricity between inert electrodes in a dilute solution of potassium sulfate.

10-14. Write equations for the anode reaction, the cathode reaction, and the over-all reaction for electrolysis of the following systems, with inert electrodes:
(a) Molten potassium bromide.
(b) Molten sodium oxide.
(c) Dilute aqueous solution of sodium hydroxide.
(d) Dilute aqueous solution of hydrochloric acid.
(e) Molten silver bromide, Ag^+Br^-.
(f) Dilute solution of silver nitrate, $AgNO_3$ (metallic silver deposits on the cathode).

10-15. How much copper would be deposited from a solution of copper sulfate, $CuSO_4$, by a current of 1 amp in the time 1 hour? (Ans. 1.18 g)

10-16. Sodium metal is sometimes made commercially by the electrolysis of fused sodium hydroxide, NaOH.
(a) Write equations for the anode and cathode reactions and the over-all reaction. (b) Calculate the weight of sodium formed per hour in a cell through which 1000 amperes is flowing.

10-17. A current operating for a period of 15 hours deposited 2.400 g of silver. Calculate the average current in amperes. (Ans. 0.0398)

10-18. The annual production of chlorine in the United States (1954) is approximately 2,500,000 tons. Assuming no loss, how many faradays of electricity and how many tons of sodium chloride would be required to produce this much chlorine by electrolysis? If the cells are operated at 2.4 volts, what fraction of the total hydroelectric power of the country, about 90,000,000 kilowatts, would be required to produce the chlorine?

10-19. Compare the quantities of electricity required to deposit the same weight of iron from a solution containing ferrous iron and a solution containing ferric iron. (Ans. $\frac{2}{3}$)

10-20. It was found in an experiment that an electric current passing through a series of cells deposited 10.78 g of silver, 6.967 g of bismuth, and 3.178 g of copper, and liberated 0.560 liter of oxygen and 1.12 liters of chlorine, at standard conditions. Calculate the equivalent weight of each of these elements, except oxygen (assumed to be 8), from these data. Multiply each equivalent weight by a suitable factor, to obtain a value for the atomic weight.

10-21. Sodium hydroxide, which is extensively used in industry, is made in large quantities by an electrochemical process. A brine (concentrated aqueous solution of sodium chloride) is electrolyzed in an apparatus in which the region around the cathode is separated by a membrane from the region around the anode. Chlorine is liberated at the anode and hydrogen at the cathode, and the solution around the cathode becomes a solution of sodium hydroxide as the chloride ion migrates away and hydroxide ion is produced by the cathode reaction. Write the equations for the electrode reactions occurring in this process. How much chlorine, hydrogen, and sodium hydroxide are produced per faraday? (Ans. 36.5 g, 1 g, 40 g)

References

Rosemary G. Ehl and A. J. Ihde, "Faraday's Electrochemical Laws and the Determination of Equivalent Weights" (historical), *J. Chem. Ed.* **31,** 226 (1954).

W. C. Gardiner, "Electrolytic Caustic and Chlorine Industries," *J. Chem. Ed.,* **30** 116 (1953).

Chapter 11

Covalence and
Electronic Structure

11-1. *The Nature of Covalence*

In the preceding chapter we have discussed chemical compounds that contain *ions*, and that owe their stability to the tendency of certain atoms to lose electrons and of others to gain them. When these ionic substances are melted or are dissolved in water the ions become able to move about independently in the molten substance or solution, which for this reason is a conductor of electricity.

There are many other substances, however, that do not have these properties. These non-ionic substances are so numerous that it is not necessary to search for examples—nearly every substance except the salts is in this class. Thus molten sulfur, like solid sulfur, is an electric insulator; it does not conduct electricity. Liquid air (liquid oxygen, liquid nitrogen), bromine, gasoline, carbon tetrachloride, and many other liquid substances are insulators. Gases, too, are insulators, and do not contain ions, unless they have been ionized by an electric discharge or in some similar way.

These non-ionic substances consist of *molecules* made of atoms that are bonded tightly together. Thus the pale straw-colored liquid that is obtained by melting sulfur contains S_8 molecules, each molecule being built of eight sulfur atoms; liquid air contains the stable diatomic molecules O_2 and N_2, bromine the molecules Br_2, carbon tetrachloride the molecules CCl_4, etc.

The atoms of these molecules are held tightly together by a very important sort of bond, the *shared-electron-pair bond* or *covalent bond*. This bond is so important, so nearly universally present in substances that Professor Gilbert Newton Lewis of the University of California (1875–

217

1946), who discovered its electronic structure, called it *the* chemical bond.

It is the covalent bond that is represented by a dash in the valence-bond formulas, such as Br—Br and $Cl—\overset{\displaystyle Cl}{\underset{\displaystyle Cl}{|\ \ |}}C—Cl$, that have been written by chemists for nearly a hundred years. We have described these formulas in Chapter 6 and have used them in Chapter 7.

Modern chemistry has been greatly simplified through the development of the theory of the covalent bond. It is now easier to understand and to remember chemical facts, by connecting them with our knowledge of the nature of the chemical bond and the electronic structure of molecules, than was possible fifty years ago. It is accordingly wise for the student of chemistry to study this chapter carefully, and to get a clear picture of the covalent bond.

11–2. *Covalent Molecules*

The Hydrogen Molecule.   The simplest example of a covalent molecule is the hydrogen molecule, H_2. For this molecule the electronic structure H : H is written, indicating that the two electrons are shared between the two hydrogen atoms, forming the bond between them. This structure corresponds to the valence-bond structure H—H.

By the study of its spectrum and by calculations made on the basis of the theory of quantum mechanics, the hydrogen molecule has been shown to have the structure represented in Figure 11-1. The two nuclei are fimly held at a distance of about 0.74 Å apart—they oscillate relative to each other with an amplitude of a few hundredths of an Ångström at room temperature, and with a somewhat larger amplitude at higher temperatures. The two electrons move very rapidly about in the region

FIGURE 11-1

The electron distribution in a hydrogen molecule. The two nuclei in the molecule are 0.74 Å apart.

of the two nuclei, their time-average distribution being indicated by the shading in the figure. It can be seen that the motion of the two electrons is largely concentrated into the small region between the two nuclei. (The nuclei are in the positions where the electron density is greatest.) We might draw an analogy with two steel balls (the nuclei) vulcanized into a tough piece of rubber (the two electrons, moving rapidly about) that surrounds them and binds them together. *The two electrons held jointly by the two nuclei constitute the chemical bond between the two hydrogen atoms in the hydrogen molecule.*

We have seen in the consideration of ionic valence that there is a very strong tendency for atoms of the stronger metals and the non-metals to achieve the electron number of an inert gas by losing or gaining one or more electrons. It was pointed out by Professor Lewis that the same tendency is operating in the formation of molecules containing covalent bonds, and that the electrons in a covalent bond are to be counted for each of the bonded atoms.

Thus the hydrogen atom, with one electron, can achieve the helium structure by taking up another electron, to form the hydride anion, H : ⁻, as in the salt lithium hydride, Li⁺H⁻. But the hydrogen atom can also achieve the helium structure by sharing its electron with the electron of another hydrogen atom, to form a shared-electron-pair bond. Each of the two atoms thus contributes one electron to the shared electron pair. The shared electron pair is to be counted first for one hydrogen atom, and then for the other; if this is done, it is seen that in the hydrogen molecule each of the atoms has the helium structure:

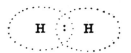

The Covalent Bond in Other Molecules. The covalent bond in other molecules is closely similar to that in the hydrogen molecule. For each covalent bond a pair of electrons is needed; also, two orbitals are needed, one of each atom.

The covalent bond consists of a pair of electrons shared between two atoms, and occupying two stable orbitals, one of each atom.

For example, reference to the energy-level diagram (Figure 5-5 or inside the back cover) shows that the carbon atom has four stable orbitals, in its L shell, and four electrons which may be used in bond formation. Hence it may combine with four hydrogen atoms, each of which has one stable orbital (the $1s$ orbital) and one electron, forming four covalent bonds:

$$
\begin{array}{c}
\text{H} \\
\text{H}:\overset{\displaystyle\cdot\cdot}{\underset{\displaystyle\cdot\cdot}{\text{C}}}:\text{H} \\
\text{H}
\end{array}
\qquad \text{equivalent to} \qquad
\begin{array}{c}
\text{H} \\
| \\
\text{H}-\text{C}-\text{H} \\
| \\
\text{H}
\end{array}
$$

In this molecule each atom has achieved a noble-gas structure; the shared electron pairs are to be counted for each of the atoms sharing them. The carbon atom, with four shared pairs in the L shell and one unshared pair in the K shell, has achieved the neon structure, and each hydrogen atom has achieved the helium structure.

It has been found that the atoms of the principal groups of the periodic table (that is, all atoms except the transition elements) usually have a noble-gas structure in their stable compounds.

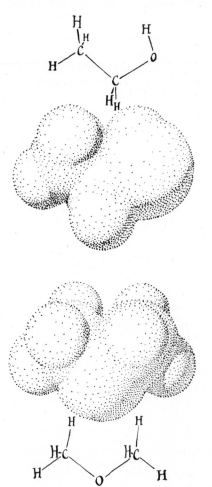

FIGURE 11-2

The structures of the isomeric molecules ethyl alcohol, C_2H_5OH, and dimethyl ether, $(CH_3)_2O$.

Stable molecules and complex ions usually have structures such that each atom has the electronic structure of a noble-gas atom, the shared electrons of each covalent bond being counted for each of the two atoms connected by the covalent bond.

The noble-gas atoms, except for helium, have eight electrons in the outermost shell, occupying four orbitals (one *s* orbital and three *p* orbitals). These eight electrons are called the *octet*. When an atom achieves a noble-gas structure, either by transferring electrons to or from other atoms or by sharing electron pairs with other atoms, it is said to *complete the octet*.

11–3. *The Structure of Covalent Compounds*

The electronic structure of molecules of covalent compounds involving the principal groups of the periodic table can usually be written by counting up the number of valence electrons in the molecule and then distributing the valence electrons as unshared electron pairs and shared electron pairs in such a way that each atom achieves a noble-gas structure.

It is often necessary to have some experimental information about the way in which the atoms are bonded together. This is true especially of organic compounds. Thus there are two compounds with the composition C_2H_6O, ethyl alcohol and dimethyl ether.* The chemical properties of these two substances show that one of them, ethyl alcohol, contains one hydrogen atom attached to an oxygen atom, whereas dimethyl ether does not contain such a hydroxyl group. The structures of these two isomeric molecules are the following (see also Figure 11-2):

Ethyl alcohol   Dimethyl ether

Compounds of Hydrogen with Non-metals.   Let us consider first the structure expected for a compound between hydrogen and fluorine, the lightest element of the seventh group. Hydrogen has a single orbital and one electron. Accordingly it could achieve the helium configuration by forming a single covalent bond with another element. Fluorine has in its outer shell, the *L* shell, seven electrons, occupying the four orbitals of the *L* shell. These seven electrons accordingly constitute three electron pairs in three of the orbitals and a single electron in the fourth orbital. Hence fluorine also can achieve a noble-gas configuration by

---

* Another example is the pair *n*-butane and isobutane, Section 7–6.

forming a single covalent bond with use of its odd electron. We are thus led to the following structure for hydrogen fluoride:

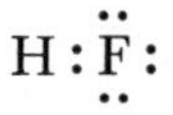

$$H : \overset{..}{\underset{..}{F}} :$$

In this molecule, the hydrogen fluoride molecule, there is a single covalent bond (shared-electron-pair bond), that holds the hydrogen atom and the fluorine atom firmly together.

It is often convenient to represent this electronic structure by using a dash as a symbol for the covalent bond instead of the dots representing the shared electron pair. Sometimes, especially when the electronic structure of the molecule is under discussion, the unshared pairs in the outer shell of each atom are represented but often they are omitted:

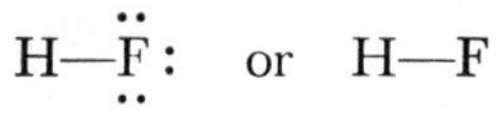

$$H—\overset{..}{\underset{..}{F}} : \quad \text{or} \quad H—F$$

The other halogens form similar compounds:

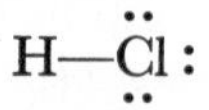

$$H—\overset{..}{\underset{..}{Cl}} : \qquad H—\overset{..}{\underset{..}{Br}} : \qquad H—\overset{..}{\underset{..}{I}} :$$

Hydrogen chloride 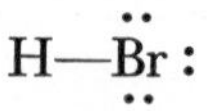   Hydrogen bromide 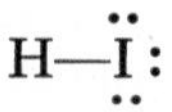   Hydrogen iodide

These substances are strong acids: when they are dissolved in water the proton leaves the molecule, and attaches itself to a water molecule, to form a hydronium ion, H_3O^+, the halogen being left as a halogenide

ion, $: \overset{..}{\underset{..}{Cl}} : ^-$, $: \overset{..}{\underset{..}{Br}} : ^-$, or $: \overset{..}{\underset{..}{I}} : ^-$. Hydrogen fluoride is a weak acid.

Elements of the sixth group (oxygen, sulfur, selenium, tellurium) can achieve the noble-gas structure by forming two covalent bonds. Oxygen has six electrons in its outer shell. These can be distributed among the four orbitals by putting two unshared pairs in two of the orbitals and an odd electron in each of the other two orbitals. These two odd electrons can be used in forming covalent bonds with two hydrogen atoms, to give a water molecule, with the following electronic structure:

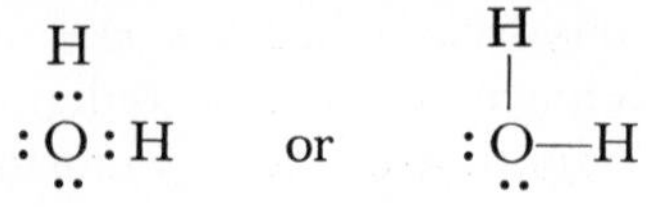

$$\begin{array}{cc} H & H \\ \overset{..}{:O}:H & \underset{}{:O}—H \\ \overset{..}{} & \overset{..}{} \end{array}$$

$$\text{or}$$

If a proton is removed from the water molecule, a hydroxide ion, OH^-, is formed:

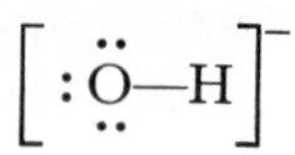

$$\left[: \overset{..}{\underset{..}{O}}—H \right]^-$$

If a proton is added to a water molecule (attaching itself to one of the unshared electron pairs) a hydronium ion, OH_3^+, is formed:

$$\begin{bmatrix} \text{H} \\ | \\ :\text{O—H} \\ | \\ \text{H} \end{bmatrix}^{+}$$

All three of the hydrogen atoms in the hydronium ion are held to the oxygen atom by the same kind of bond, a covalent bond.

In hydrogen peroxide, H_2O_2, each oxygen atom achieves the neon configuration by forming one covalent bond with the other oxygen atom and one covalent bond with a hydrogen atom:

$$\begin{array}{cc} \text{H} & \text{H} \\ | & | \\ :\text{O—O}: \end{array}$$

Hydrogen sulfide, hydrogen selenide, and hydrogen telluride have the same electronic structure as water:

$$\begin{array}{ccc} \text{H} & \text{H} & \text{H} \\ | & | & | \\ :\text{S—H} & :\text{Se—H} & :\text{Te—H} \end{array}$$

Nitrogen and the other fifth-group elements, with five outer electrons, can achieve the noble-gas configuration by forming three covalent bonds. The structures of ammonia, phosphine, arsine, and stibine are the following:

$$\begin{array}{cccc} \text{H} & \text{H} & \text{H} & \text{H} \\ | & | & | & | \\ :\text{N—H} & :\text{P—H} & :\text{As—H} & :\text{Sb—H} \\ | & | & | & | \\ \text{H} & \text{H} & \text{H} & \text{H} \end{array}$$

The ammonia molecule can attach a proton to itself, to form an ammonium ion, NH_4^+, in which all four hydrogen atoms are held to the nitrogen atom by covalent bonds:

$$\begin{bmatrix} \text{H} \\ | \\ \text{H—N—H} \\ | \\ \text{H} \end{bmatrix}^{+}$$

In the ammonium ion all four of the L orbitals are used in forming covalent bonds. The formation of the ammonium ion from ammonia is similar to the formation of hydronium ion from water.

The Electronic Structure of Some Other Compounds.   Electronic structures of other molecules containing covalent bonds may be readily written, by keeping in mind the importance of completing the octets of atoms of non-metallic elements. The structures of some compounds of non-metallic elements with one another are shown below:

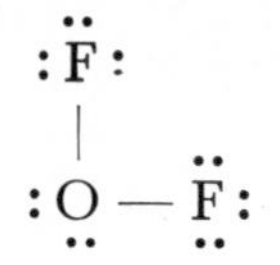

:F̈:
 |
:O̤ — F̈:   Oxygen difluoride

:C̈l:
 |
:S̤ — C̈l: Sulfur dichloride

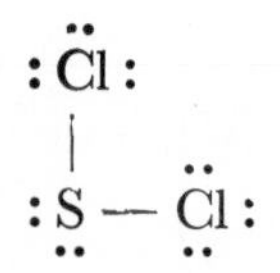

      C̈l
    /
  /
:N——C̈l: Nitrogen trichloride*
  \
    \
      C̈l

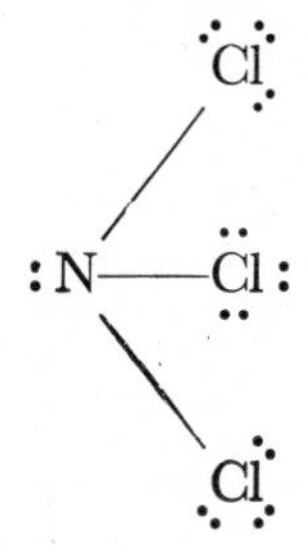

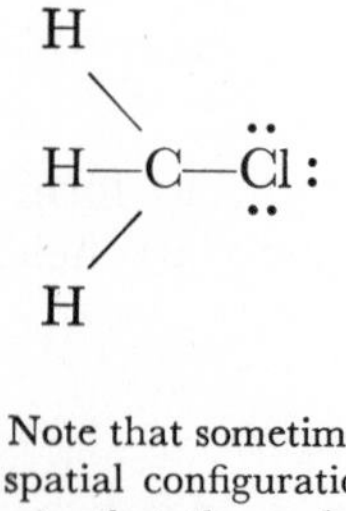

H
 \
H—C—C̈l: Methyl chloride
 /
H

---

* Note that sometimes an effort is made in drawing the structure of a molecule to indicate the spatial configuration; the structure shown here for nitrogen trichloride is supposed to indicate that the molecule is pyramidal, with the chlorine atoms approximately at three corners of a tetrahedron about the nitrogen atom. The spatial configuration of molecules is discussed in the following section.

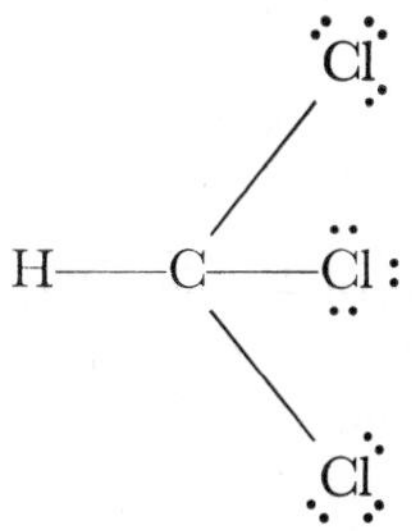

$$H—C \begin{matrix} \ddot{\ddot{Cl}} \\ \ddot{Cl}: \\ \ddot{Cl} \end{matrix}$$ Chloroform

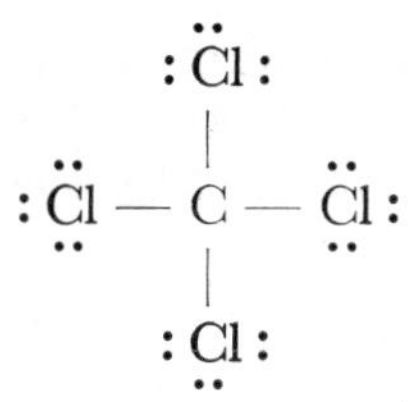

$$:\ddot{Cl}—C—\ddot{Cl}:$$ Carbon tetrachloride

with $:\ddot{Cl}:$ above and $:\ddot{Cl}:$ below

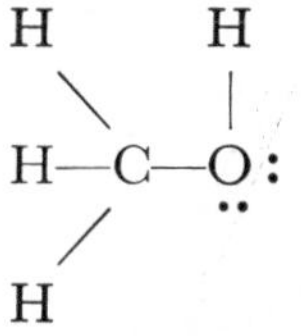

Methyl alcohol

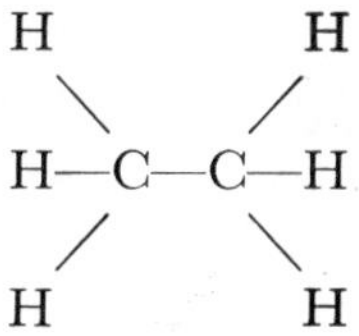

$$\begin{matrix} H \\ \diagdown \\ H—C—\ddot{O}: \\ \diagup \\ H \end{matrix}$$

Ethane

$$\begin{matrix} H \quad\quad H \\ \diagdown \quad\quad \diagup \\ H—C—C—H \\ \diagup \quad\quad \diagdown \\ H \quad\quad H \end{matrix}$$

$$H—C≡N:$$ Hydrogen cyanide

Illustrative Exercises

11-1. Silicon and hydrogen form the compound silane, SiH_4. (a) What is its electronic structure? (b) What orbitals of the silicon atom are used in forming the four covalent bonds?

11-2. Write electronic structures for silicon tetrachloride, $SiCl_4$, and phosphorus trichloride, PCl_3, showing all electron pairs in the outermost shell of each atom.

11-3. The acetylene molecule contains two carbon atoms and two hydrogen atoms. What is its electronic structure?

11-4. Write the electronic structure of ethyl chloride. What noble-gas structure does each atom achieve?

11-5. In the second paragraph of Section 11–3 it is said that there are two compounds with the composition C_2H_6O. Can you prove that there are only two ways of connecting these atoms together and keeping carbon quadrivalent, oxygen bivalent, and hydrogen univalent?

11–4. *The Direction of Valence Bonds in Space*

It was mentioned in Section 7–6 that the methane molecule, CH_4, is a tetrahedral molecule. The four bonds formed by the carbon atoms are directed in space toward the four corners of a tetrahedron, so that the four hydrogen atoms are tetrahedrally arranged about the carbon atom. The relation of the tetrahedron to the cube is shown in Figure 11-3. This tetrahedral arrangement of four hydrogen atoms around each carbon atom in methane is the expression of an important property of the octet:

The four electron pairs of an octet, whether shared or unshared, tend to arrange themselves in space at the corners of a regular tetrahedron.

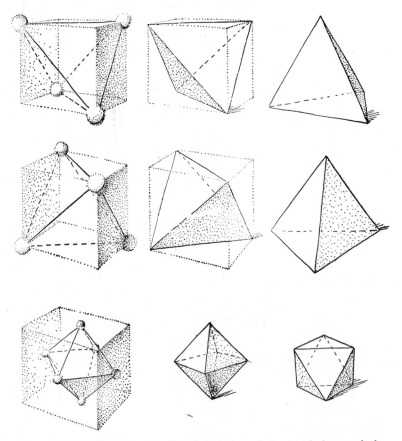

FIGURE 11-3. *Drawing showing the relation of the tetrahedron and the octahedron to the cube. These polyhedra are important in molecular structure.*

The angle between two single bonds formed by a tetrahedral atom is 109° 28′. It is the bond angle in methane, and also in the ammonium ion, NH_4^+. When an atom forms only three or two covalent bonds, its octet being completed by one or two unshared electron pairs, the bond angles tend to be a little less than the tetrahedral angle. In ammonia, NH_3, the H—N—H bond angle is 107°, and in water the H—O—H bond angle is 105°. The values of these bond angles have been found experimentally by the study of the spectra of the substances.

Sometimes two valence bonds of an atom are used in the formation of a double bond with another atom. There is a double bond between two carbon atoms in the molecules of ethylene, C_2H_4:

$$
\begin{array}{ccc}
\text{H} & & \text{H} \\
\diagdown & & \diagup \\
& \text{C}{=}\text{C} & \\
\diagup & & \diagdown \\
\text{H} & & \text{H}
\end{array}
$$

Ethylene

Such a double bond between two atoms may be represented by two tetrahedra sharing two corners: that is, sharing an edge, as shown in Figure 11-4. It is interesting to note that the four single bonds which the two carbon atoms in ethylene can also form lie in the same plane.

In acetylene, C_2H_4, there is a triple bond between the two carbon atoms:

$$ \text{H—C}{\equiv}\text{C—H} $$

Acetylene

The triple bonds between two atoms may be represented by two tetrahedra sharing a face (Figure 11-4). Note that this causes the acetylene molecule to be linear.

Hybrid Bond Orbitals. In the discussion of the electronic structure of methane, CH_4, in Section 11–2 it was said that the carbon atom forms four covalent bonds by

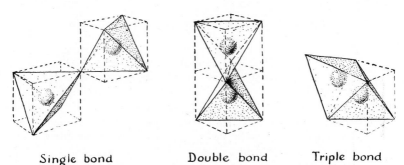

Single bond   Double bond   Triple bond

FIGURE 11-4 *Tetrahedral atoms forming single, double, and triple bonds.*

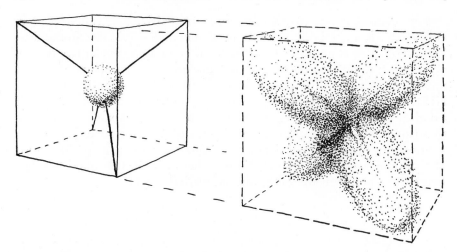

FIGURE 11-5   *Diagram illustrating (left) the 1s orbital in the K shell of the carbon atom, and (right) the four tetrahedral orbitals of the L shell.*

using the four orbitals of its L shell. These orbitals are given in Chapter 5 as the $2s$ orbital and the three $2p$ orbitals. We might hence ask whether or not the bonds to the four hydrogen atoms are all alike. Would not the $2s$ electron form a bond of one kind, and the three $2p$ electrons form bonds of a different kind?

Chemists have made many experiments to answer this question, and have concluded that the four bonds of the carbon atom are alike. A theory of the tetrahedral carbon atom was developed in 1931. According to this theory, the *theory of hybrid bond orbitals*, the $2s$ orbital and the three $2p$ orbitals of the carbon atom are hybridized (combined) to form four *tetrahedral bond orbitals*. They are exactly equivalent to one another, and are directed toward the corners of a regular tetrahedron, as shown in Figure 11-5.

Illustrative Exercises

11-6.   Three isomers of dichloroethylene, $C_2H_2Cl_2$, exist. Can you assign structural formulas to them? (Their names are 1,1-dichloroethylene, *cis*-1,2-dichloroethylene, and *trans*-1,2-dichloroethylene. The prefix *cis* means on the same side, and *trans* means on opposite sides.)

11-7.   The compound allene, C_3H_4, has the valence-bond structure

$$\overset{\displaystyle H \qquad\qquad\quad H}{\underset{\displaystyle H \qquad\qquad\quad H}{C\!\!=\!\!C\!\!=\!\!C}}$$

(a) Write the electronic structure for the molecule. (b) Draw the molecule, showing each carbon atom as a tetrahedron. (c) Are the four hydrogen atoms in one plane, or not?

11-8.   If you have studied trigonometry, you can verify that the angle between two tetrahedral bonds is 109° 28′. Refer to Figure 11-3, and note that the distance from the central atom (at the center of the cube, not shown) to a corner atom is one half of the body diagonal of the cube, and hence equal to $\sqrt{3}\,a/2$, where a is the length of the edge of the cube, and the distance between two corner atoms is the face diagonal of the cube, equal to $\sqrt{2}\,a$.

11–5. *Molecules and Crystals of the Non-Metallic Elements*

The Halogen Molecules.   A halogen atom such as fluorine can achieve the noble-gas structure by forming a single covalent bond with another halogen atom:

$$\ddot{\underset{\cdot\cdot}{\text{F}}}\!-\!\ddot{\underset{\cdot\cdot}{\text{F}}}\colon \qquad \colon\ddot{\underset{\cdot\cdot}{\text{Cl}}}\!-\!\ddot{\underset{\cdot\cdot}{\text{Cl}}}\colon \qquad \colon\ddot{\underset{\cdot\cdot}{\text{Br}}}\!-\!\ddot{\underset{\cdot\cdot}{\text{Br}}}\colon \qquad \colon\ddot{\underset{\cdot\cdot}{\text{I}}}\!-\!\ddot{\underset{\cdot\cdot}{\text{I}}}\colon$$

This single covalent bond holds the atoms together into diatomic mole. cules, which are present in the elementary halogens in all states of aggre. gation—crystal, liquid, and gas.

The Elements of the Sixth Group.   An atom of a sixth-group element, such as sulfur, lacks two electrons of having a completed octet. It can complete its octet by forming single covalent bonds with two other atoms. These bonds may hold the molecule together either into a ring, such as an S_8 ring, or into a very long chain, with the two end atoms having an abnormal structure:

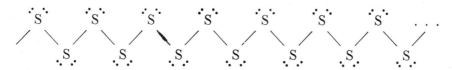

The elementary substance **sulfur** occurs in both these forms. Ordinary sulfur (orthorhombic sulfur) consists of molecules made of eight atoms. The molecule S_8 has the configuration shown in Figure 11-6; it is a

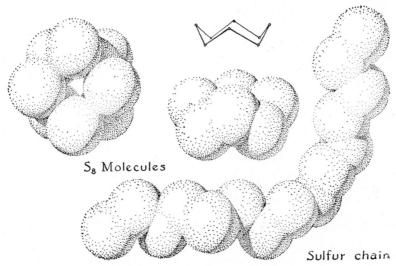

S_8 Molecules

Sulfur chain

FIGURE 11-6   *The S_8 ring, and a long chain of sulfur atoms.*

staggered octagonal ring. When sulfur is melted, it is converted into a straw-colored liquid, which also consists of the staggered ring S_8. However, when molten sulfur is heated to a temperature considerably above its melting point it becomes deep red in color and extremely viscous, so that it will not pour out of the test tube when it is inverted. This change in properties is the result of the formation of very large molecules containing hundreds of atoms into a long chain—the S_8 rings break open, and then combine together in a "high polymer." * The deep red color is due to the abnormal atoms at the ends of the chains, which are forming only one bond instead of the two bonds that a sulfur atom is expected to form. The great viscosity of the liquid is due to the interference with molecular motion caused by entanglement of the long chains of atoms with one another.

Selenium, which is just under sulfur in the periodic table, crystallizes as red crystals containing Se_8 molecules, and also as semi-metallic gray crystals which contain long staggered chains, stretching from one end of the crystal to the other. **Tellurium** crystals also contain long chains.

Ordinary **oxygen** consists of diatomic molecules with an unusual electronic structure. We might expect these molecules O_2 to contain a double bond:

$$:\overset{..}{O}::\overset{..}{O}: \qquad \text{or} \qquad :\overset{..}{O}=\overset{..}{O}:$$

Instead only one shared pair is formed, leaving two unshared electrons:

$$:\overset{..}{O}-\overset{.}{O}:$$

These two unshared electrons are responsible for the paramagnetism of oxygen. †

Ozone, the triatomic form of oxygen, has the electronic structure

---

* A *polymer* is a molecule made by combination of two or more identical smaller molecules. A *high polymer* is made by the combination of a great many smaller molecules.

† It has been found by study of the oxygen spectrum that the force of attraction between the oxygen atoms is much greater than that expected for a single covalent bond. This shows that the unpaired electrons are really involved in the formation of bonds of a special sort. The oxygen molecule may be said to contain a single covalent bond plus two *three-electron bonds*, and its structure may be written as

$$:\overset{..}{O}\overset{\cdot}{\underset{\cdot}{\vdots}}\overset{..}{O}:$$

Here one of the end atoms of the molecule resembles a fluorine atom in that it completes its octet by sharing only one electron pair. It may be considered to be the negative ion: $: \overset{..}{\underset{..}{O}} \cdot ~^{-}$, which forms one covalent bond.

The central oxygen atom of the ozone molecule resembles a nitrogen atom (see the following section), and may be considered to be the posi-

tive ion $: \overset{.}{\underset{.}{O}} \cdot ~^{+}$, which forms three covalent bonds (one double bond and one single bond).

Two structures for ozone are shown above, in brackets. This indicates that the two end oxygen atoms are not different, but are equivalent. The molecule has a structure represented by the superposition of the two structures shown; that is, each bond is a *hybrid* of a single covalent bond and a double covalent bond.

Nitrogen and Its Congeners.   The nitrogen atom, lacking three electrons of a completed octet, may complete the octet by forming three covalent bonds. It does this in elementary **nitrogen** by forming a triple bond in the molecule N_2. Three electron pairs are shared by the two nitrogen atoms:

$: N : : : N :$ or $: N \equiv N :$

This bond is extremely strong, and the N_2 molecule is a very stable molecule.

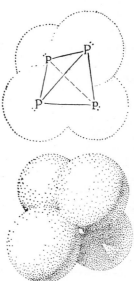

FIGURE 11-7

The P₄ molecule.

FIGURE 11-8

A layer of atoms from the arsenic crystal. Each atom is attached by single bonds to three other atoms.

Phosphorus gas at very high temperatures consists of P_2 molecules, with a similar structure, $: P \equiv P :$. At lower temperatures, however, phosphorus forms a molecule containing four atoms, P_4. This molecule has the structure shown in Figure 11-7. The four phosphorus atoms are arranged at the corners of a regular tetrahedron. Each phosphorus atom forms covalent bonds with the three other phosphorus atoms. This P_4 molecule exists in phosphorus vapor, in solutions of phosphorus in carbon disulfide and other non-polar solvents, and in solid white phosphorus. In other forms of elementary phosphorus (red phosphorus, black phosphorus) the atoms are bonded together into larger aggregates.

Arsenic and **antimony** also form tetrahedral molecules, As_4 and Sb_4, in the vapor phase. At higher temperatures these molecules dissociate into diatomic molecules, As_2 and Sb_2. Crystals of these elementary substances and of bismuth, however, contain high polymers—layers of atoms in which each atom is bonded to three neighbors by single covalent bonds, as shown in Figure 11-8.

Carbon and Its Congeners. Carbon, with four electrons missing from a completed octet, can form four covalent bonds. The structures of diamond and graphite have been discussed in Section 7–2. **Silicon, germanium,** and **gray tin** crystallize with the diamond structure. Ordinary tin (white tin) and lead have metallic structures (see Chapter 24).

Illustrative Exercises

11-9. Write the electronic structures of P_2, As_4, S_8, and S_x (x very large), showing all electron pairs in the outermost shell of each atom. Which noble-gas structure is assumed, in each case?

11-10. Describe the electronic structure of diamond.

11-11 Can you explain by use of the theory of the tetrahedral atom why elementary carbon is not a gas C_2, with structural formula $C \equiv C$?

11–6. *Resonance*

In the foregoing section it was mentioned that ozone has the structure

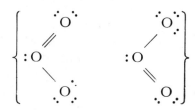

The reason for this statement is that it is known from experiment that the two oxygen-oxygen bonds in ozone are not different, but are equivalent. Equivalence of the bonds can be explained by the assumption of a *hybrid structure*. Each of the bonds in ozone is a hybrid between a single bond and a double bond, and its properties are intermediate between those of these two kinds of bonds.

It is customary to say that the double bond *resonates* between the two positions in ozone. *The resonance of molecules between two or more electronic structures* is an important concept. Often it is found difficult to assign to a molecule a single electronic structure of the valence-bond type which represents its properties satisfactorily. Often, also, two or more electronic structures seem to be about equally good. In these cases it is usually wise to say that the actual molecule resonates among the reasonable structures, and to indicate the molecule by writing the various resonating structures together in brackets. These various structures do not correspond to different kinds of molecules; there is only one kind of molecule present, with an electronic structure which is a hybrid structure of two or more valence bond structures.

The following resonating structures represent important molecules:

$$\left\{ : \text{C--} \overset{..}{\underset{..}{\text{O}}} : \qquad : \text{C} \!=\! \overset{..}{\text{O}} : \qquad : \text{C} \!\equiv\! \text{O} : \right\} \qquad \text{Carbon monoxide}$$

$$\left\{ : \overset{..}{\text{O}} \!=\! \text{C} \!=\! \underset{..}{\text{O}} : \qquad : \overset{..}{\underset{..}{\text{O}}} \!-\! \text{C} \!\equiv\! \text{O} : \qquad : \text{O} \!\equiv\! \text{C} \!-\! \overset{..}{\underset{..}{\text{O}}} : \right\} \qquad \begin{array}{l} \text{Carbon dioxide} \\ \text{(linear molecule)} \end{array}$$

$$\left\{ : \overset{..}{\text{S}} \!=\! \text{C} \!=\! \text{S} : \qquad : \overset{..}{\underset{..}{\text{S}}} \!-\! \text{C} \!\equiv\! \text{S} : \qquad : \text{S} \!\equiv\! \text{C} \!-\! \overset{..}{\underset{..}{\text{S}}} : \right\} \qquad \begin{array}{l} \text{Carbon disulfide} \\ \text{(linear molecule)} \end{array}$$

$$\left\{ : \overset{..}{\text{N}} \!=\! \text{N} \!=\! \underset{..}{\text{O}} : \qquad : \text{N} \!\equiv\! \text{N} \!-\! \overset{..}{\underset{..}{\text{O}}} : \right\} \qquad \begin{array}{l} \text{Nitrous oxide} \\ \text{(linear molecule)} \end{array}$$

There is experimental evidence showing that these molecules have the resonating structures indicated above. Perhaps the simplest evidence is that given by the distances between the atoms. It has been observed that in general the distance between two atoms connected by a double bond is approximately 0.21 Å less than the distance between the same two atoms connected by a single bond, and that the distance for a triple bond is approximately 0.13 Å less than that for a double bond. For example, the single-bond distance between two carbon atoms (as in diamond or ethane, H_3C—CH_3) is 1.54 Å; the double-bond distance is 1.33 Å, and the triple-bond distance is 1.20 Å. The distance between a carbon atom and an oxygen atom connected by a double bond as found in compounds such as formaldehyde,

$$
\begin{array}{c}
H \\
\diagdown \\
\quad\; C \!=\! \overset{\cdot\cdot}{O} : \\
\diagup \\
H
\end{array}
$$

is 1.22 Å. In carbon dioxide, however, for which the structure O=C=O was accepted for many years, the distance between the carbon atom and an oxygen atom has been found to be 1.16 Å. The shortening of 0.06 Å is due to the triple-bond character introduced by the two structures O≡C—O and O—C≡O (the effect of the triple bond on the inter-atomic distance is greater than the effect of the single bond).

11–7. *The Partial Ionic Character of Covalent Bonds*

Often a decision must be made as to whether a molecule is to be considered as containing an ionic bond or a covalent bond. There is no question about a salt of a strong metal and a strong non-metal; an ionic structure is to be written for it. Thus for lithium chloride we write

$$
Li^+Cl^- \qquad \text{or} \qquad Li^+ : \overset{\cdot\cdot}{\underset{\cdot\cdot}{Cl}} : ^-
$$

Similarly there is no doubt about nitrogen trichloride, NCl_3, an oily molecular substance composed of two non-metals. Its molecules have the covalent structure

$$
\begin{array}{c}
\overset{\cdot\;\cdot}{\underset{\cdot}{Cl}} \\
\diagup \\
: N \!\!-\!\!\! \overset{\cdot\cdot}{\underset{\cdot\cdot}{Cl}} : \\
\diagdown \\
\overset{\cdot}{\underset{\cdot\;\cdot}{Cl}}
\end{array}
$$

Between LiCl and NCl₃ there are the compounds $BeCl_2$, BCl_3, and CCl_4. Where does the change from an ionic structure to a covalent structure occur? Should CCl_4 be written

$$Cl^- \quad C^{++++}Cl^- \quad \text{or} \quad :\ddot{C}l - C - \ddot{C}l:\,?$$

(with Cl⁻ above and below on the left; and $:\ddot{C}l:$ above and below on the right)

The answer to this question is provided by the theory of resonance. *The transition from an ionic bond to a normal covalent bond does not occur sharply, but gradually.* The structure of the carbon tetrachloride molecule is best represented by the resonance hybrid of the structures given above, and the related ones

$$Cl^- \quad {}^+C - \ddot{C}l: \qquad Cl^- \quad \overset{++}{C} - \ddot{C}l:, \text{ etc.}$$

(each with $:\ddot{C}l:$ above and $:\ddot{C}l:$ below the central carbon)

Often only the covalent structure is shown, and the chemist bears in mind that the covalent bonds have a certain amount of ionic character. These bonds are called *covalent bonds with partial ionic character*.

For example, the hydrogen chloride molecule may be assigned the resonating structure

$$\left\{ H^+ \quad :\ddot{C}l:^- \qquad H-\ddot{C}l: \right\}$$

This is usually represented by the simple structural formula

$$H-\ddot{C}l: \quad \text{or} \quad H-Cl$$

It is then borne in mind that the hydrogen-chlorine bond has a certain amount (about 20%) of ionic character, which gives the hydrogen end of the molecule a small positive electric charge and the chlorine end a small negative charge.

In practice it is customary to indicate bonds between the highly electropositive metals and the non-metals as ionic bonds, and bonds between non-metals and non-metals or metalloids as covalent bonds, which are understood to have a certain amount of partial ionic character.

11–8. *The Electronegativity Scale of the Elements*

It has been found possible to assign to the elements numbers representing their power of attraction for the electrons in a covalent bond, by means of which the amount of partial ionic character of the bond may be estimated. This power of attraction for the electrons in a covalent bond is called the *electronegativity* of the element. In Figure 11-9 the elements other than the transition elements (which all have electronegativity values close to 1.6) and the rare-earth metals (which have values close to 1.3) are shown on an *electronegativity scale*. The way in which this scale was set up is described in Chapter 23.

The scale extends from cesium, with electronegativity 0.7, to fluorine, with electronegativity 4.0. Fluorine is by far the most electronegative element, with oxygen in second place, and nitrogen and chlorine in third place. Hydrogen and the metalloids are in the center of the scale, with electronegativity values close to 2. The metals have values about 1.7 or less.

The electronegativity scale as drawn in Figure 11-9 is seen to be similar in a general way to the periodic table, but deformed by pushing the top to the right and the bottom to the left. In describing the periodic table we have said that the strongest metals are in the lower left-hand corner and the strongest non-metals in the upper right-hand corner of the table: because of this deformation, the electronegativity scale shows the metallic or non-metallic character of an element simply as a function of the value of the horizontal coordinate, the electronegativity.

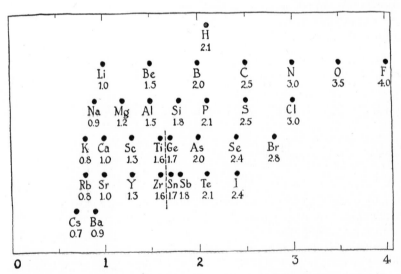

FIGURE 11-9   *The electronegativity scale. The dashed line indicates approximate values for the transition metals.*

The farther away two elements are from one another in the electronegativity scale (horizontally in Figure 11-8), the greater is the amount of ionic character of a bond between them. When the separation on the scale is 1.7 the bond has about 50% ionic character. If the separation is greater than this, it would seem appropriate to write an ionic structure for the substance, and if it is less to write a covalent structure. However, it is not necessary to adhere rigorously to this rule.

An important use of the electronegativity scale is to indicate roughly the stability or strength of a bond. *The greater the separation of two elements on the electronegativity scale, the greater is the strength of the bond between them.* Thus a bond between boron and nitrogen or between nitrogen and fluorine is a strong bond, whereas the bond between nitrogen and chlorine, as in nitrogen trichloride (which explodes when subjected to a blow), is a weak bond. In general great bond strength leads to the evolution of a large amount of energy when the bond is formed. Hydrogen burns in fluorine with the evolution of a great amount of energy, 64 kcal per mole of HF formed. This very large heat of reaction is correlated with the large electronegativity difference, 1.9 units, between hydrogen and fluorine.

The heat of formation of hydrogen chloride is 22 kcal per mole of hydrogen chloride formed, that of hydrogen bromide is 13 kcal per mole, and that of hydrogen iodide is 1.6 kcal per mole. The close relation between the heats of formation of these substances and the difference in partial ionic character of the atoms that are bonded together is evident. Reactions between elements with nearly the same electronegativity usually are accompanied by very small evolution or absorption of heat. (See also Section 23-3.)

Illustrative Exercises

11-12. Explain why the heat of formation of cesium fluoride from cesium and fluorine is very large (129 kcal/mole), and that of phosphine, PH_3, from red phosphorus and hydrogen is very small (2.2 kcal/mole).

11-13. Why is a great amount of heat liberated when metals combine with oxygen, but only a small amount when metals combine with other metals?

11-14. In which of the substances Al_2O_3, SiC, $MgCl_2$, and PI_3 do the bonds have more than 50% ionic character? Write a reasonable electronic structure for each substance.

11–9. Deviations from the Octet Rule

Sometimes heavy atoms form so many covalent bonds as to surround themselves with more than four electron pairs. An example is phosphorus pentachloride, PCl_5; in the molecule of this substance the phosphorus atom is surrounded by five chlorine atoms, with each of which it forms a covalent bond (with some ionic character).

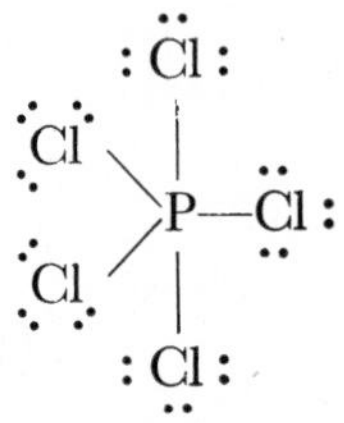

$$: \overset{\cdot\cdot}{\underset{\cdot\cdot}{Cl}} :$$

$$\overset{\cdot\cdot}{\underset{\cdot\cdot}{Cl}} \diagdown \mid$$

$$\overset{\cdot\cdot}{\underset{\cdot\cdot}{Cl}} \diagup P—\overset{\cdot\cdot}{\underset{\cdot\cdot}{Cl}} :$$

$$: \overset{}{\underset{\cdot\cdot}{Cl}} :$$

The phosphorus atom in this compound seems to be using five of the nine orbitals of the *M* shell, rather than only the four most stable orbitals, which are occupied by electrons in the argon configuration. It seems likely that of the nine or more orbitals in the *M* shell, the *N* shell, and the *O* shell four are especially stable, but that one or more others may occasionally be utilized.

11–10. *The Oxygen Acids*

It is customary to write the following structures for the simpler oxygen acids:

Silicic acid

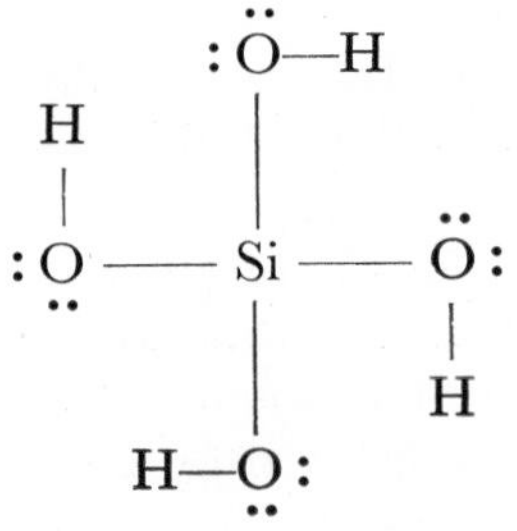

Phosphoric acid

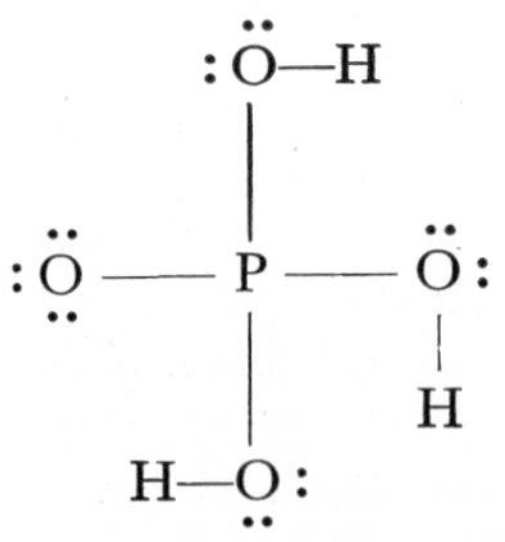

Sulfuric acid

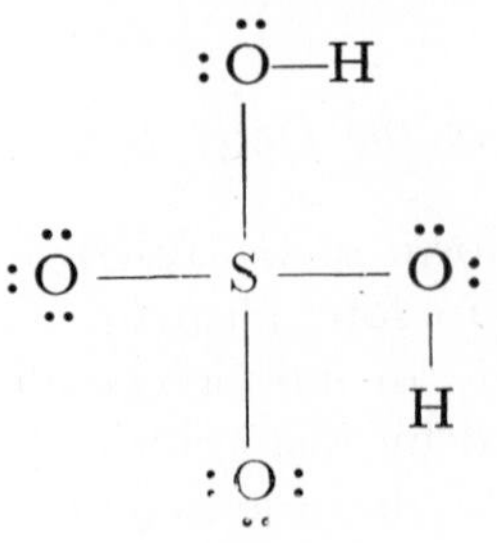

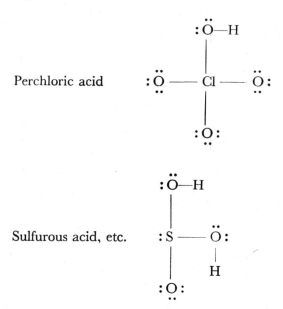

Perchloric acid

Sulfurous acid, etc.

The structures that are shown here are those in which the central atom makes use of the four orbitals corresponding to a noble-gas structure. There is evidence, however, that the central atom deviates from the octet rule, making use of additional orbitals and the unshared pairs of the oxygen atoms to form bonds with considerable double-bond character. Thus perchloric acid might be shown with the following structure, in which the chlorine atom forms double bonds with three oxygen atoms and a single bond with the fourth:

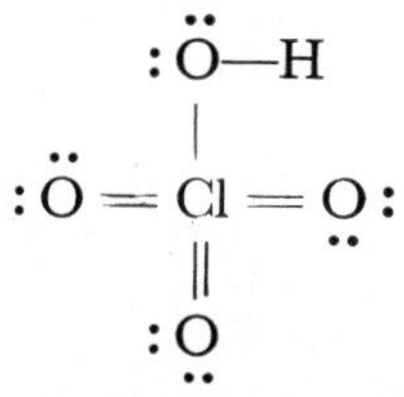

$$: \overset{\cdot\cdot}{O}\!-\!H$$
$$: \overset{\cdot\cdot}{O} = Cl = \overset{\cdot\cdot}{O} :$$
$$\overset{\parallel}{\underset{\cdot\cdot}{: O}}$$

In general it is satisfactory to write the simpler, single-bonded structures shown above for these oxygen acids and their anions.

Salts of these acids are ionic. Thus sodium sulfate has the structure

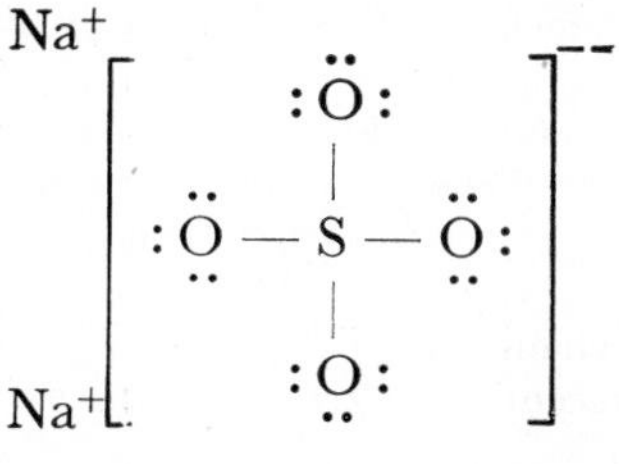

11–11. *How to Make Use of Electronic Structures*

In the study of descriptive chemistry it is a good practice to write electronic structures for all the new substances encountered, and to see whether they fit into the simple scheme with all atoms having noble-gas structures, or whether they constitute exceptions. It is possible in this way to gain an understanding of chemical phenomena and a systematization of the facts of chemistry that should be useful in your work.

You should write the electronic structures in such a way as to reproduce the actual structure of the molecule as closely as can conveniently be done. For example, the angle between two valence bonds formed by an oxygen atom is 105° to 110° (the tetrahedral angle); hence we

$$\begin{array}{c} H \\ | \\ \text{write} \; : \!\!\underset{\cdot\cdot}{O} \!\!-\!\! H \end{array} \text{ for the water molecule rather than } H\!\!-\!\!\overset{\cdot\cdot}{\underset{\cdot\cdot}{O}}\!\!-\!\!H.$$

11–12. *The Development of the Electronic Theory of Valence*

During the first decade of the nineteenth century many investigators made use of the electric battery newly discovered by Volta to carry out studies of the phenomenon of electrolysis of solutions and of molten salts. It was observed that in the electrolysis of water hydrogen is liberated at the cathode and oxygen at the anode, and that in the electrolysis of molten salts and metal hydroxides metals are liberated at the cathode and non-metals (chlorine, oxygen) at the anode.

On the basis of these results Berzelius in 1811 developed his *dualistic theory of chemical combination*. This theory involved the idea that in a salt the base and the acid have positive and negative charges, respectively, and that when the salt is electrolyzed they are drawn to the oppositely charged electrodes and liberated by neutralization of their charges. The theory is seen to have foreshadowed closely the present theory of ionic valence.

With the development of organic chemistry during the latter part of the nineteenth century the dualistic theory fell largely into disuse, because of the impossibility of applying it satisfactorily to the compounds of carbon, which in the main contain covalent bonds. The theory of the valence bond was then developed, as described in Section 7–1.

Soon after the discovery of the electron by J. J. Thomson efforts were made to formulate a more detailed structural theory of valence, based upon the electronic structure of molecules. The general ideas of electron transfer and of electron sharing were developed at this time, but detailed electronic structures could not be assigned to molecules with confidence because of lack of knowledge of the number of electrons in an atom and lack of information about atomic structures in general.

The determination of the atomic numbers of the elements by Moseley and the development of the quantum theory of the atom by Bohr, both in 1913, provided the basis for further progress. An important contribution was made in 1916 by Gilbert Newton Lewis, who pointed out the significance of completed shells of two and eight electrons and identified the covalent bonds with a pair of electrons shared by two atoms and counting as part of the outer shell of each.

After the discovery of the theory of quantum mechanics in 1925 a detailed quantitative theory of covalent bonds was developed. In recent years great progress has been made in understanding valence and chemical combination through the experimental determination of the structures of molecules and crystals and through theoretical studies. The theory of resonance was developed around 1930.

Concepts, Facts, and Terms Introduced in This Chapter

Shared-electron pair bond (covalent bond).

Completion of noble-gas configuration by the sharing of electrons.

The structure of covalent compounds. Isomers.

Formation of one covalent bond by the hydrogen atom and halogen atoms; formation of two covalent bonds by oxygen and its congeners; formation of three covalent bonds by nitrogen and other fifth-group elements; formation of four covalent bonds by carbon and its congeners.

The tetrahedral atom; angles between valence bonds; hybrid bond orbitals; equivalence of the four bonds formed by a carbon atom.

The structure of F_2, Cl_2, O_2, O_3, S_8, the sulfur chain, N_2, P_4, diamond, graphite.

Resonance; hybrid structures.

Partial ionic character of covalent bonds.

Electronegativity; the electronegativity scale; relation between electronegativity and strength of bond.

Deviations from the octet rule: PCl_5.

The electronic structure of the oxygen acids.

Exercises

11-15.   Make a drawing of each of the noble gases, He, Ne, A, Kr, Xe, and Rn, showing by dots the electrons in the outermost electron shell.

11-16.   Write electronic structures for hydrogen iodide, HI; hydrogen selenide, H_2Se; phosphine, PH_3; arsenic trichloride, $AsCl_3$; chloroform, $HCCl_3$; ethane, C_2H_6.

11-17.   Assuming that the following compounds contain ionic bonds only, write the electron-dot formula for each ion, and put in parentheses the symbol of the noble gas with the same structure:

HF   LiCl Na_2O MgO $KMgF_3$

11-18.   Write electronic structures for the following polyatomic ions, indicating all the electrons in the outer shell of each atom; assume that the various atoms of the ion are held together by covalent bonds:

Peroxide ion, O_2^{--}
Trisulfide ion, S_3^{--}
Borohydride ion, BH_4^-
Phosphonium ion, PH_4^+
Tetramethyl ammonium ion, $N(CH_3)_4^+$

For each of these ions, what corresponding neutral molecule has the same electronic structure? Example: HS^+, the hydrogen sulfide ion, has the same electronic structure as HCl.

11-19.   Write electronic structures for the molecules NH_3 (ammonia) and BF_3 (boron trifluoride). When these substances are mixed they react to form a compound

H_3NBF_3; such a compound is called an "addition compound." What is the electronic structure of this compound? What is the similarity in the electronic rearrangement in the following chemical reactions:

$$NH_3 + H^+ \longrightarrow NH_4^+$$

$$NH_3 + BF_3 \longrightarrow H_3NBF_3$$

11-20. Assuming covalent bonds, write electronic structures for the molecules ClF (chlorine fluoride), BrF_3 (bromine trifluoride), $SbCl_5$ (antimony pentachloride), H_2S_2 (hydrogen disulfide). In which of these molecules are there atoms with electron configurations that are not noble-gas configurations?

11-21. Write the resonating electronic structures for the nitrate ion, NO_3^-; the nitrite ion, NO_2^-; the carbonate ion, CO_3^{--}, ozone.

11-22. How does the difference in the structures of diamond and graphite manifest itself in some of the physical properties of these substances?

11-23. By reference to the electronegativity scale, arrange the following binary compounds in rough order of their stability, placing those that you think would be especially stable at the top of the list, and the most unstable at the bottom of the list:

Phosphine, PH_3 Cesium fluoride, CsF
Aluminum oxide, Al_2O_3 Sodium iodide, NaI
Hydrogen iodide, HI   Nitrogen trichloride, NCl_3
Lithium fluoride, LiF   Selenium diiodide, SeI_2

11-24. What is the electronic structure of tin tetraiodide, SnI_4? What noble-gas structure is assumed by each atom?

References

G. N. Lewis, *Valence and the Structure of Atoms and Molecules*, Chemical Catalog Co., **1923**. This is a famous book, in which the author summarizes his work on the chemical bond.

L. Pauling, *The Nature of the Chemical Bond and the Structure of Molecules and Crystals*, Cornell University Press, Second Edition, **1940**. Later developments in chemical bond theory are described in this book.

Chapter 12

Oxidation-Reduction Reactions

We shall now make use of our knowledge of electronic structure, ionic valence, and covalence in the discussion of some chemical reactions.

There are many different kinds of chemical reactions. Sometimes it is possible to classify a chemical reaction by use of suitable words. The reaction of hydrogen and oxygen with one another to form water may be described as the *combination* of these elements to form the compound, or their *direct union*. The reaction of mercuric oxide when it is heated to form mercury and oxygen may be called the *decomposition* of this substance. Chlorine reacts with a compound such as methane, CH_4, in the sunlight or in the presence of catalysts to produce hydrogen chloride and methyl chloride, CH_3Cl:

$$CH_4 + Cl_2 \longrightarrow CH_3Cl + HCl$$

This reaction has been described in Chapter 7 as the *substitution* of chlorine for hydrogen in methane.

Although different kinds of chemical reactions are thus easily recognized, it has not been found very useful in general to attempt to classify reactions in a rigorous way. Nevertheless, there is one very important class of chemical reactions that deserves special study. These reactions are *oxidation-reduction reactions*, to which we now turn our attention.

12–1. *Oxidation and Reduction*

The Generalized Use of the Word Oxidation.   When charcoal burns in air it forms the gases carbon monoxide and carbon dioxide:

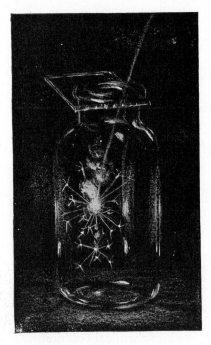

FIGURE 12-1

An iron wire burning in oxygen.

$$2C + O_2 \longrightarrow 2CO$$
$$2CO + O_2 \longrightarrow 2CO_2$$

When hydrogen burns in air it forms water:

$$2H_2 + O_2 \longrightarrow 2H_2O$$

When an iron wire heated red-hot at one end is introduced into a bottle of pure oxygen the iron burns to form iron oxide (Figure 12-1); iron also reacts slowly with air ("rusts") under ordinary conditions:

$$4Fe + 3O_2 \longrightarrow 2Fe_2O_3$$

In all of these reactions an element combines with oxygen to form an oxide. This process of combining with oxygen was named oxidation many years ago.

It was then recognized by chemists that combination with a non-metallic element other than oxygen closely resembles combination with oxygen. Carbon burns in fluorine even more vigorously than in oxygen:

$$C + 2F_2 \longrightarrow CF_4$$

Hydrogen burns in fluorine and in chlorine:

$$H_2 + F_2 \longrightarrow 2HF$$
$$H_2 + Cl_2 \longrightarrow 2HCl$$

Iron burns in fluorine and when heated combines readily with chlorine and also with sulfur:

$$2Fe + 3F_2 \longrightarrow 2FeF_3$$

$$2Fe + 3Cl_2 \longrightarrow 2FeCl_3$$

$$Fe + S \longrightarrow FeS$$

Because of the similarity of these reactions to combination with oxygen they have come to be described as involving a generalized sort of oxidation.

Oxidation and Electron Transfer.   In accordance with this usage we would say that metallic sodium is oxidized when it burns in chlorine to form sodium chloride:

$$2Na + Cl_2 \longrightarrow 2Na^+Cl^-$$

Here we have written sodium chloride as Na^+Cl^- to show that it consists of ions.

The oxidation of metallic sodium is the process of removing an electron from each sodium atom:

$$Na \longrightarrow Na^+ + e^-$$

Reduction.   The reverse process to that of oxidation is called reduction. In its restricted usage *reduction* is the removal of oxygen from an oxide, to produce the element: we speak of an ore, such as an iron ore, as being reduced to the metal in a blast furnace.

The reverse of the process of oxidation of metallic sodium to sodium ion is the reduction of sodium ion to metallic sodium. This reduction is not an easy process. It was first achieved by Davy, by electrolysis (Chapter 10).

In the electrolysis of molten sodium chloride there occurs at the cathode the reaction

$$Na^+ + e^- \longrightarrow Na$$

This reaction, the reduction of sodium ion to metallic sodium by the addition of an electron from the cathode, is called *cathodic reduction.*

The Electronic Definitions of Oxidation and Reduction.   From these examples we see the justification for the modern usage of the words oxidation and reduction:

Oxidation is the removal of electrons from an atom or group of atoms.

Reduction is the addition of electrons to an atom or group of atoms.

Professor E. C. Franklin of Stanford University made use of the terms *de-electronation* in place of oxidation and *electronation* in place of reduction. It may help you to remember the nature of oxidation and reduction by remembering the following statements: **Oxidation is de-electronation. Reduction is electronation.**

When molten sodium chloride is decomposed by electrolysis free chlorine is formed at the anode:

$$2Cl^- \longrightarrow Cl_2 + 2e^-$$

This is an example of *anodic oxidation*. The electrons that are liberated in this reaction move into the anode and along the wire connecting the anode with the generator or battery.

Oxidation and reduction reactions can take place either at the electrodes, which supply electrons and take up electrons, or by direct contact of atoms or molecules, with direct transfer of electrons. Thus when sodium burns in chlorine the sodium atoms transfer their electrons directly to the chlorine atoms at the time that the molecule of chlorine strikes the surface of the metal (Figure 12-2):

$$2Na \longrightarrow 2Na^+ + 2e^-$$
$$\underline{Cl_2 + 2e^- \longrightarrow 2Cl^-}$$
$$2Na + Cl_2 \longrightarrow 2Na^+Cl^-$$

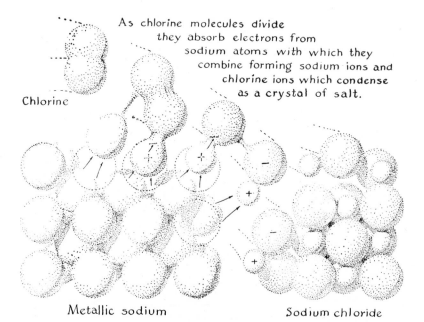

As chlorine molecules divide
they absorb electrons from
sodium atoms with which they
combine forming sodium ions and
chlorine ions which condense
as a crystal of salt.

Chlorine

Metallic sodium   Sodium chloride

FIGURE 12-2   *The reaction of sodium and chlorine to form sodium chloride.*

The Simultaneous Occurrence of Oxidation and Reduction. Oxidation or reduction of a substance could be carried out without simultaneous reduction or oxidation of another substance if one had at hand a very large electric condenser from which to remove electrons or in which to store them. Ordinarily such an electron reservoir is not available; even the very largest electric condenser charged to its maximum potential holds so few electrons (compared with Avogadro's number) that only a very small amount of chemical reaction can be produced by it. *There accordingly occur equivalent processes of oxidation and reduction in every oxidation-reduction reaction.*

Oxidizing Agents and Reducing Agents. An atom, molecule, or ion which takes up electrons is called an *oxidizing agent*, and one which liberates electrons is called a *reducing agent.*

For example, in the formation of magnesium fluoride by combination of magnesium and fluorine magnesium is the reducing agent and fluorine is the oxidizing agent:

$$Mg + F_2 \longrightarrow Mg^{++}(F^-)_2$$

In the electrolytic production of sodium at the cathode of an electrolytic cell we may say that the cathode, with its excess of electrons, is the reducing agent that reduces sodium ion to metallic sodium. Similarly we may say that the anode, with its deficiency of electrons, is the oxidizing agent that oxidizes chloride ion to free chlorine.

It is interesting to note that *every electron reaction involves an oxidizing agent and a reducing agent, which are closely related to one another.* Thus sodium ions in molten sodium chloride can be reduced to metallic sodium by the cathode of the cell:

$$Na^+ + e^- \longrightarrow Na$$

In this electron reaction the oxidizing agent Na^+ is reduced by the cathode. But when sodium combines with chlorine to form sodium chloride the metallic sodium Na is oxidized to Na^+, by giving its electron up to chlorine:

$$Na \longrightarrow Na^+ + e^-$$

In this reaction metallic sodium is the reducing agent. Metallic sodium and sodium ion are called an *oxidation-reduction pair*, or *oxidation-reduction couple.* The interconversion of metallic sodium and sodium ion by an electron reaction can be expressed by a single equation, with a double arrow:

$$Na \rightleftarrows Na^+ + e^-$$

The direction in which this reaction proceeds in any system depends upon the nature of the system.

An example of the reversal of an electron reaction involving an oxidation-reduction pair is the bromine-bromide ion pair:

$$Br_2 + 2e^- \rightleftarrows 2Br^-$$

Here elementary bromine, Br_2, is the oxidizing agent of the pair and bromide ion is the reducing agent. Bromine is a strong enough oxidizing agent to liberate iodine from iodide ion; that is to oxidize iodide ion to iodine:

$$Br_2 + 2e^- \longrightarrow 2Br^-$$
$$2I^- \longrightarrow I_2 + 2e^-$$
$$\overline{Br_2 + 2I^- \longrightarrow 2Br^- + I_2}$$

However, chlorine is a still stronger oxidizing agent; it is able to liberate bromine from bromide ion:

$$Cl_2 + 2e^- \longrightarrow 2Cl^-$$
$$2Br^- \longrightarrow Br_2 + 2e^-$$
$$\overline{Cl_2 + 2Br^- \longrightarrow 2Cl^- + Br_2}$$

Thus in one of these two oxidation-reduction reactions the bromine-bromide ion electron reaction proceeds in one direction, and in the other reaction it proceeds in the other direction.

The conditions determining the direction in which an electron reaction proceeds are discussed later in this chapter and also in Chapter 23. It has been found that the oxidation-reduction pairs can be arranged in a series with increasing strength of the oxidizing agent and decreasing strength of the reducing agent. Thus as oxidizing agents the halogens lie in the order

$$F_2 > Cl_2 > Br_2 > I_2$$

and as reducing agents their ions lie in the reverse order:

$$I^- > Br^- > Cl^- > F^-$$

The non-metallic elements are strong oxidizing agents, and the metals are strong reducing agents. There is rough correspondence between the strength of an elementary substance as an oxidizing or reducing agent and its electronegativity, discussed in the preceding chapter. Fluorine, the element with the greatest electronegativity, is also the strongest oxidizing agent known. The alkali metals, with the smallest electronegativity, are the strongest reducing agents.

Illustrative Exercises

12-1. Aluminum wire will burn in an atmosphere of fluorine, forming aluminum fluoride. (a) By reference to the periodic table, predict the ionic valence of aluminum and the formula of aluminum fluoride. (b) What is the oxidizing agent and what is the reducing agent in this reaction?

12-2.   (a) What halogen might you use to oxidize chloride ion to chlorine? (b) What halogenide ion might you use to reduce chlorine to chloride ion? (c) Write equations for the two reactions.

12–2. Oxidation Numbers of Atoms

The examples given above of oxidation-reduction reactions have involved the interconversion of atoms and monatomic ions. It is convenient to extend the idea of electron transfer in such a way as to permit it to be applied to all substances. This is done by introducing the concept of *oxidation number*.

For example, let us consider the reduction of the permanganate ion. Potassium permanganate, $KMnO_4$, is a purple crystalline substance soluble in water to produce a magenta solution. It is a strong oxidizing agent, and it is sometimes used in the jungle to disinfect water (it oxidizes the bacteria). The solution of potassium permanganate contains the magenta-colored permanganate ion, MnO_4^-. In the presence of alkali this ion is easily reduced to the manganate ion, MnO_4^{--}, which has a green color. The reduction can be carried out by electrolysis; the electrons are then transferred from the cathode to the permanganate ion to produce the manganate ion:

$$MnO_4^- + e^- \longrightarrow MnO_4^{--}$$

It is clear that the permanganate ion has served as the oxidizing agent in this electron reaction, having been reduced by the cathode, which transferred an electron to it. If we knew enough about the electronic structure of the permanganate ion and the manganate ion we might be able to say that the added electron had attached itself to a particular atom. It is, in fact, convenient to do so—we say that the added electron has attached itself to the manganese atom, which has been reduced; the oxygen atoms in the permanganate ion are considered not to have changed, in this respect, on conversion of the permanganate ion to the manganate ion. We say that the *oxidation number* of manganese has changed from $+7$ to $+6$, whereas that of oxygen has remained unchanged at -2.

The **oxidation number** *of an atom is a number that represents the electric charge that the atom would have if the electrons in a compound were assigned to the atoms in a certain way.*

The assignment of electrons is somewhat arbitrary, but the procedure described below is useful because it permits a simple statement to be made about the valences of the elements in a compound without considering its electronic structure in detail and because it can be made the basis of a simple method of balancing equations for oxidation-reduction reactions.

An oxidation number may be assigned to each atom in a substance by the application of simple rules. These rules, while simple, are not completely unambiguous. Although their application is usually a straightforward procedure, it sometimes requires considerable chemical insight and knowledge of molecular structure. The rules are given in the following sentences:

1. *The oxidation number of a monatomic ion in an ionic substance is equal to its electric charge.*
2. *The oxidation number of an atom in an elementary substance is zero.*
3. *In a covalent compound of known structure, the oxidation number of each atom is the charge remaining on the atom when each shared electron pair is assigned completely to the more electronegative of the two atoms sharing it. An electron pair shared by two atoms of the same element is usually split between them.*
4. *The oxidation number of an element in a compound of uncertain structure may be calculated from a reasonable assignment of oxidation numbers to the other elements in the compounds.*

The application of the first three rules is illustrated by the following examples; the number by the symbol of each atom is the oxidation number of that atom:

$Na^{+1}Cl^{-1}$ $Mg^{+2}(Cl^{-1})_2$ $(B^{+3})_2(O^{-2})_3$

H_2^0 O_2^0 C^0 (diamond or graphite)

H^{+1} (hydrogen cation) $(O^{-2}H^{+1})^-$ (hydroxide ion)

$N^{-3}(H^{+1})_3$ $Cl^{+1}F^{-1}$ $C^{+4}(O^{-2})_2$

$C^{+2}O^{-2}$ $C^{-4}(H^{+1})_4$ $K^{+1}Mn^{+7}(O^{-2})_4$

Fluorine, the most electronegative element, has the oxidation number -1 in all of its compounds with other elements.

Oxygen is second only to fluorine in electronegativity, and in its compounds it usually has oxidation number -2; examples are $Ca^{+2}O^{-2}$, $(Fe^{+3})_2(O^{-2})_3$, $C^{+4}(O^{-2})_2$. Oxygen fluoride, OF_2, is an exception; in this compound, in which oxygen is combined with the only element that is more electronegative than it is, oxygen has the oxidation number $+2$. The peroxides, which are discussed in the section following the next one, are also exceptional; oxygen has the oxidation number -1 in these compounds.

Hydrogen when bonded to a non-metal has oxidation number $+1$, as in $(H^{+1})_2O^{-2}$, $(H^{+1})_2S^{-2}$, $H^{+1}Cl^{-1}$, etc. In compounds with metals, such as $Li^{+1}H^{-1}$, its oxidation number is -1, corresponding to the electronic structure $H:^{-1}$ for a negative hydrogen ion with completed K shell (helium structure). On electrolysis of fused alkali hydride hydrogen is liberated at the anode, according to the equation

$$2H^- \longrightarrow H_2 \uparrow + 2e^-$$

Values of Oxidation Numbers of Elements.   Some of the elements are well-behaved in their compounds, in that they assume only certain standard oxidation numbers, whereas other elements are much more variable.

The elements of the first three groups of the periodic table have normal oxidation numbers, $+1$, $+2$, and $+3$, respectively, in all of their compounds, with rare exceptions. The processes of oxidation and reduction that these elements undergo are simply the interconversion of the elementary substances and their ions.

It will be found in later chapters that the non-metals, in groups V, VI, and VII of the periodic table, show a variety of oxidation numbers, usually extending over a range of 8, with the important ones tending to differ by 2. Thus the halogens (aside from fluorine, which has oxidation numbers 0 and -1 only) have oxidation numbers ranging from -1 to $+7$, with $+1$, $+3$, and $+5$ the important intermediate values. The congeners of oxygen have oxidation numbers ranging from -2 to $+6$, and nitrogen and its congeners have oxidation numbers ranging from -3 to $+5$.

Each of the transition elements tends to have several oxidation numbers. Thus iron forms one series of compounds with oxidation number $+2$ (ferrous compounds) and another series with oxidation number $+3$ (ferric compounds). For chromium the principal oxidation numbers are $+3$ and $+6$, and for manganese they are $+2$ and $+7$. It would be of great value to chemistry if a simple and reliable theory of the oxidation states of the transition elements were to be developed; but this has not yet been done.

Illustrative Exercises

12-3.   Verify that the oxidation number of manganese is $+7$ in permanganate ion, MnO_4^-, and $+6$ in manganate ion, MnO_4^{--}.

12-4.   What is the oxidation number of sulfur in hydrogen sulfide, H_2S? In elementary sulfur, S_8? In sulfur dioxide, SO_2? In sulfuric acid, H_2SO_4? In the sulfate ion, SO_4^{--}?

12-5.   What is the oxidation number of manganese in the elementary substance? In manganous chloride, $MnCl_2 \cdot 4H_2O$? In manganese dioxide, MnO_2?

12–3. Oxidation Number and Chemical Nomenclature

The principal classification of the compounds of an element is made on the basis of its oxidation state. In our discussions of the compounds formed by the various elements or groups of elements in the following chapters of this book we begin by a statement of the oxidation states represented by the compounds. The compounds are grouped together in classes, representing those with the principal element in the same oxidation state. For example, in the discussion of the compounds of iron, in Chapter 27, they are divided into two classes, representing the compounds of iron in oxidation state $+2$ and those in oxidation state $+3$, respectively.

The nomenclature of the compounds of the metals is also based upon their oxidation states. At the present time there are two principal nomenclatures in use. We may illustrate the two systems of nomenclature by taking the compounds $FeCl_2$ and $FeCl_3$ as examples. In the older system a compound of a metal in the lower of two important oxidation states is named by use of the name of the metal (usually the Latin name) with the suffix *ous*. Thus the salts of iron in oxidation state $+2$ are *ferrous* salts; $FeCl_2$ is called *ferrous chloride*. The compounds of a metal in the higher oxidation state are named with use of the suffix *ic*. The salts of iron in oxidation state $+3$ are called *ferric* salts; $FeCl_3$ is *ferric chloride*.

Note that the suffixes ous and ic do not tell what the oxidation states are. For copper compounds, such as $CuCl$ and $CuCl_2$, the compounds in which copper has oxidation number $+1$ are called cuprous compounds, and those in which it has oxidation number $+2$ are called cupric compounds.

A new system of nomenclature for inorganic compounds was drawn up by a committee of the International Union of Chemistry in 1940.* According to this system the value of the oxidation number of a metal is represented by a Roman numeral given in parentheses following the name (usually the English name rather than the Latin name) of the metal. Thus $FeCl_2$ is given the name iron(II) chloride, and $FeCl_3$ is given the name iron(III) chloride. These names are read simply by stating the numeral after the name of the metal: thus iron(II) chloride is read as iron two chloride.

It may be noted that it is not necessary to give the oxidation number of a metal in naming a compound if the metal forms only one principal series of compounds. The compound $BaCl_2$ may be called barium chloride rather than barium(II) chloride, because barium forms no compounds other than those in which it has oxidation number $+2$. Also, if one oxidation state is represented by many compounds, and another by only a few, the oxidation state does not need to be indicated for the compounds of the important series. Thus the compounds of copper with oxidation number $+2$ are far more important than those of copper with oxidation number $+1$, and for this reason $CuCl_2$ may be called simply copper chloride, whereas $CuCl$ would have to be called copper(I) chloride.

We shall in general make use of the new system of nomenclature in the following chapters of our book, except that, for convenience, we shall use the old nomenclature for the following common metals:

* The system is described in the Journal of the American Chemical Society, **63**, 889 (1941).

Iron: $+2$, ferrous; $+3$, ferric
Copper: $+1$, cuprous; $+2$, cupric (or copper)
Mercury: $+1$, mercurous; $+2$, mercuric
Tin: $+2$, stannous; $+4$, stannic

Compounds of metalloids and non-metals are usually given names in which the numbers of atoms of different kinds are indicated by prefixes, as described in Chapter 6. The compounds PCl_3 and PCl_5, for example, are called phosphorus trichloride and phosphorus pentachloride, respectively.

12–4. *How to Balance Equations for Oxidation-Reduction Reactions*

The principal use of the oxidation numbers that we have been discussing in the preceding section is in writing equations for oxidation-reduction reactions.

The first step in writing the equation for an oxidation-reduction reaction is the same as for any other chemical reaction: **be sure that you know what the reactants are and what the products are.**

The chemist finds what the reactants and the products are by studying the reaction as it occurs in the laboratory or in nature, or by reading in journals or books to find out what other chemists have learned about the reaction. Sometimes, of course, a knowledge of chemical theory permits a safe prediction about the nature of the reaction to be made.

The next step is to balance the equation for the reaction. In balancing the equation for an oxidation-reduction reaction it is often wise to write the electron reactions separately (as they would occur in an electrolytic cell), and then to add them so as to cancel out the electrons. For example, ferric ion, Fe^{+++}, oxidizes stannous ion, Sn^{++}, to stannic ion, Sn^{++++}; that is, from the bipositive state to the quadripositive state. The ferric ion is itself reduced to ferrous ion, Fe^{++}. The two electron reactions are

$$Fe^{+++} + e^- \longrightarrow Fe^{++}$$

and

$$Sn^{++} \longrightarrow Sn^{++++} + 2e^-$$

Note that there is conservation of electric charge as well as conservation of atoms in each of these equations.

Before adding these two equations the first must be multiplied by 2 to use up the two electrons that are given by the second; then the two equations may be added together:

$$2Fe^{+++} + 2e^- \longrightarrow 2Fe^{++}$$
$$Sn^{++} \longrightarrow Sn^{++++} + 2e^-$$
$$\overline{2Fe^{+++} + Sn^{++} \longrightarrow 2Fe^{++} + Sn^{++++}}$$

The consideration of the electrode reactions has shown that two ferric ions are required to oxidize one stannous ion, because the reduction of ferric ion requires only one electron, whereas in the oxidation of stannous ion two electrons are given up.

The process of balancing a more complicated equation is illustrated by the example given below.

Example 1. If potassium permanganate, $KMnO_4$, is dissolved in water and a solution of ferrous salt, such as ferrous sulfate, $FeSO_4$, containing some sulfuric acid is added, the permanganate ion is reduced to manganese(II) ion, Mn^{++}, and the ferrous ion is oxidized to ferric ion. Write the equation for the reaction.

    Solution. The oxidation number of manganese in permanganate ion, MnO_4^-, is $+7$. The oxidation number of manganese in manganese(II) ion, Mn^{++}, is $+2$. Hence 5 electrons are involved in the reduction of permanganate ion to manganese(II) ion. The electron reaction is accordingly

$$[Mn^{+7}(O^{-2})_4]^- + 5e^- + \text{other reactants} \longrightarrow Mn^{++}$$
$$+ \text{other products} \quad (1a)$$

In reactions in aqueous solution water, hydrogen ion, and hydroxide ion may come into action as reactants or products. For example, in an acidic solution hydrogen ion may be either a reactant or a product, and water may also be either a reactant or a product in the same reaction. In an acidic solution hydroxide ion exists only in extremely low concentration and would hardly be expected to enter into the reaction. Hence water and hydrogen ion may enter into the reaction now under consideration.

Equation 1a is not balanced electrically; there are 6 negative charges on the left side and 2 positive charges on the right side. The only other ion that can enter into the reaction is hydrogen ion, H^+. The number of hydrogen ions needed to give conservation of electric charge is 8. Thus we obtain, as the second step in our process, the following equation:

$$MnO_4^- + 5e^- + 8H^+ \longrightarrow Mn^{++} + \text{other products} \quad (1b)$$

Oxygen and hydrogen occur here on the left side and not on the right side of the equation; conservation of atoms is satisfied if $4H_2O$ is written in as the "other products":

$$MnO_4^- + 5e^- + 8H^+ \longrightarrow Mn^{++} + 4H_2O \quad (1)$$

We now check this equation on three points—*proper change in oxidation number* (5 electrons were used, corresponding to the change of -5 in oxidation number of manganese from Mn^{+7} in permanganate ion to Mn^{+2} in manganese(II) ion), *conservation of electric charge* (from $-1 - 5 + 8$ to $+2$), and *conservation of atoms*—and convince ourselves that it is correct.

The electron reaction for the oxidation of ferrous ion to ferric ion is now written:

$$Fe^{++} \longrightarrow Fe^{+++} + e^- \tag{2}$$

This equation checks on all three points.

The equation for the oxidation-reduction reaction itself is obtained by combining the two electron reactions in such a way that the electrons liberated in one are used up in the other. We see that this is to be achieved by multiplying Equation 2 by 5 and adding it to Equation 1:

$$5Fe^{++} \longrightarrow 5Fe^{+++} + 5e^-$$
$$\underline{MnO_4^- + 5e^- + 8H^+ \longrightarrow Mn^{++} + 4H_2O}$$
$$MnO_4^- + 5Fe^{++} + 8H^+ \longrightarrow Mn^{++} + 5Fe^{+++} + 4H_2O \tag{3}$$

It is good practice to check this final equation also on all three points to be sure that no mistake has been made:

1. *Change in oxidation number:* Mn^{+7} to Mn^{+2}, change -5; $5Fe^{++}$ to $5Fe^{+++}$, change $+5$.
2. *Conservation of electric charge:* left side, $-1 + 10 + 8 = +17$; right side, $+2 + 15 = +17$
3. *Conservation of atoms:* Left side, 1Mn, 4O, 5Fe, 8H; right side, 1 Mn, 5Fe, 8H, 4O

It is not always necessary to carry through this entire procedure. Sometimes an equation is so simple that it can be written at once and verified by inspection. An example is the oxidation of iodide ion by chlorine:

$$Cl_2 + 2I^- \longrightarrow 2Cl^- + I_2$$

Illustrative Exercises

12-6. Balance the equation for the reaction of aluminum and fluorine to form aluminum fluoride, writing first the equations for the electron reactions and then that for the over-all reaction.

12-7. Ferric ion, Fe^{+++}, in aqueous solution is reduced to ferrous ion, Fe^{++}, by metallic zinc, which is oxidized to zinc ion, Zn^{++}. Write equations for the electron reactions and the over-all reaction.

12-8. Under certain conditions silver dissolves in nitric acid, HNO_3, to form silver ion, Ag^+, and nitric oxide gas, NO. (a) What is the oxidation number of nitrogen in nitric acid? In nitric oxide? (b) Balance the following equations for the electron reactions and the over-all reaction:

$$Ag \longrightarrow Ag^+ + e^-$$
$$\underline{H^+ + HNO_3 \longrightarrow H_2O + NO}$$
$$Ag + H^+ + HNO_3 \longrightarrow Ag^+ + H_2O + NO$$

12–5. *An Example: The Reactions of Hydrogen Peroxide*

Preparation, Properties, and Structure of Hydrogen Peroxide.
When barium oxide, BaO, is heated to a dull red heat in a stream of
air it adds oxygen to form a similar compound, BaO_2, *barium peroxide:*

$$2BaO + O_2 \longrightarrow 2BaO_2$$

This salt contains the *peroxide ion*, O_2^{--}, which has the electronic structure

$$\left[:\overset{..}{O}-\overset{..}{O}: \right]^{--}$$

There is a single covalent bond between the two oxygen atoms. The
oxidation number of oxygen in the peroxide ion and in peroxides is -1.
These substances represent an intermediate oxidation state between
free oxygen (oxygen with oxidation number 0 in O_2) and oxides (O^{-2}).

The electrolysis of a peroxide solution leads to the liberation of one
mole of oxygen at the anode by two moles of electrons, the anode
reaction being

$$O_2^{--} \longrightarrow O_2 \uparrow + 2e^-$$

Care must be taken to distinguish between *peroxides*, which contain
two oxygen atoms with a single covalent bond between them, and

dioxides. Thus BaO_2 is a peroxide, containing Ba^{++} and $\left[:\overset{..}{O}-\overset{..}{O}: \right]^{--}$,

and TiO_2, titanium dioxide, is a dioxide, containing Ti^{++++} and two
oxygen ions, O^{--}. A peroxide usually liberates hydrogen peroxide when
treated with acid, whereas a dioxide does not.

Hydrogen peroxide, H_2O_2, is made by treating barium peroxide with
sulfuric acid or phosphoric acid, and distilling:*

$$BaO_2 + H_2SO_4 \longrightarrow BaSO_4 + H_2O_2$$

Pure hydrogen peroxide is a colorless, sirupy liquid, with density
1.47 g/cm^3, melting point $-1.7°$ C, and boiling point $151°$ C. It is a
very strong oxidizing agent, which spontaneously oxidizes organic substances. Its uses are in the main determined by its oxidizing power.

Commercial hydrogen peroxide is an aqueous solution, sometimes
containing a small amount of a stabilizer, such as phosphate ion, to
decrease its rate of decomposition to water and oxygen by the reaction

$$2H_2O_2 \longrightarrow 2H_2O + O_2 \uparrow$$

* A method involving organic compounds is used in industry.

Drug-store hydrogen peroxide is a 3% solution (containing 3 g H_2O_2 per 100 g), for medical use as an antiseptic, or a 6% solution, for bleaching hair. A 30% solution and, in recent years, an 85% solution are used in chemical industries. The 85% solution (nearly pure hydrogen peroxide) has found some use as the oxidizing agent to burn fuel in rockets and for submarine propulsion.

The structure of the hydrogen peroxide molecule is

$$\text{H} \quad \text{H}$$
$$| \quad |$$
$$:\text{O}\!-\!\text{O}:$$

Hydrogen Peroxide as an Oxidizing Agent.   It is the oxidizing power of hydrogen peroxide that causes it to be used for bleaching hair and other materials and that is responsible for its effectiveness as an antiseptic. Oil paintings that have been discolored by the formation of lead sulfide, PbS, which is black in color, from the white lead (a hydroxide-carbonate of lead) in the paint may be bleached by washing with hydrogen peroxide. The reaction that occurs is the oxidation of lead sulfide to lead sulfate (which is white):

$$\text{PbS} + 4\text{H}_2\text{O}_2 \longrightarrow \text{PbSO}_4 + 4\text{H}_2\text{O}$$

The electron reaction for the reduction of hydrogen peroxide in acidic solution is

$$\text{H}_2\text{O}_2 + 2\text{H}^+ + 2e^- \longrightarrow 2\text{H}_2\text{O}$$

Two electrons are required, because each of the two oxygen atoms of the H_2O_2 molecule changes its oxidation number from -1 to -2.

Hydrogen Peroxide as a Reducing Agent.   Hydrogen peroxide can also serve as a reducing agent, with increase in oxidation number of oxygen from -1 to 0, and the liberation of molecular oxygen.

This activity is shown, for example, by the decolorizing of an acidic solution of potassium permanganate by addition of hydrogen peroxide. The permanganate ion, MnO_4^-, is reduced to the manganese(II) ion, Mn^{++}, and free oxygen is liberated. The electron reactions are

$$\text{H}_2\text{O}_2 \longrightarrow \text{O}_2 + 2\text{H}^+ + 2e^-$$
$$\text{MnO}_4^- + 5e^- + 8\text{H}^+ \longrightarrow \text{Mn}^{++} + 4\text{H}_2\text{O}$$

or, with the proper factors to balance the electrons,

$$5\text{H}_2\text{O}_2 \longrightarrow 5\text{O}_2 + 10\text{H}^+ + 10e^-$$
$$\underline{2\text{MnO}_4^- + 10e^- + 16\text{H}^+ \longrightarrow 2\text{Mn}^{++} + 8\text{H}_2\text{O}}$$
$$2\text{MnO}_4^- + 5\text{H}_2\text{O}_2 + 6\text{H}^+ \longrightarrow 2\text{Mn}^{++} + 5\text{O}_2\uparrow + 8\text{H}_2\text{O}$$

Hydrogen peroxide also reduces permanganate ion in basic solution, forming a precipitate of MnO_2, manganese dioxide:

$$H_2O_2 + 2OH^- \longrightarrow O_2 + 2H_2O + 2e^-$$

$$MnO_4^- + 3e^- + 2H_2O \longrightarrow MnO_2 + 4OH^-$$

or

$$3H_2O_2 + 6OH^- \longrightarrow 3O_2 + 6H_2O + 6e^-$$

$$\underline{2MnO_4^- + 6e^- + 4H_2O \longrightarrow 2MnO_2 + 8OH^-}$$

$$2MnO_4^- + 3H_2O_2 \longrightarrow 2MnO_2 \downarrow + 3O_2 \uparrow + 2H_2O + 2OH^-$$

The Auto-Oxidation of Hydrogen Peroxide.   When hydrogen peroxide decomposes, by the reaction

$$2H_2O_2 \longrightarrow 2H_2O + O_2$$

it is carrying on an *auto-oxidation-reduction process* (usually called *auto-oxidation*), in which the substance acts simultaneously as an oxidizing agent and as a reducing agent; half of the oxygen atoms are reduced to O^{-2} (forming water), and the other half are oxidized to O^0 (free oxygen).

It is interesting that this process occurs only extremely slowly in pure hydrogen peroxide and its pure aqueous solutions. It is accelerated by catalysts, such as dust particles and active spots on ordinary solid surfaces. If some grains of a catalytic material such as manganese dioxide are dropped into a solution of hydrogen peroxide there is a vigorous evolution of free oxygen. The stabilizers that are added to hydrogen peroxide inactivate these catalysts.

It will be recalled that a catalyst is a substance which causes a chemical reaction to go faster than in its absence, but which is itself not changed by the reaction. It is probable that a catalyst for the hydrogen peroxide decomposition exerts its effect by attracting the molecules of hydrogen peroxide to its surface, and subjecting them to a strain, which causes the molecules to decompose. Presumably a stabilizer is attracted to the active surface of the catalyst, and firmly held there, thus preventing the hydrogen peroxide molecules from reaching this region.

The most effective catalysts for the decomposition of hydrogen peroxide are certain complex organic substances, with molecular weights of 100,000 or more, which occur in the cells of plants and animals. These substances, which are called *catalases* (a special kind of enzyme), have the specific job in the organism of causing the decomposition of peroxides.

The Peroxy Acids.   Acids containing a peroxide group are called *peroxy acids*. Examples are peroxysulfuric acid, H_2SO_5

$$: \overset{..}{\underset{..}{O}}-H$$
$$: \overset{..}{\underset{..}{O}}-\overset{|}{\underset{|}{S}}-\overset{..}{\underset{..}{O}}:$$
$$: \overset{..}{\underset{..}{O}}: \quad : \overset{}{\underset{..}{O}}-H$$

peroxydisulfuric acid, $H_2S_2O_8$

$$: \overset{..}{\underset{..}{O}}-H$$
$$: \overset{..}{\underset{..}{O}}-\overset{|}{\underset{|}{S}}-\overset{..}{\underset{..}{O}}: \quad : \overset{..}{\underset{..}{O}}:$$
$$: \overset{..}{\underset{..}{O}}: \quad : \overset{}{\underset{..}{O}}-\overset{|}{\underset{|}{S}}-\overset{..}{\underset{.}{O}}:$$
$$H-\overset{}{\underset{..}{O}}:$$

When moderately concentrated (50%) sulfuric acid is electrolyzed, hydrogen is formed at the cathode and peroxydisulfuric acid at the anode:

Cathode reaction: $2H^+ + 2e^- \longrightarrow H_2 \uparrow$

Anode reaction: $2H_2SO_4 \longrightarrow H_2S_2O_8 + 2H^+ + 2e^-$

When this solution is heated peroxysulfuric acid is formed:

$$H_2S_2O_8 + H_2O \longrightarrow H_2SO_5 + H_2SO_4$$

If the solution is heated to a higher temperature it forms hydrogen peroxide, which can then be separated by distillation:

$$H_2SO_5 + H_2O \longrightarrow H_2SO_4 + H_2O_2$$

This method is used commercially for making 30% hydrogen peroxide. The peroxy acids and their salts are strong oxidizing agents.

Illustrative Exercises

12-9. The over-all reaction of decomposition of hydrogen peroxide is described by the reaction

$$2H_2O_2 \longrightarrow 2H_2O + O_2 \uparrow$$

(a) Write equations for the two electron reactions. (b) What is the oxidizing agent and what is the reducing agent? What is the oxidized product, and what is the reduced product? (c) What changes in oxidation number have occurred?

12-10. How many liters of oxygen at standard conditions would be produced by complete decomposition of 10 kg (22 lbs.) of 34% hydrogen peroxide?

12–6. *The Electromotive-Force Series of the Elements*

If a piece of one metal is put into a solution containing ions of another metallic element the first metal may dissolve, with the deposition of the second metal from its ions. Thus a strip of zinc placed in a solution of copper salt causes a layer of metallic copper to deposit on the zinc, as the zinc goes into solution (Figure 12-3). The chemical reaction that is involved is the reduction of copper ion, Cu^{++}, by metallic zinc:

$$Zn + Cu^{++} \longrightarrow Zn^{++} + Cu$$

On the other hand, a strip of copper placed in a solution of zinc salt does not cause metallic zinc to deposit.* Many experiments of this sort have been carried out, and it has been found that the metallic elements can be arranged in a table showing their ability to reduce ions of other metals. This table is given as Table 12-1.

The metal with the greatest reducing power is at the head of the list. It is able to reduce the ions of all the other metals.

This series is called the *electromotive-force series* because the tendency of one metal to reduce ions of another can be measured by setting up an *electric cell* and measuring the voltage which it produces. (Electromotive

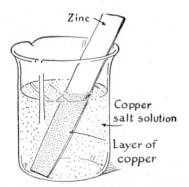

Zinc

Copper
salt solution

Layer of
copper

FIGURE **12-3**

Replacement of copper ion by zinc.

---

* It is not strictly correct to say that zinc can replace copper in solution and that copper cannot replace zinc. If a piece of metallic copper is placed in a solution containing zinc ions in appreciable concentration, say 1 mole per liter, and no cupric ion at all, the reaction

$$Cu + Zn^{++} \rightarrow Cu^{++} + Zn$$

will occur to a very small extent, stopping when a certain very small concentration of copper ion has been produced. If metallic zinc is added to a solution of cupric ion, the reaction

$$Zn + Cu^{++} \rightarrow Zn^{++} + Cu$$

will take place almost to completion, stopping when the concentration of cupric ion has become very small. It will be shown in a later chapter (Chapter 23) that the ratio of concentration of the two ions Cu^{++} and Zn^{++} in equilibrium with solid copper and solid zinc must be the same whether the equilibrium is reached by adding metallic copper to a zinc solution or metallic zinc to a copper solution. The statement "zinc replaces copper from solution" means that at equilibrium the amount of copper ion in the solution is very small relative to the amount of zinc ion.

TABLE 12-1   *The Electromotive-Force Series of the Elements**

			$E°$				$E°$	
	1.	$Li \rightleftarrows Li^+ + e^-$	3.05	17.	$Cd \rightleftarrows Cd^{++} + 2e^-$	0.40	
	2.	$Cs \rightleftarrows Cs^+ + e^-$	2.92	18.	$Co \rightleftarrows Co^{++} + 2e^-$	.28	
	3.	$Rb \rightleftarrows Rb^+ + e^-$	2.92	19.	$Ni \rightleftarrows Ni^{++} + 2e^-$	.25	
	4.	$K \rightleftarrows K^+ + e^-$	2.92	20.	$Sn \rightleftarrows Sn^{++} + 2e^-$	.14	
	5.	$Ba \rightleftarrows Ba^{++} + 2e^-$	2.90	21.	$Pb \rightleftarrows Pb^{++} + 2e^-$	.13	
	6.	$Sr \rightleftarrows Sr^{++} + 2e^-$	2.89	22.	$H_2 \rightleftarrows 2H^+ + 2e^-$	0.00	
	7.	$Ca \rightleftarrows Ca^{++} + 2e^-$	2.87	23.	$Cu \rightleftarrows Cu^{++} + 2e^-$	−0.34	
	8.	$Na \rightleftarrows Na^+ + e^-$	2.71	24.	$2I^- \rightleftarrows I_2 + 2e^-$	−0.53	
	9.	$La \rightleftarrows La^{+++} + 3e^-$	2.52	25.	$Ag \rightleftarrows Ag^+ + e^-$	−0.80	
	10.	$Mg \rightleftarrows Mg^{++} + 2e^-$	2.34	26.	$Hg \rightleftarrows Hg^{++} + 2e^-$	−0.85	
	11.	$Be \rightleftarrows Be^{++} + 2e^-$	1.85	27.	$2Br^- \rightleftarrows Br_2(1) + 2e^-$	−1.06	
	12.	$Al \rightleftarrows Al^{+++} + 3e^-$	1.67	28.	$Pt \rightleftarrows Pt^{++} + 2e^-$	−1.2	
	13.	$Mn \rightleftarrows Mn^{++} + 2e^-$	1.18	29.	$2H_2O \rightleftarrows O_2 + 4H^+ + 4e^-$	−1.23	
	14.	$Zn \rightleftarrows Zn^{++} + 2e^-$	0.76	30.	$2Cl^- \rightleftarrows Cl_2 + 2e^-$	−1.36	
	15.	$Cr \rightleftarrows Cr^{+++} + 3e^-$	.74	31.	$Au \rightleftarrows Au^+ + e^-$	−1.68	
	16.	$Fe \rightleftarrows Fe^{++} + 2e^-$	.44	32.	$2F^- \rightleftarrows F_2 + 2e^-$	−2.65	

Strongest reducing action (left margin, upward arrow)
Strongest oxidizing action (right margin, downward arrow)

* For a longer table see Chapter 23. Note that it is customary in the United States to represent the electromotive force of a couple involving a strong reducing agent as positive in sign, as in this table, but that European scientists usually use the opposite convention, writing $E° = -3.05$ v for $Li \rightleftarrows Li^+ + e^-$ and $+2.65$ v for $2F^- \rightleftarrows F_2 + 2e^-$.

The value 0.00 v is arbitrarily assumed for the standard hydrogen electrode, as the reference point for values of $E°$.

force is here a synonym for voltage.) Thus the cell shown in Figure 12-4 would be used to measure the voltage between the electrodes at which occur the electrode reactions

$$Zn \longrightarrow Zn^{++} + 2e^-$$

and

$$Cu^{++} + 2e^- \longrightarrow Cu$$

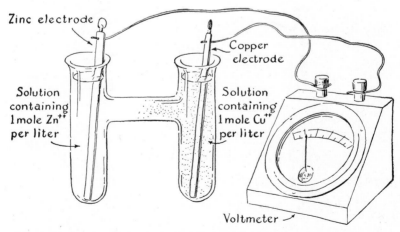

FIGURE 12-4   *A cell involving the Zn, Zn^{++} electrode and the Cu, Cu^{++} electrode.*

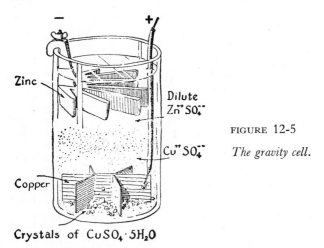

FIGURE 12-5

The gravity cell.

This cell produces a voltage of about 1.1 volts, the difference of the values of $E°$ shown in the table. The cell is used to some extent in practice; it is called the *gravity cell* when it is made as shown in Figure 12-5.

The values of the voltages shown in Table 12-1 refer to an idealized cell in which each metal ion is present at an effective concentration of 1 mole per liter of solution, and in which interactions between ions, especially the effects of any anions present, have been neglected. Actually the presence of other substances in solution changes the voltage produced by a cell of this sort, and often reverses the relative positions of two metals that are not far apart in the table. Nevertheless, the table is a very useful one in indicating whether an oxidation-reduction re-

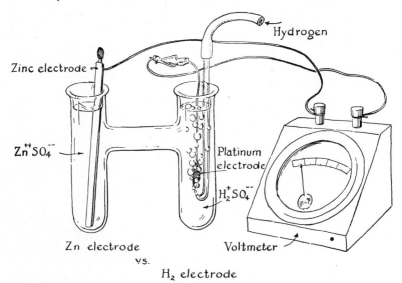

FIGURE 12-6   *A cell involving the zinc electrode and the hydrogen electrode.*

action involving two of the electron reactions shown is apt to take place or is apt not to take place.

The standard reference point in the electromotive-force series is the *hydrogen electrode*, which consists of gaseous hydrogen at 1 atm bubbling over a platinum electrode in an acidic solution (Figure 12-6). Similar electrodes can be made for some other non-metallic elements, and a few of these elements are included in the table.

The table can be extended to include also many other oxidation-reduction pairs. An extended table is given in Chapter 23, in which its use is discussed.

Illustrative Exercises

12-11. Would you expect iron to replace lead ion, Pb^{++}, from solution? Refer to Table 12-1. Write the equations for the electron reactions and the over-all reaction.

12-12. Which of the following metals would you expect to liberate hydrogen, if placed in a solution of sulfuric acid: zinc, gold, nickel, tin, platinum, silver, copper, iron?

12-13. (a) Write equations for the electrode reactions in the gravity cell, shown in Figure 12-5. (b) Why is the zinc electrode marked negative and the copper electrode positive?

12-14. What voltage would you expect to read on the voltmeter in Figure 12-6? Would the zinc electrode be positive or negative?

12–7. Primary Cells and Storage Cells

The production of an electric current through chemical reaction is achieved in *primary cells* and *storage cells*.

Primary cells are cells in which an oxidation-reduction reaction can be carried out in such a way that its driving force produces an electric potential. This is achieved by having the oxidizing agent and the reducing agent separated; the oxidizing agent then removes electrons from one electrode and the reducing agent gives electrons to another electrode, the flow of current through the cell itself being carried by ions.

Storage cells are similar cells, which, however, can be returned to their original state after current has been drawn from them (can be *charged*) by applying an impressed electric potential between the electrodes, and thus reversing the oxidation-reduction reaction.

The Common Dry Cell.   One primary cell, the gravity cell, has been described in the preceding section. This cell is called a *wet cell*, because it contains a liquid electrolyte. A very useful primary cell is the *common dry cell*, shown in Figure 12-7. The common dry cell consists of a zinc cylinder that contains as electrolyte a paste of ammonium chloride (NH_4Cl), a little zinc chloride ($ZnCl_2$), water, and diatomaceous earth or other filler.*   The central electrode is a mixture of carbon and

---

* The dry cell is not dry; water must be present in the paste that serves as electrolyte.

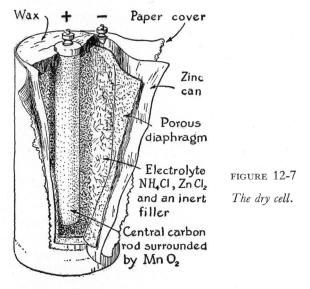

Wax + − Paper cover
Zinc can
Porous diaphragm
Electrolyte NH₄Cl, ZnCl₂ and an inert filler
Central carbon rod surrounded by MnO₂

FIGURE 12-7

The dry cell.

manganese dioxide, embedded in a paste of these substances. The electrode reactions are

$$Zn \longrightarrow Zn^{++} + 2e^-$$

$$2NH_4^+ + 2MnO_2 + 2e^- \longrightarrow 2MnHO_2 + 2NH_3$$

(The zinc ion combines to some extent with ammonia to form the zinc-ammonia complex ion, $Zn(NH_3)_4^{++}$.) This cell produces a potential of about 1.48 v.

The Lead Storage Battery. The most common storage cell is that in the *lead storage battery* (Figure 12-8). The electrolyte in this cell is a mixture of water and sulfuric acid with density about 1.290 g/cm³ in the charged cell (38% H_2SO_4 by weight). The plates are lattices made of a lead alloy, the pores of one plate being filled with spongy metallic lead, and those of the other with lead dioxide, PbO_2. The spongy lead is the reducing agent, and the lead dioxide the oxidizing agent in the chemical reaction which takes place in the cell. The electrode reactions which occur as the cell is being discharged are

$$Pb + SO_4^{--} \longrightarrow PbSO_4 + 2e^-$$

$$PbO_2 + SO_4^{--} + 4H^+ + 2e^- \longrightarrow PbSO_4 + 2H_2O$$

Each of these reactions produces the insoluble substance $PbSO_4$, lead sulfate, which adheres to the plates. As the cell is discharged sulfuric acid is removed from the electrolyte, which decreases in density. The state of charge or discharge of the cell can accordingly be determined with use of a hydrometer, by measuring the density of the electrolyte.

The cell can be charged again by applying an electric potential across

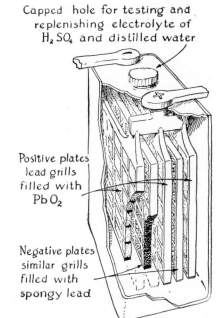

Capped hole for testing and
replenishing electrolyte of
H_2SO_4 and distilled water

FIGURE 12-8

The lead storage cell.

Positive plates
lead grills
filled with
PbO_2

Negative plates
similar grills
filled with
spongy lead

the terminals, and causing the above electrode reactions to take place in the opposite directions. The charged cell produces an electromotive force of slightly over 2 volts.

It is interesting that in this cell the same element changes its oxidation state in the two plates: the oxidizing agent is PbO_2 (containing lead with oxidation number $+4$, which changes to $+2$ as the cell discharges), and the reducing agent is Pb (lead with oxidation number 0, which changes to $+2$).

Illustrative Exercises

12-15. Write equations for the electrode reactions that take place in a lead storage battery while it is being charged.

12-16. (a) If a fully charged lead storage battery has 2000 g of spongy lead on its plates, how much lead dioxide should it have on the other plates? (b) How much sulfuric acid would it need in the electrolyte?

12-17. (a) How many faradays of electricity could a lead storage battery with 2000 g of spongy lead and a corresponding amount of lead dioxide produce? (b) For how many hours could it deliver a current of 10 amperes?

Concepts, Facts, and Terms Introduced in This Chapter

Generalized concept of oxidation, removal of electrons.

Generalized concept of reduction, addition of electrons.

Anodic oxidation; cathodic reduction.

Simultaneous occurrence of oxidation and reduction in a chemical reaction.

Oxidizing agent; reducing agent; oxidation-reduction pair (couple).

Oxidation number; a way to balance oxidation-reduction reactions; chemical nomenclature.

Barium peroxide; hydrogen peroxide.

Hydrogen peroxide as an oxidizing agent; as a reducing agent.

The auto-oxidation-reduction of hydrogen peroxide.

Peroxy acids.

The electrolytic method of making peroxydisulfuric acid, peroxysulfuric acid, and hydrogen peroxide.

Electromotive-force series of the elements.

Primary electric cells and storage cells. The common dry cell. The lead storage battery.

Exercises

12-18. Give three examples of oxidation-reduction reactions in everyday life. In each case designate the oxidizing agent and the reducing agent.

12-19. Define an oxidation-reduction pair, and write an electron equation in illustration.

12-20. Assign oxidation numbers to elements in the following compounds:

Sodium hydride, NaH	Ammonia, NH_3
Nitric acid, HNO_3	Lead sulfide, PbS
Lead sulfate, $PbSO_4$	Phosphorus, P_4
Potassium chromate, K_2CrO_4	Potassium dichromate, $K_2Cr_2O_7$
Silica, SiO_2	Nitrous acid, HNO_2
Ammonium chloride, NH_4Cl	Ammonium nitrite, NH_4NO_2
Sodium peroxide, Na_2O_2	Sodium oxide, Na_2O
Permanganate ion, MnO_4^-	Peroxysulfate ion, SO_5^{--}
Cuprous oxide, Cu_2O	Cupric oxide, CuO
Ferrous oxide, FeO	Ferric oxide, Fe_2O_3
Magnetite, Fe_3O_4	Borax, $Na_2B_4O_7 \cdot 10H_2O$
Garnet, $Ca_3Al_2Si_3O_{12}$	Topaz, $Al_2SiO_4F_2$

12-21. Using the new nomenclature described in Section 12–3, assign names to the following compounds:

$TiCl_3$ $AuCl$ $SnBr_2$ $FeSO_4 \cdot 7H_2O$ $AgNO_3$ $CuSO_4 \cdot 5H_2O$

$TiCl_4$ $AuCl_3$ SnI_4 $KFe(SO_4)_2 \cdot 12H_2O$ CuI $MgCO_3$

12-22. Complete and balance the following oxidation-reduction equations:

$$Cl_2 + I^- \longrightarrow I_2 + Cl^-$$
$$Sn + I_2 \longrightarrow SnI_4$$
$$KClO_3 \longrightarrow KClO_4 + KCl$$
$$MnO_2 + H^+ + Cl^- \longrightarrow Mn^{++} + Cl_2$$
$$ClO_4^- + Sn^{++} \longrightarrow Cl^- + Sn^{+++}$$

12-23. Write electrode equations for the electrolytic production of (a) ferric ion from ferrous ion; (b) magnesium metal from molten magnesium chloride; (c) perchlorate ion, ClO_4^-, from chlorate ion, ClO_3^-, in aqueous solution; (d) permanganate ion, MnO_4^-, from manganate ion, MnO_4^{--}, in aqueous solution; (e) fluorine from fluoride ion in a molten salt. State in each case whether the reaction occurs at the anode or at the cathode.

12-24. What weight of 3.00% hydrogen peroxide solution would be required to oxidize 1.00 g of lead sulfide, PbS, to lead sulfate, $PbSO_4$?

12-25. Would you expect zinc to reduce cadmium ion? (Refer to the electromotive-force series.) Iron to reduce mercuric ion? Zinc to reduce lead ion? Potassium to reduce magnesium ion?

12-26. Which metal ions would you expect gold to reduce? Suggest a reason for calling gold and platinum noble metals.

12-27. What would you expect to happen if a large piece of lead were put in a beaker containing a solution of stannous salt (a solution giving the ion Sn^{++})? Note the values of the electromotive force in Table 12-1.

12-28. What would happen if chlorine gas were bubbled into a solution containing fluoride ion and bromide ion? If chlorine were bubbled into a solution containing both bromide ion and iodide ion?

12-29. Why are hydrogen peroxide and potassium permanganate both antiseptics? Would you expect fluorine to be an antiseptic?

12-30. A sample of commercial hydrogen peroxide weighing 10.0 g was found to evolve 112 ml of oxygen (at standard conditions) when a little catalase was added to it. What was the strength of the hydrogen peroxide solution, in weight percentage? (Ans. 3.4%)

12-31. After reference to the electromotive-force series of the elements, would you expect potassium to reduce zinc ion in significant amount? Nickel to reduce magnesium ion? Silver to reduce lead ion? Lead to reduce silver ion? Barium to reduce gold ion?

12-32. Write a balanced equation for the reaction of chromate ion, CrO_4^{--}, with stannite ion, $Sn(OH)_4^{--}$, in basic solution, to give stannate ion, $Sn(OH)_6^{--}$, and chromite ion, $Cr(OH)_4^-$.

12-33. A compound containing phosphorus and chlorine is found on analysis to contain 22.5% phosphorus. The molecular weight of the compound is about 137. What is the oxidation number of phosphorus in this compound, and what is the formula of the substance?

12-34. Write electronic formulas for calcium peroxide, CaO_2, and zirconium dioxide, ZrO_2. Write equations for the reactions of these two substances with sulfuric acid.

12-35. When a solution of a ferrous salt, containing the hydrated ferrous ion, Fe^{++}, is treated with sodium hydroxide, the precipitate of ferrous hydroxide that is first formed is rapidly oxidized by oxygen from the air, converting it into ferric hydroxide, $Fe(OH)_3$. Write the equation for this reaction.

References

E. S. Shanley, "Hydrogen Peroxide" (manufacture, properties, industrial uses), *J. Chem. Ed.*, **28**, 260 (1951).

P. Walden, "The Beginnings of the Doctrine of Chemical Affinity" (the electromotive-force series, historical), *J. Chem. Ed.*, **31**, 27 (1954).

PART THREE

Some Non-Metallic Elements and Their Compounds

We have now obtained, through the study of the five chapters that constitute Part II of our book, an understanding of weight relations in chemical reactions and of the properties of gases that permits us to discuss such questions as the amount of a product that might be produced by the reaction of substances with one another, and also, through the study of ionic valence, covalence, electronic structure, and oxidation-reduction reactions, an understanding of the structure of substances and the combining power of atoms that permits us to write and balance equations for chemical reactions and to discuss the properties of substances in terms of their structure. With this background we now begin the study of the chemistry of some of the non-metallic elements.

In Chapters 6 and 7 there was given a discussion of the chemistry of hydrogen, oxygen, and carbon. The chemistry of the non-metallic elements is amplified in the next four chapters of the book. Chapter 13 deals with the halogens, the elements of group VII. These elements have been selected for the chapter immediately following that on oxidation-reduction reactions because they provide a number of interesting examples of reactions of this sort. Chapter 14 deals with the chemistry of sulfur, selenium, and tellurium, which, together with oxygen, constitute group VI. The chemistry of the elements of group V is then discussed in Chapter 15, on nitrogen, and Chapter 16, on phosphorus, arsenic, antimony, and bismuth.

In the study of these four chapters you may find it useful to correlate the properties of the elements and their compounds with the periodic system. The formulas and properties of the compounds of these non-metallic elements change in a regular way from group to group (horizontally in the periodic system), and from period to period (vertically). The theory of electronic structure, which has been developed during the past fifty years, is still far from complete, and you will probably find that there are some compounds described that you have difficulty in fitting into the system. Nevertheless, even though it is not perfect, the present system of electronic structure can be of great value by serving as the framework to which you can tie the facts of chemistry in the course of your studies.

Chapter 13

The Halogens

The halogens, fluorine, chlorine, bromine, and iodine, are the elements that immediately precede the noble gases in the periodic table. Their neutral atoms, with the electronic structures given in Table 13-1, have one electron less than the corresponding noble gas. They have a strong tendency to assume the electronic structure of the noble gas, either by adding an electron, to form a halogenide ion, as was discussed in Chapter 10, or by sharing an electron pair with another atom, forming a covalent bond (Chapters 7 and 11).

TABLE 13-1   *Electronic Structure of the Halogens*

Z	ELEMENT	K	L		M			N			O	
		1s	2s	2p	3s	3p	3d	4s	4p	4d	5s	5p
9	Fluorine	2	2	5								
17	Chlorine	2	2	6	2	5						
35	Bromine	2	2	6	2	6	10	2	5			
53	Iodine	2	2	6	2	6	10	2	6	10	2	5

Sometimes more than one electron pair is shared by a halogen atom with other atoms, especially atoms of oxygen. The oxygen compounds of the halogens are important substances. A few of them, such as potassium chlorate, have been mentioned in earlier chapters. The chemistry of these substances is complex, but it can be systematized and clarified by correlation with the electronic theory of valence.

13-1. *The Oxidation States of the Halogens*

The oxidation states which are represented by known compounds of the halogens are shown in the diagram on the following page. It is seen that the range of the oxidation states extends from −1, corresponding

271

to the achievement for each halogen atom of the structure of the adjacent noble gas, to +7, corresponding for chlorine to the inner noble-gas structure (neon). In general the odd oxidation states are represented by compounds. The importance of the odd oxidation states is the result of the stability of electronic structures involving pairs of electrons, either shared or unshared. Structures involving only pairs of electrons lead to even oxidation states for elements in even groups of the periodic system and to odd oxidation states for elements in odd groups. The exceptional compounds chlorine dioxide, ClO_2, bromine dioxide, BrO_2, and iodine dioxide, IO_2, corresponding to oxidation number +4, have molecules containing an odd number of electrons.

+7		$HClO_4$, Cl_2O_7		H_5IO_6
+6		Cl_2O_6		
+5		$HClO_3$	$HBrO_3$	HIO_3, I_2O_5
+4		ClO_2	BrO_2	IO_2
+3		$HClO_2$		
+2				
+1		$HClO$, Cl_2O	$HBrO$, Br_2O	HIO
0	F_2	Cl_2	Br_2	I_2
−1	HF, F^-	HCl, Cl^-	HBr, Br^-	HI, I^-

Fluorine differs significantly from the other halogens. Whereas chlorine, bromine, and iodine form many compounds with oxygen, fluorine forms very few. There are no oxygen acids of fluorine.

This fact can be correlated with the position of fluorine in the electronegativity scale (Section 11–8). Fluorine, with electronegativity 4.0, is the most electronegative of the elements. It is more electronegative than oxygen (electronegativity 3.5), whereas the other halogens (chlorine 3.0, bromine 2.8, iodine 2.5) are less electronegative than oxygen. The large electronegativity of fluorine causes instability of positive oxidation states of fluorine, and great stability of its negative oxidation state.

Fluorine forms one compound with oxygen, OF_2. It is produced by

$$:\overset{\cdot\cdot}{\underset{|}{F}}:$$

reaction of fluorine with water. Its electronic structure is $:\overset{\cdot\cdot}{\underset{\cdot\cdot}{O}}-\overset{\cdot\cdot}{\underset{\cdot\cdot}{F}}:$, and

it is considered to contain fluorine with oxidation number −1, because the electronegativity of fluorine is greater than that of oxygen; it is hence called *oxygen fluoride*, rather than fluorine oxide.

Illustrative Exercises

13-1. Write the equation for the reaction of fluorine with water, producing oxygen fluoride. What is the other product of the reaction?

13-2. What are the oxidation numbers of hydrogen, oxygen, and fluorine in the reactants and the products of the reaction of Exercise 13-1? What is the oxidizing agent in this reaction? What has been oxidized?

13-3. How many liters of oxygen fluoride could be prepared by reaction of 10 l of fluorine with water?

13–2. *The Halogens and Halogenides*

The halogens consist of diatomic molecules, F_2, Cl_2, Br_2, and I_2. Some physical properties of the halogens are given in Table 13-2.

Fluorine.   Fluorine, the lightest of the halogens, is the most reactive of all the elements, and it forms compounds with all the elements except the inert gases. Substances such as wood and rubber burst into flame when held in a stream of fluorine, and even asbestos (a silicate of magnesium and aluminum) reacts vigorously with it and becomes incandescent. Platinum is attacked only slowly by fluorine. Copper and steel can be used as containers for the gas; they are attacked by it, but become coated with a thin layer of copper fluoride or iron fluoride which then protects them against further attack.

Fluorine was first made in 1886 by the French chemist Henri Moissan (1852–1907), by the method described in the following section. In recent years methods for its commercial production and transport (in steel tanks) have been developed, and it is now used in chemical industry in moderate quantities.

TABLE 13-2   *Properties of the Halogens*

FORMULA		ATOMIC NUMBER	ATOMIC WEIGHT	COLOR AND FORM	MELTING POINT	BOILING POINT	IONIC RADIUS*
Fluorine	F_2	9	19.00	Pale yellow gas	$-223°$ C	$-187°$ C	1.36 Å
Chlorine	Cl_2	17	35.457	Greenish yellow gas	$-101.6°$	$-34.6°$	1.81
Bromine	Br_2	35	79.916	Reddish brown liquid	$-7.3°$	$58.7°$	1.95
Iodine	I_2	53	126.91	Grayish black lustrous solid	$113.5°$	$184°$	2.16

* For negatively charged ion with ligancy 6, such as Cl^- in the NaCl crystal.

Fluorine occurs in nature in the combined state in minerals such as *fluorite*, CaF_2; *fluor-apatite*, $Ca_5(PO_4)_3F$, which is a constituent of bones and teeth; and *cryolite*, Na_3AlF_6; and in small quantities in sea water and most supplies of drinking water, as fluoride ion. If there is not a sufficient (very small) quantity of fluoride ion in the drinking water of children their teeth will not be properly resistant to decay.

The name fluorine, from Latin *fluere*, to flow, refers to the use of fluorite as a flux (a material that forms a melt with metal oxides).

Hydrogen fluoride, HF, can be made by treating fluorite with sulfuric acid:

$$H_2SO_4 + CaF_2 \longrightarrow CaSO_4 + 2HF \uparrow$$

This method is used industrially. The reaction is usually carried out in the laboratory in a lead dish, because hydrogen fluoride attacks glass, porcelain, and other silicates. It is a colorless gas (m.p. $-92.3°$ C, b.p. $19.4°$ C), very soluble in water.

The solution of hydrogen fluoride in water is called hydrofluoric acid. This solution, and also hydrogen fluoride gas, may be used for etching glass.* The glass is covered with a thin layer of paraffin, through which the design to be etched, such as the graduations on a buret, is scratched with a stylus. The object is then treated with the acid. The reactions that occur are similar to those for quartz, SiO_2:

$$SiO_2 + 4HF \longrightarrow SiF_4 \uparrow + 2H_2O$$

The product, SiF_4, silicon tetrafluoride, is a gas.

Hydrofluoric acid must be handled with great care, because on contact with the skin it produces sores which heal very slowly. The acid is stored in bottles made of polyethylene (a resistant plastic).

The salts of hydrofluoric acid are called fluorides. Sodium fluoride, NaF, is used as an insecticide.

Chlorine. Chlorine (from Greek *chloros*, greenish-yellow), the most common of the halogens, is a greenish-yellow gas, with a sharp irritating odor. It was first made by the Swedish chemist K. W. Scheele (1742–1786) in 1774, by the action of manganese dioxide on hydrochloric acid. It is now manufactured on a large scale by the electrolysis of a strong solution of sodium chloride.

Chlorine is a very reactive substance, but less reactive than fluorine. It combines with most elements, to form chlorides, at room temperature or on gentle heating. Hydrogen burns in chlorine, after being ignited, to form hydrogen chloride:

$$H_2 + Cl_2 \longrightarrow 2HCl$$

Iron burns in chlorine, producing ferric chloride, a brown solid,

---

* Metals, such as copper, may be etched with nitric acid. Nitric acid and other acids, except hydrofluoric acid, do not attack glass.

$$2Fe + 3Cl_2 \longrightarrow 2FeCl_3$$

and other metals react similarly with it.

Chlorine is a strong oxidizing agent, and because of this property it is effective in killing bacteria. It is used extensively to sterilize drinking water, and is also used in many ways throughout the chemical industry.

Hydrogen chloride, HCl, is a colorless gas (m.p. $-112°$ C, b.p. $-83.7°$ C) with an unpleasant sharp odor. It is easily made by heating sodium chloride with sulfuric acid:

$$NaCl + H_2SO_4 \longrightarrow NaHSO_4 + HCl \uparrow$$

The gas dissolves readily in water, with the evolution of a large amount of heat. The solution is called hydrochloric acid. Hydrochloric acid is a strong acid—it has a very acidic taste, turns blue litmus paper red, dissolves zinc and other active metals with the evolution of hydrogen gas, and combines with bases to form salts. The salts formed by hydrochloric acid are called chlorides. A representative chloride is sodium chloride, which has been mentioned often in the preceding chapters; other chlorides will be discussed in later sections of the book.

Bromine.   The element bromine (from Greek *bromos*, stench) occurs in the form of compounds in small quantities in sea water and in natural salt deposits. It is an easily volatile, dark reddish-brown liquid with a strong, disagreeable odor and an irritating effect on the eyes and throat. It produces painful sores when spilled on the skin. The free element can be made by treating a bromide with an oxidizing agent, such as chlorine.

Hydrogen bromide, HBr, is a colorless gas (m.p. $-88.5°$ C, b.p. $-67.0°$ C). Its solution in water, hydrobromic acid, is a strong acid. The principal salts of hydrobromic acid are sodium bromide, NaBr, and potassium bromide, KBr, which are used in medicine, and silver bromide, AgBr, which, like silver chloride, AgCl, and silver iodide, AgI, is used in making photographic emulsions.

Iodine.   The element iodine (from Greek *iodes*, violet) occurs as iodide ion, I^-, in very small quantities in sea water, and, as **sodium iodate,** $NaIO_3$, in deposits of Chile saltpeter. It is made commercially from sodium iodate obtained from saltpeter, and also from kelp, which concentrates it from the sea water, and from oil-well brines.

The free element is an almost black crystalline solid with a slightly metallic luster. On gentle warming it gives a beautiful blue-violet vapor. Its solutions in chloroform, carbon tetrachloride, and carbon disulfide are also blue-violet in color, indicating that the molecules I_2 in these solutions closely resemble the gas molecules. The solutions of iodine in water containing potassium iodide and in alcohol (tincture of iodine) are brown; this change in color suggests that the iodine molecules have undergone chemical reaction in these solutions. The brown compound KI_3, potassium triiodide, is present in the first solution, and a compound with alcohol in the second.

Hydrogen iodide, HI, is a colorless gas (m.p. $-50.8°$ C, b.p. $-35.3°$ C), whose solution in water, called hydriodic acid, is a strong acid.

Periodicity and Atomic Number.   The value of the periodic table is clearly illustrated by the halogens. All four of the elementary substances form diatomic molecules X_2; their hydrogen compounds all have the formula HX, and their sodium salts the formula NaX. The free elements are all oxidizing agents, and their oxidizing power decreases regularly in the order F_2, Cl_2, Br_2, I_2.

The color of the free elements becomes increasingly deeper, from pale yellow to nearly black, with increase in atomic number. Some of the salts also show a trend in color; for example, from AgF and AgCl, colorless, to AgBr, pale yellow, and AgI, yellow.

In general the weak intermolecular forces that hold molecules together in liquids and crystals increase rapidly in magnitude with increase in atomic number of the atoms in the molecules. This is shown for example by the trend in melting points and boiling points of the noble gases, Table 5-2. It causes the physical state of the free halogens to vary, from a difficulty condensable gas (fluorine), through an easily condensable gas (chlorine), and a liquid (bromine), to a solid (iodine). The melting points of the halogens show nearly regular increments of about $100°$ C from each period to the next, and the boiling points show similar increments.

In your study of descriptive chemistry you may find it valuable often to compare the properties of substances with the positions of their component elements in the periodic table, in the way illustrated above.

Illustrative Exercises

13-4.   Write the equation for the reaction of methane with an excess of fluorine. What are the oxidation numbers of carbon, hydrogen, and oxygen in the reactants and the products?

13-5.   Write the electronic structure of silicon tetrafluoride.

13-6.   Can you explain by the consideration of electronegativities why hydrofluoric acid attacks glass, such as silica glass, SiO_2, whereas hydrochloric acid does not? (Compare the stability of the Si—F bond with that of the Si—Cl bond.)

13-7   Assuming asbestos to have the formula $Ca_2Mg_5Si_8O_{24}H_2$, list the products that might be obtained by its reaction with an excess of fluorine. Write the equation for the reaction.

13-8.   How many grams of salt and how many grams of sulfuric acid (pure H_2SO_4) would be needed to prepare 22.4 l (at standard conditions) of hydrogen chloride, by the reaction given above in the discussion of hydrogen chloride?

13–3. The Preparation of the Elementary Halogens

The original method of preparing **fluorine** was the electrolysis of a solution of potassium fluoride, KF, in liquid hydrogen fluoride, HF, using as the material of the containing vessel an alloy of platinum and

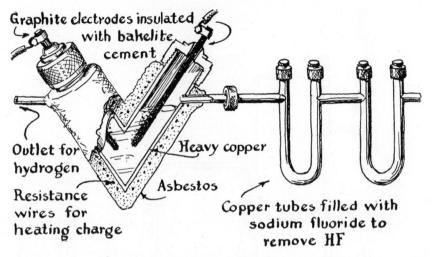

Graphite electrodes insulated with bakelite cement

Outlet for hydrogen

Heavy copper

Resistance wires for heating charge

Asbestos

Copper tubes filled with sodium fluoride to remove HF

FIGURE 13-1   *Apparatus used for preparing fluorine by electrolysis of potassium hydrogen fluoride.*

iridium. It has since been learned that copper can be used for this purpose. The copper is attacked by the fluorine, forming, however, a surface layer of copper fluoride which protects the tube from further corrosion.

The modern method of preparing fluorine in the laboratory is illustrated in Figure 13-1. The container is filled with perfectly dry potassium hydrogen fluoride, KHF_2, which is melted by passing an electric current through the resistance wires surrounding the copper tube. A direct potential is then applied between the two graphite electrodes, causing the liberation of hydrogen at the cathode, on the left, and fluorine at the anode. Hydrogen fluoride is removed from the fluorine gas by passage through a U-tube filled with sodium fluoride, which combines with hydrogen fluoride to form the crystalline substance sodium hydrogen fluoride, $NaHF_2$.

Chlorine is conveniently made in the laboratory by the oxidation of hydrochloric acid with either manganese dioxide or potassium permanganate. Manganese dioxide is placed in a flask, as shown in Figure 13-2, and concentrated hydrochloric acid is added through a funnel. Chlorine is evolved according to the equation

$$MnO_2 + 4HCl \longrightarrow MnCl_2 + 2H_2O + Cl_2 \uparrow$$

This equation represents the over-all reaction, which in fact takes place in two stages. At room temperature manganese is reduced from the quadripositive state to the terpositive state, with liberation of a corresponding amount of chlorine:

$$2MnO_2 + 8HCl \longrightarrow 2MnCl_3 + 4H_2O + Cl_2 \uparrow$$

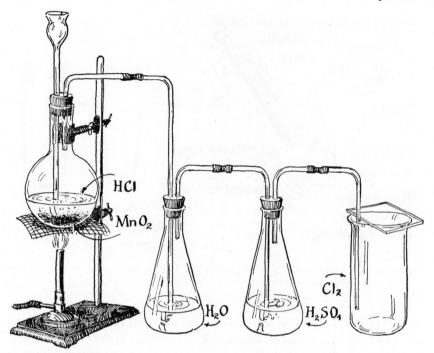

FIGURE 13-2   *The preparation of chlorine by the reaction of hydrochloric acid and manganese dioxide.*

When the mixture is heated a further reaction takes place, with reduction of manganese to the bipositive state:

$$2MnCl_3 \longrightarrow 2MnCl_2 + Cl_2 \uparrow$$

The liberated chlorine is bubbled through a small amount of water, to remove hydrogen chloride, and then through concentrated sulfuric acid, to remove water vapor. The gas is over twice as heavy as air (molecular weight 71, as compared with average molecular weight 29 for air) and can accordingly be collected by upward displacement of air.

The preparation of chlorine by use of potassium permanganate is carried out in the same way, except that it is not necessary to heat the reaction mixture. Crystals of potassium permanganate are placed in a flask of an apparatus similar to that of Figure 13-2, except that the funnel for introducing the hydrochloric acid is provided with a stopcock. Hydrochloric acid is then permitted to drip into the funnel, the stopcock being closed after the reaction has begun to take place at a sufficiently rapid rate. The equation for the over-all reaction is

$$2KMnO_4 + 16HCl \longrightarrow 2MnCl_2 + 2KCl + 8H_2O + 5Cl_2$$

Chlorine can also be prepared, with such an apparatus, by allowing concentrated hydrochloric acid to react with bleaching powder.

Chlorine for commercial use is made by electrolysis of molten sodium chloride, as described in Chapter 10, or of brine.

Bromine can be prepared in the laboratory by the action of sulfuric acid on a mixture of sodium bromide and manganese dioxide, in the apparatus shown in Figure 13-2. Until recently most of the bromine used commercially was made in this way, from sodium bromide and potassium bromide mined from the Stassfurt deposits in Germany, or from brines pumped from wells in the eastern and central United States. During the past twenty-five years there has occurred a very great increase in the amount of bromine manufactured, until at present over 10,000 tons a year is being made.

Most of the bromine produced is converted into ethylene dibromide, $C_2H_4Br_2$, which is an important constituent of "ethyl gas," together with tetraethyl lead, $(C_2H_5)_4Pb$. Tetraethyl lead has valuable anti-knock properties, but its continued use would cause damage to a motor through the deposition of metallic lead, unless some way were found to eliminate this deposit. The ethylene dibromide that is added to the gasoline provides bromine on combustion, which combines with the lead, permitting its elimination as lead bromide, $PbBr_2$.

The great amount of bromine required for this purpose and other uses at the present time is obtained by extraction of the element from sea water, which contains about 70 parts of bromine, as bromide ion, per million of water. The process of extraction involves four steps: oxidation with chlorine to convert the bromide ion to free bromine, removal of the bromine from the solution by bubbling a stream of air through it, absorption of the bromine from the air by bubbling through a solution of sodium carbonate, and treatment of the solution with sulfuric acid to liberate the elementary bromine. The equations for the successive reactions are

$$2Br^- + Cl_2 \longrightarrow Br_2 + 2Cl^-$$
$$3Br_2 + 6CO_3^{--} + 3H_2O \longrightarrow 5Br^- + BrO_3^- + 6HCO_3^-$$
$$5Br^- + BrO_3^- + 6H^+ \longrightarrow 3Br_2 + 3H_2O$$

The acidified reaction mixture is boiled, and the bromine is condensed from the vapor.

Iodine is conveniently made in the laboratory from sodium iodide, by the method described above for making bromine from a bromide.

Illustrative Exercises

13-9. Write the electrode reactions and the over-all reaction for the preparation of fluorine by electrolysis of potassium hydrogen fluoride.

13-10. How many liters of fluorine at $0°$ C and 1 atm would be produced by a current of 10 amperes in 9650 seconds?

13-11. Write the equation for production of chlorine by reaction of permanganate ion, MnO_4^-, with hydrogen ion and chloride ion, in aqueous solution. Manganese(II) ion, Mn^{++}, is also a product.

13-12. Write the equations for the combustion of tetraethyl lead to form carbon dioxide, water, and lead, the combustion of ethylene dibromide to form carbon dioxide, water, and bromine, and the reaction of lead and bromine to form lead(II) bromide. These reactions take place in a gasoline engine using ethyl gasoline.

13-13. How many grams of ethylene dibromide would you calculate to be needed in ethyl gasoline per gram of tetraethyl lead?

13-14. Write an equation for the reaction of sulfuric acid, manganese dioxide, and sodium iodide to prepare iodine.

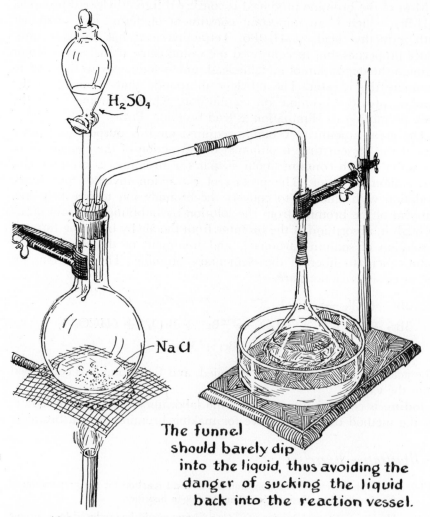

FIGURE 13-3 *Apparatus for the preparation of hydrogen chloride and hydrochloric acid.*

13–4. *The Preparation of the Hydrogen Halides*

It was mentioned in Section 13–2 that **hydrogen fluoride,** HF, is made
by treating fluorite with sulfuric acid. This reaction is usually carried
out in a lead dish or a platinum dish; in the commercial manufacture
of hydrofluoric acid it is carried out in an iron pot, which is connected
with a series of lead boxes containing water, in which the hydrogen
fluoride dissolves to form aqueous hydrofluoric acid. Pure, anhydrous
hydrogen fluoride is best made by heating potassium hydrogen fluoride,
KHF$_2$. This salt can be easily crystallized from a potassium fluoride
solution to which hydrofluoric acid has been added.

Hydrogen chloride is made by the reaction of sodium chloride and

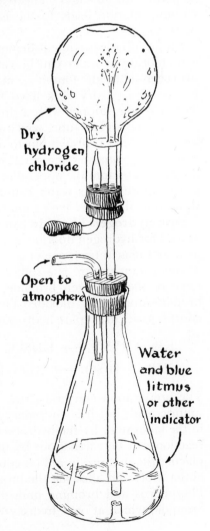

FIGURE 13-4

The hydrogen chloride fountain; the same ex-
periment can be carried out with ammonia in-
stead of hydrogen chloride.

sulfuric acid. The apparatus shown in Figure 13-3 may be used for this purpose. The sulfuric acid is dropped onto sodium chloride as shown; since concentrated sulfuric acid absorbs water, the gas that is evolved is dry, and it may be collected directly in bottles by upward displacement of air. In case that a solution of hydrochloric acid is to be prepared, care must be taken in leading the gas into water, because its great solubility in water might cause the solution to be sucked back into the reaction vessel. A safety device designed to prevent this is shown in the figure; it consists of an inverted funnel, through which the gas is led into the water. The mouth of the funnel is dipped only a small distance under the surface of the water, in such a way that if the solution begins to be sucked back the water level is lowered enough to permit air to enter. The reaction between cold sulfuric acid and sodium chloride leads to the formation of sodium hydrogen sulfate, $NaHSO_4$.

An amusing experiment demonstrating the great solubility of hydrogen chloride in water can be carried out. This experiment, called the hydrogen chloride fountain, makes use of the apparatus shown in Figure 13-4. A dry flask filled with hydrogen chloride and equipped with a 2-hole stopper with a dropper with rubber bulb in one hole is placed over a glass tube, which dips beneath the surface of water in a lower flask and is drawn out to a nozzle at its upper end. The reaction is begun by pressing the small rubber bulb, so as to introduce a few drops of water into the upper flask. The immediate solution of the hydrogen chloride in this water causes a decrease in pressure, which sucks water into the upper flask from the lower flask in a rapid stream.

Pure **hydrogen bromide** cannot be prepared by the same methods as used for hydrogen fluoride and hydrogen chloride, involving displacement of the acid from one of its salts by sulfuric acid. Sulfuric acid even at room temperature is a sufficiently strong oxidizing agent to oxidize some of the hydrogen bromide, causing it to be contaminated with bromine and sulfur dioxide. The reactions that take place when the effort is made to prepare hydrogen bromide in this way are the following:

$$KBr + H_2SO_4 \longrightarrow KHSO_4 + HBr \uparrow$$

$$2HBr + H_2SO_4 \longrightarrow 2H_2O + SO_2 \uparrow + Br_2 \uparrow$$

The preparation can be carried out with phosphoric acid in place of sulfuric acid, but it is customary instead to prepare hydrogen bromide in the laboratory by the hydrolysis of phosphorus tribromide, PBr_3. The reaction can be carried out by mixing red phosphorus with wet sand, placing the mixture in a flask equipped with a dropping funnel and an outlet tube, and allowing the bromine to drip onto the red phosphorus. Phosphorus and bromine immediately react, to form phosphorus tribromide, which at once hydrolyzes with the water present:

$$2P + 3Br_2 \longrightarrow 2PBr_3$$

$$PBr_3 + 3H_2O \longrightarrow P(OH)_3 + 3HBr \uparrow$$

The gas that is evolved is passed through a U-tube containing glass beads mixed with red phosphorus, which combines with any bromine that may be carried along with it. The hydrogen bromide may be collected by upward displacement of air, or may be absorbed in water, with use of a safety device such as shown in Figure 13-3, to form hydrobromic acid.

Hydrogen bromide can also be made by direct combination of the elements. If a stream of hydrogen is bubbled through bromine contained in a flask heated on a water bath to 38° C, the gas mixture that is produced contains hydrogen and bromine in approximately equimolecular proportions. This gas may be passed over platinized silicic acid, which acts as a catalyst, causing the combination of hydrogen and bromine:

$$H_2 + Br_2 \longrightarrow 2HBr$$

The reaction can also be made to take place in a heated tube filled with pieces of porous clay plate.

Hydrogen bromide can also be made by the reduction of bromine with hydrogen sulfide:

$$H_2S + Br_2 \longrightarrow 2HBr + S$$

The gas that is produced can be purified of bromine by passing over red phosphorus, as described in the first method.

Hydrogen iodide, which is still more easily oxidized than hydrogen bromide, can be prepared by similar methods. The customary method of preparation involves the reaction of water, iodine, and red phosphorus. Iodine and red phosphorus are mixed and placed in a flask, to which water is admitted from a dropping funnel. The reaction involved is

$$2P + 3I_2 + 6H_2O \longrightarrow 2P(OH)_3 + 6HI \uparrow$$

Illustrative Exercises

13-15. Hydrogen chloride can be made by heating a mixture of sodium hydrogen sulfate and sodium chloride. Write the equation for the reaction.

13-16. Why cannot pure hydrogen iodide be made by use of sulfuric acid and sodium iodide? Write equations for two reactions that might take place if these substances were mixed.

13-17. It is stated above that when a stream of hydrogen is bubbled through bromine at 38° C the gas mixture produced is equimolecular in H_2 and Br_2. What is the vapor pressure of liquid bromine at 38° C? (Ans. About 380 mm Hg)

13–5. *The Oxygen Acids and Oxides of Chlorine*

The oxygen acids of chlorine and their anions have the following formulas and names:

$HClO_4$, perchloric acid	ClO_4^-, perchlorate ion
$HClO_3$, chloric acid	ClO_3^-, chlorate ion
$HClO_2$, chlorous acid	ClO_2^-, chlorite ion
$HClO$, hypochlorous acid	ClO^-, hypochlorite ion

The electronic structures of the four anions are shown in Figure 13-5.

In the following sections these acids and their salts, and also the oxides of chlorine, are discussed in the order of increasing oxidation number of the halogen.

Hypochlorous Acid and the Hypochlorites. Hypochlorous acid, $HClO$, and most of its salts are known only in aqueous solution; they decompose when the solution is concentrated. A mixture of chloride ion and hypochlorite ion is formed when chlorine is bubbled through a solution of sodium hydroxide:

$$Cl_2 + 2OH^- \longrightarrow Cl^- + ClO^- + H_2O$$

A solution of **sodium hypochlorite,** $NaClO$, made in this way or by electrolysis of sodium chloride solution is a popular household sterilizing and bleaching agent. The hypochlorite ion is an active oxidizing agent, and its oxidizing power is the basis of its sterilizing and bleaching action.

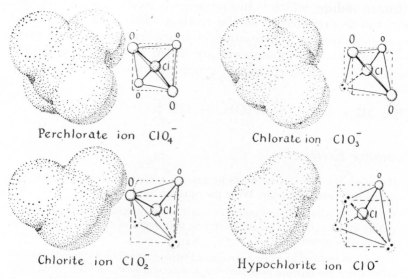

Perchlorate ion ClO_4^- Chlorate ion ClO_3^-

Chlorite ion ClO_2^- Hypochlorite ion ClO^-

FIGURE 13-5   *The structure of ions of the four oxygen acids of chlorine.*

Bleaching powder is a compound obtained by passing chlorine over calcium hydroxide:

$$Ca(OH)_2 + Cl_2 \longrightarrow CaCl(ClO) + H_2O$$

The formula $CaCl(ClO)$, which approximates the composition of commercial bleaching powder, indicates it to be a calcium chloride-hypochlorite, containing the two anions Cl^- and ClO^-. Bleaching powder is a white, finely-powdered substance which usually smells of chlorine, because of its decomposition by water vapor in the air. It is often called by the incorrect name "chloride of lime." It is used as a household bleaching and sterilizing agent; in its former industrial use, for bleaching paper pulp and textile fabrics, it has been largely displaced by liquid chlorine. Pure **calcium hypochlorite,** $Ca(ClO)_2$, is also manufactured and used as a bleaching agent.

Hypochlorous acid is a weak acid. The solution obtained by adding another acid, such as sulfuric acid, to a solution of a hypochlorite contains molecules $HClO$, and very few hypochlorite ions ClO^-:

$$ClO^- + H^+ \longrightarrow HClO$$

Dichlorine monoxide, Cl_2O, is a yellow gas obtained by gently heating hypochlorous acid in a partially evacuated system (that is, under reduced pressure):

$$2HClO \longrightarrow H_2O + Cl_2O \uparrow$$

or by passing chlorine over mercuric oxide:

$$2Cl_2 + HgO \longrightarrow HgCl_2 + Cl_2O \uparrow$$

The gas condenses to a liquid at about 4° C. It is the anhydride of hypochlorous acid: that is, it reacts with water to give hypochlorous acid:

$$Cl_2O + H_2O \longrightarrow 2HClO$$

The electronic structure of chlorine monoxide is $: \overset{\displaystyle ..}{\underset{\displaystyle ..}{O}} - \overset{\displaystyle ..}{\underset{\displaystyle ..}{Cl}} :$, in which

chlorine and oxygen have their normal covalences of 1 and 2, respectively.

Chlorous Acid and the Chlorites.   When chlorine dioxide, ClO_2, is passed into a solution of sodium hydroxide or other alkali a chlorite ion and a chlorate ion are formed:

$$2ClO_2 + 2OH^- \longrightarrow ClO_2^- + ClO_3^- + H_2O$$

This is an auto-oxidation-reduction reaction, the chlorine with oxidation number $+4$ in chlorine dioxide being reduced and oxidized simultaneously to oxidation numbers $+3$ and $+5$. Pure sodium chlorite, $NaClO_2$, can be made by passing chlorine dioxide into a solution of sodium peroxide:

$$2ClO_2 + Na_2O_2 \longrightarrow 2Na^+ + 2ClO_2^- + O_2$$

In this reaction the peroxide oxygen serves as a reducing agent, decreasing the oxidation number of chlorine from $+4$ to $+3$.

Sodium chlorite is an active bleaching agent, used in the manufacture of textile fabrics.

Chlorine Dioxide. Chlorine dioxide, ClO_2, is the only compound of quadripositive chlorine. It is a reddish-yellow gas, which is very explosive, decomposing readily to chlorine and oxygen. The violence of this decomposition makes it very dangerous to add sulfuric acid or any other strong acid to a chlorate or to any dry mixture containing a chlorate.

Chlorine dioxide can be made by carefully adding sulfuric acid to potassium chlorate, $KClO_3$. It would be expected that this mixture would react to produce chloric acid, $HClO_3$, and then, because of the dehydrating power of sulfuric acid, to produce the anhydride of chloric acid, Cl_2O_5:

$$KClO_3 + H_2SO_4 \longrightarrow KHSO_4 + HClO_3$$
$$2HClO_3 \longrightarrow H_2O + Cl_2O_5$$

However, dichlorine pentoxide, Cl_2O_5, is very unstable—its existence has never been verified. If it is formed at all, it decomposes at once to give chlorine dioxide and oxygen:

$$2Cl_2O_5 \longrightarrow 4ClO_2 + O_2$$

The over-all reaction may be written as

$$4KClO_3 + 4H_2SO_4 \longrightarrow 4KHSO_4 + 4ClO_2\uparrow + O_2\uparrow + 2H_2O$$

Chlorine dioxide is an **odd molecule;** that is, a molecule containing an odd number of electrons. It was pointed out by G. N. Lewis in 1916 that odd molecules (other than those containing transition elements) are rare, and that they are usually colored and are always paramagnetic (attracted by a magnet). Every electronic structure that can be written for chlorine dioxide contains one unpaired electron. This unpaired electron presumably resonates among the three atoms, the electronic structure of the molecule being a resonance hybrid:

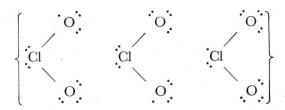

It was mentioned in the preceding section that when chlorine dioxide is dissolved in an alkaline solution chlorate ion and chlorite ion are formed.

Chloric Acid and Its Salts.   Chloric acid, $HClO_3$, is an unstable acid which, like its salts, is a strong oxidizing agent. The most important salt of chloric acid is **potassium chlorate, $KClO_3$**, which is made by passing an excess of chlorine through a hot solution of potassium hydroxide or by heating a solution containing hypochlorite ion and potassium ion:

$$3ClO^- \longrightarrow ClO_3^- + 2Cl^-$$

The potassium chlorate can be separated from the potassium chloride formed in this reaction by crystallization, its solubility at low temperatures being much less than that of the chloride (3 g and 28 g, respectively, per 100 g of water at 0° C). A cheaper way of making potassium chlorate is to electrolyze a solution of potassium chloride, using inert electrodes and keeping the solution mixed. The electrode reactions are

Cathode reaction: $2e^- + 2H_2O \longrightarrow 2OH^- + H_2 \uparrow$

Anode reaction: $Cl^- + 3H_2O \longrightarrow ClO_3^- + 6H^+ + 6e^-$

In the stirred solution the hydroxide ions and the hydrogen ions are brought into contact with one another, and combine to form water. The over-all reaction is

$$Cl^- + 3H_2O \xrightarrow{\text{electr.}} ClO_3^- + 3H_2 \uparrow$$

Potassium chlorate is a white crystalline substance, which is used as the oxidizing agent in matches and fireworks, and in the manufacture of dyes.

A solution of the similar salt **sodium chlorate, $NaClO_3$**, is used as a weed-killer. Potassium chlorate would be as good as sodium chlorate for this purpose; however, sodium salts are cheaper than potassium salts, and for this reason they are often used when only the anion is important. Sometimes the sodium salts have unsatisfactory properties, such as *deliquescence* (attraction of water from the air to form a solution), which make the potassium salts preferable for some uses, even though more expensive.

All of the chlorates form sensitive explosive mixtures when mixed with reducing agents; **great care must be taken in handling them.** The use of sodium chlorate as a weed-killer is attended with danger, because combustible material such as wood or clothing that has become saturated with the chlorate solution will ignite by friction after it has dried. Also *it is very dangerous to grind a chlorate with sulfur, charcoal, or other reducing agent.*

Perchloric Acid and the Perchlorates. Potassium perchlorate, $KClO_4$, is made by heating potassium chlorate just to its melting point:

$$4KClO_3 \longrightarrow 3KClO_4 + KCl$$

At this temperature very little decomposition with evolution of oxygen occurs in the absence of a catalyst. Potassium perchlorate may also be made by long-continued electrolysis of a solution of potassium chloride, potassium hypochlorite, or potassium chlorate.

Potassium perchlorate and other perchlorates are oxidizing agents, somewhat less vigorous and less dangerous than the chlorates. Potassium perchlorate is used in explosives, such as the propellent powder of the bazooka and other rockets. This powder is a mixture of potassium perchlorate and carbon together with a binder; the equation for the principal reaction accompanying its burning is

$$KClO_4 + 4C \longrightarrow KCl + 4CO$$

Anhydrous **magnesium perchlorate,** $Mg(ClO_4)_2$, and **barium perchlorate,** $Ba(ClO_4)_2$, are used as drying agents (*desiccants*). These salts have a very strong attraction for water. Nearly all of the perchlorates are highly soluble in water; potassium perchlorate is exceptional for its low solubility, 0.75 g/100 g at 0° C.

Sodium perchlorate, $NaClO_4$, made by the electrolytic method, is used as a weed-killer; it is safer than sodium chlorate. In general the mixtures of perchlorates with oxidizable materials are less dangerous than the corresponding mixtures of chlorates.

Perchloric acid, $HClO_4 \cdot H_2O$, is a colorless liquid made by distilling, under reduced pressure, a solution of a perchlorate to which sulfuric acid has been added. The perchloric acid distills as the monohydrate, and on cooling it forms crystals of the monohydrate. These crystals are isomorphous with ammonium perchlorate, NH_4ClO_4, and the substance is presumably hydronium perchlorate, $(H_3O)^+(ClO_4)^-$.

Dichlorine heptoxide, Cl_2O_7, is the anhydride of perchloric acid. It can be made by heating perchloric acid with P_2O_5, a strong dehydrating agent:

$$2HClO_4 \cdot H_2O + P_2O_5 \longrightarrow 2H_3PO_4 + Cl_2O_7$$

It is a colorless, oily liquid having a boiling point of $80°$ C. It is the most stable oxide of chlorine, but is exploded by heat or shock.

Illustrative Exercises

13-18. When chlorine is passed into a solution of potassium hydroxide, chloride ions and hypochlorite ions are formed. If the solution is heated the hypochlorite ions undergo auto-oxidation to chlorate ions and chloride ions. Write equations for the two reactions.

13-19. What reaction takes place when Cl_2O is added to water? When ClO_2 is added to water? When Cl_2O_7 is added to water? Would you consider each of these oxides to be an acid anhydride?

13–6. The Oxygen Acids and Oxides of Bromine

Bromine forms only two stable oxygen acids—hypobromous acid and bromic acid—and their salts:

HBrO, hypobromous acid   KBrO, potassium hypobromite
$HBrO_3$, bromic acid $KBrO_3$, potassium bromate

Their preparation and properties are similar to those of the corresponding compounds of chlorine. They are somewhat weaker oxidizing agents than their chlorine analogs.

The bromite ion, BrO_2^-, has been reported to exist in solution. However, no effort to prepare perbromic acid or any perbromate has succeeded.

Three very unstable oxides of bromine, Br_2O, BrO_2, and Br_3O_8, have been described. The structure of Br_3O_8 is not known.

None of the oxygen compounds of bromine has found important practical use.

13–7. The Oxygen Acids and Oxides of Iodine

Iodine reacts with hydroxide ion in cold alkaline solution to form the **hypoiodite ion, IO^-,** and iodide ion:

$$I_2 + 2OH^- \longrightarrow IO^- + I^- + H_2O$$

On warming the solution it reacts further to form **iodate ion, IO_3^-:**

$$3IO^- \longrightarrow IO_3^- + 2I^-$$

The salts of hypoiodous acid and iodic acid may be made in these ways. **Iodic acid** itself, HIO_3, is usually made by oxidizing iodine with concentrated nitric acid:

$$I_2 + 10HNO_3 \longrightarrow 2HIO_3 + 10NO_2 \uparrow + 4H_2O$$

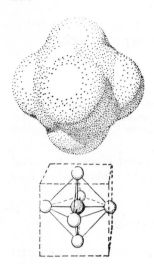

FIGURE 13-6

The periodate ion, IO_6^{5-}.

Iodic acid is a white solid, which is only very slightly soluble in concentrated nitric acid; it accordingly separates out during the course of the reaction. Its principal salts, **potassium iodate,** KIO_3, and **sodium iodate,** $NaIO_3$, are white crystalline solids.

Periodic acid has the normal formula H_5IO_6, with an octahedral arrangement of the oxygen atoms around the iodine atom, as shown in Figure 13-6. This difference in composition from its analog perchloric acid, $HClO_4$, results from the large size of the iodine atom, which permits this atom to coordinate six oxygen atoms about itself, instead of four. The ligancy of iodine in periodic acid is hence 6.

There exists a series of periodates corresponding to the formula H_5IO_6 for periodic acid, and also a series corresponding to HIO_4. Salts of the first series are **dipotassium trihydrogen periodate,** $K_2H_3IO_6$, **silver periodate,** Ag_5IO_6, etc. **Sodium periodate,** $NaIO_4$, a salt of the second series, occurs in small amounts in crude Chile saltpeter. A solution of sodium periodate usually crystallizes as $Na_2H_3IO_6$, a salt of the first series.

The two forms of periodic acid, H_5IO_6 and HIO_4 (the latter being unstable, but forming stable salts), represent the same oxidation state of iodine, $+7$. The equilibrium between the two forms is a hydration reaction:

$$HIO_4 + 2H_2O \rightleftharpoons H_5IO_6$$

The Oxides of Iodine. Iodine pentoxide, I_2O_5, is obtained as a white powder by gently heating either iodic acid or periodic acid:

$$2HIO_3 \longrightarrow I_2O_5 + H_2O \uparrow$$

$$2H_5IO_6 \longrightarrow I_2O_5 + 5H_2O \uparrow + O_2 \uparrow$$

The anhydride of periodic acid, I_2O_7, seems not to be stable.

The lower oxide of iodine, IO_2, can be made by treating an iodate with concentrated sulfuric acid and then adding water. This oxide is a yellow solid. The magnetic properties of the substance show that its formula is not I_2O_4; the substance is paramagnetic, which shows that it has an odd number of electrons in the molecule.

13–8. *The Oxidizing Strength of the Oxygen Compounds of the Halogens*

Elementary fluorine, F_2, is able to oxidize the halide ions of its congeners to the free halogens, by reactions such as

$$F_2 + 2Cl^- \longrightarrow 2F^- + Cl_2$$

Fluorine is more electronegative than the other elements, and it accordingly is able to take electrons away from the anions of these elements. Similarly chlorine is able to oxidize both bromide ion and iodide ion, and bromine is able to oxidize iodide ion:

$$Cl_2 + 2Br^- \longrightarrow 2Cl^- + Br_2$$
$$Cl_2 + 2I^- \longrightarrow 2Cl^- + I_2$$
$$Br_2 + 2I^- \longrightarrow 2Br^- + I_2$$

The order of strength as an oxidizing agent for the elementary halogens is accordingly $F_2 > Cl_2 > Br_2 > I_2$.

At first sight there seems to be an anomaly in the reactions involving the free halogens and their oxygen compounds. Thus, although chlorine is able to liberate iodine from iodide ion, iodine is able to liberate chlorine from chlorate ion, according to the reaction

$$I_2 + 2ClO_3^- \longrightarrow 2IO_3^- + Cl_2$$

In this reaction, however, it is to be noted that elementary iodine is acting as a reducing agent, rather than as an oxidizing agent. During the course of the reaction the oxidation number of iodine is increased, from 0 to $+5$, and that of chlorine is decreased, from $+5$ to 0. The direction in which the reaction takes place predominantly is accordingly that which would be predicted by the electronegativity scale; iodine, the heavier halogen and less electronegative element, tends to have a high positive oxidation number, and chlorine tends to have a low oxidation number. (Remember that in this case, as in nearly all chemical reactions, we may be dealing with chemical equilibrium. The foregoing statement is to be interpreted as meaning that at equilibrium there are present in the system larger amounts of iodate ion and free chlorine than of chlorate ion and free iodine.)

Chlorate ion also has the power of oxidizing free bromine to bromate ion, and bromate ion has the power of oxidizing free iodine to iodate ion:

$$Br_2 + 2ClO_3^- \longrightarrow 2BrO_3^- + Cl_2$$
$$I_2 + 2BrO_3^- \longrightarrow 2IO_3^- + Br_2$$

Chlorate ion is hence a stronger oxidizing agent than bromate ion, which in turn is a stronger oxidizing agent than iodate ion; conversely, iodine is a stronger reducing agent than bromine, which is itself a stronger reducing agent than chlorine. All of these relations correspond to the electronegativity scale. The oxidizing and reducing strengths of hypochlorite ion, hypobromite ion, and hypoiodite ion also correspond to expectation; hypochlorite ion is the strongest oxidizing agent and the weakest reducing agent of the three.

Illustrative Exercises

13-20. Would you predict that iodine would react with chloride ion? With chlorate ion?

13-21. Write an equation for the reaction of bromine with a solution of potassium hydroxide.

13-22. Would you expect iodine to be a stronger or a weaker disinfectant than chlorine? Why?

13-23. Bromine forms only two oxygen acids, HBrO and HBrO₃. Write an equation for the reaction that you would expect to occur when the oxide BrO_2 is added to water.

13–9. Compounds of Halogens with Non-Metals and Metalloids

The halogens form covalent compounds with most of the non-metallic elements (including each other) and the metalloids. These compounds are usually molecular substances, with the relatively low melting points and boiling points characteristic of substances with small forces of intermolecular attraction.

An example of a compound involving a covalent bond between a halogen and a non-metal is chloroform, $CHCl_3$ (Chapter 7). In this molecule, the structure of which is shown in Figure 13-7, the carbon atom is attached by single covalent bonds to one hydrogen atom and three chlorine atoms. Chloroform is a colorless liquid, with a characteristic sweetish odor. Its boiling point is 61° C and its density is 1.498 g/ml. Chloroform is only slightly soluble in water, but it dissolves readily in alcohol, ether, and carbon tetrachloride.

FIGURE 13-7

The chloroform molecule, CHCl₃.

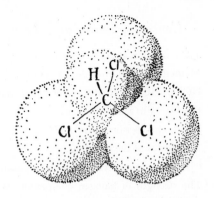

The melting points and boiling points of some binary covalent chlorides are the following:

	CCl₄	NCl₃	Cl₂O	ClF
m.p.	−23°	−40°	−20°	−154° C
b.p.	77°	70°	4°	−100°

	SiCl₄	PCl₃	SCl₂	Cl₂
m.p.	−70°	−112°	−78°	−102°
b.p.	60°	74°	59°	−34°

	GeCl₄	AsCl₃
m.p.	−50°	−18°
b.p.	83°	130°

	SnCl₄	SbCl₃	TeCl₂	ICl
m.p.	−33°	73°	209°	27°
b.p.	114°	223°	327°	97°

In addition to these compounds, many compounds, such as PCl₅, ClF₃, SCl₄, etc., exist, to which a normal covalent structure with noble-gas configuration for the central atom cannot be assigned.

Many of these substances react readily with water, to form a hydride of one element and a hydroxide of the other:

$$ClF + H_2O \longrightarrow HClO + HF$$

$$PCl_3 + 3H_2O \longrightarrow P(OH)_3 + 3HCl$$

In general, in a reaction of this sort, called *hydrolysis*, the more electronegative element combines with hydrogen, and the less electronegative element combines with the hydroxide group. This rule is seen to be followed in the above examples.

Concepts, Facts, and Terms Introduced in This Chapter

The oxidation states of the halogens. Properties of the halogens and halogenides.

Methods of preparing the halogens and the hydrogen halogenides.

$HClO_4$, $HClO_3$, $HClO_2$, $HClO$, and their salts.

$HBrO_3$, $HBrO$, and their salts.

H_5IO_6 and its salts; salts of HIO_4.

The oxides of the halogens.

ClO_2, an odd molecule; color and paramagnetism of odd molecules.

The strength of halogen compounds as oxidizing and reducing agents in relation to electronegativity.

Compounds of halogens with non-metals and metalloids; hydrolysis.

Bleaching powder; potassium chlorate; sodium chlorate; potassium perchlorate; magnesium perchlorate and barium perchlorate.

Exercises

13-24.   What chemical reaction do you expect to take place when a solution of bleaching powder is acidified? Could this be used as a method of producing hypochlorous acid?

13-25.   What chemical reaction takes place at each electrode in the electrolytic preparation of sodium hypochlorite from sodium chloride? Would a well stirred solution become more acidic or more basic during the course of this electrolysis?

13-26.   Which is the stronger oxidizing agent, hypochlorite ion, ClO^-, or hypoiodite ion, IO^-? Which is the stronger reducing agent?

13-27.   Why is potassium chlorate rather than sodium chlorate usually used in the chemical laboratory when a chlorate is needed? Why is sodium chlorate solution, rather than potassium chlorate solution, used as a weed-killer?

13-28.   Write the equation for the formation of potassium iodate by the reaction of powdered iodine with a hot solution of potassium hydroxide.

13-29.   Under what conditions does potassium chlorate decompose to give oxygen and potassium chloride, and under what conditions does it react to form potassium perchlorate and potassium chloride?

13-30.   What is the equation for the hydrolysis of chlorine monoxide? Is there any oxidation or reduction in this chemical reaction? If so, what element changes its oxidation number?

13-31.   Write an equation for the reaction of chlorine with carbon disulfide, CS_2. The products of the reaction are carbon tetrachloride, CCl_4, and disulfur dichloride, S_2Cl_2. What do you think the structure of disulfur dichloride is?

13-32.   Phosgene, $COCl_2$, is made by mixing carbon monoxide with chlorine in the sunlight or in the presence of a catalyst. Write the equation for this reaction, assigning oxidation numbers to the elements in the reactants and the product. What do you think the electronic structure of phosgene is?

13-33.   What halogen forms no oxygen acids? Does this halogen form any compounds containing oxygen?

13-34. What are the names of the compounds $CaCl_2$, $Ca(ClO)_2$, $Ca(ClO_2)_2$, $Ca(ClO_3)_2$, $Ca(ClO_4)_2$? What is the oxidation number of chlorine in each compound?

13-35. If liquid chlorine costs 5 cents per pound, and bleaching powder approximating the formula $CaOCl_2$ costs 3 cents per pound, which is the less expensive material to use to purify the water of a swimming pool?

13-36. In a mixture of sodium iodide, sodium bromide, sodium chloride, and sodium fluoride, what oxidizing agent could be used to oxidize the iodide to free iodine without affecting any of the others? After the oxidation of the iodide, what substance could be used to oxidize only the bromide? Then only the chloride? Can the fluoride be oxidized?

13-37. How can each of the four halogens be conveniently prepared from compounds in the laboratory? Write equations for all reactions.

13-38. How can each of the four hydrogen halides be prepared in moderately pure form in the laboratory? Write equations.

13-39. The German chemist Liebig is said to have prepared bromine several years before the discovery of this element, but to have failed to recognize it as a new element because of its close similarity in physical properties to ICl. How would you tell a sample of bromine from a sample of ICl?

13-40. It is stated in Section 13–9 that in hydrolysis of a binary compound the more electronegative element combines with hydrogen, and the less electronegative element combines with the OH group. Can you explain why this is to be expected? What would be the products of hydrolysis of ICl?

Chapter 14

Sulfur

The sixth-group elements sulfur, selenium, and tellurium are much less electronegative than their congener oxygen, which was discussed in Chapter 6, and their chemical properties are correspondingly distinctive.

The electronic structures of the atoms of these elements are given in Table 14-1. The atoms have two electrons less than the corresponding noble gas. They can assume the electronic structure of the noble gas by adding two electrons, to form doubly charged anions, or by sharing two electron pairs with other atoms (that is, by forming two covalent bonds), or in other ways.

TABLE 14-1 *Electronic Structure of the Sixth-group Elements*

Z	ELEMENT	K	L		M			N			O	
		1s	2s	2p	3s	3p	3d	4s	4p	4d	5s	5p
8	Oxygen	2	2	4								
16	Sulfur	2	2	6	2	4						
34	Selenium	2	2	6	2	6	10	2	4			
52	Tellurium	2	2	6	2	6	10	2	6	10	2	4

14–1. The Oxidation States of Sulfur

The principal oxidation states of sulfur are -2, 0, $+4$, and $+6$. These states are represented by many important substances, including those given in the diagram on the next page.

14–2. Elementary Sulfur

Orthorhombic and Monoclinic Sulfur. Sulfur exists in several allotropic forms. Ordinary sulfur is a yellow solid substance which forms crystals with orthorhombic symmetry; it is called **orthorhombic sulfur**

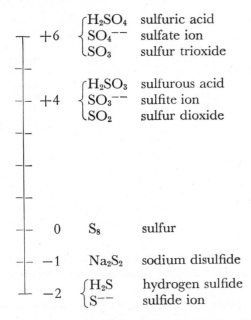

$+6$ $\begin{cases} H_2SO_4 & \text{sulfuric acid} \\ SO_4{}^{--} & \text{sulfate ion} \\ SO_3 & \text{sulfur trioxide} \end{cases}$

$+4$ $\begin{cases} H_2SO_3 & \text{sulfurous acid} \\ SO_3{}^{--} & \text{sulfite ion} \\ SO_2 & \text{sulfur dioxide} \end{cases}$

0 S_8 sulfur

-1 Na_2S_2 sodium disulfide

-2 $\begin{cases} H_2S & \text{hydrogen sulfide} \\ S^{--} & \text{sulfide ion} \end{cases}$

or, usually, **rhombic sulfur.** It is insoluble in water, but soluble in carbon disulfide (CS_2), carbon tetrachloride, and similar non-polar solvents, giving solutions from which well formed crystals of sulfur can be obtained (Figure 14-1). Some of its physical properties are given in Table 14-2.

At 112.8° C orthorhombic sulfur melts to form a straw-colored liquid. This liquid crystallizes in a monoclinic crystalline form, called β-sulfur or **monoclinic sulfur** (Figure 14-1). The sulfur molecules in both orthorhombic sulfur and monoclinic sulfur, as well as in the straw-colored liquid, are S_8 molecules, with a staggered-ring configuration (Figure 11-6). The formation of this large molecule (and of the similar molecules Se_8 and Te_8) is the result of the tendency of the sixth-group elements to form two single covalent bonds, instead of one double bond. Diatomic molecules S_2 are formed by heating sulfur vapor (S_8

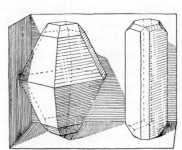

FIGURE 14-1

Crystals of orthorhombic and monoclinic sulfur.

Orthorhombic   Monoclinic
Sulfur

TABLE 14-2   *Properties of Oxygen, Sulfur, Selenium, and Tellurium*

	ATOMIC NUMBER	MELTING POINT	BOILING POINT	DENSITY
Oxygen	8	$-218.4°$ C	$-183.0°$ C	1.429 g/l
Sulfur (orthorhombic)	16	119.25°, 112.8°	444.6°	2.07 g/cm³
Selenium (gray)	34	217°	688°	4.79
Tellurium (gray)	52	452°	1390°	6.25

at lower temperatures) to a high temperature, but these molecules are less stable than the large molecules containing single bonds. This fact is not isolated, but is an example of the generalization that stable double bonds and triple bonds are formed readily by the light elements carbon, nitrogen, and oxygen, but only rarely by the heavier elements. Carbon

disulfide, CS_2, with electronic structure $: \overset{..}{S}=C=\overset{..}{S} :$, and other compounds containing a carbon-sulfur double bond are the main exceptions to this rule.

Monoclinic sulfur is the stable form above 95.5° C, which is the *equilibrium temperature* (*transition temperature* or *transition point*) between it and the orthorhombic form. Monoclinic sulfur melts at 119.25° C.

Liquid Sulfur.   Sulfur which has just been melted is a mobile, straw-colored liquid. The viscosity of this liquid is low because the S_8 molecules which compose it are nearly spherical in shape (Figure 11-6) and roll easily over one another. When molten sulfur is heated to a higher temperature, however, it gradually darkens in color and becomes more viscous, finally becoming so thick (at about 200°) that it cannot be poured out of its container. Most substances decrease in viscosity with increasing temperature, because the increased thermal agitation causes the molecules to move around one another more easily. The abnormal behavior of liquid sulfur results from the production of molecules of a different kind—long chains, containing scores of atoms. These very long molecules get entangled with one another, causing the liquid to be very viscous. The dark red color is due to the ends of the chains, which consist of sulfur atoms with only one valence bond instead of the normal two.

The straw-colored liquid, S_8, is called λ-sulfur, and the dark red liquid consisting of very long chains is called μ-sulfur. When this liquid is rapidly cooled by being poured into water it forms a rubbery *super-cooled liquid*, insoluble in carbon disulfide. On standing at room temperature the long chains slowly rearrange into S_8 molecules, and the rubbery mass changes into an aggregate of crystals of orthorhombic sulfur.

A form of crystalline sulfur with rhombohedral symmetry can be made by extracting an acidified solution of sodium thiosulfate with chloroform and evaporating the chloroform solution. These crystals, which are orange in color, consist of S_6 molecules; they are unstable, and change into long chains and then into orthorhombic sulfur (S_8) in a few hours.

Sulfur boils at 444.6°, forming S_8 vapor, which on a cold surface condenses directly to orthorhombic sulfur.

The Mining of Sulfur. Free sulfur occurs in large quantities in Sicily, Louisiana, and Texas. The Sicilian deposits consist of rock

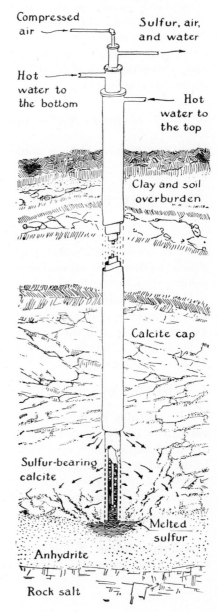

Compressed
air

Sulfur, air,
and water

Hot
water to
the bottom

Hot
water to
the top

Clay and soil
overburden

Calcite cap

Sulfur-bearing
calcite

Melted
sulfur

Anhydrite

Rock salt

FIGURE 14-2

The Frasch process for mining sulfur. (The mineral anhydrite which lies below the sulfur-calcite layer is anhydrous calcium sulfate, $CaSO_4$.)

(clay, gypsum, limestone) mixed with about 20 percent of free sulfur
The material is heated by burning part of the sulfur, and molten sulfur
is drawn off, and then purified by sublimation.

Over 80 percent of the world's production of sulfur is mined in
Louisiana and Texas by a very clever method, the Frasch process. The
sulfur, mixed with limestone, occurs at depths of about one thousand
feet, under strata of sand, clay, and rock. A boring is made to the deposit, and four concentric pipes are sunk (Figure 14-2). Superheated
water (155°) under pressure is pumped down the two outer pipes. This
melts the sulfur, which collects in a pool around the open end. Air is
forced down the innermost pipe, and a bubbly froth of air, sulfur, and
water rises through the space between the innermost pipe and the next
one. This mixture is allowed to flow into a very large wooden vat, where
the sulfur hardens as a product 99.5% pure.

14–3. Hydrogen Sulfide and the Sulfides of the Metals

Hydrogen sulfide, H_2S, is analogous to water, its electronic structure

$$H$$
$$|$$

being $:\overset{..}{S}$—H. It is far more volatile (m.p. $-85.6°$ C, b.p. $-60.7°$)

than water. It is appreciably soluble in cold water (2.6 l of gas dissolves
in 1 l of water at 20°), forming a slightly acidic solution. The solution is
slowly oxidized by atmospheric oxygen, giving a milky precipitate of
sulfur.

Hydrogen sulfide has a powerful odor, resembling that of rotten
eggs. It is very poisonous, and care must be taken not to breathe the
gas while using it in the analytical chemistry laboratory.

Hydrogen sulfide is readily prepared by action of hydrochloric acid
on ferrous sulfide:

$$2HCl + FeS \longrightarrow FeCl_2 + H_2S \uparrow$$

The **sulfides** of the alkali and alkaline-earth metals are colorless
substances easily soluble in water. The sulfides of most other metals
are insoluble or only very slightly soluble in water, and their precipitation under varying conditions is an important part of the usual
scheme of qualitative analysis for the metallic ions. Many metallic
sulfides occur in nature; important sulfide ores include FeS, Cu_2S, CuS,
ZnS, Ag_2S, HgS, and PbS.

The Polysulfides.   Sulfur dissolves in a solution of an alkali or alkaline-
earth sulfide, forming a mixture of polysulfides:

$$S^{--} + S \longrightarrow S_2^{--}, \text{ disulfide ion}$$
$$S^{--} + 2S \longrightarrow S_3^{--}, \text{ trisulfide ion}$$
$$S^{--} + 3S \longrightarrow S_4^{--}, \text{ tetrasulfide ion}$$

The **disulfide ion** has the structure $\left[\; :\!\overset{..}{\underset{..}{S}}\!-\!\overset{..}{\underset{..}{S}}\!: \; \right]^{--}$, analogous to that

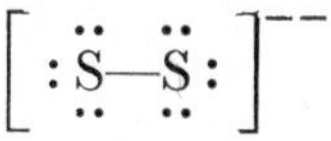

of the peroxide ion, and the polysulfide ions have similar structures, involving chains of sulfur atoms connected by single covalent bonds:

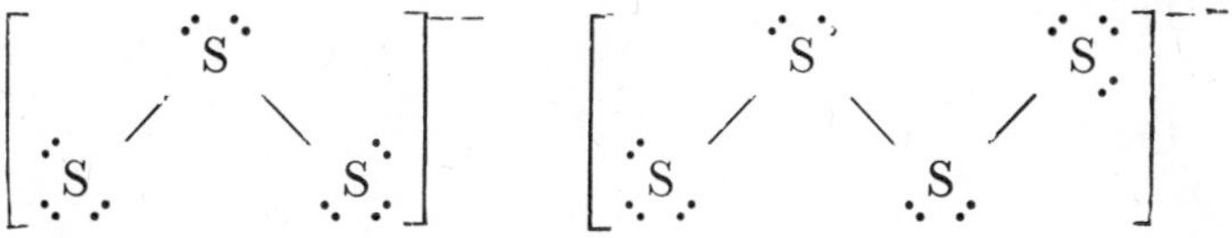

Hydrogen disulfide, H_2S_2, analogous to hydrogen peroxide, can be made by careful treatment of a disulfide with acid; it is a pale yellow oily liquid. The hydrogen polysulfides readily decompose to hydrogen sulfide and sulfur.

The common mineral *pyrite*, FeS_2, is ferrous disulfide.

14–4. *Sulfur Dioxide and Sulfurous Acid*

Sulfur dioxide, SO_2, is the gas formed by burning sulfur or a sulfide, such as pyrite:

$$S + O_2 \longrightarrow SO_2$$
$$4FeS_2 + 11O_2 \longrightarrow 2Fe_2O_3 + 8SO_2 \uparrow$$

It is colorless, and has a characteristic choking odor.

Sulfur dioxide is conveniently made in the laboratory by adding a strong acid to solid sodium hydrogen sulfite:

$$H_2SO_4 + NaHSO_3 \longrightarrow NaHSO_4 + H_2O + SO_2 \uparrow$$

It may be purified and dried by bubbling it through concentrated sulfuric acid, and, since it is over twice as dense as air, it may be collected by displacement of air.

A solution of **sulfurous acid,** H_2SO_3, is obtained by dissolving sulfur dioxide in water. Both sulfurous acid and its salts, the **sulfites,** are active reducing agents. They form sulfuric acid, H_2SO_4, and sulfates on oxidation by oxygen, the halogens, hydrogen peroxide, and similar oxidizing agents.

The electronic structure of sulfur dioxide is

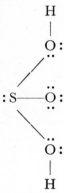

It is a resonating structure in which each sulfur-oxygen bond is a hybrid between a single bond and a double bond. The structure of sulfurous acid is

In each of these molecules the sulfur atom has one unshared pair of electrons; this is characteristic of atoms with oxidation number two less than the maximum.

Sulfur dioxide is used in great quantities in the manufacture of sulfuric acid, sulfurous acid, and sulfites. It destroys fungi and bacteria, and is used as a preservative in the preparation of dried prunes, apricots, and other fruits. A solution of **calcium hydrogen sulfite,** $Ca(HSO_3)_2$, made by reaction of sulfur dioxide and calcium hydroxide, is used in the manufacture of paper pulp from wood. The solution dissolves lignin, a substance which cements the cellulose fibers together, and liberates these fibers, which are then processed into paper.

14–5. *Sulfur Trioxide*

Sulfur trioxide, SO_3, is formed in very small quantities when sulfur is burned in air. It is usually made by oxidation of sulfur dioxide by air, in the presence of a catalyst. The reaction

$$2SO_2 + O_2 \rightleftarrows 2SO_3$$

is exothermic; it liberates 45 kcal of heat for two moles of sulfur trioxide produced. The nature of the equilibrium is such that at low temperatures a satisfactory yield can be obtained; the reaction proceeds nearly to completion. However, the rate of the reaction is so small at low temperatures as to make the direct combination of the substances unsuitable as a commercial process, and at higher temperatures, where the rate is satisfactory, the yield is low because of the unfavorable equilibrium.

The solution to this problem was the discovery of certain catalysts (platinum, vanadium pentoxide), which speed up the reaction without affecting the equilibrium. The catalyzed reaction proceeds not in the gaseous mixture, but on the surface of the catalyst, as the gas molecules strike it. In practice sulfur dioxide, made by burning sulfur or pyrite, is mixed with air and passed over the catalyst at a temperature of 400° to 450° C. About 99% of the sulfur dioxide is converted into sulfur trioxide under these conditions. It is used mainly in the manufacture of sulfuric acid.

Sulfur trioxide is a corrosive gas, which combines vigorously with water to form sulfuric acid:

$$SO_3 + H_2O \longrightarrow H_2SO_4$$

It also dissolves readily in sulfuric acid, to form *oleum* or *fuming sulfuric acid*, which consists mainly of disulfuric acid, $H_2S_2O_7$ (also called pyrosulfuric acid):

$$SO_3 + H_2SO_4 \rightleftarrows H_2S_2O_7$$

Sulfur trioxide condenses at 44.5° to a colorless liquid, which freezes at 16.8° to transparent cystals. The substance is polymorphous, these crystals being the unstable form (the α-form). The stable form consists of silky asbestos-like crystals, which are produced when the α-crystals or the liquid stands for some time, especially in the presence of a trace of moisture. There exist also one or more other forms of this substance, which are hard to investigate because the changes from one form to another are very slow. The asbestos-like crystals slowly evaporate to SO_3 vapor at temperatures above 50°.

The Structure of Sulfur Trioxide and Its Derivatives. The sulfur trioxide molecule in the gas phase, the liquid, and the α-crystals has the electronic structure

The molecule is planar, and each bond is a resonance hybrid, as indicated.

The properties of sulfur trioxide may be in large part explained as resulting from the instability of the sulfur-oxygen double bond. Thus by reaction with water the double bond can be replaced by two single bonds, in sulfuric acid:

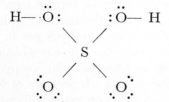

The increased stability of the product is reflected in the large amount of heat evolved in the reaction. A second sulfur trioxide molecule can eliminate its double bond by combining with a molecule of sulfuric acid to form a molecule of disulfuric acid:

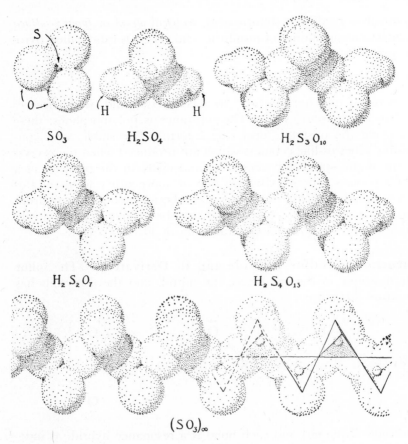

FIGURE 14-3   *Sulfur trioxide and some oxygen acids of sulfur.*

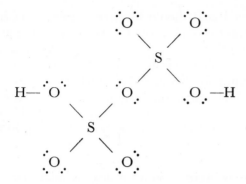

Similarly molecules of trisulfuric acid, $H_2S_3O_{10}$, tetrasulfuric acid, $H_2S_4O_{13}$, etc., can be formed (Figure 14-3), culminating in a chain $HO_3SO(SO_3)_\infty SO_3H$ of nearly infinite length—essentially a high polymer of sulfur trioxide, $(SO_3)_x$, with x large. It is these very long molecules which constitute the asbestos-like crystalline form of sulfur trioxide. We can understand why the crystals are fibrous, like asbestos—they consist of extremely long chain molecules, arranged together side by side, but easily separated into fibers, because, although the chains themselves are strong, the forces between them are relatively weak.

The molecular structures explain why the formation of the asbestos-like crystals, and also their decomposition to SO_3 vapor, are slow processes, whereas crystallization and evaporation are usually rapid. In this case these processes are really *chemical reactions*, involving the formation of new chemical bonds. The role of a trace of water in catalyzing the formation of the asbestos-like crystals can also be understood; the molecules of water serve to start the chains, which can then grow to great length.

14–6. *Sulfuric Acid and the Sulfates*

Sulfuric acid, H_2SO_4, is one of the most important of all chemicals, finding use throughout the chemical industry and related industries. About 10,000,000 tons of the acid is made each year. It is a heavy, oily liquid (density 1.838 g/cm³), which fumes slightly in air, as the result of the liberation of traces of sulfur trioxide which then combine with water vapor to form droplets of sulfuric acid. When heated, pure sulfuric acid yields a vapor rich in sulfur trioxide, and then boils, at $338°$ with the constant composition 98% H_2SO_4, 2% water. This is the ordinary "concentrated sulfuric acid" of commerce.

Concentrated sulfuric acid is very corrosive. It has a strong affinity for water, and a large amount of heat is liberated when it is mixed with water, as the result of the formation of hydronium ion:

$$H_2SO_4 + 2H_2O \rightleftharpoons 2H_3O^+ + SO_4^{--}$$

In diluting it, the concentrated acid should be poured into water in a thin stream, with stirring; water should never be poured into the acid, because it is apt to sputter and throw drops of acid out of the container. The diluted acid occupies a smaller volume than its constituents, the concentration being a maximum at $H_2SO_4 + 2H_2O$ $[(H_3O)_2{}^+(SO_4)^{--}]$.

The crystalline phases which form on cooling sulfuric acid containing varying amounts of sulfur trioxide or water are $H_2S_2O_7$, H_2SO_4, $H_2SO_4 \cdot H_2O$ [presumably $(H_3O)^+(HSO_4)^-$], $H_2SO_4 \cdot 2H_2O$ $[(H_3O)_2{}^+$ $(SO_4)^{--}]$, and $H_2SO_4 \cdot 4H_2O$.

The Manufacture of Sulfuric Acid. Sulfuric acid is made by two processes, the *contact process* and the *lead-chamber process*, which are now about equally important.

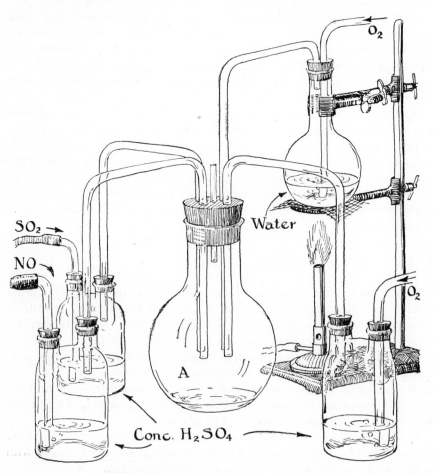

O_2

$SO_2 \rightarrow$

$NO \searrow$

Water

O_2

A

Conc. $H_2SO_4 \longrightarrow$

FIGURE 14-4 *A demonstration experiment illustrating the lead-chamber process for making sulfuric acid.*

In the **contact process** sulfur trioxide is made by the catalytic oxidation of sulfur dioxide (the name of the process refers to the fact that reaction occurs on contact of the gases with the solid catalyst). The catalyst formerly used was finely divided platinum; it has now been largely replaced by vanadium pentoxide, V_2O_5. The gas containing sulfur trioxide is then bubbled through sulfuric acid, which absorbs the sulfur trioxide. Water is added at the proper rate, and 98% acid is drawn off.

The principle of the **lead-chamber process** is shown by the following experiment (Figure 14-4). A large flask is fitted with four inlet tubes and a small outlet tube. Three of the tubes come from wash bottles, and the fourth from a flask in which water may be boiled. When oxygen, sulfur dioxide, nitric oxide, and a small amount of water vapor are introduced into the large flask, white crystals of nitrososulfuric acid,

$$\begin{array}{c} HO \qquad\quad O{-}N{=}O \\ \diagdown\quad\diagup \\ S \\ \diagup\quad\diagdown \\ O \qquad O \end{array}$$

(sulfuric acid in which one hydrogen atom is replaced by the nitroso

group, $-\ddot{N}{=}\ddot{O}:$), are formed. When steam is sent into the flask by boiling the water in the small flask, the crystals react to form drops of sulfuric acid, liberating oxides of nitrogen. In effect, the oxides of nitrogen serve to catalyze the oxidation of sulfur dioxide by oxygen. The complex reactions which occur may be summarized as

$$2SO_2 + NO + NO_2 + O_2 + H_2O \longrightarrow 2HSO_4NO$$
$$2HSO_4NO + H_2O \longrightarrow 2H_2SO_4 + NO\uparrow + NO_2\uparrow$$

The oxides of nitrogen, NO and NO_2, which take part in the first reaction are released by the second reaction, and can serve over and over again.

In practice the reactions take place in large lead-lined chambers (Figure 14-5). The acid produced, called *chamber acid*, is 65% to 70% H_2SO_4. It may be concentrated to 78% H_2SO_4 by the evaporation of water by the hot gases from the sulfur burner or pyrite burner. This process occurs as the acid trickles down over acid-resistant tile in a lead-lined tower (the Glover tower). A similar tower (the Gay-Lussac tower) is used to remove the nitrogen oxides from the exhaust gases; the oxides of nitrogen are then reintroduced into the chamber.

The Chemical Properties and Uses of Sulfuric Acid. The uses of sulfuric acid are determined by its chemical properties—as an **acid,** a **dehydrating agent,** and an **oxidizing agent.**

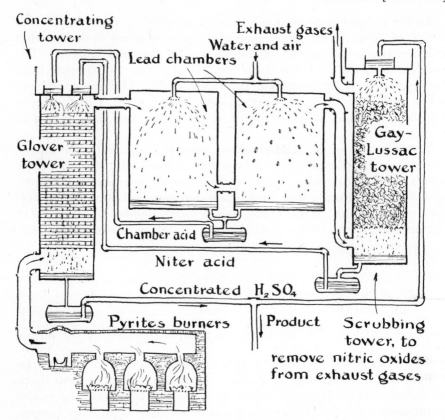

Concentrating tower

Exhaust gases

Water and air

Lead chambers

Glover tower

Gay-Lussac tower

Chamber acid

Niter acid

Concentrated H₂SO₄

Pyrites burners

Product

Scrubbing tower, to remove nitric oxides from exhaust gases

FIGURE 14-5   *The lead-chamber process for making sulfuric acid.*

Sulfuric acid has a high boiling point, 330° C, which permits it to be used with salts of more volatile acids in the preparation of these acids. Nitric acid, for example, can be made by heating a nitrate, such as sodium nitrate, with sulfuric acid:

$$NaNO_3 + H_2SO_4 \longrightarrow NaHSO_4 + HNO_3 \uparrow$$

The nitric acid distills off at 86° C. It is also used for the manufacture of soluble phosphate fertilizers (Chapter 16), of ammonium sulfate for use as a fertilizer, of other sulfates, and in the manufacture of many chemicals and drugs. Steel is usually cleaned of iron rust (is "pickled") by immersion in a bath of sulfuric acid before it is coated with zinc, tin, or enamel. The use of sulfuric acid as the electrolyte in ordinary storage cells has been mentioned (Chapter 12).

Sulfuric acid has such a strong affinity for water as to make it an effective dehydrating agent. Gases which do not react with the substance may be dried by being bubbled through sulfuric acid. The dehydrating power of the concentrated acid is great enough to cause it to remove hydrogen and oxygen as water from organic compounds, such as sugar:

$$\underset{\text{sugar (sucrose)}}{C_{12}H_{22}O_{11}} \xrightarrow[H_2SO_4]{} 12C + 11H_2O$$

(The symbol $\xrightarrow[H_2SO_4]{}$ is used to show that H_2SO_4 assists in causing the reaction to go to the right.) Many explosives, such as glyceryl trinitrate (nitroglycerine), are made by reaction of organic substances with nitric acid, producing the explosive substance and water:

$$\underset{\text{glycerine}}{C_3H_5(OH)_3} + 3HNO_3 \xrightarrow[H_2SO_4]{} \underset{\text{glyceryl trinitrate}}{C_3H_5(NO_3)_3} + 3H_2O$$

These reversible reactions are made to proceed to the right by mixing the nitric acid with sulfuric acid, which by its dehydrating action favors the products.

Hot concentrated sulfuric acid is an effective oxidizing agent, the product of its reduction being sulfur dioxide. It will dissolve copper, and will even oxidize carbon:

$$Cu + 2H_2SO_4 \longrightarrow CuSO_4 + 2H_2O + SO_2\uparrow$$

$$C + 2H_2SO_4 \longrightarrow CO_2\uparrow + 2H_2O + 2SO_2\uparrow$$

The solution of copper by hot concentrated sulfuric acid illustrates a general reaction—*the solution of an unreactive metal in an acid under the influence of an oxidizing agent.* The reactive metals, above hydrogen in the electromotive-force series, are oxidized to their cations by hydrogen ion, which is itself reduced to elementary hydrogen; for example,

$$Zn + 2H^+ \longrightarrow Zn^{++} + H_2\uparrow$$

Copper is below hydrogen in the series, and does not undergo this reaction. It can be oxidized to cupric ion, however, by a stronger oxidizing agent, such as chlorine or nitric acid or, as illustrated above, hot concentrated sulfuric acid.

Sulfates. Sulfuric acid combines with bases to form **normal sulfates,** such as K_2SO_4, potassium sulfate, and **hydrogen sulfates** or **acid sulfates,** such as $KHSO_4$, potassium hydrogen sulfate.

The sparingly soluble sulfates occur as minerals: these include $CaSO_4 \cdot 2H_2O$ (*gypsum*), $SrSO_4$, $BaSO_4$ (*barite*), and $PbSO_4$. Barium sulfate is the least soluble of the sulfates, and its formation as a white precipitate is used as a test for sulfate ion.

Common soluble sulfates include $Na_2SO_4 \cdot 10H_2O$, $(NH_4)_2SO_4$, $MgSO_4 \cdot 7H_2O$ (Epsom salt), $CuSO_4 \cdot 5H_2O$ (blue vitriol), $FeSO_4 \cdot 7H_2O$, $(NH_4)_2Fe(SO_4)_2 \cdot 6H_2O$ (a well-crystallized, easily purified salt used in analytical chemistry in making standard solutions of ferrous ion), $ZnSO_4 \cdot 7H_2O$, $KAl(SO_4)_2 \cdot 12H_2O$ (alum), $NH_4Al(SO_4)_2 \cdot 12H_2O$ (ammonium alum), and $KCr(SO_4)_2 \cdot 12H_2O$ (chrome alum).

The Peroxysulfuric Acids. Sulfuric acid contains sulfur in its highest oxidation state. When a strong oxidizing agent (hydrogen peroxide or an anode at suitable electric potential) acts on sulfuric acid, the only oxidation which can occur is that of oxygen atoms, from -2 to -1. The products of this oxidation, **peroxysulfuric acid**, H_2SO_5, and **peroxydisulfuric acid**, $H_2S_2O_8$, have been mentioned in Chapter 12. These acids and their salts are used as bleaching agents.

14–7. *The Thio or Sulfo Acids*

Sodium thiosulfate, $Na_2S_2O_3 \cdot 5H_2O$ (incorrectly called "hypo," from an old name sodium hyposulfite), is a substance used in photography (Chapter 28). It is made by boiling a solution of sodium sulfite with free sulfur:

$$SO_3^{--} + S \longrightarrow S_2O_3^{--}$$
$$\text{sulfite ion} \qquad\qquad \text{thiosulfate ion}$$

Thiosulfuric acid, $H_2S_2O_3$, is unstable, and sulfur dioxide and sulfur are formed when a thiosulfate is treated with acid.

The structure of the thiosulfate ion, $S_2O_3^{--}$, is interesting in that the two sulfur atoms are not equivalent. This ion is a sulfate ion, SO_4^{--}, in which one of the oxygen atoms has been replaced by a sulfur atom. The central sulfur atom may be assigned oxidation number $+6$, and the attached sulfur atom oxidation number -2.

Thiosulfate ion is easily oxidized, especially by iodine, to **tetrathionate ion**, $S_4O_6^{--}$:

$$2S_2O_3^{--} \longrightarrow S_4O_6^{--} + 2e^-$$

or

$$2S_2O_3^{--} + I_2 \longrightarrow S_4O_6^{--} + 2I^-$$

This reaction, between thiosulfate ion and iodine, is very useful in the quantitative analysis of oxidizing and reducing agents. The structure of tetrathionate ion is shown in Figure 14-6; it contains a disulfide group $-\overset{..}{\underset{..}{S}}-\overset{..}{\underset{..}{S}}-$ in place of the peroxide group of the peroxydisulfate ion. The oxidation of thiosulfate ion to tetrathionate ion is analogous to the oxidation of sulfide ion S^{--} to disulfide ion $\left[:\overset{..}{\underset{..}{S}}-\overset{..}{\underset{..}{S}}: \right]^{--}$

$$2S^{--} \longrightarrow S_2^{--} + 2e^-$$

Thiosulfuric acid is representative of a general class of acids, called **thio acids** or **sulfo acids**, in which one or more oxygen atoms of an oxygen acid are replaced by sulfur atoms. For example, diarsenic penta-

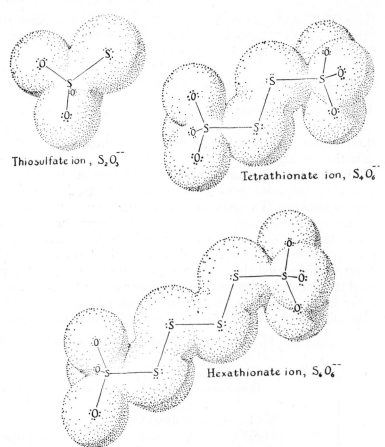

Thiosulfate ion, $S_2O_3^{--}$

Tetrathionate ion, $S_4O_6^{--}$

Hexathionate ion, $S_6O_6^{--}$

FIGURE 14-6   *The thiosulfate ion and related ions.*

sulfide dissolves in a sodium sulfide solution to form the thioarsenate ion, AsS_4^{---}, completely analogous to the arsenate ion, AsO_4^{---}:

$$As_2S_5 + 3S^{--} \longrightarrow 2AsS_4^{---}$$

Diarsenic trisulfide also dissolves, to form the thioarsenite ion:

$$As_2S_3 + 3S^{--} \longrightarrow 2AsS_3^{---}$$

In case that disulfide ion, S_2^{--}, is present in the solution, the thio-arsenite ion is oxidized to thioarsenate ion:

$$AsS_3^{---} + S_2^{--} \longrightarrow AsS_4^{---} + S^{--}$$

An alkaline solution of sodium sulfide and sodium disulfide (or of the ammonium sulfides) is used in the usual systems of qualitative analysis as a means of separating the precipitated sulfides of certain metals and metalloids. This separation depends upon the ability of certain sulfides (HgS, As_2S_3, As_2S_5, Sb_2S_3, Sb_2S_5, SnS, SnS_2) to form thio anions (HgS_2^{--}, AsS_4^{---}, SbS_4^{---}, SnS_4^{----}), whereas others (Ag_2S, PbS, Bi_2S_3, CuS, CdS) remain undissolved.

14–8. *Selenium and Tellurium*

The elementary substances selenium and tellurium differ from sulfur in their physical properties in ways expected from their relative positions in the periodic table. Their melting points, boiling points, and densities are higher, as shown in Table 14–2.

The increase in metallic character with increase in molecular weight is striking. Sulfur is a non-conductor of electricity, as is the red allotropic form of selenium. The gray form of selenium has a small but measurable electronic conductivity, and tellurium is a semi-conductor, with conductivity a fraction of one percent of that of metals. An interesting property of the gray form of selenium is that its electric conductivity is greatly increased during exposure to visible light. This property is used in "selenium cells" for the measurement of light intensity.

Selenium is also used to impart a ruby-red color to glass, and to neutralize the green color in glass which is due to the presence of iron.

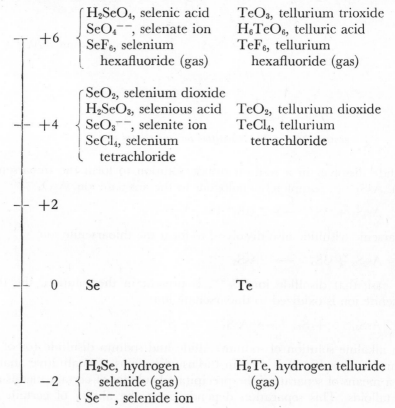

Selenium and tellurium are similar to sulfur in chemical properties, but are less electronegative (more metallic) in character. In addition, sexipositive tellurium shows increase in ligancy from 4 to 6, telluric acid being H_6TeO_6. Representative compounds are shown in the chart on the preceding page.

Concepts, Facts, and Terms Introduced in This Chapter

The principal oxidation states of sulfur: -2, 0, $+4$, $+6$.

Orthorhombic sulfur, monoclinic sulfur, liquid λ-sulfur, liquid μ-sulfur; S_8, S_6, S_2.

The Frasch process of mining sulfur. Hydrogen sulfide, metal sulfides, hydrogen disulfide, polysulfides, pyrite.

Transition temperature or transition point between crystalline forms of a substance. Supercooled liquid.

Sulfur dioxide, sulfurous acid, calcium hydrogen sulfite.

Sulfur trioxide, sulfuric acid, fuming sulfuric acid (oleum), disulfuric acid (pyrosulfuric acid).

The contact process and the lead-chamber process.

Sulfuric acid as an acid, a dehydrating agent, an oxidizing agent.

Gypsum: barite; blue vitriol; Epsom salt; alum; ammonium alum; chrome alum; other sulfates.

Peroxysulfuric acid and peroxydisulfuric acid.

Sodium thiosulfate; the thiosulfate ion; the tetrathionate ion; thio acids (sulfo acids).

Selenium and tellurium and their compounds.

Exercises

14-1. Write an oxidation-reduction equation for the formation of an acid of each of the important oxidation states of sulfur.

14-2. Describe the Frasch process of mining sulfur.

14-3. What is the electronic structure of Na_2S_4?

14-4. What happens when a polysulfide is treated with acid? Write an equation.

14-5. Write chemical equations for the preparation of each of the substances H_2S, SO_2, and SO_3 by (a) a chemical reaction in which there is an oxidation or reduction of the sulfur atom; (b) a chemical reaction in which there is no change in the oxidation number of the sulfur.

14-6. Give the names and formulas of two natural sources of sulfur.

14-7. What is the role of a catalyst in the oxidation of SO_2 to SO_3?

14-8. Explain as fully as you can the properties of sulfur trioxide in terms of its electronic structure.

14-9. How would you make up a solution approximately $1M$ in H^+ from concentrated sulfuric acid (98%, density 1.838 g/cm^3)?

14-10. List all the examples that have been cited in this chapter and previous chapters of the use of concentrated sulfuric acid for the preparation of more volatile acids. Why cannot this method be applied to the preparation of hydrogen iodide gas?

14-11. Write chemical reactions illustrating the three important kinds of uses of sulfuric acid.

14-12. What is the electronic structure of pyrosulfuric acid?

14-13. What are the electronic structures of peroxysulfuric acid and peroxydisulfuric acid?

14-14. Write electronic-structure equations for
(a) sulfite ion and sulfur to give thiosulfate ion.
(b) thiosulfate ion and iodine to give tetrathionate ion plus iodide ion.

14-15. Give the names and formulas of the oxides and oxygen acids of selenium and tellurium.

14-16. What volume of sulfur dioxide at standard conditions would be produced by burning 1 ton of pyrite, FeS_2?

14-17. A sample of an alloy of aluminum and copper weighing 1.000 g was dissolved in acid, the solution was saturated with hydrogen sulfide and filtered, and the precipitate, consisting of cupric sulfide, CuS, was dried and weighed. It was found to weigh 95.5 mg. What was the percentage of copper in the alloy?

14-18. (a) Carbon disulfide, which has boiling point 46.3° C, is made by passing sulfur vapor over red-hot carbon. The carbon burns in the sulfur vapor, forming carbon disulfide. Write the equation for this reaction. (b) In the presence of iodine as catalyst carbon disulfide reacts with chlorine to form carbon tetra-chloride and disulfur dichloride, S_2Cl_2. Write the equation for this reaction. (c) Assuming that the sulfur vapor is in its low-temperature form (S_8), state what the gas-volume relations are for these two reactions.

14-19. Potassium pyrosulfate, $K_2S_2O_7$, is formed by heating potassium hydrogen sulfate at moderate temperatures. Metallic oxides, such as ferric oxide, can be dissolved in the molten potassium pyrosulfate. Write the equations for the reactions involved.

Chapter 15

Nitrogen

Nitrogen is the lightest element of group V of the periodic table; the others are phosphorus, arsenic, antimony, and bismuth (Chapter 16). The chemistry of nitrogen is very interesting and important. Nitrogen is an essential element in most of the substances that make up living matter, including the proteins. Its important compounds include explosives, fertilizers, and other industrial materials.

Elementary nitrogen occurs in nature in the atmosphere, of which it constitutes 78% by volume. It is a colorless, odorless, and tasteless gas, composed of diatomic molecules, N_2. At 0° C and 1 atm pressure a liter of nitrogen weighs 1.2506 g. The gas condenses to a colorless liquid at −195.8° C, and to a white solid at −209.86° C. Nitrogen is slightly soluble in water, 1 liter of which dissolves 23.5 ml of the gas at 0° C and 1 atm.

Nitrogen is chemically unreactive; it does not burn, and at ordinary temperature does not react with other elements. At high temperatures it combines with lithium, magnesium, calcium, and boron, to form *nitrides*, with the formulas Li_3N, Mg_3N_2, Ca_3N_2, and BN, respectively. In a mixture with oxygen through which electric sparks are passed it reacts slowly to form *nitric oxide*, NO.

Nitrogen is made commercially by the fractional distillation of liquid air. In the laboratory it is conveniently made, in slightly impure form, by removing oxygen from air. It may also be made by the oxidation of ammonia by hot copper oxide:

$$2NH_3 + 3CuO \longrightarrow 3H_2O + 3Cu + N_2$$

A convenient method is by the reaction of ammonium ion and nitrite ion:

$$NH_4^+ + NO_2^- \longrightarrow 2H_2O + N_2$$

Ammonium nitrite is an unstable substance, which cannot be kept ready for use. Accordingly in preparing nitrogen in this way sodium

315

nitrite and ammonium chloride may be mixed in solution; decomposition occurs rapidly in the presence of a small amount of acid.

15–1. *The Oxidation States of Nitrogen*

Compounds of nitrogen are known representing all oxidation levels from -3 to $+5$. Some of these compounds are shown in the following chart:

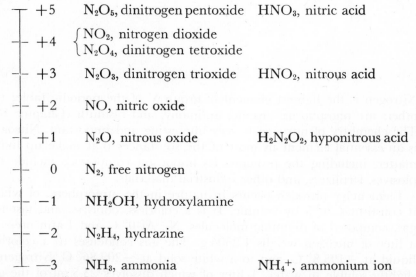

$+5$		N_2O_5, dinitrogen pentoxide	HNO_3, nitric acid
$+4$		{ NO_2, nitrogen dioxide	
		{ N_2O_4, dinitrogen tetroxide	
$+3$		N_2O_3, dinitrogen trioxide	HNO_2, nitrous acid
$+2$		NO, nitric oxide	
$+1$		N_2O, nitrous oxide	$H_2N_2O_2$, hyponitrous acid
0		N_2, free nitrogen	
-1		NH_2OH, hydroxylamine	
-2		N_2H_4, hydrazine	
-3		NH_3, ammonia	NH_4^+, ammonium ion

Free nitrogen is surprisingly stable, and this stability is responsible for the explosive properties of many nitrogen compounds. Usually a triple bond in a molecule causes the molecule to be less stable than molecules containing only single bonds; for example, acetylene, $H—C{\equiv}C—H$, is explosive, and sometimes undergoes violent detonation. The triple bond in the nitrogen molecule $:N{\equiv}N:$, however, seems to be especially stable. It has been estimated that the nitrogen molecule is 110 kcal/mole more stable than it would be if its bonds were normal, with the same energy as single bonds (as in a tetrahedral N_4 molecule, like the P_4 molecule described in Chapter 11).

An example of an unstable nitrogen compound is nitrogen trichloride,

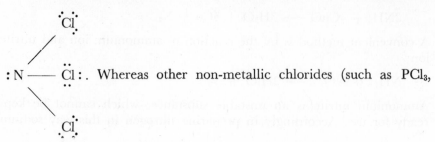

Whereas other non-metallic chlorides (such as PCl_3,

CCl_4, SCl_2, OCl_2) are stable, this substance explodes with great violence when jarred, with the evolution of a large amount of heat:

$$2NCl_3 \longrightarrow N_2 + 3Cl_2 + 110 \text{ kcal}$$

The amount of heat liberated is in this case just equal to the extra stability of the nitrogen molecule.

15–2. Ammonia and Its Compounds

Ammonia, NH_3, is an easily condensable gas (b.p. $-33.3°$ C; m.p. $-77.7°$ C), readily soluble in water. The gas is colorless and has a pungent odor, often detected around stables and manure piles, where ammonia is produced by decomposition of organic matter. The solution of ammonia in water, called ammonium hydroxide solution (or sometimes *aqua ammonia*), contains the molecular species NH_3, NH_4OH (ammonium hydroxide), NH_4^+, and OH^-. Ammonium hydroxide is a weak base, and is only slightly ionized to ammonium ion, NH_4^+, and hydroxide ion (Figure 15-1):

$$NH_3 + H_2O \rightleftarrows NH_4OH \rightleftarrows NH_4^+ + OH^-$$

In the ammonium hydroxide molecule the ammonium ion and the hydroxide ion are held together by a hydrogen bond.

The Preparation of Ammonia.   Ammonia is easily made in the laboratory by heating an ammonium salt, such as ammonium chloride, NH_4Cl, with a strong alkali, such as sodium hydroxide or calcium hydroxide:

$$2NH_4Cl + Ca(OH)_2 \longrightarrow CaCl_2 + 2H_2O + 2NH_3$$

The gas may also be made by warming concentrated ammonium hydroxide.

The principal commercial method of production of ammonia is the *Haber process*, the direct combination of nitrogen and hydrogen under high pressure (several hundred atmospheres) in the presence of

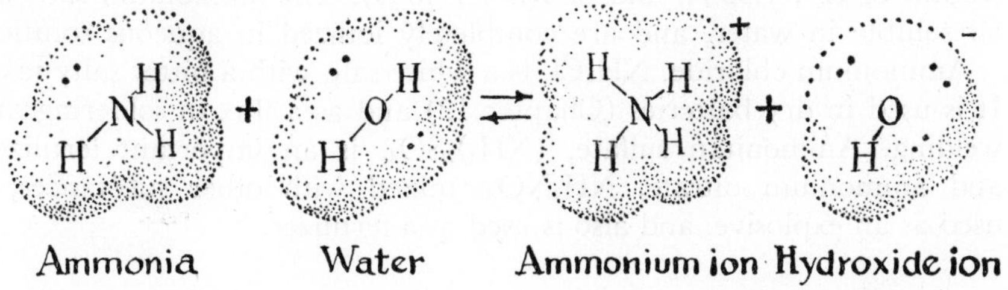

Ammonia   Water   Ammonium ion   Hydroxide ion

FIGURE 15-1   *The reaction of ammonia and water to produce ammonium ion and hydroxide ion.*

a catalyst (usually iron, containing molybdenum or other substances to increase the catalytic activity). The gases used must be specially purified, to prevent "poisoning" the catalyst. The reaction

$$N_2 + 3H_2 \longrightarrow 2NH_3$$

is exothermic, and the yield of ammonia at equilibrium is less at a high temperature than at a lower temperature. However, the gases react very slowly at low temperatures, and the reaction became practical as a commercial process only when a catalyst was found which speeded up the rate satisfactorily at 500° C. Even at this relatively low temperature the equilibrium is unfavorable if the gas mixture is under atmospheric pressure, less than 0.1% of the mixture being converted to ammonia. Increase in the total pressure favors the formation of ammonia; at 500 atmospheres pressure the equilibrium mixture is over one third ammonia.

Smaller amounts of ammonia are obtained as a by-product in the manufacture of coke and illuminating gas by the distillation of coal, and are made by the cyanamide process. In the *cyanamide process* a mixture of lime and coke is heated in an electric furnace, forming **calcium acetylide** (*calcium carbide*), CaC_2:

$$CaO + 3C \longrightarrow CO + CaC_2$$

Nitrogen, obtained by fractionation of liquid air, is passed over the hot calcium acetylide, forming **calcium cyanamide,** $CaCN_2$:

$$CaC_2 + N_2 \longrightarrow CaCN_2 + C$$

Calcium cyanamide may be used directly as a fertilizer, or may be converted into ammonia by treatment with steam under pressure:

$$CaCN_2 + 3H_2O \longrightarrow CaCO_3 + 2NH_3$$

Ammonium Salts. The ammonium salts are similar to the potassium salts and rubidium salts in crystal form, molar volume, color, and other properties. This similarity is due to the close approximation in size of the ammonium ion (radius 1.48 Å) to these alkali ions (radius of K^+, 1.33 Å, and of Rb^+, 1.48 Å). The ammonium salts are all soluble in water, and are completely ionized in aqueous solution.

Ammonium chloride, NH_4Cl, is a white salt, with a bitter salty taste. It is used in dry batteries (Chapter 12) and as a flux in soldering and welding. Ammonium sulfate, $(NH_4)_2SO_4$, is an important fertilizer; and ammonium nitrate, NH_4NO_3, mixed with other substances, is used as an explosive, and also is used as a fertilizer.

Liquid Ammonia as a Solvent. Liquid ammonia (b.p. $-33.4°$ C) has a high dielectric constant, and is a good solvent for salts, forming ionic solutions. It also has the unusual power of dissolving the alkali metals and alkaline-earth metals without chemical reaction, to form blue solutions which have an extraordinarily high electric conductivity and a metallic luster. These metallic solutions slowly decompose, with evolution of hydrogen, forming **amides,** such as sodium amide, $NaNH_2$:

$$2Na + 2NH_3 \longrightarrow 2Na^+ + 2NH_2^- + H_2 \uparrow$$

The amides are ionized in the solution into sodium ion and the amide

ion, $\left[\begin{matrix} H \\ \diagup \\ :\ddot{N} \\ \diagdown \\ H \end{matrix} \right]^-$, which is analogous to the hydroxide ion in aqueous sys-

tems. The ammonium ion in liquid ammonia is analogous to the hydronium ion in aqueous systems.

Ammonium Amalgam. The similarity of the ammonium ion to an alkali ion suggests that it might be possible to reduce ammonium ion to ammonium metal, NH_4. This has not been accomplished; however, a solution of ammonium metal in mercury, *ammonium amalgam*, can be made by cathodic reduction of ammonium ion.

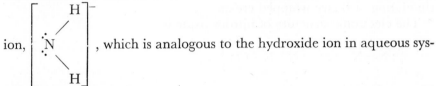

Hydrazine, N_2H_4, has the structure $H-\overset{..}{N}-\overset{..}{N}-H$, in which nitrogen has oxidation number -2. It can be made by oxidizing ammonia with sodium hypochlorite. Hydrazine is a liquid with weak basic properties, similar to those of ammonia. It has found some use as a rocket fuel. It forms salts such as $(N_2H_5)^+Cl^-$ and $(N_2H_6)^{++}Cl_2^-$.

Hydroxylamine, NH_2OH, has the structure $H-\overset{..}{N}-\overset{..}{O}:$, with uni-negative nitrogen. It can be made by reducing nitric oxide or nitric acid under suitable conditions. It is a weak base, forming salts such as hydroxylammonium chloride, $(NH_3OH)^+Cl^-$ (also called hydroxylamine hydrochloride).

15–3. *The Oxides of Nitrogen*

Nitrous oxide, N_2O, is made by heating ammonium nitrate:

$$NH_4NO_3 \longrightarrow 2H_2O + N_2O \uparrow$$

It is a colorless, odorless gas, which has the power of supporting combustion, by giving up its atom of oxygen, leaving molecular nitrogen. When breathed for a short time the gas causes a condition of hysteria; this effect discovered in 1799 by Humphry Davy) led to the use of the name *laughing gas* for the substance. Longer inhalation causes unconsciousness, and the gas, mixed with air or oxygen, is used as a general anesthetic for minor operations. The gas also finds use in making whipped cream; under pressure it dissolves in the cream, and when the pressure is released it fills the cream with many small bubbles, simulating ordinary whipped cream.

The electronic structure of nitrous oxide is

$$\left\{: \ddot{N}\!=\!N\!=\!\ddot{O}: \quad : N\!\equiv\!N\!-\!\ddot{O}: \right\}$$

The position of the oxygen atom at the end of the linear molecule explains the ease with which nitrous oxide acts as an oxidizing agent.

Nitric oxide, NO, can be made by reduction of dilute nitric acid with copper or mercury:

$$3Cu + 8H^+ + 2NO_3^- \longrightarrow 3Cu^{++} + 4H_2O + 2NO \uparrow$$

When made in this way the gas usually contains impurities such as nitrogen and nitrogen dioxide. If the gas is collected over water, in which it is only slightly soluble, the nitrogen dioxide is removed by solution in the water.

A metal or other reducing agent may reduce nitric acid to any lower stage of oxidation, producing nitrogen dioxide, nitrous acid, nitric oxide, nitrous oxide, nitrogen, hydroxylamine, hydrazine, or ammonia (ammonium ion), depending upon the conditions of the reduction. Conditions may be found which strongly favor one product, but usually appreciable amounts of other products are also formed. Nitric oxide is produced preferentially under the conditions mentioned above.

Nitric oxide is a colorless, difficultly condensable gas (b.p. $-151.7°$, m.p. $-163.6°$ C). It combines readily with oxygen to form the red gas nitrogen dioxide, NO_2.

Dinitrogen trioxide, N_2O_3, can be obtained as a blue liquid by cooling an equimolal mixture of nitric oxide and nitrogen dioxide. It is the anhydride of nitrous acid, and produces this acid on solution in water:

$$N_2O_3 + H_2O \longrightarrow 2HNO_2$$

Nitrogen dioxide, NO_2, a red gas, and its dimer **dinitrogen tetroxide,** N_2O_4, a colorless, easily condensable gas, exist in equilibrium with one another:

$$2NO_2 \rightleftarrows N_2O_4$$
red   colorless

The mixture of these gases may be made by adding nitric oxide to oxygen, or by reducing concentrated nitric acid with copper:

$$Cu + 4H^+ + 2NO_3^- \longrightarrow Cu^{++} + 2H_2O + 2NO_2$$

It is also easily obtained by decomposing lead nitrate by heat:

$$2Pb(NO_3)_2 \longrightarrow 2PbO + 4NO_2 + O_2$$

The gas dissolves readily in water or alkali, forming a mixture of nitrate ion and nitrite ion.

Dinitrogen pentoxide, N_2O_5, the anhydride of nitric acid, can be made, as white crystals, by carefully dehydrating nitric acid with diphosphorus pentoxide or by oxidizing nitrogen dioxide with ozone. It is unstable, decomposing spontaneously at room temperature into nitrogen dioxide and oxygen.

The electronic structures of the oxides of nitrogen are shown below Most of these molecules are resonance hybrids, and the contributing structures are not all shown; for dinitrogen pentoxide, for example, the various single and double bonds may change places.

Oxidation number +5 — Dinitrogen pentoxide

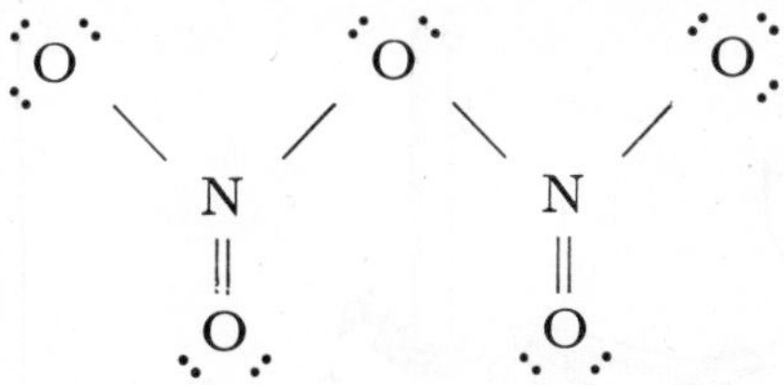

Oxidation number +4 — Nitrogen dioxide 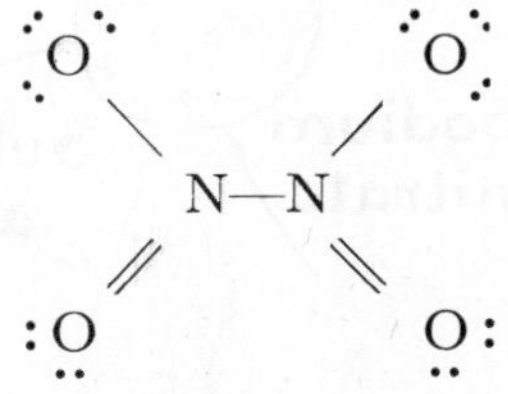 — Dinitrogen tetroxide

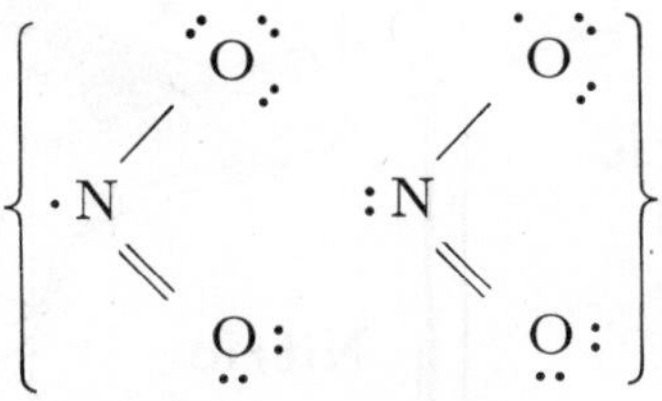

+3 — Dinitrogen trioxide

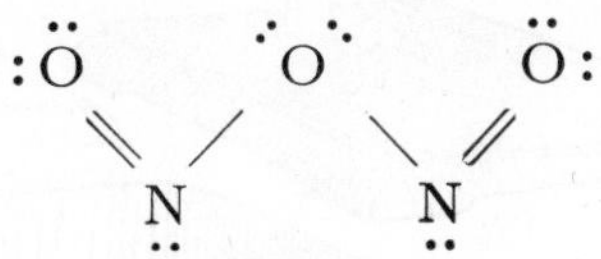

+2 — Nitric oxide

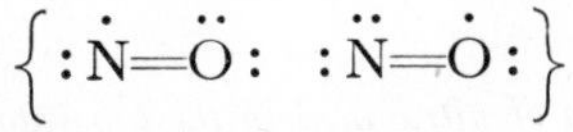

$+1$ $\left\{ :\overset{..}{N}=N=\overset{..}{O}: \quad :N\equiv N-\overset{..}{\underset{..}{O}}: \right\}$ Nitrous oxide

We may well ask why it is that two of the most stable of these substances, NO and NO$_2$, are odd molecules, representing oxidation levels for nitrogen not occurring in other compounds, and also why N$_2$O$_3$ and N$_2$O$_5$, the anhydrides of the important substances HNO$_2$ and HNO$_3$, are so unstable that they decompose at room temperature. The answer to these questions probably is that the resonance of the odd electron between the two or three atoms of the molecule stabilizes the substances NO and NO$_2$ enough to make them somewhat more stable than the two anhydrides.

15–4. Nitric Acid and the Nitrates

Nitric acid, HNO$_3$, is a colorless liquid with melting point $-42°$ C, boiling point $86°$ C, and density 1.52 g/cm^3. It is a strong acid, completely ionized to hydrogen ion and nitrate ion (NO$_3^-$) in aqueous solution; and it is a strong oxidizing agent. It attacks the skin, and gives it a yellow color.

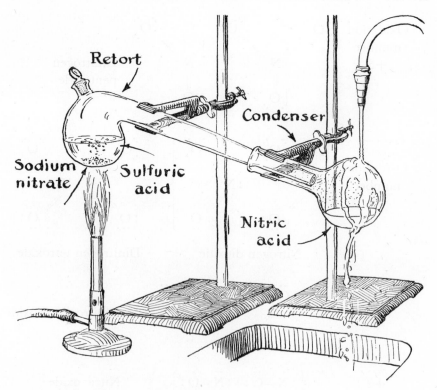

FIGURE 15-2   *The preparation of nitric acid in the laboratory.*

Nitric acid can be made in the laboratory by heating sodium nitrate with sulfuric acid in an all-glass apparatus (Figure 15-2):

$$NaNO_3 + H_2SO_4 \longrightarrow NaHSO_4 + HNO_3$$

The substance is also made commercially in this way, from natural sodium nitrate (Chile saltpeter).

The Manufacture of Nitric Acid from Ammonia. Much nitric acid is made by the oxidation of ammonia. This oxidation occurs in several steps. Ammonia mixed with air burns on the surface of a platinum catalyst to form nitric oxide:

$$4NH_3 + 5O_2 \longrightarrow 4NO + 6H_2O$$

On cooling, the nitric oxide is further oxidized to nitrogen dioxide:

$$2NO + O_2 \longrightarrow 2NO_2$$

The gas is passed through a tower packed with pieces of broken quartz through which water is percolating. Nitric acid and nitrous acid are formed:

$$2NO_2 + H_2O \longrightarrow HNO_3 + HNO_2$$

As the strength of the acid solution increases, the nitrous acid decomposes:

$$3HNO_2 \rightleftarrows HNO_3 + 2NO + H_2O$$

The nitric oxide is re-oxidized by the excess oxygen present and again enters the reaction.

The Fixation of Nitrogen as Nitric Oxide. A method (the arc process) formerly used for fixation of atmospheric nitrogen but now abandoned is the direct combination of nitrogen and oxygen to nitric oxide at the high temperature of the electric arc. The reaction

$$N_2 + O_2 \longrightarrow 2NO$$

is slightly endothermic, and the equilibrium yield of nitric oxide increases with increasing temperature, from 0.4% at 1500° to 5% at 3000°. The reaction was carried out by passing air through an electric arc in such a way that the hot gas mixture was cooled very rapidly, thus "freezing" the high-temperature equilibrium mixture. The nitric oxide was then converted into nitric acid in the way described above.

Nitrates and Their Properties. Sodium nitrate, $NaNO_3$, forms colorless crystals closely resembling crystals of calcite, $CaCO_3$ (Figure 7-6). This resemblance is not accidental. The crystals have the same structure, with Na^+ replacing Ca^{++} and NO_3^- replacing CO_3^{--}. The crystals of sodium nitrate have the same property of birefringence (double refraction) as calcite. Sodium nitrate is used as a fertilizer, and for conversion into nitric acid and other nitrates. **Potassium nitrate, KNO₃** (*saltpeter*), is used in pickling meat (ham, corned beef), in medicine, and in the manufacture of *gun powder*, which is an intimate mixture of potassium nitrate, charcoal, and sulfur, which explodes when ignited in a closed space.

The nitrate ion has a planar structure, with each bond a hybrid of a single bond and a double bond:

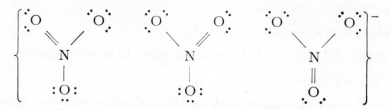

The nitrates of all metals are soluble in water.

A useful test for nitrates is the *brown-ring test*. Ferrous ion has the property of combining with nitric oxide to form an intensely colored brown complex ion, $(FeNO)^{++}$. Since ferrous ion also reduces nitrate ion or nitrite ion in acidic solution to nitric oxide, the test can be carried out by mixing the solution to be tested with concentrated sulfuric

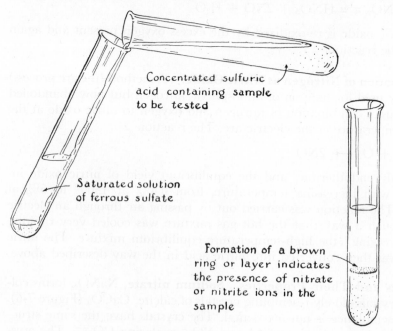

Concentrated sulfuric
acid containing sample
to be tested

Saturated solution
of ferrous sulfate

Formation of a brown
ring or layer indicates
the presence of nitrate
or nitrite ions in the
sample

FIGURE 15-3   *The brown-ring test for nitrate ion or nitrite ion.*

acid and pouring the mixture down the side of a test tube containing a saturated solution of ferrous sulfate, beneath which it forms a layer. If even a very small amount of nitrate ion or nitrite ion is present, a brown ring can be seen at the interface between the two solutions (Figure 15-3).

15–5. Nitrous Acid and the Nitrites

Nitrous acid, HNO_2, forms in small quantity together with nitric acid when nitrogen dioxide is dissolved in water. Nitrite ion can be made together with nitrate ion by solution of nitrogen dioxide in alkali:

$$2NO_2 + 2OH^- \longrightarrow NO_2^- + NO_3^- + H_2O$$

Sodium nitrite, $NaNO_2$, and **potassium nitrite,** KNO_2, can be made also by decomposing the nitrates by heat:

$$2NaNO_3 \longrightarrow 2NaNO_2 + O_2$$

or by reduction with lead:

$$NaNO_3 + Pb \longrightarrow NaNO_2 + PbO$$

These nitrites are slightly yellow crystalline substances, and their solutions are yellow. They are used in the manufacture of dyes, and in the chemical laboratory.

The nitrite ion is a reducing agent, being oxidized to nitrate ion by bromine, permanganate ion, chromate ion, and similar oxidizing agents. It is also itself an oxidizing agent, able to oxidize iodide ion to iodine. This property may be used, with the starch test (blue color) for iodine, to distinguish nitrite from nitrate ion, which does not oxidize iodide ion readily.

The electronic structure of the nitrite ion is

15–6. Other Compounds of Nitrogen

Hyponitrous Acid and the Hyponitrites. Hyponitrous acid, $H_2N_2O_2$, is formed in small quantity by reaction of nitrous acid and hydroxylamine:

$$H_2NOH + HNO_2 \longrightarrow H_2N_2O_2 + H_2O$$

It is a very weak acid, with structure

$$\begin{array}{cc} H—\overset{..}{O}: & :\overset{..}{O}—H \\ \diagdown & \diagup \\ N & = N \\ .. & .. \end{array}$$

. The acid

decomposes to form nitrous oxide, N_2O; it is not itself formed in appreciable concentration by reaction of nitrous oxide and water. Its salts have no important uses.

Hydrogen Cyanide and Its Salts. Hydrogen cyanide, HCN (structural formula $H—C\equiv N:$), is a gas which dissolves in water and acts as a very weak acid. It is made by treating a cyanide, such as **potassium cyanide,** KCN, with sulfuric acid, and is used as a fumigant and rat poison. It smells like bitter almonds and crushed fruit kernels, which in fact owe their odor to it. Hydrogen cyanide and its salts are very poisonous.

Cyanides are made by action of carbon and nitrogen on metallic oxides. For example, barium cyanide is made by heating a mixture of barium oxide and carbon to a red heat in a stream of nitrogen:

$$BaO + 3C + N_2 \longrightarrow Ba(CN)_2 + CO$$

The cyanide ion, $: C\equiv N\overline{:}$, is closely similar to a halogenide ion in its properties. By oxidation it can be converted into **cyanogen,** C_2N_2 $(: N\equiv C—C\equiv N:)$, which is analogous to the halogen molecules F_2, Cl_2, etc.

The Cyanate Ion, Fulminate Ion, Azide Ion, and Thiocyanate Ion. By suitable procedures three anions can be made which are similar in structure to the carbon dioxide molecule $: \overset{..}{O}=C=\overset{..}{O}:$ and the nitrous oxide molecule $: \overset{..}{N}=N=\overset{..}{O}:$ (these structures are hybridized with other structures, such as $: O\equiv C—\overset{..}{\underset{..}{O}}:$ and its analogs). These anions are

$: \overset{..}{N}=C=\overset{..}{O}:^{-}$ cyanate ion

$: \overset{..}{C}=N=\overset{..}{O}:^{-}$ fulminate ion

$: \overset{..}{N}=N=\overset{..}{N}:^{-}$ azide ion

A related ion is the thiocyanate ion, $: \overset{..}{N}=C=\overset{..}{S} :$, which forms a deep red complex with ferric ion, used as a test for iron. The azide ion also forms a deep red complex with ferric ion.

The fulminates and azides of the heavy metals are very sensitive explosives. **Mercuric fulminate,** $Hg(CNO)_2$, and **lead azide,** $Pb(N_3)_2$, are used as detonators.

15–7. *The Nitrogen Cycle in Nature*

Nitrogen is essential to plant and animal life. In particular, the proteins, which are important constituents of plant and animal tissues, contain about 16% nitrogen (Chapter 31).

Man obtains all of his nitrogen from the nitrogen compounds present in plant and animal food, and the combined nitrogen present in animal tissues came originally from plant food. When plant and animal tissues decay, the nitrogen is in large part returned to the atmosphere as free nitrogen. Some animal waste products containing nitrogen, such as urea, $(NH_2)_2CO$, and ammonia, are returned to the soil, and utilized by plants, but there is a continual loss of nitrogen to the atmosphere as free nitrogen.

The steady state in the nitrogen cycle is achieved by the action of several different processes of converting the free nitrogen of the air into compounds that can be utilized by plants and animals. First, there are the *nitrogen-fixing bacteria,* which are associated with plants such as beans (including soy beans), peas, clover, and alfalfa. These bacteria, which exist on the root cells of these plants, have the power of converting free nitrogen from the atmosphere into nitrate ion, which is then assimilated by the plant and converted into protein. Bacteria are also involved in the process of conversion of organic matter into nitrate ion in the soil (the process of *nitrification*), and in the production of free nitrogen, which is returned to the atmosphere.

A significant amount of atmospheric nitrogen is also fixed into compounds which can be utilized by plants through the action of lightning, which causes the nitrogen and the oxygen of the air to combine. The nitrogen oxides are then carried down to the soil by falling rain, converted into nitrates, and utilized by the plants.

During recent years the natural fertilizers that provide combined nitrogen for the growth of plants have been supplemented by artificial fertilizers, made through the fixation of nitrogen by man. The processes by which atmospheric nitrogen is artificially converted into compounds have been described earlier in this chapter.

The nitrogen cycle in nature is summarized in the diagram given on the following page.

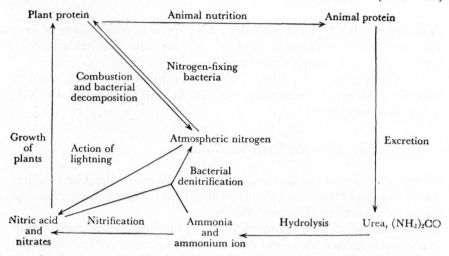

Several of the processes indicated in the chart have been described in the preceding paragraphs. The hydrolysis of urea, a waste product of animals, occurs according to the reaction

$$(NH_2)_2CO + H_2O \longrightarrow 2NH_3 + CO_2$$

Ammonia is not easily utilized by plants. It is converted by the action of nitrifying bacteria into nitrite ion and nitrate ion. Bacterial denitrification, with loss of the utilizable nitrogen (nitrate) in the soil, sometimes occurs through conversion of nitrate ion to nitrite ion and its reaction with ammonium ion:

$$NH_4^+ + NO_2^- \longrightarrow 2H_2O + N_2 \uparrow$$

In order to avoid loss of nitrogen, the farmer must take care not to mix fertilizers containing nitrates and ammonium salts, and not to add nitrate fertilizer to a compost heap (which contains ammonia).

Concepts, Facts, and Terms Introduced in This Chapter

The oxidation states of nitrogen, -3 to $+5$.

Free nitrogen, its great stability.

Ammonia, ammonium hydroxide, ammonia water (aqua ammonia), ammonium ion, ammonium salts. The Haber process and the cyanamide process of making ammonia.

Liquid ammonia as a' solvent; sodium amide; ammonium amalgam; hydrazine; hydroxylamine.

Nitrous oxide, nitric oxide, dinitrogen trioxide, nitrogen dioxide, dinitrogen tetroxide, dinitrogen pentoxide: their properties, method of formation, and electronic structure.

Nitric acid and the nitrates; the manufacture of nitric acid from ammonia; the fixation of nitrogen as nitric oxide; the brown-ring test for nitrates.

Nitrous acid, sodium nitrite, potassium nitrite; hyponitrous acid and the hyponitrites; hydrogen cyanide, potassium cyanide, cyanogen; the cyanate ion, fulminate ion, azide ion, and thiocyanate ion.

Mercuric fulminate and lead azide as detonators.

The nitrogen cycle in nature.

Exercises

15-1. What are the commercial methods of preparing a) nitrogen, b) ammonia, c) nitric acid, and d) calcium cyanamide?

15-2. Describe laboratory methods of preparing a) ammonia, b) nitrous oxide, c) nitric oxide, d) dinitrogen trioxide, e) nitrogen dioxide, f) nitric acid, g) sodium nitrite, h) hydrazine, i) ammonium amalgam.

15-3. Write the electronic structure of the nitrate ion. Compare it with that of the carbonate ion.

15-4. Write a balanced chemical equation to represent the formation of potassium sulfate, carbon dioxide, and nitrogen from potassium nitrate, carbon, and sulfur.

15-5. What chemical reaction takes place between nitrous acid and bromine? Between nitrous acid and iodide ion?

15-6. What chemical reaction takes place between nitrogen dioxide and a solution of sodium hydroxide?

15-7. What is the electronic structure of hydrazine? Compare this molecule with hydrogen peroxide and hydroxylamine.

15-8. Balance the equation

$$N_2H_5^+ + Cr_2O_7^{--} \longrightarrow Cr^{+++} + N_2$$

15-9. What is the electronic structure of the azide ion?

15-10. How does the electronic structure of the cyanide ion compare with that of nitrogen?

15-11. What is the electronic structure of nitrous oxide?

15-12. What are possible electronic structures for dinitrogen tetroxide?

15-13. Why are ammonium salts similar in their properties to the corresponding salts of potassium and rubidium?

15-14. Write the equation for the formation of hydrazine from ammonia and sodium hypochlorite.

15-15. How much nitric acid would be produced from 25 tons of Chile saltpeter, assuming it to be pure sodium nitrate?

15-16. Under what conditions are amides, such as sodium amide, formed? To what ions in aqueous systems are the amide ion and the ammonium ion analogous?

15-17. Write the equation for the synthesis of dinitrogen pentoxide from nitrogen dioxide and ozone. Why is it necessary to be careful when synthesizing dinitrogen pentoxide in this way?

15-18. When aluminum is heated in an atmosphere of nitrogen, aluminum nitride, AlN, is formed. Aluminum nitride reacts with water to give ammonia and aluminum hydroxide. Write the equations for these reactions.

Chapter 16

Phosphorus, Arsenic, Antimony, and Bismuth

The electronic structures of phosphorus, arsenic, antimony, and bismuth, as well as of nitrogen (Chapter 15), the elements of group V of the periodic table, are given in Table 16-1. Each element has three fewer electrons than the following noble gas. In general, the compounds of these elements have electronic structures representing the formation of covalent bonds in sufficient number to complete the octet of electrons in the outermost shell of the group V atom.

The chemical properties of the heavier elements of group V differ significantly from those of nitrogen, the difference being smallest for phosphorus and greatest for bismuth. The differences can be attributed largely to the differences in electronegativity of the five elements: nitrogen (electronegativity 3.0) is the most electronegative, the others having electronegativities equal to or smaller than that of hydrogen (P 2.1, As 2.0, Sb 1.8, Bi 1.7).

TABLE 16-1   *Electronic Structures of Elements of Group V*

Z	ELEMENT	K	L		M			N				O			P	
		1s	2s	2p	3s	3p	3d	4s	4p	4d	4f	5s	5p	5d	6s	6p
7	N	2	2	3												
15	P	2	2	6	2	3										
33	As	2	2	6	2	6	10	2	3							
51	Sb	2	2	6	2	6	10	2	6	10		2	3			
83	Bi	2	2	6	2	6	10	2	6	10	14	2	6	10	2	3

16–1. *Properties of the Fifth-group Elements*

The members of group V of the periodic table show the expected trend in properties with increasing atomic number (Table 16-2): nitrogen is a gas which can be condensed to a liquid only at very low temperatures; phosphorus (in the modification called *white phosphorus*) is a low-melting non-metal; and arsenic, antimony, and bismuth are metalloids with increasing metallic character.

TABLE 16-2   *Properties of the Elements of Group V*

	ATOMIC NUMBER	ATOMIC WEIGHT	MELTING POINT	BOILING POINT	DENSITY OF SOLID	COLOR
Nitrogen	7	14.008	−209.8° C	−195.8° C	1.026 g/cm³	White
Phosphorus	15	30.975	44.1°	280°	1.81	White
Arsenic	33	74.91	814°*	715°†	5.73	Gray
Antimony	51	121.76	630°	1380°	6.68	Silvery white
Bismuth	83	209.00	271°	1470°	9.80	Reddish white

* At 36 atm.   † It sublimes.

The similarity of the elements is indicated by the formulas of their hydrides, NH_3 (ammonia), PH_3 (phosphine), AsH_3 (arsine), SbH_3, and BiH_3, and of their highest oxides, N_2O_5, P_2O_5, As_2O_5, Sb_2O_5, and Bi_2O_5. This similarity is far from complete, however; the principal acids formed by nitrogen, phosphorus, arsenic, and antimony have different formulas:

HNO_3	Nitric acid
H_3PO_4	Phosphoric acid
H_3AsO_4	Arsenic acid
H_7SbO_6	Antimonic acid

The most striking deviation from regularity in properties of these elements is the smaller stability and greater reactivity of the heavier elements than of elementary nitrogen. Whereas nitrogen can be made to combine directly with oxygen only at extremely high temperatures, as in the electric arc, and then only to a small extent, less than one percent of nitric oxide, NO, being formed, white phosphorus ignites spontaneously in air, and the heavier elements of the fifth group burn when they are heated in air.

16–2. *The Oxidation States of Phosphorus*

Phosphorus, like nitrogen and the other members of the fifth group, has oxidation states ranging from −3 to +5. The principal compounds of phosphorus are indicated in the following chart:

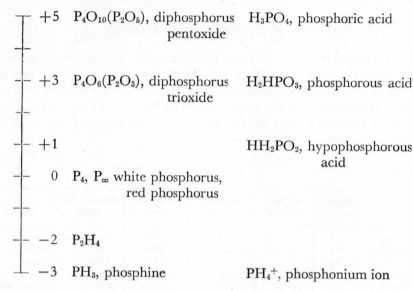

+5	$P_4O_{10}(P_2O_5)$, diphosphorus pentoxide	H_3PO_4, phosphoric acid
+3	$P_4O_6(P_2O_3)$, diphosphorus trioxide	H_2HPO_3, phosphorous acid
+1		HH_2PO_2, hypophosphorous acid
0	P_4, P_∞ white phosphorus, red phosphorus	
−2	P_2H_4	
−3	PH_3, phosphine	PH_4^+, phosphonium ion

Phosphorus, although it is less electronegative than nitrogen, is a non-metallic element, its oxides being acid-forming and not amphoteric. The quinquepositive oxidation state of phosphorus is more stable than that of nitrogen; phosphoric acid and the phosphates are not effective oxidizing agents, whereas nitric acid is a strong oxidizing agent.

16–3. *Elementary Phosphorus*

Phosphorus occurs in nature mainly as the minerals *apatite*, $Ca_5(PO_4)_3F$, *hydroxy-apatite*, $Ca_5(PO_4)_3(OH)$, and tricalcium phosphate (*phosphate rock*, ranging in composition from $Ca_3(PO_4)_2$ to hydroxy-apatite). Hydroxy-apatite is the main mineral constituent of the bones and teeth of animals, and complex organic compounds of phosphorus are essential constituents of nerve and brain tissue and of many proteins, and are involved significantly in the metabolic reactions of living organisms.

Phosphorus was discovered in 1669 by a German alchemist, Dr. Hennig Brand, in the course of his search for the Philosopher's Stone. Brand heated the residue left on evaporation of urine, and collected the distilled phosphorus in a receiver. The name given the element (from Greek *phosphoros*, giving light) refers to its property of glowing in the dark.

Elementary phosphorus is now made by heating calcium phosphate with silica and carbon in an electric furnace (Figure 16-1). The silica forms calcium silicate, displacing diphosphorus pentoxide, P_4O_{10}, which is then reduced by the carbon. The phosphorus leaves the furnace as vapor, and is condensed under water to *white phosphorus*.

Phosphorus vapor is tetratomic: the P_4 molecule has a structure

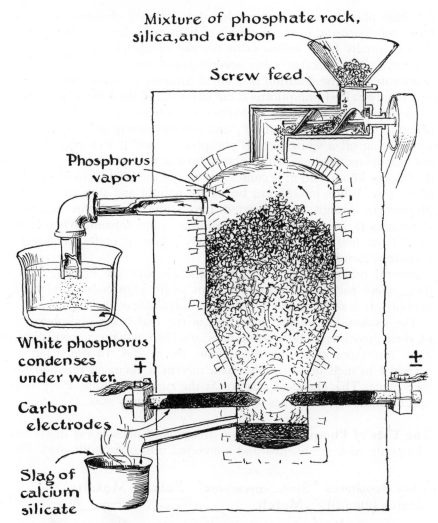

FIGURE 16-1 *Electric furnace for the manufacture of elementary phosphorus.*

with each atom having one unshared electron pair and forming a single bond with each of its three neighbors (Figure 11-7).

At 1600° C the vapor is dissociated slightly, forming a few percent of diatomic molecules P_2, with the structure $:P{\equiv}P:$, analogous to that of the nitrogen molecule.

Phosphorus vapor condenses at 280.5° C to liquid white phosphorus, which freezes at 44.1° C to solid white phosphorus, a soft, waxy, colorless material, soluble in carbon disulfide, benzene, and other non-polar solvents. Both solid and liquid white phosphorus contain the same P_4 molecules as the vapor.

White phosphorus is metastable, and it slowly changes to a stable form, *red phosphorus*, in the presence of light or on heating. White phosphorus usually has a yellow color because of partial conversion to the red form. The reaction takes several hours even at 250°; it can be accelerated by the addition of a small amount of iodine, which serves as a catalyst. Red phosphorus is far more stable than the white form—it does not catch fire in air at temperatures below 240°, whereas white phosphorus ignites at about 40°, and oxidizes slowly at room temperature, giving off a white light ("phosphorescence"). Red phosphorus is not poisonous, whereas white phosphorus is very poisonous, the lethal dose being about 0.15 g; it causes necrosis of the bones, especially those of the jaw. White phosphorus burns are painful and slow to heal. Red phosphorus cannot be converted into white phosphorus except by vaporizing it. It is not appreciably soluble in any solvent. When heated to 500° or 600° red phosphorus slowly melts (if under pressure) or vaporizes, forming P_4 vapor.

Several other allotropic forms of the element are known. One of these, *black phosphorus*, is formed from white phosphorus under high pressure. It is still less reactive than red phosphorus.

The explanation of the properties of red and black phosphorus lies in their structure. These substances are high polymers, consisting of giant molecules extending throughout the crystal. In order for such a crystal to melt or to dissolve in a solvent a chemical reaction must take place. This chemical reaction is the rupture of some P—P bonds and formation of new ones. Such processes are very slow.

The Uses of Phosphorus. Large amounts of phosphorus made from phosphate rock are burned and converted into phosphoric acid. Phos-

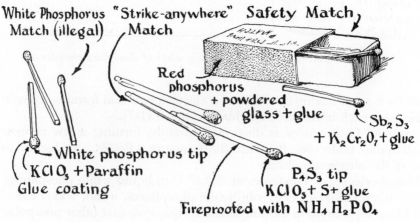

White Phosphorus "Strike-anywhere" Safety Match
Match (illegal) Match

Red phosphorus + powdered glass + glue

Sb_2S_3 + $K_2Cr_2O_7$ + glue

White phosphorus tip
$KClO_3$ + Paraffin
Glue coating

P_4S_3 tip
$KClO_3$ + S + glue
Fireproofed with $NH_4H_2PO_4$

FIGURE 16-2 *The old, white phosphorus match, not used now, the ordinary match, and the safety match.*

phorus is also used in making matches. White phosphorus is no longer used for this purpose because of its danger to the health of the workers. Ordinary matches are now made by dipping the ends of the match sticks into paraffin, and then into a wet mixture of phosphorus sulfide, (P_4S_3), lead dioxide (or other oxidizing agent), and glue. The heads of safety matches contain antimony trisulfide and potassium chlorate or dichromate, and the box is coated with a mixture of red phosphorus, powdered glass, and glue (Figure 16-2).

16–4. *Phosphine*

The principal hydride of phosphorus is *phosphine*, PH_3 (with structure

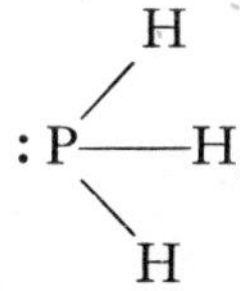

$$: P \begin{matrix} \diagup H \\ \text{—H,} \\ \diagdown H \end{matrix}$$

analogous to ammonia). Phosphine is not made by direct union of the elements. It is formed, together with the hypophosphite ion $H_2PO_2^-$, when white phosphorus is heated in a solution of alkali:

$$P_4 + 3OH^- + 3H_2O \longrightarrow 3H_2PO_2^- + PH_3 \uparrow$$

The gas made in this way, which contains some impurities, ignites spontaneously on contact with air and burns, forming white fumes of oxide. To avoid explosion, the air in the flask must be displaced by hydrogen or illuminating gas before the mixture in the flask is heated. Phosphine is exceedingly poisonous.

Phosphine has far less affinity for hydrogen ion than has ammonia. Its only salts are phosphonium iodide, PH_4I; phosphonium bromide, PH_4Br; and phosphonium chloride, PH_4Cl. These salts decompose on contact with water, liberating phosphine.

16–5. *The Oxides of Phosphorus*

Diphosphorus pentoxide, usually assigned the formula P_2O_5, consists of molecules P_4O_{10}, with the structure shown in Figure 16-3. It is formed when phosphorus is burned with a free supply of air. It reacts with water with great violence, to form phosphoric acid, and it is used in the laboratory as a drying agent for gases.

Diphosphorus trioxide, P_2O_3 or P_4O_6 (Figure 16-3), is made, together with the pentoxide, by burning phosphorus with a restricted supply of air. It is much more volatile than the pentoxide (P_4O_6, m.p. 22.5° C, b.p. 173.1° C; P_4O_{10}, sublimes at 250° C), and is easily purified by distillation in an apparatus from which air is excluded.

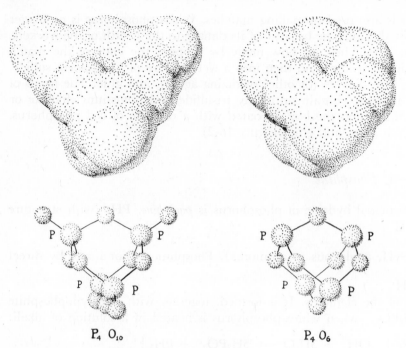

$P_4 O_{10}$ $P_4 O_6$

FIGURE 16-3   *Molecules of the oxides of phosphorus.*

16–6. *Phosphoric Acid*

Pure phosphoric acid, H_3PO_4 (also called *orthophosphoric acid*), is a deliquescent crystalline substance, with melting point 42° C. Commercial phosphoric acid is a viscous liquid. It is made by dissolving diphosphorus pentoxide in water.

Phosphoric acid is a weak acid. It is a stable substance, without effective oxidizing power.

Orthophosphoric acid forms three series of salts, with one, two, and three of its hydrogen atoms replaced by metal. The salts are usually made by mixing phosphoric acid and the metal hydroxide or carbonate, in proper proportion. Sodium dihydrogen phosphate, NaH_2PO_4, is faintly acidic in reaction. It is used (mixed with sodium hydrogen carbonate) in baking powder, and also for treating boiler water, to prevent formation of scale. Disodium hydrogen phosphate, Na_2HPO_4, is slightly basic in reaction. Trisodium phosphate, Na_3PO_4 is basic. It is used as a detergent (for cleaning woodwork, etc.) and for treating boiler water.

Phosphates are valuable fertilizers. Phosphate rock itself (tricalcium phosphate, $Ca_3(PO_4)_2$, and hydroxy-apatite) is too slightly soluble to serve as an effective source of phosphorus for plants. It is accordingly converted into the more soluble substance calcium dihydrogen phosphate, $Ca(H_2PO_4)_2$. This may be done by treatment with sulfuric acid:

$$Ca_3(PO_4)_2 + 2H_2SO_4 \longrightarrow 2CaSO_4 + Ca(H_2PO_4)_2$$

Enough water is added to convert the calcium sulfate to its dihydrate, gypsum, and the mixture of gypsum and calcium dihydrogen phosphate is sold as "superphosphate of lime." Sometimes the phosphate rock is treated with phosphoric acid:

$$Ca_3(PO_4)_2 + 4H_3PO_4 \longrightarrow 3Ca(H_2PO_4)_2$$

This product is much richer in phosphorus than the "superphosphate"; it is called "triple phosphate." Over ten million tons of phosphate rock is converted into phosphate fertilizer each year.

The Condensed Phosphoric Acids.   Phosphoric acid easily undergoes the process of *condensation*. Condensation is the reaction of two or more molecules to form larger molecules, either without any other products (in which case the condensation is also called *polymerization*), or with the elimination of small molecules, such as water. Condensation of two phosphoric acid molecules occurs by the reaction of two

hydroxyl groups $:\overset{\cdot\cdot}{O}\!-\!H$ to form water and an oxygen atom held

by single bonds to two phosphorus atoms.

When orthophosphoric acid is heated it loses water and condenses to **diphosphoric acid** or **pyrophosphoric acid**, $H_4P_2O_7$:

$$2H_3PO_4 \rightleftharpoons H_4P_2O_7 + H_2O \uparrow$$

(The name pyrophosphoric acid is the one customarily used.) This acid is a white crystalline substance, with melting point 61° C. Its salts may be made by neutralization of the acid or by strongly heating the hydrogen orthophosphates or ammonium orthophosphates of the metals. Magnesium pyrophosphate, $Mg_2P_2O_7$, is obtained in a useful method for quantitative analysis for either magnesium or orthophosphate. A solution containing orthophosphate ion may be mixed with a solution of magnesium chloride (or sulfate), ammonium chloride, and ammonium hydroxide. The very slightly soluble substance magnesium ammonium phosphate, $MgNH_4PO_4 \cdot 6H_2O$, then slowly precipitates. The precipitate is washed with dilute ammonium hydroxide, dried, and heated to a dull red heat, causing it to form magnesium pyrophosphate, which is then weighed:

$$2MgNH_4PO_4 \cdot 6H_2O \longrightarrow Mg_2P_2O_7 + 2NH_3 \uparrow + 13H_2O \uparrow$$

Larger condensed phosphoric acids also occur, such as **triphosphoric acid,** $H_5P_3O_{10}$. The interconversion of triphosphates, pyrophosphates, and phosphates is important in many bodily processes, including the absorption and metabolism of sugar. These reactions occur at body temperature under the influence of special enzymes (Chapter 31).

An important class of condensed phosphoric acids is that in which each phosphate tetrahedron is bonded by oxygen atoms to two other tetrahedra. These acids have the composition $(HPO_3)_x$, with $x = 3, 4, 5, 6, \cdots$. They are called the **metaphosphoric acids.** Among these acids are **tetrametaphosphoric acid** and **hexametaphosphoric acid.**

Metaphosphoric acid is made by heating orthophosphoric acid or pyrophosphoric acid or by adding water to phosphorus pentoxide. It is a viscous sticky mass, which contains, in addition to ring molecules such as $H_4P_4O_{12}$, long chains approaching $(HPO_3)_\infty$ in composition. It is the long chains, which may also be condensed together to form branched chains, which, by becoming entangled, make the acid viscous and sticky.

The process of condensation may continue further, ultimately leading to phosphorus pentoxide.

The metaphosphates are used as water softeners (Chapter 17). Sodium hexametaphosphate, $Na_6P_6O_{18}$, is especially effective for this purpose.

16–7. *Phosphorous Acid*

Phosphorous acid, H_2HPO_3, is a white substance, m.p. 74° C, which is made by dissolving diphosphorus trioxide in cold water:

$$P_4O_6 + 6H_2O \longrightarrow 4H_2HPO_3$$

It may also be conveniently made by the action of water on phosphorus trichloride:

$$PCl_3 + 3H_2O \longrightarrow H_2HPO_3 + 3HCl$$

Phosphorous acid is an unstable substance. When heated it undergoes auto-oxidation-reduction to phosphine and phosphoric acid:

$$4H_2HPO_3 \longrightarrow 3H_3PO_4 + PH_3 \uparrow$$

The acid and its salts, the *phosphites*, are powerful reducing agents. Its reaction with silver ion is used as a test for phosphite ion; a black precipitate is formed, which consists of silver phosphate, Ag_3PO_4, colored black by metallic silver formed by reduction of silver ion. Phosphite ion also reduces iodate ion to free iodine, which can be detected by the starch test (blue color) or by its coloration of a small volume of carbon tetrachloride shaken with the aqueous phase.

Phosphorous acid is a weak acid, which forms two series of salts. Ordinary sodium phosphite is $Na_2HPO_3 \cdot 5H_2O$. Sodium hydrogen phosphite, $NaHHPO_3 \cdot 5H_2O$, also exists, but the third hydrogen atom cannot be replaced by a cation. The non-acidic character of this third hydrogen atom is due to its attachment directly to the phosphorus atom, rather than to an oxygen atom:

$$
\begin{array}{ccc}
\text{H} & & \overset{\cdot\cdot}{\text{O}}\text{---H} \\
& \diagdown \diagup & \\
& \text{P} & \\
& \diagup \diagdown & \\
\overset{\cdot\cdot}{\underset{\cdot\cdot}{\text{O}}} & & \overset{\cdot\cdot}{\underset{\cdot\cdot}{\text{O}}}\text{---H}
\end{array}
$$

The phosphite ion is HPO_3^{--}, not PO_3^{---}.

16–8. *Hypophosphorous Acid*

The solution remaining from the preparation of phosphite from phosphorus and alkali contains the *hypophosphite ion*, $H_2PO_2^-$. The corresponding acid, hypophosphorous acid, HH_2PO_2, can be prepared by using barium hydroxide as the alkali, thus forming barium hypophosphite, $Ba(H_2PO_2)_2$, and then adding to the solution the calculated amount of sulfuric acid, which precipitates barium sulfate and leaves the hypophosphorous acid in solution.

Hypophosphorous acid is a weak monoprotic acid, forming only one series of salts. The two non-acidic hydrogen atoms are bonded to the phosphorus atom:

$$
\begin{array}{ccc}
\text{H} & & \overset{\cdot\cdot}{\text{O}}\text{---H} \\
& \diagdown \diagup & \\
& \text{P} & \\
& \diagup \diagdown & \\
\text{H} & & \overset{\cdot\cdot}{\underset{\cdot\cdot}{\text{O}}}
\end{array}
$$

The acid and the hypophosphite ion are powerful reducing agents, able to reduce the cations of copper and the more noble metals.

16–9. *The Halogenides and Sulfides of Phosphorus*

By direct combination of the elements or by other methods the halogenides of terpositive phosphorus (PF_3, PCl_3, PBr_3, PI_3) and of quinquepositive phosphorus (PF_5, PCl_5) can be formed. These halogenides are gases or easily volatile liquids or solids, which hydrolyze with water, forming the corresponding oxygen acids of phosphorus. The electronic structures of the phosphorus trihalogenides and pentahalogenides have been discussed in earlier chapters. These halogenides are useful in the preparation of inorganic and organic substances.

Phosphorus pentachloride, PCl_5, is a useful chemical reagent. It reacts in general with the inorganic oxygen acids and with organic substances containing hydroxyl groups, in such a way as to introduce a chlorine atom in place of the hydroxyl group —OH. Thus from sulfuric acid it produces chlorosulfuric acid, HSO_3Cl:

$$SO_2(OH)_2 + PCl_5 \longrightarrow SO_2(OH)Cl + POCl_3 + HCl$$

With an excess of phosphorus pentachloride the substance sulfuryl chloride, SO_2Cl_2, is formed:

$$SO_2(OH)_2 + 2PCl_5 \longrightarrow SO_2Cl_2 + 2POCl_3 + 2HCl$$

Sulfur and phosphorus combine when heated together to form various compounds, including P_2S_5, P_4S_7, and P_4S_3. The last of these, tetraphosphorus trisulfide, is used as a constituent of match heads.

16–10. Arsenic, Antimony, and Bismuth

Arsenic, antimony, and bismuth differ from their congeners nitrogen and phosphorus in the decreasing electronegativity which accompanies increasing atomic number. The principal compounds of these elements correspond to the oxidation states $+5$ and $+3$. The state -3 also occurs; it is represented by the gaseous hydrides AsH_3, SbH_3, and BiH_3, which, however, do not form salts analogous to the ammonium and phosphonium salts.

Representative compounds of the fifth-group elements are shown in the chart on the following page.

The oxides of arsenic are acidic; with water they form arsenic acid, H_3AsO_4, and arsenious acid, H_3AsO_3, which resemble the corresponding acids of phosphorus. Antimony pentoxide is also acidic, and its trioxide is amphoteric, behaving both as an acid and as a base (forming the antimony ion, Sb^{+++}). Bismuth trioxide is primarily a basic oxide, forming the ion Bi^{+++}; its acidic activity is slight.

Arsenic and Its Ores. Elementary arsenic exists in several forms. Ordinary *gray arsenic* is a semi-metallic substance, steel-gray in color, with density 5.73 and melting point (under pressure) 814°. It sublimes rapidly at about 450°, forming gas molecules As_4 similar in structure to P_4. An unstable yellow crystalline allotropic form containing As_4 molecules, and soluble in carbon disulfide, also exists. The gray form has a covalent layer structure.

The chief minerals of arsenic include *orpiment*, As_2S_3 (from Latin *auripigmentum*, yellow pigment), *realgar*, AsS (a red substance), *arseno-lite*, As_4O_6, and *arsenopyrite*, FeAsS. Diarsenic trioxide (arsenious oxide)

Oxidation state	N	P	As	Sb	Bi
+5	N_2O_5	P_4O_{10}	As_2O_5	Sb_2O_5	Bi_2O_5
	HNO_3	H_3PO_4	H_3AsO_4	$HSb(OH)_6$	
		PCl_5	$AsCl_5$	$SbCl_5$	
+4	NO_2				
+3	N_2O_3	P_4O_6	As_4O_6	Sb_4O_6	Bi_4O_6
	HNO_2	H_2HPO_3	H_3AsO_3	H_3SbO_3	
	NCl_3	PCl_3	$AsCl_3$	$SbCl_3$	$BiCl_3$
				Sb^{+++}	Bi^{+++}
+2	NO				
+1	N_2O	HH_2PO_2			
	$H_2N_2O_2$				
0	N_2	P_4	As	Sb	Bi
−1	NH_2OH				
−2	N_2H_4	P_2H_4			
−3	NH_3	PH_3	AsH_3	SbH_3	BiH_3
	NH_4^+	PH_4^+			

is obtained by roasting ores of arsenic. The element is made by reducing the trioxide with carbon or by heating arsenopyrite:

$$4FeAsS \longrightarrow 4FeS + As_4 \uparrow$$

Arsenic is inert at room temperature, but ignites when heated, burning with a lavender flame to produce white clouds of the trioxide. It is oxidized to arsenic acid, H_3AsO_4, by hot nitric acid and other powerful oxidizing agents. Arsenic combines with many other elements, both metallic and non-metallic.

Arsenic is used with lead (0.5% As) in making lead shot. It makes the metal harder than pure lead, and also improves the properties of the molten metal—the shot are made by pouring the metal through a sieve at the top of a tall tower, which permits the liquid drops to assume a spherical form and then to harden before falling into water at the base of the tower.

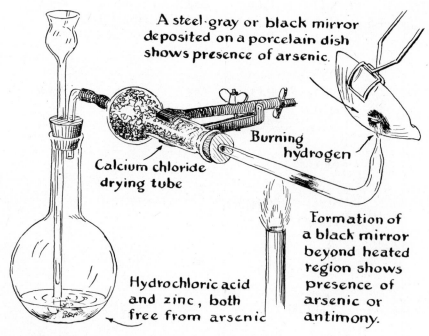

A steel-gray or black mirror deposited on a porcelain dish shows presence of arsenic.

Calcium chloride drying tube

Burning hydrogen

Hydrochloric acid and zinc, both free from arsenic

Formation of a black mirror beyond heated region shows presence of arsenic or antimony.

FIGURE 16-4   *The Marsh test for arsenic. The sample is introduced through the thistle tube. Both arsenic and antimony produce a mirror in this test; the chemical properties of the deposit permit a distinction to be made between an arsenic mirror and an antimony mirror.*

Arsine.   Arsine, AsH_3, is a colorless, very poisonous gas with a garlic-like odor. It is made by reaction of a metallic arsenide, such as zinc arsenide, with acid:

$$Zn_3As_2 + 6HCl \longrightarrow 3ZnCl_2 + 2AsH_3 \uparrow$$

It also is formed by reduction of soluble arsenic compounds by zinc in acidic solution. This reaction is the basis of an important and sensitive test for arsenic, the *Marsh test* (Figure 16-4). The arsenic is deposited as a steel-gray or black mirror from the burning gas onto a cold glazed porcelain dish held in the flame. Antimony produces a velvety brown or black deposit, which is not soluble in sodium hypochlorite solution, whereas the arsenic deposit is. The antimony deposit, but not that of arsenic, dissolves in ammonium polysulfide solution. The deposit may be made to form inside the tube by heating the tube. This test for arsenic will detect as small an amount as 1×10^{-6} g.

The Oxides and Acids of Arsenic.   **Diarsenic trioxide** (*arsenious oxide,* As_4O_6) is a white solid substance which sublimes readily, and is easily purified by sublimation. Its molecules have the same structure as diphosphorus trioxide, shown in Figure 16-3. It is a violent poison, and is used as an insecticide and for preserving skins.

Diarsenic trioxide dissolves in water to form **arsenious acid,** H_3AsO_3. This acid differs from phosphorous acid in that all three of its hydrogen atoms are attached to oxygen atoms, and are replaceable by metal. It is a very weak acid ($K_1 = 6 \times 10^{-10}$). Cupric hydrogen arsenite, $CuHAsO_3$, and a cupric arsenite-acetate (called *Paris green*) are used as insecticides.

Diarsenic pentoxide, As_2O_5, is not obtained by burning arsenic, but can be made by boiling diarsenic trioxide with concentrated nitric acid. With water it forms **arsenic acid,** H_3AsO_4, which is closely similar to phosphoric acid. Sodium arsenate, Na_3AsO_4, is used as a weed killer, and other arsenates (especially of calcium and lead) are used as insecticides.

The toxicity of arsenic compounds to living organisms is utilized in chemotherapy; several organic compounds of arsenic have been discovered which are able to attack invading organisms, such as the spirochete of syphilis, when taken in amounts smaller than the amount poisonous to man.

Antimony.   The principal ore of antimony is *stibnite*, Sb_2S_3, a steel-gray or black mineral which forms beautiful crystals. The metal is usually made by heating stibnite with iron:

$$Sb_2S_3 + 3Fe \longrightarrow 3FeS + 2Sb$$

Antimony is a brittle metal, silvery-gray in color. It has the property of expanding on freezing, and its main use is as a constituent of type metal (82% lead, 15% antimony, 3% tin), to which it confers this property, thus giving sharp reproductions of the mold. It is also used as a constituent of other alloys, especially for making the grids in storage batteries and for bearings.

The oxides and acids of antimony resemble those of arsenic, except that antimony in **antimonic acid** has coordination number 6, the formula of antimonic acid being $HSb(OH)_6$. A solution of potassium antimonate, $K^+[Sb(OH)_6]^-$, finds use as a test reagent for sodium ion; sodium antimonate, $NaSb(OH)_6$, one of the very few sodium salts with slight solubility in water (about 0.03 g per 100 g), is precipitated. The antimonate ion condenses to larger complexes when heated; this condensation may ultimately lead to macromolecular structures, such as that of dehydrated potassium antimonate, $KSbO_3$ (Figure 16-5).

Diantimony trioxide, Sb_4O_6, is amphoteric. In addition to reacting with bases to form *antimonites*, it reacts with acids to form antimony salts, such as antimony sulfate, $Sb_2(SO_4)_3$. The antimony ion Sb^{+++} hydrolyzes readily to form the antimonyl ion, SbO^+.

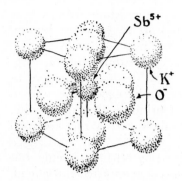

FIGURE 16-5

The cubic unit of structure of the crystal of dehy-drated potassium antimonate, KSbO₃.

Antimony trichloride, $SbCl_3$, is a soft, colorless substance, which hydrolyzes with water, precipitating antimonyl chloride, $SbOCl$. The reaction may be reversed by adding hydrochloric acid, forming the complex anion $SbCl_4^-$. This anion can be oxidized by iodate ion to a similar complex anion of quinquevalent antimony:

$$5SbCl_4^- + 2IO_3^- + 12H^+ + 10Cl^- \longrightarrow 5SbCl_6^- + I_2 + 6H_2O$$

This reaction may be used for the quantitative determination of antimony.

Potassium antimonyl tartrate (tartar emetic, $KSbOC_4H_4O_6$) and some other compounds of antimony are used in medicine.

Bismuth.   Bismuth occurs in nature as the free element, and as the sulfide Bi_2S_3 and oxide Bi_2O_3. The metal is won from its compounds by roasting and reducing the oxide with carbon. It is a brittle metal, with a silvery color showing a reddish tinge. It expands slightly on freezing. Its principal use is in making low-melting alloys.

The oxides of bismuth are basic, forming salts such as bismuth chloride, $BiCl_3 \cdot H_2O$, and bismuth nitrate, $Bi(NO_3)_3 \cdot 5H_2O$. These salts when dissolved in water hydrolyze, and precipitate the corresponding bismuthyl compounds, $BiOCl$ and $Bi(OH)_2NO_3$ (or $BiONO_3 \cdot H_2O$). The compounds of bismuth have found little use; bismuthyl nitrate and some other compounds are used to some extent in medicine.

Concepts, Facts, and Terms Introduced in This Chapter

Electronic structure and properties of the elements of group V. Oxidation numbers -3 to $+5$.

Ores of phosphorus: apatite, hydroxy-apatite, tricalcium phosphate (phosphate rock). White phosphorus, red phosphorus, black phosphorus. High polymers and their properties. Manufacture and uses of phosphorus. Ordinary matches, safety matches.

Compounds of phosphorus: phosphine, diphosphorus pentoxide, diphosphorus trioxide, orthophosphoric acid, sodium dihydrogen phosphate, disodium hydrogen phosphate, trisodium phosphate, magnesium ammonium phosphate, diphosphoric acid (pyrophosphoric acid), magnesium pyrophosphate, triphosphoric acid, metaphosphoric acid and the metaphosphates, phosphorus acid and the phosphites, hypophosphorous acid, phosphorus pentachloride, tetraphosphorus trisulfide. Phosphate as fertilizers; superphosphate of lime, triple phosphate. Condensation of phosphoric acid to poly-phosphoric acids.

Ores of arsenic: orpiment, realgar, arsenolite, arsenopyrite. Compounds of arsenic: arsine, diarsenic trioxide, arsenious acid, cupric hydrogen arsenite, diarsenic pentoxide, arsenic acid, sodium arsenate. The Marsh test for arsenic. Uses of arsenic and its compounds: lead shot, insecticides, weed killers, chemotherapy.

Antimony, its properties and uses—type metal, other alloys. Stibnite, Sb_2S_3. Compounds of antimony: antimonic acid, potassium antimonate, sodium antimonate, diantimony trioxide, antimony sulfate, antimony trichloride, antimonyl chloride, potassium antimonyl tartrate (tartar emetic).

Bismuth, its properties, occurrence in nature, and use in alloys. Compounds of bismuth: bismuth trichloride, bismuth nitrate, bismuthyl chloride, bismuthyl nitrate.

Exercises

16-1. What are the formulas and structures of the oxygen acids of the $+5$ oxidation states of the fifth-group elements?

16-2. What are the formulas and structures of the oxygen acids of the $+3$ oxidation states of the fifth-group elements (include $Bi(OH)_3$ in this tabulation)? How do the properties of these compounds vary with atomic number?

16-3. What are apatite and hydroxy-apatite?

16-4. Write the chemical equation for the preparation of phosphorus in the electric furnace.

16-5. Write the equations for the hydrolysis of phosphorus tribromide and for the hydrolysis of phosphorus pentachloride.

16-6. Calculate the amount of phosphorus (as percent of P_2O_5) in "superphosphate of lime" and in "triple phosphate."

16-7. Describe the Marsh test, and explain how it is possible to detect the presence of arsenic, antimony, or both elements in the sample tested.

16-8. Write the chemical equation for the condensation of orthophosphoric acid to pyrophosphoric acid.

16-9. What is the structure of trimetaphosphoric acid, $H_3P_3O_9$?

16-10. Write a chemical equation for the reduction of Ag^+ by a solution of sodium phosphite.

16-11. Compare the properties of PCl_3 and $BiCl_3$.

16-12. Write chemical equations illustrating the acidic and the basic properties of the $+3$ oxidation state of antimony.

16-13. Which are the most metallic of the fifth-group elements?

16-14. Give the name and formula of an ore of antimony and an ore of arsenic.

16-15. Write a chemical equation for the preparation of Sb_2O_5 from Sb_2O_3.

16-16. What chemical reaction takes place when bismuth nitrate is dissolved in water?

16-17. How much phosphorus could be made from 1 ton of calcium phosphate, $Ca_3(PO_4)_2$? How much phosphorus sulfide, P_4S_3, could be made from this amount of phosphorus?

PART FOUR

Water, Solutions,
Chemical Equilibrium

In the study of some aspects of chemical theory in Part II of our book we learned how to write equations for chemical reactions, and to discuss the relations between the weights of the reacting substances and their products, and also the volumes, if the substances are gases. For example, we know how to write an equation for the reaction of nitrogen and hydrogen to form ammonia. The correctly balanced equation is

$$N_2 + 3H_2 \rightleftarrows 2NH_3$$

We can say that 28 g (2 gram-atoms) of nitrogen and 6 g (6 gram-atoms) of hydrogen might react to form 34 g (two moles) of ammonia, and that, at given temperature and pressure, one volume of nitrogen and three volumes of hydrogen might produce two volumes of ammonia.

In the preceding sentence we have to say "might produce" rather than "would produce" because we have not yet discussed the question, in any detail, as to whether a certain chemical reaction would take place or not. If we mix nitrogen and hydrogen at room temperature, will any reaction take place? If we raise the temperature, will any reaction take place? If reaction does begin to take place, will it continue until all of the nitrogen or all of the hydrogen has been converted into ammonia?

The questions above are examples of two general kinds of questions. First, how fast may we expect a chemical reaction to take place—what is the rate of the reaction? A chemist in the business of manufacturing ammonia is far more interested in a reaction that would produce his product in a few minutes than in a reaction that would require years.

The second question is the following: If a chemical reaction begins to take place, can it be expected to continue until all of the reacting materials are used up, or might it stop before this point? Questions of this sort relate to the subject of *chemical equilibrium.*

It has been found by experiment that if nitrogen and hydrogen are mixed at room temperature the reaction does not take place at all—the rate of the reaction is so small that it is impossible to detect any ammonia in the mixture, even after a long time. If the temperature is raised, the formation of ammonia begins to take place. If the temperature is very high the nitrogen and hydrogen begin to react rapidly, but the reaction apparently ceases when only a small amount of the gas has been converted into ammonia. The problem of the manufacturer who wants to make ammonia by reaction of nitrogen and hydrogen is to find conditions at which the rate of the reaction is great enough to give him some ammonia in a few minutes or hours, and at which the chemical equilibrium permits the reaction to provide a satisfactory yield of ammonia.

The seven chapters that constitute Part IV of our book are devoted largely to the study of chemical equilibrium, with some discussion also of the rate of chemical reactions. Many chemical reactions take place in solution, especially solution in water, and Part IV begins with a chapter on water, Chapter 17. This chapter is followed by a chapter on solutions, Chapter 18. In Chapter 19 there is a general discussion of the theory of the rate of chemical reaction and the theory of chemical equilibrium. These subjects are closely related, because in fact a system in chemical equilibrium, in which no change in composition of the system takes place with time, is not a static system; instead, chemical reactions may be taking place at a great rate. The equilibrium is a dynamic one, in which a reaction that produces a product is taking place at the same rate as the reaction that decomposes the product. For example, when a mixture of nitrogen and hydrogen is heated to high temperature, some ammonia is formed, and after a time the composition of the mixture becomes constant; under these equilibrium conditions the reaction of nitrogen and hydrogen to form ammonia continues, and the reverse reaction, the decomposition of ammonia to form nitrogen and hydrogen, also takes place, at such a rate that the amount of ammonia being decomposed is just equal to the amount being formed. In Chapter 20 there is a detailed discussion of acids and bases, with special attention to the reactions of acids and bases that involve chemical equilibria. Other applications of the principles of chemical equilibrium are given in Chapter 21, which deals with the solubility of precipitates, and Chapter 22, which deals with the formation of complex ions.

There is a close relation between the energy that is given out or taken up during a chemical reaction and the effect of temperature on the corresponding equilibrium state. This relation and other chemical aspects of energy are discussed in the last chapter of Part IV, Chapter 23.

The aspects of chemical theory discussed in Chapters 17 to 23 are especially significant to the procedures of qualitative analysis and quantitative analysis of substances and to industrial chemistry. The systems of analysis and methods used in chemical industries provide many illustrations of the application of these principles.

Some aspects of chemical equilibrium can be treated quantitatively, with use of an equilibrium equation, which is discussed in Chapter 19 and applied in the following chapters. Mathematical equations like this one are, of course, very valuable, and they must be used if it is necessary to carry out numerical calculations. A student or a scientist who relies on equations may, however, occasionally find that he has made a very bad mistake, because of a misunderstanding as to how the equation should be used. The student (or the scientist) would be wise to refrain from using the mathematical equation unless he understands the theory that it represents, and can make a statement about the theory that does not consist just in reading the equation.

It is fortunate that there is a general qualitative principle, called *Le Chatelier's principle*, that relates to all the applications of the principles of chemical equilibrium. *When you have obtained a grasp of Le Chatelier's principle, you will be able to think about any problem of chemical equilibrium that arises, and, by use of a simple argument, make a qualitative statement about it.* For example, with use of Le Chatelier's principle you can answer the question as to whether the conversion of nitrogen and hydrogen into ammonia would be favored by compressing the mixture of gases, and also the question as to whether it would be favored by raising the temperature. Le Chatelier's principle is discussed in the first chapter of Part IV, Chapter 17, and it is referred to in each of the following chapters.

Some years after you have finished your college work, you may (unless you become a chemist or work in some closely related field) have forgotten all the mathematical equations relating to chemical equilibrium. I hope, however, that you will not have forgotten Le Chatelier's principle.

Chapter 17

Water

Water is one of the most important of all chemical substances. It is a major constituent of living matter and of the environment in which we live. Its physical properties are strikingly different from those of other substances, in ways that determine the nature of the physical and biological world.

17–1. *The Composition of Water*

Water was thought by the ancients to be an element. Henry Cavendish in 1781 showed that water is formed when hydrogen is burned in air, and Lavoisier first recognized that water is a compound of the two elements hydrogen and oxygen.

The formula of water is H_2O. The relative weights of hydrogen and oxygen in the substance have been very carefully determined as $2.0160 : 16.0000$. This determination has been made both by weighing the amounts of hydrogen and oxygen liberated from water by electrolysis and by determining the weights of hydrogen and oxygen which combine to form water.

Purification of Water by Distillation. Ordinary water is impure; it usually contains dissolved salts and dissolved gases, and sometimes organic matter. For chemical work water is purified by distillation. Pure tin vessels and pipes are often used for storing and transporting distilled water. Glass vessels are not satisfactory, because the alkaline constituents of glass slowly dissolve in water. Distilling apparatus and vessels made of fused silica are used in making very pure water.

The impurity which is hardest to keep out of distilled water is carbon dioxide, which dissolves readily from the air.

Removal of Ionic Impurities from Water.   Ionic impurities can be effectively and cheaply removed from water by an interesting process which involves the use of *giant molecules*—molecular structures which are so big as to constitute visible particles. A crystal of diamond is an example of such a giant molecule (Chapter 11). Some complex inorganic crystals, such as the minerals called *zeolites*, are of this nature. These minerals are used to "soften" hard water. Hard water is water containing cations of calcium, magnesium, and iron, which are undesirable because they form a precipitate with ordinary soap. The zeolite is able to remove these ions from the water, replacing them by sodium ion.

A zeolite is an aluminosilicate, with formula such as $Na_2Al_2Si_4O_{12}$ (Chapter 26). It consists of a rigid framework formed by the aluminum, silicon, and oxygen atoms, honeycombed by corridors in which sodium ions are located. These ions have some freedom of motion, and when

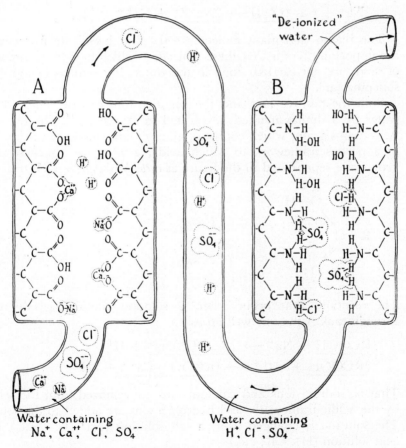

FIGURE 17-1   *The removal of ions from water by use of giant molecules with attached acidic and basic groups.*

hard water flows over zeolite grains some of the sodium ions run out of the corridors into the solution and are replaced by ions of calcium, magnesium, and iron. In this way the hardness of the water is removed. After most of the sodium ion has been replaced the zeolite is regenerated by allowing it to stand in contact with a saturated brine; the reaction is then reversed, Na^+ replacing Ca^{++} and the other cations in the corridors of the zeolite.

The reactions that occur may be written with symbols. If Z^- is used to represent a small portion of the zeolite framework, carrying one negative charge, the replacement of calcium ion in the water by sodium ion may be written*

$$2Na^+Z^- + Ca^{++} \longrightarrow Ca^{++}(Z^-)_2 + 2Na^+ \tag{1}$$

When concentrated salt solution (brine) is run through the zeolite the reverse reaction occurs:

$$2Na^+ + Ca^{++}(Z^-)_2 \longrightarrow 2Na^+Z^- + Ca^{++} \tag{2}$$

The reason that giant molecules—the aluminosilicate framework—are important here is that these molecules, which look like large grains of sand, are not carried along in the water, but remain in the water-softening tank.

Both the positive ions and the negative ions can be removed from water by a similar method, illustrated in Figure 17-1. The first tank, A, contains grains which consist of giant organic molecules in the form of a porous framework to which acidic groups are attached. These groups are represented in the figure as *carboxyl groups*, —COOH:

$$
\begin{array}{c}
:\overset{\cdot\cdot}{O}\text{---H} \\
\diagup \\
R\text{---C} \\
\diagdown \\
\underset{\cdot\cdot}{O}:
\end{array}
$$

The reactions that occur when a solution containing salts passes through tank A may be written as

$$RCOOH + Na^+ \longrightarrow (RCOO^-)Na^+ + H^+$$
$$2RCOOH + Ca^{++} \longrightarrow (RCOO^-)_2Ca^{++} + 2H^+$$

That is, sodium ions and calcium ions are removed from the solution by the acidic framework, and hydrogen ions are added to the solution. The solution is changed from a salt solution (Na^+, Cl^-, etc.) to an acid solution (H^+, Cl^-, etc.).

* A line is drawn under the formula for a substance to indicate that it is a solid.

This acid then runs through tank B, which contains grains of giant organic molecules with basic groups attached. These groups are shown as *substituted ammonium hydroxide** groups, $(RNH_3^+)(OH^-)$:

$$\left[\begin{array}{c} H \\ | \\ R-N-H \\ | \\ H \end{array}\right]^+ \qquad \left[:\ddot{O}-H\right]^-$$

The hydroxide ion of these groups combines with the hydrogen ion in the water:

$$OH^- + H^+ \longrightarrow H_2O$$

The negative ions then remain, held by the ammonium ions of the framework. The reactions are

$$(RNH_3^+)(OH^-) + Cl^- + H^+ \longrightarrow (RNH_3^+)Cl^- + H_2O$$
$$2(RNH_3^+)(OH^-) + SO_4^{--} + 2H^+ \longrightarrow (RNH_3^+)_2(SO_4^{--}) + 2H_2O$$

The water which passes out of the second tank contains practically no ions, and may be used in the laboratory and in industrial processes in place of distilled water.

The giant molecules in tank A may be regenerated after use by passing moderately concentrated sulfuric acid through the tank:

$$2(RCOO^-)Na^+ + H_2SO_4 \longrightarrow 2RCOOH + 2Na^+ + SO_4^{--}$$

Those in tank B may be regenerated by use of a moderately concentrated solution of sodium hydroxide:

$$(RNH_3^+)Cl^- + OH^- \longrightarrow (RNH_3^+)OH^- + Cl^-$$

17–2. The Principle of Le Chatelier

The reactions that occur in the softening of water by a zeolite and the regeneration of the zeolite provide a good example of an important general principle, **the principle of Le Chatelier.** This principle, which is named after the French chemist Henri Louis Le Chatelier (1850–1936), may be expressed in the following way: **if the conditions of a system, initially at equilibrium, are changed, the equilibrium will shift in such a direction as to tend to restore the original conditions.**

Let us recall the reaction that occurs when a hard water, containing calcium ions, is brought into contact with a sodium zeolite; this reaction is

* R represents a part of the framework, shown as a carbon atom in Figure 17-1.

$$2Na^+Z^- + Ca^{++} \longrightarrow Ca^{++}(Z^-)_2 + 2Na^+ \tag{1}$$

After a large amount of hard water has been run through the zeolite, no further replacement of calcium ions by sodium ions occurs; a *steady state* has been reached. The reason for the existence of the steady state is that there is also the possibility of the reverse reaction:

$$2Na^+ + Ca^{++}(Z^-)_2 \longrightarrow 2Na^+Z^- + Ca^{++} \tag{2}$$

Even a very few sodium ions in the water might react with the calcium zeolite to cause this reaction to take place. The steady state occurs when the concentrations of calcium ion and sodium ion in the water and bound into the zeolite are such that the rate at which calcium ion is replacing sodium ion is just equal to the rate at which sodium ion is replacing calcium ion; this equilibrium of the two rates can be expressed by a single equation, with a double arrow:

$$2Na^+Z^- + Ca^{++} \rightleftarrows Ca^{++}(Z^-)_2 + 2Na^+$$

If, now, conditions are changed by the addition of a large quantity of sodium ion, in high concentration (the addition of a concentrated salt solution), the equilibrium shifts in the way stated by Le Chatelier's principle, namely, in the direction that reduces the concentration of sodium ion in the solution. This is the direction to the left: the sodium zeolite is thus regenerated.

It is often possible to reach a useful qualitative conclusion about a chemical system by applying Le Chatelier's principle. The example that we are discussing shows that a chemical reaction may be made to proceed first in one direction and then in the opposite direction simply by changing the concentration of one or more of the reacting substances.

17–3. *Other Ways of Softening Water*

Hard water may also be softened by chemical treatment. In practice the use of giant organic molecules (synthetic resins) for de-ionizing water, described above, is restricted to industries requiring very pure water, as in making medicinal products. The zeolite method is sometimes used on a large scale, to treat the water for an entire city, but it is more often applied only for an individual house or building. Water for a city is usually treated by the addition of chemicals, followed by sedimentation when the water is allowed to stand in large reservoirs, and then by filtration through beds of sand. The settling process removes suspended matter in the water together with precipitated substances that might be produced by the added chemicals, and some living microorganisms. After filtration, the remaining living organisms may be destroyed by treatment with chlorine, bleaching powder, sodium hypochlorite or calcium hypochlorite, or ozone.

The hardness of water is due mainly to calcium ion, ferrous ion (Fe^{++}), and magnesium ion; it is these ions which form insoluble compounds with ordinary soap. Hardness is usually reported in parts per million (ppm), calculated as calcium carbonate (or sometimes in grains per gallon: 1 grain per gallon is equal to 17.1 ppm). Domestic water with hardness less than 100 ppm is good, and that with hardness between 100 and 200 ppm is fair.

Ground water in limestone regions may contain a large amount of calcium ion and hydrogen carbonate ion, HCO_3^-. Although calcium carbonate itself is insoluble, calcium hydrogen carbonate, $Ca(HCO_3)_2$, is a soluble substance. A water of this sort (which is said to have *temporary hardness*) can be softened simply by boiling, which causes the excess carbon dioxide to be driven off, and the calcium carbonate to precipitate:

$$Ca^{++} + 2HCO_3^- \longrightarrow CaCO_3 \downarrow + H_2O + CO_2 \uparrow$$

This method of softening water cannot be applied economically in the treatment of the water supply of a city, however, because of the large fuel cost. Instead, the water is softened by the addition of calcium hydroxide, slaked lime:

$$Ca^{++} + 2HCO_3^- + Ca(OH)_2 \longrightarrow 2CaCO_3 \downarrow + 2H_2O$$

If sulfate ion or chloride ion is present in solution instead of hydrogen carbonate ion, the hardness of the water is not affected by boiling— the water is said to have *permanent hardness*. Permanently hard water can be softened by treatment with sodium carbonate:

$$Ca^{++} + CO_3^{--} \longrightarrow CaCO_3 \downarrow$$

The sodium ions of the sodium carbonate are left in solution in the water, together with the sulfate or chloride ions that were already there.

In softening water by use of calcium hydroxide or sodium carbonate enough of the substance is used to cause magnesium ion to be precipitated as magnesium hydroxide and iron as ferrous hydroxide or ferric hydroxide. Sometimes, in addition to the softening agent, a small amount of aluminum sulfate, alum, or ferric sulfate is added as a coagulant. These substances, with the alkaline reagents, form a flocculent, gelatinous precipitate, of aluminum hydroxide, $Al(OH)_3$, or ferric hydroxide, $Fe(OH)_3$, which entraps the precipitate produced in the softening reaction, and helps it to settle out. The gelatinous precipitate also tends to adsorb coloring matter and other impurities in the water.*

---

* *Adsorption* is the adhesion of molecules of a gas, liquid, or dissolved substance or of particles to the surface of a solid substance. *Absorption* is the assimilation of molecules into a solid or liquid substance, with the formation of a solution or a compound. Sometimes the word *sorption* is used to include both of these phenomena. We say that a heated glass vessel *adsorbs* water vapor from the air on cooling, and becomes coated with a very thin layer of water: a dehydrating agent such as concentrated sulfuric acid *absorbs* water, forming hydrates.

A water that is used in a steam boiler often deposits a scale of calcium sulfate, which is left as the water is boiled away. In order to prevent this, boiler water is sometimes treated with sodium carbonate, causing the precipitation of calcium carbonate as a sludge, and preventing the formation of the calcium sulfate scale. Sometimes trisodium phosphate, Na_3PO_4, is used, leading to the precipitation of calcium as hydroxy-apatite, $Ca_5(PO_4)_3OH$, as a sludge. In either case the sludge is removed from the boiler by draining at intervals.

17–4. *The Ionic Dissociation of Water*

An acidic solution contains hydrogen ions, H^+ (actually hydronium ions, H_3O^+). A basic solution contains hydroxide ions, OH^-. A number of years ago chemists asked, and answered, the question, "Are these ions present in pure neutral water?" The answer is that they are present, in equal but very small concentrations.

Pure water contains hydrogen ions in concentration 1×10^{-7} moles per liter, and hydroxide ions in the same concentration. These ions are formed by the dissociation of water:

$$H_2O \rightleftharpoons H^+ + OH^-$$

When a small amount of acid is added to pure water the concentration of hydrogen ion is increased. The concentration of hydroxide ion then decreases, *but not to zero*. Acidic solutions contain hydrogen ion in large concentration and hydroxide ion in very small concentration.

17–5. *Physical Properties of Water*

Water is a clear, transparent liquid, colorless in thin layers. Thick layers of water have a bluish-green color.

The physical properties of water are used to define many physical constants and units. The freezing point of water (saturated with air at 1 atm pressure) is taken as $0°$ C, and the boiling point of water at 1 atm is taken as $100°$ C. The unit of volume in the metric system is chosen so that 1 ml of water at $3.98°$ C (the temperature of its maximum density) weighs 1.00000 gram. A similar relation holds in the English system: 1 cu. ft. of water weighs approximately 1000 ounces. The unit of energy, the calorie, is defined in relation to water (Section 1–6).

Most substances diminish in volume, and hence increase in density, with decrease in temperature. Water has the very unusual property of having a temperature at which its density is a maximum. This temperature is $3.98°$ C. With further cooling below this temperature the volume of a sample of water increases somewhat (Figure 17-2).

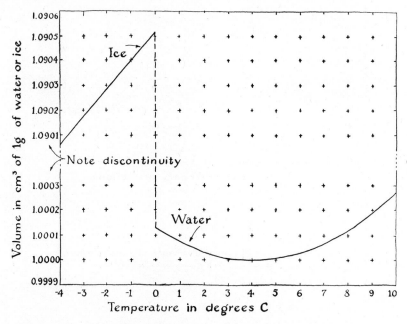

FIGURE 17-2   *Dependence of the volume of ice and water on temperature.*

A related phenomenon is the increase in volume which water undergoes on freezing. These properties are discussed in detail in the last
section of this chapter.

17–6. *The Melting Points and Boiling Points of Substances*

All molecules exert a weak attraction upon one another. This attraction, the *electronic van der Waals attraction,* is the result of the mutual
interaction of the electrons and nuclei of the molecules; it has its origin
in the electrostatic attraction of the nuclei of one molecule for the electrons of another, which is largely but not completely compensated by
the repulsion of electrons by electrons and nuclei by nuclei. The van
der Waals attraction is significant only when the molecules are very
close together—almost in contact with one another. At small distances
(about 4 Å for argon, for example) the force of attraction is balanced
by a force of repulsion due to interpenetration of the outer electron
shells of the molecules (Figure 17-3).

It is these intermolecular forces of electronic van der Waals attraction which cause substances such as the noble gases, the halogens, etc.,
to condense to liquids and to freeze into solids at sufficiently low temperatures. The boiling point is a measure of the amount of molecular
agitation necessary to overcome the forces of van der Waals attraction,
and hence is an indication of the magnitude of these forces. In general

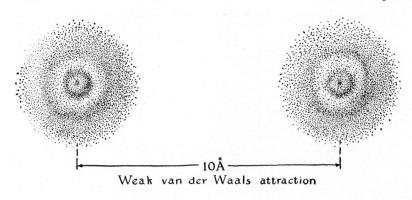

— 10Å —
Weak van der Waals attraction

Very strong van der Waals attraction
— 5Å —

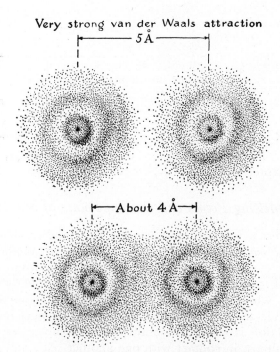

|— About 4 Å —|

Van der Waals attraction just
balanced by repulsive forces due to
interpenetration of outer electron shells

FIGURE 17-3 *Diagram illustrating van der Waals attraction and repulsion
in relation to electron distribution of monatomic molecules of argon.*

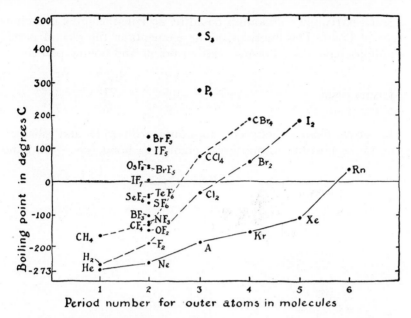

FIGURE 17-4   *Diagram showing increase in boiling point with increase in molecular complexity.*

the electronic van der Waals attraction between molecules increases with increase in the number of electrons per molecule. Since the molecular weight is roughly proportional to the number of electrons in the molecule, usually about twice the number of electrons, the van der Waals attraction usually increases with increase in the molecular weight. **Heavy molecules attract one another more strongly than light molecules; hence normal molecular substances with large molecular weight have high boiling points, and those with small molecular weight have low boiling points.**

This generalization is indicated in Figure 17-4, in which the boiling points of some molecular substances are shown. The steady increase in boiling point for sequences such as He, Ne, A, Kr, Xe, Rn, and H_2, F_2, Cl_2, Br_2, I_2 is striking.

The similar effect of increase in the number of atoms (with nearly the same atomic number) in the molecule is shown by the following sequences:

	A	Cl_2	P_4	S_8	
Boiling point	$-185.7°$	$-34.6°$	$280°$	$444.6°$ C	

	Ne	F_2	CF_4	SF_6	IF_7	OsF_8
Boiling point	$-245.9°$	$-187°$	$-161.4°$	$-62°$	$4.5°$	$47.5°$ C

Bond Type and Atomic Arrangement.   It has sometimes been thought that an abrupt change in melting point or boiling point in a series of related compounds could be accepted as proof of a change in type of bond. The fluorides of the elements of the second period, for example, have the following melting points and boiling points:

	NaF	MgF$_2$	AlF$_3$	SiF$_4$*	PF$_5$	SF$_6$*
Melting point	980°	1400°	1040°	−77°	−83°	−55° C
Boiling point	1700°	2240°	——	−96°	−75°	−64°

The great change between aluminum trifluoride and silicon tetra-fluoride is not due to any great change in bond type—the bonds are

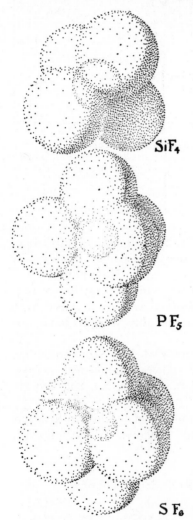

SiF$_4$

PF$_5$

SF$_6$

FIGURE 17-5

Molecules of silicon tetrafluoride, phosphorus pentafluoride, and sulfur hexafluoride, three very volatile substances.

* Note that silicon tetrafluoride and sulfur hexafluoride have the interesting property, described in Chapter 7 for carbon dioxide, of subliming at 1 atm pressure without melting. The temperatures given in the table as the boiling points of these two substances are in fact the subliming points, when the vapor pressure of the crystals becomes equal to 1 atm.

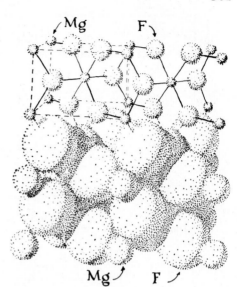

FIGURE 17-6

*The structure of magnesium fluoride; this
substance has high melting point and boiling point.*

in all cases intermediate in character between extreme ionic bonds

M^+F^- and normal covalent bonds $M : \overset{..}{\underset{..}{F}} : $ —but rather to a *change*

in atomic arrangement. The three easily volatile substances exist as discrete
molecules SiF_4, PF_5, and SF_6 (with no dipole moments) in the liquid
and crystalline states as well as the gaseous state (Figure 17-5), and the
thermal agitation necessary for fusion or vaporization is only that needed
to overcome the weak intermolecular forces, and is essentially independent of the strength or nature of the interatomic bonds within a molecule.
On the other hand, the other three substances in the crystalline state
are giant molecules, with strong bonds between neighboring ions holding the whole crystal together (NaF, sodium chloride arrangement,
Figure 4-6; MgF_2, Figure 17-6). To melt such a crystal some of these
strong bonds must be broken, and to boil the liquid more must be
broken; hence the melting point and boiling point are high.

The extreme case is that in which the entire crystal is held together
by very strong covalent bonds; this occurs for diamond, with melting
point above 3500° and boiling point 4200° C.

17–7. *The Hydrogen Bond—the Cause of the Unusual Properties of Water*

The unusual properties of water mentioned above are due to the
power of its molecules to attract one another especially strongly. This
power is associated with a structural feature called the **hydrogen bond.**

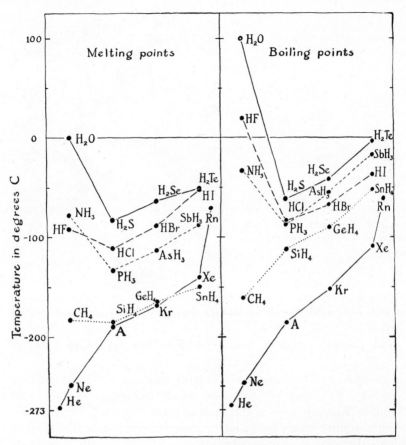

FIGURE 17-7   *Melting points and boiling points of hydrides of non-metallic elements, showing abnormally high values for hydrogen fluoride, water, and ammonia, caused by hydrogen-bond formation.*

The Abnormal Melting and Boiling Points of Hydrogen Fluoride, Water, and Ammonia.   The melting points and boiling points of the hydrides of some non-metallic elements are shown in Figure 17-7. The variation for a series of congeners is normal for the sequence CH_4, SiH_4, GeH_4, and SnH_4, but is abnormal for the other sequences. The curves through the points for H_2Te, H_2Se, and H_2S show the expected trend, but when extrapolated they indicate values of about $-100°$ C and $-80°$ C, respectively, for the melting point and boiling point of water. The observed value of the melting point is $100°$ greater, and that of the boiling point is $180°$ greater, than would be expected for water if it were a normal substance; and hydrogen fluoride and ammonia show similar, but smaller, deviations.

The Nature of the Hydrogen Bond.   The hydrogen ion is a bare nucleus, with charge $+1$. If hydrogen fluoride, HF, had an extreme

FIGURE 17-8

The hydrogen fluoride molecule (A) and the hydrogen difluoride ion, containing a hydrogen bond (B).

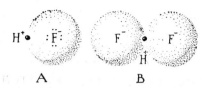

ionic structure, it could be represented as in A of Figure 17-8. The positive charge of the hydrogen ion could then strongly attract a negative ion, such as a fluoride ion, forming an $[F^-H^+F^-]^-$ or HF_2^- ion, as shown in B. This does indeed occur, and the stable ion HF_2^-, called the *hydrogen bifluoride ion*, exists in considerable concentration in acidic fluoride solutions, and in salts such as KHF_2, potassium hydrogen bifluoride. The bond holding this complex ion together, called the **hydrogen bond,** is weaker than ordinary ionic or covalent bonds, but stronger than ordinary van der Waals forces of intermolecular attraction.

Hydrogen bonds are also formed between hydrogen fluoride mole-

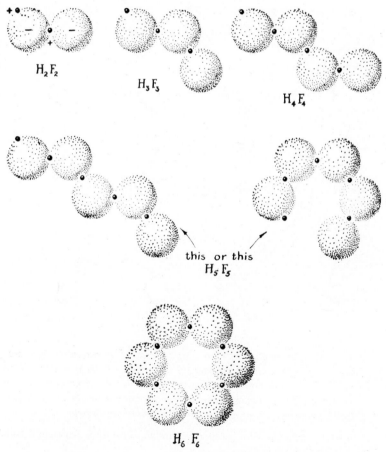

FIGURE 17-9   *Some polymers of hydrogen fluoride.*

cules, causing the gaseous substance to be largely polymerized into the molecular species H_2F_2, H_3F_3, H_4F_4, H_5F_5, and H_6F_6 (Figure 17-9).

In a hydrogen bond the hydrogen atom is usually attached more strongly to one of the two electronegative atoms which it holds together than to the others.* The structure of the dimer of hydrogen fluoride

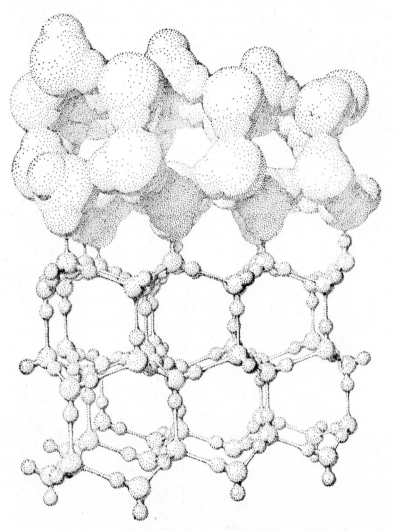

FIGURE 17-10   *A small part of a crystal of ice. The molecules above are shown with approximately their correct size (relative to the interatomic distances). Note hydrogen bonds, and the open structure which gives ice its low density. The molecules below are indicated diagrammatically as small spheres for oxygen atoms and still smaller spheres for hydrogen atoms.*

* In KHF_2 and a few other exceptional substances the hydrogen atom is midway between the hydrogen-bonded atoms.

may be represented by the formula

$$F^- \!\!-\!\! H^+ \;-\;-\;-\; F^- \!\!-\!\! H^+$$

in which the dashed line represents the hydrogen bonding.

Because of the electrostatic origin of the hydrogen bond, only the most electronegative atoms—fluorine, oxygen, nitrogen—form these bonds. Usually an unshared electron pair of the attracted atom approaches closely to the attracting hydrogen ion. Water is an especially suitable substance for hydrogen-bond formation, because each molecule has two attached hydrogen atoms and two unshared electron pairs, and hence can form four hydrogen bonds. The tetrahedral arrangement of the shared and unshared electron pairs causes these four bonds to extend in the four tetrahedral directions in space, and leads to the characteristic crystal structure of ice (Figure 17-10). This structure, in which each molecule is surrounded by only four immediate neighbors, is a very open structure, and accordingly ice is a substance with abnormally low density. When ice melts this tetrahedral structure is partially destroyed, and the water molecules are packed more closely together, causing water to have greater density than ice. Many of the hydrogen bonds remain, however, and aggregates of molecules with the open tetrahedral structure persist in water at the freezing point. With increase in temperature some of these aggregates break up, causing a further increase in density of the liquid; only at 4° C does the normal expansion due to increase in molecular agitation overcome this effect, and cause water to begin to show the usual decrease in density with increasing temperature.

17–8. *The Importance of Water as an Electrolytic Solvent*

Salts are insoluble in most solvents. Gasoline, benzene, carbon disulfide, carbon tetrachloride, alcohol, ether—these substances are "good solvents" for grease, rubber, organic materials generally; but they do not dissolve salts.

The reasons that water is so effective in dissolving salts are that *it has a very high dielectric constant* and *its molecules tend to combine with ions, to form hydrated ions*. Both of these properties are due to the *large electric dipole moment* of the water molecule.

The water molecule has a considerable amount of ionic character; it can be thought of (somewhat idealized) as an oxygen ion O^{--} with two hydrogen ions H^+ attached near its surface. These hydrogen ions are 0.96 Å from the oxygen nucleus, and on the same side of the oxygen atom, the angle H—O—H being 105°. Hence there is a separation of positive charge and negative charge within the molecule, causing the center of the positive charge in the molecule to be to one side of

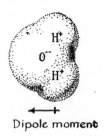

Dipole moment

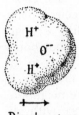

1 Å

FIGURE 17-11

Two water molecules with their electric dipole moment vectors oriented in opposite directions.

Dipole moment

the center of the negative charge. *Such a combination of separated positive and negative charge is called an* **electric dipole moment** (Figure 17-11).

The Effect of the High Dielectric Constant. In an electric field, as between the electrostatically charged plates of a condenser, water molecules tend to orient themselves, pointing their positive ends toward the negative plate and their negative ends toward the positive plate (Figure 17-12). This partially neutralizes the applied field, an effect described by saying that the medium (water) has a *dielectric constant* greater than unity.

The voltage required to put a given amount of electric charge on the plates of a condenser is inversely proportional to the dielectric constant of the medium surrounding the condenser plates. Water has dielectric constant 81 at room temperature (18° C). Hence a condenser in water can be charged by 1 volt of electric potential to the same extent as by 81 volts in a vacuum (dielectric constant 1) or in air (dielectric constant 1.0006).

The force of attraction or repulsion of electric charges is inversely proportional to the dielectric constant of the medium surrounding the charges. This means that two opposite electric charges in water attract each other with a force only $\frac{1}{81}$ as strong as in air (or a vacuum). It is clear that the ions of a crystal of sodium chloride placed in water could dissociate away from the crystal far more easily than if the crystal were in air, since the electrostatic force bringing an ion back to the surface of the crystal from the aqueous solution is only $\frac{1}{81}$ as strong as from air. It is accordingly not surprising that the thermal agitation of the ions in a salt crystal at room temperature is not great enough to

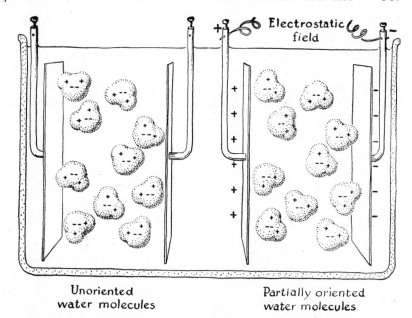

FIGURE 17-12   *Orientation of polar molecules in an electrostatic field, produc-ing the effect of a high dielectric constant.*

cause the ions to dissociate away into the air, but that it is great enough to overcome the relatively weak attraction when the crystal is surrounded by water, thus allowing large numbers of the ions to dissociate into aqueous solution.

The Hydration of an Ion.   A related effect which stabilizes the dis-solved ions is the formation of *hydrates* of the ions. Each negative ion attracts the positive ends of the adjacent water molecules, and tends to hold several water molecules attached to itself. The positive ions, which are usually smaller than the negative ions, show this effect still more strongly; each positive ion attracts the negative ends of the water mole-cules, and binds several molecules tightly about itself, forming a hydrate which may have considerable stability, especially for the bipositive and terpositive cations.

The number of water molecules attached to a cation, its **ligancy,**[*] is determined by the size of the cation. The small cation Be^{++} forms the tetrahydrate[†] $Be(OH_2)_4^{++}$. A somewhat larger ion, such as Mg^{++} or Al^{+++}, forms a hexahydrate, $Mg(OH_2)_6^{++}$ or $Al(OH_2)_6^{+++}$ (Figure 17-13).

---

[*] The ligancy was formerly called the *coordination number*.

[†] In these formulas water is written OH_2 instead on H_2O, to indicate that the oxygen atom of the water molecule is near the metal ion, the hydrogen atoms being on the outside. Usually the formulas are written $Be(H_2O)_4$ [++], etc.

The forces between cations and water molecules are so strong that the ions often retain a layer of water molecules in crystals. This water is called *water of crystallization*. This effect is more pronounced for bipositive and terpositive ions than for unipositive ions. The tetrahedral complex $Be(H_2O)_4^{++}$ occurs in various salts, including $BeCO_3 \cdot 4H_2O$, $BeCl_2 \cdot 4H_2O$, and $BeSO_4 \cdot 4H_2O$, and is no doubt present also in solution. The following salts contain larger ions with six water molecules in octahedral coordination:

$MgCl_2 \cdot 6H_2O$	$AlCl_3 \cdot 6H_2O$
$Mg(ClO_3)_2 \cdot 6H_2O$	$KAl(SO_4)_2 \cdot 12H_2O$
$Mg(ClO_4)_2 \cdot 6H_2O$	$Fe(NH_4)_2(SO_4)_2 \cdot 6H_2O$
$MgSiF_6 \cdot 6H_2O$	$Fe(NO_3)_2 \cdot 6H_2O$
$NiSnCl_6 \cdot 6H_2O$	$FeCl_3 \cdot 6H_2O$

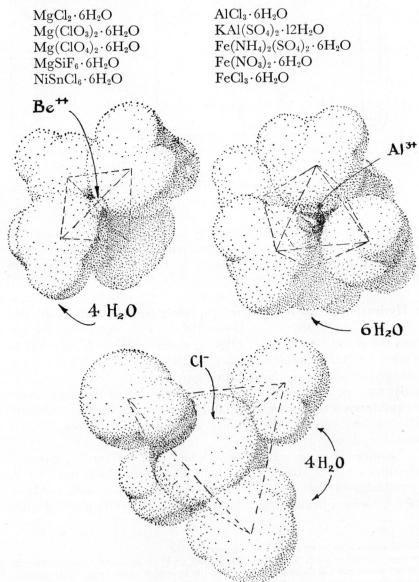

FIGURE 17-13   *Diagrams showing the structure of hydrated ions.*

In a crystal such as $FeSO_4 \cdot 7H_2O$ six of the water molecules are attached to the iron ion, in the complex $Fe(OH_2)_6^{++}$, and the seventh occupies another position, being packed near a sulfate ion of the crystal. In alum, $KAl(SO_4)_2 \cdot 12H_2O$, six of the twelve water molecules are coordinated about the aluminum ion and the other six about the potassium ion.

Crystals also exist in which some or all of the water molecules have been removed from the cations. For example, magnesium sulfate forms the three crystalline compounds $MgSO_4 \cdot 7H_2O$, $MgSO_4 \cdot H_2O$, and $MgSO_4$.

Other Electrolytic Solvents.   Some liquids other than water can serve as ionizing solvents, with the power of dissolving electrolytes to give electrically conducting solutions. These liquids include hydrogen peroxide, hydrogen fluoride, liquid ammonia, and hydrogen cyanide. All of these liquids, like water, have large dielectric constants. Liquids with low dielectric constants, such as benzene and carbon disulfide, do not act as ionizing solvents.

Liquids with large dielectric constants are sometimes called *dipolar liquids* (or simply *polar liquids*).

The large dielectric constant of water, which is responsible for the striking power of water to dissolve ionic substances, is due in part to its power to form hydrogen bonds. The hydrogen bonds help the water molecules to line up in such a direction as to neutralize part of the electric field. Hydrogen bonds are also formed in the other liquids (hydrogen peroxide, hydrogen fluoride, ammonia (boiling point $-33.4°$ C), and hydrogen cyanide) that can dissolve ionic substances.

17–9. *Heavy Water*

After the discovery of the heavy isotopes of oxygen, O^{17} and O^{18}, in 1929, and of deuterium, H^2, in 1932, it was recognized that ordinary water consists of molecules of several different kinds, built out of these isotopic atoms in various ways. Since these molecules have almost identical properties except for mass, the density of a sample of water is proportional to the average molecular weight of the molecules in it. If the sample of water consisted of ordinary oxygen combined only with deuterium, its molecular weight would be 20 instead of 18, and its density would accordingly be over 10% greater than that of ordinary water. The term *heavy water* is used to refer to this form of water, which may also be called *deuterium oxide*.

It may be pointed out that still heavier water might be made, by isolating the isotope O^{18}, and combining it with deuterium. This water would have density about 20% greater than ordinary water.

There is, in fact, a still heavier form of water. The isotope H^3, called tritium, is a radioactive substance with half-life 12.4 years. Ordinary tritium oxide has molecular weight 22, whereas water made from tritium and O^{18} would have molecular weight 24, and would be over 30% denser than ordinary water.

Shortly after the discovery of deuterium by H. C. Urey, Gilbert Newton Lewis prepared 1 ml of nearly pure deuterium oxide by the continued fractional electrolysis of ordinary water. Since then heavy water has been very carefully studied and new methods have been developed for its isolation which permit it to be made in large quantities. Its density at 20° is 1.1059 g/cm³, its freezing point is 3.82°, its boiling point 101.42°, and its temperature of maximum density 11.6° C.

Heavy water and other compounds of deuterium are used in the study of chemical reactions, especially those taking place in living organisms. For example, an investigator might want to know whether the water that is drunk by an animal serves merely as a solvent in the animal's body, or enters into chemical reactions, converting it, with other substances, into the proteins, fats, and other constituents of the cells of the organism. He could find out by having the animal drink heavy water, and then following the course of the deuterium. The content of deuterium in water can be determined either by use of the mass spectrograph or by the accurate determination of the density of carefully distilled water made from the preparation.

In recent years heavy water has been used in the field of nuclear chemistry. It is mentioned in the Smyth Report (see Chapter 32) that heavy water can be used instead of graphite as the moderator in a uranium pile. The function of the moderator is to reduce the speed of the fast neutrons emitted when nuclei undergo fission. The Canadian pile at Chalk River is a heavy-water pile.

Concepts, Facts, and Terms Introduced in This Chapter

Giant molecules; zeolites; "de-ionized" water.

The principle of Le Chatelier.

Temporary hardness and permanent hardness; methods of softening water.

Dissociation of pure water into hydrogen ions and hydroxide ions.

Dependence of density of water on temperature.

Van der Waals attraction, boiling point, melting point—dependence on molecular size.

Bond type and atomic arrangement; their effect on melting and boiling points.

The hydrogen bond, and the abnormal properties of hydrogen fluoride, water, and ammonia.

Importance of water as an electrolytic solvent. Dielectric constant. Hydration of ions. Water of crystallization. Other electrolytic solvents.

Heavy water.

Exercises

17-1. Write the fundamental chemical equations for the softening of water by a zeolite, and the regeneration of the zeolite.

17-2. Write the fundamental chemical equations for the removal of most of the ionic impurities in water by the "ion-exchange" process. Why do you suppose this process is sometimes preferred to distillation for the preparation of moderately pure water for industrial use? What do you think is the simplest method of determining when the absorbers in Tanks A and B of Figure 17-1 are saturated with ions and should be regenerated?

17-3. Describe briefly the forces responsible for the attraction between molecules.

17-4. Why are there no strong hydrogen bonds in phosphine, PH_3?

17-5. Explain the effect of the hydrogen bond on the density of ice and water.

17-6.   By reference to Figure 17-8, estimate the melting points and boiling points that hydrogen fluoride, water, and ammonia would be expected to have if these substances did not form hydrogen bonds. What would you expect the relative density of ice and water to be if hydrogen bonds were not formed?

17-7.   Distinguish between permanently hard water and temporarily hard water, and suggest methods for softening each.

17-8.   Why are glass vessels not suitable for storing pure water for chemical use? What impurity is hardest to keep out of distilled water?

17-9.   In softening water, aluminum sulfate or ferric sulfate is often added as well as calcium hydroxide, with the formation of a flocculent precipitate of aluminum hydroxide or ferric hydroxide. Write equations for the formation of these two hydroxides. Why are these hydroxides useful in the process of purifying water?

17-10. Correct the following statement: An acidic solution is a solution containing hydronium ions.

17-11. What explanation can you give of the fact that calcium fluoride, CaF_2 (the mineral fluorite), is a crystalline substance with high melting point, whereas stannic chloride, $SnCl_4$, is an easily volatile liquid?

17-12. Describe the structure of ice. Explain why ice floats, and mention some ways in which this property affects our lives.

17-13. Explain why sodium chloride crystallizes from solution as unhydrated NaCl, beryllium chloride as $BeCl_2 \cdot 4H_2O$, and magnesium chloride as $MgCl_2 \cdot 6H_2O$.

17-14. What is the fraction by weight of tritium in tritium oxide? The atomic weight of tritium is 3.0.

17-15. Can you apply the principle of Le Chatelier to predict whether the melting point of ice becomes greater than or less than $0°$ C when the pressure is increased? Compare the volume of ice and that of the water obtained by melting it.

Chapter 18

The Properties
of Solutions

One of the most striking properties of water is its ability to dissolve many substances, forming *aqueous solutions*. Solutions are very important kinds of matter—important for industry and for life. The ocean is an aqueous solution which contains thousands of components: ions of the metals and non-metals, complex inorganic ions, many different organic substances. It was in this solution that the first living organisms developed, and from it that they obtained the ions and molecules needed for their growth and life. In the course of time organisms were evolved which could leave this aqueous environment, and move out onto the land and into the air. They achieved this ability by carrying the aqueous solution with them, as tissue fluid, blood plasma, and intracellular fluids containing the necessary supply of ions and molecules.

The properties of solutions have been extensively studied, and it has been found that they can be correlated in large part by some simple laws. These laws and some descriptive information about solutions are discussed in the following sections.

18–1. *Types of Solutions. Nomenclature*

In Chapter 1 a solution was defined as a homogeneous material that does not have a definite composition.

The most common solutions are liquids. Carbonated water, for example, is a *liquid solution* of carbon dioxide in water. Air is a *gaseous solution* of nitrogen, oxygen, carbon dioxide, water vapor, and the noble gases. Coinage silver is a *solid solution* or *crystalline solution* of silver and copper. The structure of this crystalline solution is like that of crystalline copper, described in Chapter 2. The atoms are arranged in the same regular way, cubic closest packing, but atoms of silver and atoms of copper follow one another in a largely random sequence.

If one component of a solution is present in larger amount than the others, it may be called the **solvent;** the others are called **solutes.**

The concentration of a solute is often expressed as the number of grams per 100 g of solvent or the number of grams per liter of solution. It is often convenient to give the number of gram formula weights per liter of solution (the *formality*), the number of gram molecular weights per liter of solution (the *molarity*), or the number of gram equivalent weights per liter of solution (the *normality*). Sometimes these are referred to 1000 g of solvent; they are then called the *weight-formality, weight molarity,** and *weight-normality,* respectively.

The **formality** (F) *is the number of gram formula weights of solute per liter of solution.*

The **molarity** (M) *is the number of moles of solute per liter of solution.*

The **normality** (N) *is the number of gram equivalent weights per liter of solution.*

If the formula used for a substance is its correct molecular formula, describing the molecules actually present in the solution, then the formality is the same as the molarity. For example, a 1 F solution of $C_{12}H_{22}O_{11}$, sucrose (ordinary sugar) is also a 1 M solution. But a 1 F solution of NaCl, sodium chloride, is not a 1 M solution of NaCl; it is better described as 1 M in Na^+ and 1 M in Cl^-, because the substance is completely dissociated into these ions in the solution, and no NaCl molecules are present.

Example 1. A solution is made by dissolving 64.11 g of $Mg(NO_3)_2 \cdot 6H_2O$ in water enough to bring the volume to 1 l. Describe the solution.

   Answer.   The formula weight of $Mg(NO_3)_2 \cdot 6H_2O$ is 256.43; hence the solution is 0.25 F (0.25 formal) in this substance. The salt is, however, completely ionized in solution, to give magnesium ions, Mg^{++}, and nitrate ions, NO_3^-. Each formula of the salt produces one magnesium ion and two nitrate ions. Hence the solution is 0.25 M (0.25 molar) in Mg^{++} and 0.50 M in NO_3^-. Because magnesium is bivalent, its equivalent weight is one half its atomic weight. Hence the solution is 0.50 N (0.50 normal) in Mg^{++} and 0.50 N in NO_3^-.

For some purposes concentrations of the constituents of a solution are described by values of their *mole fractions.*

The **mole fraction** *of a molecular species is the ratio of the number of moles of that molecular species to the total number of moles.*

---

* Sometimes the weight-molarity is called *molality.* A few authors have used molality as the moles per liter of solution, but this usage has not been accepted.

The sum of the mole fractions of all the molecular species is equal to unity.

Example 2.   What are the mole fractions of the components of ordinary 95% ethyl alcohol?

   Solution.   Each 100 g of this solution contains 95 g of ethyl alcohol (C_2H_5OH, MW 46.07), and 5 g of water (H_2O, MW 18). The number of moles of alcohol per 100 g of solution is $\dfrac{95}{46.07} = 2.06$; the number of moles of water is $\dfrac{5}{18} = 0.28$. The total number of moles is 2.34. The mole fraction of alcohol is $x_1 = \dfrac{2.06}{2.34} = 0.88$; that of water is $x_2 = \dfrac{0.28}{2.34} = 0.12$. Note that $x_1 + x_2 = 1.00$.

It is worth noting that a $1\ M$ aqueous solution cannot be made up accurately by dissolving one mole of solute in 1 l of water, because the volume of the solution is in general different from that of the solvent. Nor is it equal to the sum of the volumes of the components; for example, 1 l of water and 1 l of alcohol on mixing give 1.93 l of solution; there occurs a volume contraction of 3.5%.

There is no way of predicting the density of a solution; tables of experimental values for important solutions are given in reference books and handbooks, such as the *International Critical Tables*, the *Handbook of Chemistry and Physics*, and *Lange's Handbook*.

Illustrative Exercises

18-1.   A solution is made containing 6.3 g of nitric acid, HNO_3, in 1 l of solution. The formula weight of HNO_3 is 63. (a) What is the formality of the HNO_3 solution? (b) Nitric acid is a strong acid. What is the molality of the solution in $H+$ and in NO_3^-?

18-2.   A solution is made by mixing one mole (18 g) of water, one mole (32 g) of methyl alcohol, CH_3OH, and one mole (46 g) of ethyl alcohol, C_2H_5OH. What are the mole fractions of the three substances in the solution?

18-3.   How many grams of $KMnO_4$ should be weighed out to make 1 l of a 0.1000 F solution?

18–2. Solubility

A system is in **equilibrium** *when its properties remain constant with the passage of time.*

If the system in equilibrium contains a solution and one of the components of the solution in the form of a pure substance, the concentration of that substance in the solution is called the *solubility* of the substance. The solution is called a *saturated solution*.

For example, at $0°$ C a solution of borax containing 1.3 g of anhydrous sodium tetraborate, $Na_2B_4O_7$, in 100 g of water is in equilibrium with the solid substance $Na_2B_4O_7 \cdot 10H_2O$, sodium tetraborate decahydrate; on standing the system does not change, the composition of the solution remaining constant. The solubility of $Na_2B_4O_7 \cdot 10H_2O$ in water is hence 1.3 g $Na_2B_4O_7$ per 100 g, or correcting for the water in hydration, 2.5 g $Na_2B_4O_7 \cdot 10H_2O$ per 100 g.

Phases.   In the discussion of solubility it is convenient to make use of the word *phase*.

A **phase** *is a homogeneous part of a system, separated from other parts by physical boundaries.*

For example, if a flask is partially full of water in which ice is floating, the system comprising the contents of the flask consists of three phases, the solid phase ice, the liquid phase water, and the gaseous phase air (Figure 18-1).

A phase in a system comprises all of the parts that have the same properties and composition. Thus if there were several pieces of ice in the system represented in Figure 18-1 they would constitute not several phases, but only one phase, the ice phase.

In the above example, a saturated solution of borax, the system consists of two phases, the solution, which is a liquid phase, and the substance $Na_2B_4O_7 \cdot 10H_2O$, a crystalline phase.

Change in the Solid Phase.   The solubility of $Na_2B_4O_7 \cdot 10H_2O$ increases rapidly with increasing temperature; at $60°$ it is 20.3 g $Na_2B_4O_7$

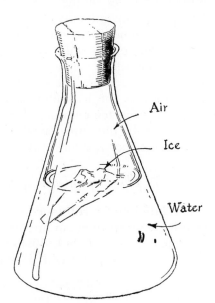

Air

Ice

Water

FIGURE 18-1

A system consisting of three phases.

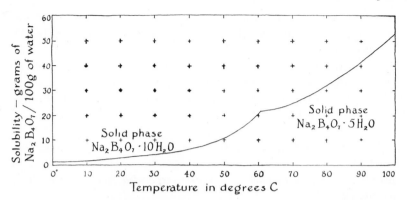

FIGURE 18-2   *Solubility of sodium tetraborate in water.*

per 100 g (Figure 18-2). If the system is heated to a temperature some-what above 60° C and held there for some time, a new phenomenon occurs. A third phase appears, a crystalline phase with composition $Na_2B_4O_7 \cdot 5H_2O$, and the other solid phase disappears. At this tempera-ture the solubility of the decahydrate is greater than that of the penta-hydrate; a solution saturated with the decahydrate is supersaturated with respect to the pentahydrate, and will deposit crystals of the penta-hydrate.* The process of solution of the unstable phase and crystal-lization of the stable phase will then continue until none of the unstable phase remains.

In this case the decahydrate is less soluble than the pentahydrate below 61°, and is hence the stable phase below this temperature. The solubility curves of the two hydrates cross at 61°, the pentahydrate being stable in contact with solution above this temperature.

Change other than solvation may occur in the stable solid phase. Thus orthorhombic sulfur (Chapter 14) is less soluble in suitable solvents than is monoclinic sulfur at temperatures below 95.5° C, the transition temperature between the two forms; above this temperature the mono-clinic form is the less soluble. The principles of thermodynamics re-quire that the temperature at which the solubility curves of the two forms cross be the same for all solvents, and be also the temperature at which the vapor pressure curves intersect.

18–3. *The Dependence of Solubility on Temperature*

The solubility of a substance may either increase or decrease with in-creasing temperature. An interesting case is provided by sodium sulfate. The solubility of $Na_2SO_4 \cdot 10H_2O$ (the stable solid phase below 32.4°) increases very rapidly with increasing temperature, from 5 g Na_2SO_4

---

* The addition of "seeds" (small crystals of the substance) is sometimes necessary to cause the process of crystallization to begin.

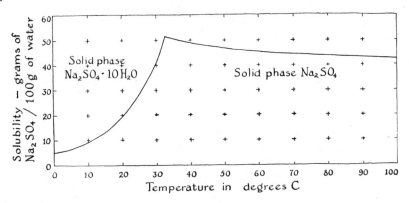

FIGURE 18-3   *Solubility of sodium sulfate in water.*

per 100 g of water at 0° to 52 g at 32.4°. Above 32.4° the stable solid phase is Na_2SO_4; the solubility of this phase decreases rapidly with increasing temperature, from 52 g at 32.4° to 42 g at 100° (Figure 18-3).

Most salts show increased solubility with increase in temperature; a good number (NaCl, K_2CrO_4) change only slightly in solubility with increase in temperature; and a few, such as Na_2SO_4 and $Na_2CO_3 \cdot H_2O$, show decreased solubility (Figures 18-4 and 18-5).

The principles of thermodynamics provide a quantitative relation

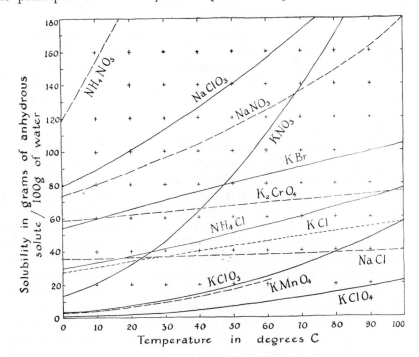

FIGURE 18-4   *Solubility curves for some salts in water.*

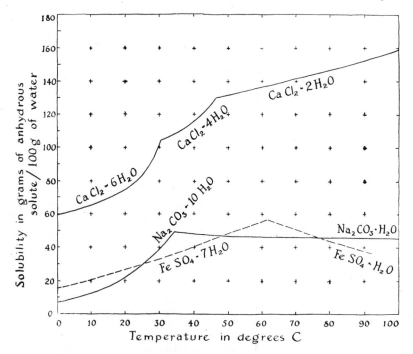

FIGURE 18-5   *Solubility curves for salts forming two or three hydrates.*

between the change in solubility with temperature of a substance (its *temperature coefficient of solubility*) and its *heat of solution,* the heat evolved as the substance dissolves in its nearly saturated solution. *If the heat of solution of a solid substance is positive* (that is, if heat is evolved on dissolving the substance in its nearly saturated solution) *the solubility of the solid decreases with increasing temperature, and if the heat of solution is negative the solubility increases.*

This rule may be derived from the principle of Le Chatelier, which has been discussed in the preceding chapter. If a system containing solute and solution is in equilibrium at a certain temperature, and the temperature is raised, the equilibrium will shift, according to this principle, in such a way as to tend to restore the system to its original temperature, by the absorption of heat from the reaction. This shift will involve the transfer of more solute into the solution if the heat of solution is negative, or the reverse process if the heat of solution is positive. Consider a solid in equilibrium with its saturated solution at one temperature. Let the temperature be increased somewhat. If the heat of solution is negative (heat being absorbed when more of the substance is dissolved) the system would be cooled in case that some of the solid phase were to dissolve, and the temperature would then drop back toward the original temperature. Hence this process will occur, and the solubility thus increases with increase in temperature.

Most salts, corresponding to their positive temperature coefficients of solubility, have negative heats of solution in water. For example, the heat of solution of $Na_2SO_4 \cdot 10H_2O$ in water is -19 kcal per gram formula weight. The formal heat of solution of sodium chloride is -1.3 kcal and that of Na_2SO_4 is 5.5 kcal.

Illustrative Exercises

18-4.   In Figure 18-3 the solubility of sodium sulfate is indicated to be 9.0 g Na_2SO_4 per 100 g of water. If 109 g of this saturated solution were allowed to evaporate, how many grams of the crystalline phase $Na_2SO_4 \cdot 10H_2O$ would be obtained?

18-5.   (a) When crystals of $FeSO_4 \cdot 7H_2O$ are dissolved in water is heat liberated or absorbed (see Figure 18-5)? (b) When crystals of $FeSO_4 \cdot H_2O$ are dissolved in water, is heat liberated or absorbed? (c) Can you predict whether heat is liberated or absorbed during the following reaction:

$$FeSO_4 \cdot H_2O + 6H_2O \longrightarrow FeSO_4 \cdot 7H_2O$$

(Hint: make use of the principle of conservation of energy and your answers to (a) and (b).)

18–4. The Dependence of Solubility on the Nature of Solute and Solvent

Substances vary greatly in their solubilities in various solvents. There are a few general rules about solubility, which, however, apply in the main to organic compounds.

One of these rules is that **a substance tends to dissolve in solvents which are chemically similar to it.** For example, the hydrocarbon naphthalene, $C_{10}H_8$, has a high solubility in gasoline, which is a mixture of hydrocarbons; it has a somewhat smaller solubility in ethyl alcohol, C_2H_5OH, whose molecules consist of short hydrocarbon chains with hydroxide groups attached, and a very small solubility in water, which is much different from a hydrocarbon. On the other hand, boric acid, $B(OH)_3$, a hydroxide compound, is moderately soluble in both water and alcohol, which themselves contain hydroxide groups, and is insoluble in gasoline. In fact, the three solvents themselves show the same phenomenon—both gasoline and water are miscible with (soluble in) alcohol, whereas gasoline and water dissolve in each other only in very small amounts.

The explanation of these facts is the following. Hydrocarbon groups (involving only carbon and hydrogen atoms) attract hydrocarbon groups only weakly, as is shown by the low melting and boiling points of hydrocarbons, relative to other substances with similar molecular weights. On the other hand, hydroxide groups and water molecules show very strong intermolecular attraction; the melting point and boiling point of water are higher than those of any other substance with low molecular weight. This strong attraction is due to the partial ionic character of the O—H bonds, which places electric charges on the atoms. The positively charged hydrogen atoms are then attracted to the negative oxygen atoms of other molecules, forming hydrogen bonds and holding the molecules firmly together (Chapter 17). The reason that the substances such as gasoline or naphthalene do not dissolve in water is that their molecules in solution would prevent water mole-

cules from forming as many of these strong

$$\begin{matrix} \text{H} & & \text{H} \\ | & & | \\ \text{O}\!\!-\!\!-\!\!\text{H}\text{---}\text{O}\!\!-\!\!-\!\!\text{H} \end{matrix}$$ bonds

as in pure water; on the other hand, boric acid is soluble in water because the decrease in the number of water-water bonds is compensated by the formation of strong hydrogen bonds between the water molecules and the hydroxide groups of the boric acid molecules.

18–5. *Solubility of Salts and Hydroxides*

In the study of inorganic chemistry, especially qualitative analysis, it is useful to know the approximate solubility of common substances. The simple rules of solubility are given below. These rules apply to compounds of the common cations Na^+, K^+, NH_4^+, Mg^{++}, Ca^{++}, Sr^{++}, Ba^{++}, Al^{+++}, Cr^{+++}, Mn^{++}, Fe^{++}, Fe^{+++}, Co^{++}, Ni^{++}, Cu^{++}, Zn^{++}, Ag^+, Cd^{++}, Sn^{++}, Hg_2^{++}, Hg^{++}, and Pb^{++}. By "soluble" it is meant that the solubility is more than about 1 g per 100 ml (roughly 0.1 M in the cation), and by "insoluble" that the solubility is less than about 0.1 g per 100 ml (roughly 0.01 M); substances with solubilities within or close to these limits are described as *sparingly soluble*.

Class of mainly soluble substances:

All **nitrates** are soluble.

All **acetates** are soluble.

All **chlorides, bromides,** and **iodides** are soluble except those of silver, mercurous mercury (mercury with oxidation number $+1$), and lead. $PbCl_2$ and $PbBr_2$ are sparingly soluble in cold water (1 g per 100 ml at 20°) and more soluble in hot water (3 g, 5 g, respectively, per 100 ml at 100°).

All **sulfates** are soluble except those of barium, strontium, and lead. $CaSO_4$, Ag_2SO_4, and Hg_2SO_4 (mercurous sulfate) are sparingly soluble.

All salts of **sodium, potassium,** and **ammonium** are soluble except $NaSb(OH)_6$ (sodium antimonate), K_2PtCl_6 (potassium hexachloroplatinate), $(NH_4)_2PtCl_6$, $K_3Co(NO_2)_6$ (potassium cobaltinitrite), and $(NH_4)_3Co(NO_2)_6$.

Class of mainly insoluble substances:

All **hydroxides** are insoluble except those of the alkali metals, ammonium, and barium. $Ca(OH)_2$ and $Sr(OH)_2$ are sparingly soluble.

All normal **carbonates** and **phosphates** are insoluble except those of the alkali metals and ammonium. Many hydrogen carbonates and phosphates, such as $Ca(HCO_3)_2$, $Ca(H_2PO_4)_2$, etc., are soluble.

All **sulfides** except those of the alkali metals, ammonium, and the alkaline-earth metals are insoluble.*

18–6. *The Dependence of Solubility on Pressure*

The effect of change of pressure on the solubility of crystalline or liquid substances in liquids is usually very small. For example, a pressure of 1000 atm increases the solubility of sodium chloride in water at 25° C only from 35.9 g per 100 g of water to 37.0 g per 100 g of water.

The **solubility of a gas in a liquid** (the weight of the dissolved gas) is, however, greatly increased by increase in pressure. At low pressures it is **directly proportional to the pressure of the gas. (Henry's law,** discovered in 1803 by the British chemist William Henry (1775–1836)). If the gas is a mixture, the solubility of each substance in the mixture is separately proportional to its partial pressure.

For example, the solubility of oxygen at 1 atm pressure in water at 18° C is 46 mg/l, and at 10 atm pressure it is 460 mg/l. Note that although the *weight* of oxygen dissolved by a liter of water is ten times as great at 10 atm pressure as at one atmosphere, the volume, at the applied pressure, is the same.

The solubilities of most gases in water are of the order of magnitude of that of oxygen. Exceptions are those gases which combine chemically with water or which dissociate largely into ions, including carbon dioxide, hydrogen sulfide, sulfur dioxide, and ammonia, which are extremely soluble.

Illustrative Exercise

18-6. It is stated above that 46 mg of oxygen can dissolve in 1 l of water at 18° when the pressure (partial pressure) of oxygen is 1 atm, and 460 mg when it is 10 atm. (a) What are the volumes of these weights of oxygen at standard conditions? (b) What are the volumes at 18° and the respective pressures, 1 atm and 10 atm?

18–7. *The Freezing Point and Boiling Point of Solutions*

It is well known that the freezing point of a solution is lower than that of the pure solvent; for example, in cold climates it is customary

---

* The sulfides of aluminum and chromium are hydrolyzed by water, precipitating $Al(OH)_3$ and $Cr(OH)_3$.

to add a solute such as alcohol or glycerol or ethylene glycol to the radiator water of automobiles to keep it from freezing. Freezing-point lowering by the solute also underlies the use of a salt-ice mixture for cooling, as in freezing ice cream; the salt dissolves in the water, making a solution, which is in equilibrium with ice at a temperature below the freezing point of water.

It is found by experiment that the freezing-point lowering of a dilute solution is proportional to the concentration of the solute. In 1883 the French chemist François Marie Raoult (1830–1901) made the useful discovery that **the weight-molar freezing-point lowering produced by different solutes is the same for a given solvent.** Thus the following freezing points are observed for 0.1 M solutions of the following solutes in water:

Hydrogen peroxide,	H_2O_2	$-0.186°$ C
Methanol,	CH_3OH	-0.181
Ethanol,	C_2H_5OH	-0.183
Dextrose,	$C_6H_{12}O_6$	-0.186
Sucrose,	$C_{12}H_{22}O_{11}$	-0.188

The *weight-molar freezing-point constant* for water has the value 1.86° C, the freezing point of a solution containing c moles of solute per 1000 g of water being $-1.86\,c$ in degrees C. For other solvents the values of this constant are the following:

SOLVENT	FREEZING POINT	WEIGHT-MOLAR* FREEZING-POINT CONSTANT
Benzene	5.6° C	4.90°
Acetic acid	17	3.90
Phenol	40	7.27
Camphor	180	40

* Moles per 1000 g of solvent.

The Determination of Molecular Weight by the Freezing-Point Method. The freezing-point method is a very useful way of determining the molecular weights of substances in solution. Camphor, with its very large constant, is of particular value for the study of organic substances.

Example 4. The freezing point of a solution of 0.244 g of benzoic acid in 20 g of benzene was observed to be 5.232° C, and that of pure benzene to be 5.478°. What is the molecular weight of benzoic acid in this solution?

Solution. The solution contains $\dfrac{0.244 \times 1000}{20} = 12.2$ g of benzoic acid per 1000 g of solvent. The number of moles of solute per 1000 g of solvent is found from the observed freezing-point lowering 0.246° to be $\dfrac{0.246}{4.90} = 0.0502$. Hence the molecular weight is

$\dfrac{12.2}{0.0502} = 243$. The explanation of this high value (the formula weight for benzoic acid, C_6H_5COOH, being 122.05) is that in this solvent the substance forms double molecules, $(C_6H_5COOH)_2$.

Evidence for Electrolytic Dissociation. One of the strongest arguments advanced by Arrhenius in support of the theory of electrolytic dissociation (Section 6–7) was the fact that the freezing-point lowering of salt solutions is much larger than that calculated for undissociated molecules, the observed lowering for a salt such as NaCl or $MgSO_4$ in very dilute solution being just twice as great and for a salt such as Na_2SO_4 or $CaCl_2$ just three times as great as expected. These results are explained by the assumption, made by Arrhenius, that NaCl and $MgSO_4$ form two ions (Na^+ and Cl^-, Mg^{++} and SO_4^{--}), whereas Na_2SO_4 and $CaCl_2$ form three ions ($2Na^+$ and SO_4^{--}, Ca^{++} and $2Cl^-$) per molecule.

Elevation of Boiling Point. *The boiling point of a solution is higher than that of the pure solvent by an amount proportional to the weight-molar concentration of the solute.* Values of the proportionality factor, the *molar boiling-point constant*, are given below for some important solvents. Boiling point measurements for a solution can be used to obtain the molecular weight of the solute in the same way as freezing-point measurements.

SOLVENT	BOILING POINT	MOLAR* BOILING-POINT CONSTANT
Water	100° C	0.52° C
Ethyl alcohol	78.5	1.19
Ethyl ether	34.5	2.11
Benzene	79.6	2.65

* Weight-molar.

Illustrative Exercises

18-7. It was found by experiment that a solution of 12.8 g of an unknown organic compound dissolved in 1000 g of benzene has freezing point 0.49° below that of pure benzene. What is the molecular weight of the compound?

18-8. (a) The freezing point of a 0.01 F aqueous solution of KCl is $-0.037°$ C. How does this fact support the Arrhenius theory of ionization? (b) What do you predict the boiling point of the solution to be?

18–8. *The Vapor Pressure of Solutions. Raoult's Law*

It was found experimentally by Raoult in 1887 that the partial pressure of solvent vapor in equilibrium with a dilute solution is directly proportional to the mole fraction of solvent in the solution. It can be expressed by the equation

$$p = p_0 x$$

in which p is the partial pressure of the solvent above the solution, p_0 is the vapor pressure of the pure solvent, and x is the mole fraction of solvent in the solution, as defined in the first section of this chapter. We may give a kinetic interpretation of this equation by saying that only x times as many solvent molecules can escape from the surface of a solution as from the corresponding surface of the pure solvent, and that accordingly equilibrium will be reached with the gas phase when the number of gas molecules striking the surface is x times the number striking the surface of the pure solvent at equilibrium.

The Derivation of Freezing-Point Depression and Boiling-Point Elevation from Raoult's Law. The laws of freezing-point lowering and boiling-point raising can be derived from Raoult's law in the following way. We first consider boiling-point raising. In Figure 18-6 the upper curve represents the vapor pressure of pure solvent as a function of the temperature. The temperature at which this becomes 1 atm is the boiling point of the pure solvent. The lower curve represents the vapor pressure of a solution of a non-volatile solute; Raoult's law requires that it lie below the curve for the pure solvent by an amount proportional to the molal concentration of solute, and that the same curve apply for all solutes, the molal concentration being the only significant quantity. This curve intersects the 1 atm line at a temperature higher than the boiling point of the solvent by an amount proportional to the

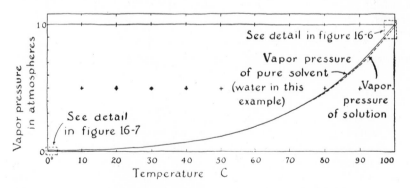

FIGURE 18-6   *Vapor-pressure curves of water in the range 0°C to 100°C.*

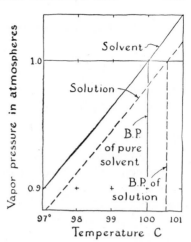

FIGURE 18-7

Vapor-pressure curves of water and an aqueous solution near the boiling point, showing elevation of the boiling point of the solution.

molal concentration of the solute (for dilute solutions), as expressed in the boiling-point law (Figure 18-7).

The argument for freezing-point lowering is similar. In Figure 18-8 the vapor pressure curves of the pure solvent in the crystalline state and the liquid state are shown intersecting at the freezing point of the pure solvent. At higher temperatures the crystal has higher vapor pressure than the liquid, and is hence unstable relative to it, and at lower temperatures the stability relation is reversed. The solution vapor pressure curve, lying below that of the liquid pure solvent, intersects the crystal curve at a temperature below the melting point of the pure solvent. This is the melting point of the solution.

Note that the assumption is made that the solid phase obtained on freezing the solution is pure solvent; if a crystalline solution is formed, as sometimes occurs, the freezing-point law does not hold.

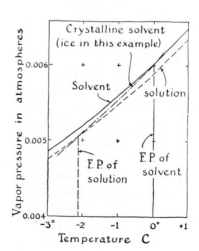

FIGURE 18-8

Vapor-pressure curves of water, ice, and an aqueous solution near the freezing point, showing depression of freezing point of the solution.

18–9. *The Osmotic Pressure of Solutions*

If red blood corpuscles are placed in pure water they swell, become round, and finally burst. This is the result of the fact that the cell wall is permeable to water but not to some of the solutes of the cell solution (mainly *hemoglobin*, the red protein in red cells); in the effort to reach a condition of equilibrium (equality of water vapor pressure) between the two liquids water enters the cell. If the cell wall were sufficiently strong, equilibrium would be reached when the hydrostatic pressure in the cell had reached a certain value, at which the water vapor pressure of the solution equals the vapor pressure of the pure water outside the cell. This equilibrium hydrostatic pressure is called the *osmotic pressure* of the solution.

A *semipermeable membrane* is a membrane with very small holes in it, of such a size that molecules of the solvent are able to pass through but molecules of the solute are not. A useful semipermeable membrane for measurement of osmotic pressure is made by precipitating cupric ferrocyanide, $Cu_2Fe(CN)_6$, in the pores of an unglazed porcelain cup, which gives the membrane mechanical support to enable it to withstand high pressures. Accurate measurements have been made in this way to over 250 atm. Cellophane membranes may also be used, if the osmotic pressure is not large (Figure 18-9).

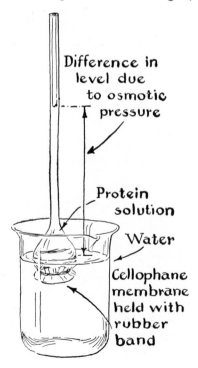

Difference in
level due
to osmotic
pressure

Protein
solution

Water

Cellophane
membrane
held with
rubber
band

FIGURE 18-9

The measurement of the osmotic pressure of a solution.

It is found experimentally that the osmotic pressure of a dilute solution satisfies the equation

$$\pi V = n_1 RT$$

with n_1 the number of moles of solute (to which the membrane is impermeable) in volume V, π the osmotic pressure, R the gas constant, and T the absolute temperature. This relation was discovered by van't Hoff in 1887. It is striking that the equation is identical in form with the perfect-gas equation; van't Hoff emphasized the similarity of a dissolved substance and a gas.

For inorganic substances and simple organic substances the osmotic-pressure method of determining molecular weight offers no advantages over other methods, such as the measurement of freezing-point lowering. It has, however, been found useful for substances of very high molecular weight; the molecular weight of hemoglobin was first reliably determined in this way by Adair in 1925. The value found by Adair, 68,000, has been verified by measurements made with the ultracentrifuge, and also by the investigation of crystals of hemoglobin by the x-ray diffraction method. The same molecular weight is found for the different kinds of hemoglobin in the blood of animals of different species.

18–10. *Colloidal Solutions*

It was found by Thomas Graham (1804–69) in the years around 1860 that substances such as glue, gelatin, albumin, starch, etc., in solution diffuse very slowly, their diffusion rates being as small as one one-hundredth of those for ordinary solutes (salt, sugar, etc.). Graham also found that substances of these two types differ markedly in their ability to pass through a membrane such as parchment paper or collodion; if a solution of sugar and glue is put into a collodion or Cellophane bag and the bag is placed in a stream of running water the sugar soon dialyzes through the bag into the water, and the glue remains behind. This process of **dialysis** gives a useful method of separating substances of these two kinds.

We now recognize that these differences in ability to pass through the pores of a membrane and in rates of diffusion are due to differences in size of the solute molecules. Graham thought that there was a deeper difference between ordinary, easily crystallizable substances and the slowly diffusing non-dialyzing substances, which he was unable to crystallize. He named the substances of the latter class *colloids* (Greek *kolla*, glue), in contradistinction to ordinary *crystalloids*. The modern usage is to define **colloids** as **substances with very large molecules.**

Some colloids consist of well-defined molecules, with constant molecular weight and definite molecular shape, permitting them to be piled in a crystalline array. Crystalline proteins include egg albumin (MW 43000) and hemoglobin (MW 68000).

Colloidal solutions may also be made by dispersing in the solvent a solid or liquid substance which is normally insoluble, such as gold, ferric oxide, arsenious sulfide, etc. A colloidal solution of this sort consists of very small particles of the dispersed substance, so small that their temperature motion (Brownian movement) prevents them from settling out in the gravitational field of the earth.

18–11. *The Activities of Ions*

During the early development of the ionic theory of electrolytic solutions it was recognized that the observed freezing-point lowering of these solutions, while greater than corresponding to undissociated solute molecules, is not so great as expected for complete ionization. For example, the freezing point of a $0.1 F$ solution of KBr is $-0.345°$ C. Since the freezing-point constant for water is $1.86°$, this lowering requires that there be effective 0.185 moles of solute, 85% more than the number of formulas KBr present, but not 100% more. For a number of years it was thought that facts such as this showed the salts to be only partially ionized; in this case KBr was said to be 85% ionized, the solution being said to be $0.085 M$ in K^+, $0.085 M$ in Br^-, and $0.015 M$ in undissociated KBr.

Then, about 1904, it was noticed that many properties of solutions of salts and strong acids (such as their color) suggest that **most salts and strong acids are completely ionized in dilute solution**. This view has been generally accepted since 1923, when a quantitative theory of the interactions of ions in solution was developed by Debye and Hückel. This theory is called the *Debye-Hückel theory of electrolytes*.

The explanation of the fact that a strong electrolyte such as potassium bromide produces a smaller freezing-point lowering than calculated for complete ionization is that there are strong *electrical forces* operating between the ions, which decrease their effectiveness, so that the properties of their solutions are different from those of ideal solutions, except at extreme dilution. The interionic attraction reduces the *activity* of the ions to a value less than their concentration.

The factor by which the ion concentration is to be multiplied to obtain the ion activity is called the *activity coefficient*. For all strong electrolytes containing only univalent ions (HCl, NaCl, KNO_3, etc.) its values are approximately 0.80 at $0.1 F$, 0.90 at $0.01 F$, and 0.96 at $0.001 F$, approaching 1 only in very dilute solutions. These activity coefficients are of significance in connection with chemical equilibrium, which is to be discussed later.

Concepts, Facts, and Terms Introduced in This Chapter

Solution, solvent, solute. Formality, molarity, normality; weight-formality, etc. Mole fraction.

Equilibrium; saturated solution; change in composition of the solid phase. Relation between temperature coefficient of solubility and heat of solution—application of the principle of Le Chatelier. Solubility in relation to nature of solute and solvent: "like dissolves like."

The solubility rules for common salts. The solubility of gases in liquids—Henry's law. The partition of a solute between two solvents.

The vapor pressure of solutions in relation to mole fraction—Raoult's law. Freezing-point lowering and boiling-point rise. Osmotic pressure. Activity of ions.

Colloids: colloidal solutions; dialysis.

Exercises

18-9. Saturated salt solution (20° C) contains 35.1 g NaCl per 100 g of water. What is its weight-formality? The density of the solution is 1.197 g/ml. What is its formality?

18-10. A 3 wt F solution of HCl is neutralized with 3 wt F NaOH. What is the weight formality of NaCl in the resulting solution?

18-11. Give an example of a gaseous solution, a liquid solution, and a crystalline solution.

18-12. A solution contains 10.00 g of anhydrous cupric sulfate in 1000 ml of solution. What is the formality of this solution in $CuSO_4$?

18-13. Calculate the mole fraction of each component in the following solutions:
(a) 1.000 g of chloroform, $CHCl_3$, in 10.00 g of carbon tetrachloride, CCl_4.
(b) 1.000 g of acetic acid, $C_2H_4O_2$, in 25.00 g of benzene, recognizing that acetic acid actually exists in benzene solution as the dimer, $(C_2H_4O_2)_2$.

18-14. The density of constant-boiling hydrochloric acid is 1.10 g/ml. It contains 20.24% HCl. Calculate the weight molarity, the volume molarity, and the mole fraction of HCl in the solution.

18-15. Make qualitative predictions about the solubility of
(a) Ethyl ether, $C_2H_5OC_2H_5$, in water, alcohol, and benzene.
(b) Hydrogen chloride in water and gasoline.
(c) Ice in liquid hydrogen fluoride and in cooled gasoline.
(d) Sodium tetraborate in water, in ether, and in carbon tetrachloride.
(e) Iodoform, HCI_3, in water and in carbon tetrachloride.
(f) Decane, $C_{10}H_{22}$, in water and in gasoline.

18-16. What can you say about the solubility in water of the substances $AgNO_3$, $PbCl_2$, PbI_2, Hg_2SO_4, $BaSO_4$, $Mg(OH)_2$, $Ba(OH)_2$, PbS, $NaSb(OH)_6$, K_2PtCl_6, KCl?

18-17. Sodium perchlorate is very soluble in water. What would happen if a solution of about 60 g of $NaClO_4$ in 100 ml of water were to be mixed with a solution of about 30 g of KCl in 100 ml of water, at 20° C? See Figure 18-4.

18-18. (a) The density of sodium chloride is 2.16 g/ml, and that of its saturated aqueous solution, containing 311 g NaCl per liter, is 1.197 g/ml. Would the solubility be increased or decreased by increasing the pressure? Give your calculations. (The assumption may be made that the change in volume that occurs when a small amount of salt is dissolved in a nearly saturated solution has the same sign as the volume change that occurs when a large amount of salt is dissolved in water.)
(b) Make a similar prediction for another salt, obtaining data from reference books.

18-19. By referring to Figures 18-3, 18-4, and 18-5, find three salts which on dissolving in a nearly saturated solution give out heat, and three which absorb heat.

18-20. Would heat be evolved or absorbed if some $Na_2CO_3 \cdot 10H_2O$ were dissolved in its nearly saturated aqueous solution at 30° C? If some $Na_2CO_3 \cdot H_2O$ were dissolved in this solution at 30° C?

18-21. What can you say about the heat of solution of common salt? (See Figure 18-4.)

18-22. The solubility of potassium hydrogen sulfate is 51.4 g per 100 g of water at 20° C, and 67.3 g per 100 g at 40° C. If you add some of the salt to a partially saturated solution and stir, will the system become colder or warmer?

18-23. Calculate approximately how much ethanol (C_2H_5OH) would be needed per gallon of radiator water to keep it from freezing at temperatures down to 10° F below the freezing point.

18-24. A solution containing 1 g of aluminum bromide in 100 g of benzene has a freezing point 0.099° below that of pure benzene. What are the apparent molecular weight and the correct formula of the solute?

18-25. The solubility of nitrogen at 1 atm partial pressure in water at 0° is 23.54 ml/l, and that of oxygen is 48.89. Calculate the amount by which the freezing points of air-saturated water and air-free water differ.

18-26. An aqueous solution of amygdalin (a sugar-like substance obtained from almonds) containing 96 g of solute per liter was found to have osmotic pressure 0.474 atm at 0° C. What is the molecular weight of the solute?

18-27. A 1% aqueous solution of gum arabic (simplest formula $C_{12}H_{22}O_{11}$) was found to have an osmotic pressure of 7.2 mm Hg at 25° C. What are the average molecular weight and degree of polymerization of the solute?

18-28. A solution containing 2.30 g of glycerol in 100 ml of water was found to freeze at −0.465°. What is the approximate molecular weight of glycerol dissolved in water? The formula of glycerol is $C_3H_5(OH)_3$. What would you predict as to the miscibility of this substance with water?

18-29. When 0.412 g of naphthalene ($C_{10}H_8$) was dissolved in 10.0 g of camphor, the freezing point was found to be 13.0° below that of pure camphor. What is the weight molar freezing-point constant for camphor, calculated from this observation? Can you explain why camphor is frequently used in molecular weight determinations?

18-30. A sample of a substance weighing 1.00 g was dissolved in 8.55 g of camphor, and was found to produce a depression of 9.5° in the freezing point of the camphor. Using the value of the molar freezing point constant found in the preceding problem, calculate the molecular weight of the substance.

18-31. Explain why the addition of heavy water to ordinary water does not cause a depression of the freezing point.

Chapter 19

Chemical Equilibrium and the Rate of Chemical Reaction

19–1. *Factors Influencing the Rate of Reaction*

Two questions may be asked in the consideration of a proposed chemical process, such as the preparation of a useful substance. One of these questions is "Are the stability relations of the reactants and the expected products such that it is possible for the reaction to occur?" The second question is equally important: it is "Under what conditions will the reaction proceed sufficiently rapidly for the method of preparation to be practicable?"

Chemists have learned a great deal about how to answer these questions, especially during the first half of the twentieth century. The question about whether it is possible for the reaction to occur is answered by the methods of *chemical thermodynamics*. We shall consider the simpler aspects of this field of science in the discussion of chemical equilibrium in the present chapter, and we shall also give a brief discussion of factors influencing the rate at which a reaction proceeds.

Every chemical reaction requires some time for its completion, but some reactions are very fast and some are very slow. Reactions between ions in solution without change in oxidation state are usually extremely fast. An example is the neutralization of a strong acid by a strong base, which proceeds as fast as the solutions can be mixed. Presumably nearly every time a hydronium ion collides with a hydroxide ion reaction occurs, and the number of collisions is very great, so that there is little delay in the reaction.

The formation of a precipitate, such as that of silver chloride when a solution containing silver ion is mixed with a solution containing chloride ion, may require a few seconds, to permit the ions to diffuse together to form the crystalline grains of the precipitate:

$$Ag^+ + Cl^- \longrightarrow AgCl \downarrow$$

On the other hand, ionic oxidation-reduction reactions are sometimes very slow. An example is the reduction of permanganate ion by hydrogen peroxide in sulfuric acid solution. When a drop of permanganate solution is added to a solution of hydrogen peroxide and sulfuric acid, the solution is colored pink, and this pink color may remain for several minutes, indicating that very little reaction has taken place. When, after a minute or so, the solution has become colorless, another drop of permanganate is found to produce a pink color that remains for a shorter time, and a third and fourth drop are found to be decolorized still more rapidly. Finally, after a considerable amount of permanganate solution has been added and has undergone reaction, with the formation of manganous ion and the liberation of free oxygen, it is found that the permanganate solution can be poured in a steady stream into the container, and that it is decolorized as rapidly as it can be stirred into the hydrogen peroxide solution. The explanation of this interesting phenomenon is that a product of the reaction, manganese in a lower state of oxidation, acts as a catalyst for the reaction; the first drop of permanganate reacts slowly, in the absence of any catalyst, but the reaction undergone by subsequent drops is the catalyzed reaction. Nobody knows the detailed mechanism of the catalytic activity of the catalysts in this reaction.

An example of a reaction which is extremely slow at room temperature is that between hydrogen and oxygen:

$$2H_2 + O_2 \longrightarrow 2H_2O$$

A mixture of hydrogen and oxygen can be kept for years without appreciable reaction. If the gas is ignited, however, a very rapid reaction —an explosion—occurs.

19–2. Chemical Equilibrium—a Dynamic Steady State

Sometimes a chemical reaction begins, continues for a while, and then appears to stop before any one of the reactants is used up: the reaction is said to have reached *equilibrium*. The reaction between nitrogen dioxide, NO_2, and dinitrogen tetroxide, N_2O_4, provides an interesting example. The gas that is obtained by heating concentrated nitric acid

with copper is found to have a density at high temperatures corresponding to the formula NO_2, and a density at low temperatures and high pressures approximating the formula N_2O_4. At high temperatures the gas
is deep red in color, and at low temperatures it becomes lighter in color,
the crystals formed when the gas is solidified being colorless. The change
in the color of the gas and in its other properties with change in temperature and change in pressure can be accounted for by assuming
that the gas is a mixture of the two molecular species NO_2 and N_2O_4,
in equilibrium with one another according to the equation

$$N_2O_4 \rightleftarrows 2NO_2$$
colorless   red

It has been found by experiment that the amounts of nitrogen dioxide
and dinitrogen tetroxide in the gas mixture are determined by a simple
equation. Let us represent the concentration of molecules of a particular
sort, in moles per liter, by enclosing the formula for the molecules in
square brackets:

$[NO_2]$ = concentration of nitrogen dioxide, in moles per liter

$[N_2O_4]$ = concentration of dinitrogen tetroxide, in moles per liter

The equilibrium equation for the above reaction is then

$$\frac{[NO_2]^2}{[N_2O_4]} = K \tag{1}$$

This equation, which is called the **equilibrium equation** for the reaction, is seen to involve in the numerator the concentration of the
substance on the right hand side of the chemical equation, with the
exponent 2, which is the coefficient shown in the chemical equation.
The denominator contains the concentration of the substance on the
left hand side. Its exponent is 1, because in the equation as written
the coefficient of N_2O_4 is 1.

The quantity K is called the **equilibrium constant** of the reaction
of dissociation of dinitrogen tetroxide to nitrogen dioxide. The equilibrium constant is independent of the pressure of the system, or of
the concentration of the reacting substances. It is, however, dependent
on the temperature.

Relation to the Principle of Le Chatelier. It can be seen that the
equilibrium equation for the reaction corresponds to the principle of
Le Chatelier.

In Section 17–2 this principle was stated in the following words:
**if the conditions of a system, initially at equilibrium, are changed,
the equilibrium will shift in such a way as to tend to restore the
original conditions.**

Let us consider an equilibrium state of the gas such that there are present nitrogen dioxide and dinitrogen tetroxide molecules in equal number, say 0.020 mole/l. The value of the equilibrium constant would then be $K = \dfrac{(0.020)^2}{0.020} = 0.020$. If, now, it were possible to inject some additional N_2O_4 molecules, by dropping a crystal of dinitrogen tetroxide into the flask, the concentration of N_2O_4 in the system would be increased, as soon as the crystal had evaporated. The concentrations of NO_2 molecules and N_2O_4 molecules would then no longer correspond to the equilibrium equation, because the denominator would be too large. The concentrations could be made to satisfy the equilibrium expression by the decomposition of some of the dinitrogen tetroxide; this would increase the concentration of nitrogen dioxide and decrease the concentration of dinitrogen tetroxide, until the equilibrium expression $[NO_2]^2/[N_2O_4]$ of Equation 1 again became equal to the value 0.020 of the equilibrium constant K.

We see, however, that this shift in concentrations is just that which would be predicted by the principle of Le Chatelier. According to this principle a change in the conditions of the system, namely, the increase in concentration of N_2O_4, should result in a reaction such as to tend to restore the original conditions. The original conditions were such as to correspond to a smaller concentration of N_2O_4; hence Le Chatelier's principle predicts that some of the N_2O_4 would decompose, to form NO_2.

The prediction made with Le Chatelier's principle is purely qualitative—it states only that some of the dinitrogen tetroxide would decompose. However, we could make use of the equilibrium equation above, to calculate exactly how much of the dinitrogen tetroxide would decompose. This calculation will be made in a following paragraph.

The Relation between the Equilibrium Equation and Rates of Reactions. It is found that if a crystal of N_2O_4 (melting point $-9.3°$ C, boiling point $21.3°$ C) is dropped into a warm flask it immediately melts, to form a yellow liquid, and then boils, to produce a red gas. It is evident that the colorless molecules of N_2O_4 undergo very rapid decomposition, according to the reaction

$$N_2O_4 \longrightarrow 2NO_2$$

We may now ask if it is not reasonable that molecules of N_2O_4 in the equilibrium mixture of N_2O_4 and NO_2 should also be undergoing decomposition. The answer to this question is that they are; it has been found in general that *the state of chemical equilibrium is not a static, frozen state, but is a dynamic state—a steady state* in which chemical reactions are occurring in opposite directions, at such rates as to lead to no over-all change in composition of the mixture. In the NO_2-N_2O_4 equilibrium mixture molecules of N_2O_4 are continually decomposing to molecules of NO_2, and they are continually being reformed by combination of the molecules of NO_2 according to the equation

$$2NO_2 \longrightarrow N_2O_4$$

The rate at which the first reaction, decomposition of the N_2O_4, occurs is exactly equal to the rate at which the second reaction, the formation of molecules of N_2O_4, occurs, when the system is in its equilibrium state.

Let us now consider the rates at which the above reactions would be expected to take place. It is believed by chemists that the N_2O_4 molecule decomposes simply by breaking a bond between two nitrogen atoms. The molecule must have enough energy to break this bond, and at a given temperature only a fraction of the molecules have this much energy. There is, at a given temperature, a certain chance that a molecule of dinitrogen tetroxide will spontaneously decompose into two molecules of nitrogen dioxide, in unit time. Let us use the symbol k' to represent the chance that a dinitrogen tetroxide molecule will decompose in 1 second. That is k' is equal to the fraction of all of the molecules of N_2O_4 that will decompose per second, and hence the number of moles of N_2O_4 per unit volume that will decompose in unit time (one second) is equal to k' multiplied by the total number of moles of N_2O_4 in the unit volume:

Number of moles of N_2O_4 per liter decomposing in
  1 second $= k'[N_2O_4]$

A reaction of this sort, in which a single molecule undergoes reaction, is called a *unimolecular reaction*.

Now let us consider the mechanism of the formation of N_2O_4 molecules by combination of NO_2 molecules. In order for an N_2O_4 molecule to be formed, two NO_2 molecules must collide with one another. The chance that a given molecule of NO_2 will collide with another molecule of NO_2 is obviously proportional to the concentration of NO_2 molecules —if the number of NO_2 molecules per liter is doubled, the chance that a given molecule of NO_2 will collide with another one will be multiplied by 2. Since the number of collisions experienced by a particular molecule is proportional to $[NO_2]$, the total number of collisions experienced by all the molecules in 1 liter of the gas is proportional to the square of this quantity. Accordingly the rate of combination of molecules of NO_2 to form N_2O_4 is proportional to $[NO_2]^2$:

Number of moles of N_2O_4 per liter formed by combination
  of NO_2 molecules in 1 second $= k'[NO_2]^2$

A reaction of this sort, in which the reaction occurs on collision of two molecules, is called a *bimolecular reaction*.

The constants k' and k are the **reaction-rate constants** for the two opposing reactions. Their values are constant at constant temperature, but change with temperature, usually increasing as the temperature is increased.

Now let us consider the steady state that exists in the equilibrium mixture. At this steady state the number of molecules of N_2O_4 decomposing in unit time is exactly equal to the number of molecules being formed from NO_2 molecules. Hence we have

$$k'[N_2O_4] = k[NO_2]^2$$

or, dividing through by $[N_2O_4]$ and by k,

$$\frac{k'}{k} = \frac{[NO_2]^2}{[N_2O_4]} = K$$

We see that the expression for $\dfrac{k'}{k}$, the ratio of the two reaction rate constants, is exactly the same as the equilibrium expression of Equation 1, and hence that the equilibrium constant K is the ratio of the rate constants for the two opposing reactions.

We repeat the statement of the general principle: **chemical equilibrium is a steady state, in which opposing chemical reactions occur at equal rates.**

In some cases it has been found possible to determine the rates of the opposing reactions, and to show experimentally that the ratio of the two rate constants is indeed equal to the equilibrium constant. This has not been done for the nitrogen dioxide-dinitrogen tetroxide equilibrium, however, because the individual chemical reactions take place so rapidly that experimenters have not been able to determine their rates.

Equilibria of this sort are very important in chemistry. Many industrial processes have been made practicable by the discovery of a way of shifting an equilibrium so as to produce a satisfactory amount of a desired product. In this chapter and later chapters we shall discuss quantitatively the principles of chemical equilibrium and the methods of shifting the equilibrium of a system in one direction or the other.

19–3. *The General Equation for the Equilibrium Constants*

The chemical equation for a general reaction can be written in the following form:

$$aA + bB + \cdots \rightleftarrows dD + eE + \cdots \tag{2}$$

Here the capital letters A, B, D, E are used to represent different molecular species, the reactants and the products, and the small letters a, b, d, e are the numerical coefficients that tell how many molecules of the different sorts are involved in the reaction.

The equilibrium equation for this reaction is

$$\frac{[D]^d[E]^e \cdots}{[A]^a[B]^b \cdots} = K \tag{3}$$

Here K is the equilibrium constant for the reaction.

It is customary to write the concentration ratio in the way given in Equation 3 for a chemical equation such as Equation 2; that is, *the concentrations of the products (to the appropriate powers) are written in the numerator and the concentrations of the reactants in the denominator*. This is a convention that has been accepted by all chemists.

Equation 3 can be derived from the equations for the rates of the forward reaction and the reverse reaction, in the same way that Equation 1 was derived in the preceding section.

Let us assume that the forward reaction occurs when a molecules of A, b molecules of B, etc. collide with one another. The chance that such a multiple collision will occur in 1 ml of the gas or solution is dependent on the concentrations [A], [B], $\cdots$. The argument given in the preceding section to show that the number of collisions between two NO_2 molecules is proportional to $[NO_2]^2$ can be extended to show that the number of collisions of aA, bB, etc. is proportional to $[A]^a[B]^b \cdots$.

Hence we derive an equation for the rate of the forward reaction:

$$\text{Rate of forward reaction} = k[A]^a[B]^b \cdots \tag{4}$$

In the same way we derive an equation for the rate of the reverse reaction:

$$\text{Rate of reverse reaction} = k'[D]^d[E]^e \cdots \tag{5}$$

The condition of dynamic equilibrium exists when the reverse rate is exactly equal to the forward rate:

$$k'[D]^d[E]^e \cdots = k[A]^a[B]^b \cdots \tag{6}$$

By dividing both sides of this equation by $k'[A]^a[B]^b \cdots$ we obtain the equilibrium equation

$$\frac{[D]^d[E]^e \cdots}{[A]^a[B]^b \cdots} = \frac{k}{k'} = K \tag{7}$$

This equation is the same as Equation 3, which was written above without being derived. We see that the equilibrium constant K is the ratio of the two rate constants k and k'.

We note that the number of collisions would be expected to increase with increase in temperature, which causes the molecules to move faster. Hence in general k and k' change with temperature, and their ratio K also changes with temperature.

The equilibrium constant K is a constant only when the temperature remains constant.

It must be emphasized that the validity of the equilibrium expression does not depend on any particular mechanism for the reaction. Sometimes a reaction does not take place by collision of all of the molecules indicated on the left side of the equation for the reaction, but instead takes place in steps. The reverse reaction then also takes place in steps, and the rates of the successive reactions involved are such as to lead to the customary equilibrium equation.

The validity of this equilibrium equation, with K a constant at constant temperature, is a consequence of the laws of thermodynamics, in case that the reactants and the products are gases obeying the perfect gas laws or are solutes in dilute solution. In gases under high pressure and in concentrated solutions there occur some deviations from this equation, similar in magnitude to the deviations from the perfect gas laws. Sometimes these deviations are taken into account by introducing *activity coefficients*, as discussed for ions in solution in Chapter 18.

Many examples of the use of the general equilibrium equation will be given in the following chapters of this book. This simple equation permits the chemist to answer many important questions that arise in his work—the equation may be compared in importance to the chemist with Newton's laws of motion in physics. As a simple example we may discuss the decomposition of hydrogen iodide.

Example 1. Hydrogen iodide, HI, is not a very stable substance. The pure gas is colorless, but whenever it is made in the laboratory the gas in the apparatus is seen to have a violet color, indicating the presence of free iodine. In fact, hydrogen iodide decomposes to an appreciable amount at room temperature and higher temperatures (Figure 19-1) according to the equation

$$2HI \rightleftharpoons H_2 + I_2(g)$$

The equilibrium constant for this decomposition reaction has been found by experiment to have the value 0.00124 at room temperature (25° C). To what extent does hydrogen iodide decompose at room temperature?

    Solution. In this example the value of the equilibrium constant is given without a statement as to its dimensions. Let us write the expression for the equilibrium constant:

$$K = \frac{[H_2][I_2]}{[HI]^2} = 0.00124 \text{ at } 25° \text{ C}$$

Each of the concentrations $[H_2]$, $[I_2]$, and $[HI]$ has the dimensions moles/l. Hence we see that for this reaction the dimensions of K are those of a pure number:

$$\text{Dimensions of } K = \frac{(\text{moles}/l)(\text{moles}/l)}{(\text{moles}/l)^2} = 1$$

When hydrogen iodide decomposes equal numbers of molecules of hydrogen and iodine are formed. Accordingly the concentrations of hydrogen and iodine present in the gas formed when hydrogen iodide undergoes some decomposition are equal. Let us use the symbol x to represent the concentration of hydrogen and also the concentration of iodine:

$$[H_2] = [I_2] = x$$

Then we have

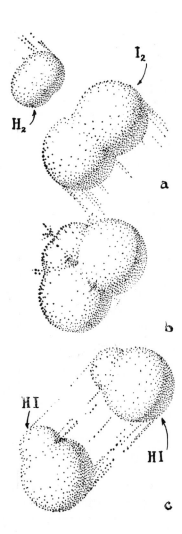

FIGURE 19-1

The mechanism of the reaction of hydrogen and iodine to form hydrogen iodide.

$$\frac{x^2}{[HI]^2} = 0.00124$$

or

$$x^2 = 0.00124[HI]^2$$

This equation can be solved for x by taking the square root of each side:

$$x = \sqrt{0.00124} \times [HI] = 0.0352[HI]$$

By solving this equation we have found that after the hydrogen iodide has decomposed enough to produce the equilibrium state at room temperature the concentration of hydrogen is equal to 3.52% of the concentration of HI. The concentration of iodine is also equal to 3.52% of concentration of HI. The question "To what extent does hydrogen iodide decompose at room temperature?" is to be interpreted as meaning "What percentage of pure hydrogen iodide originally produced decomposes to give hydrogen and iodine?" The equation for the chemical reaction shows that two molecules of HI on reaction form only one molecule of H_2 and one of I_2. Accordingly there must have been 7.04% more HI present initially than when equilibrium is reached, in order to produce 3.52% H_2 and I_2. Hence the extent of decomposition of the original hydrogen iodide is $7.04/107.04 = 0.0658$, or **6.58%**. This percentage of the hydrogen iodide originally produced decomposed at room temperature.

Example 2. By how much would the amount of decomposition of the hydrogen iodide be changed by compressing the gas into half its volume?

 Solution. If no change in the equilibrium were to occur, the concentrations $[H_2]$, $[I_2]$, and $[HI]$ would all be doubled by this compression. Since both its numerator and its denominator involve a product of two concentrations, the equilibrium expression is not changed by doubling each of the concentrations. Hence there will be no shift in the equilibrium. The amount of decomposition of the HI is not changed by doubling the pressure.

 We note that this result can be predicted by the application of the principle of Le Chatelier. In the equation for the decomposition of HI there are two molecules shown on the left side and two on the right. Hence no change in volume or pressure occurs when the reaction takes place, and accordingly change in volume or pressure of the gas mixture cannot shift the equilibrium in either direction.

It is interesting to point out that the rate of the decomposition of hydrogen iodide has been determined experimentally. It has been verified that the number of molecules of hydrogen iodide decomposing in unit time at a given temperature is proportional to the square of the concentration of hydrogen iodide:

Rate of decomposition of hydrogen iodide $= k_1 \times [HI]^2$

The rate of reaction of hydrogen and iodine gas to form hydrogen iodide has also been determined experimentally. It has been found that the rate of formation of hydrogen iodide, at a constant temperature, is proportional to the product of the concentrations of hydrogen and iodine:

Rate of formation of hydrogen iodide $= k_2[H_2][I_2]$

Moreover, the numerical values of the reaction-rate constants k_1 and k_2 as determined experimentally are such that their ratio at a given temperature is equal to the equilibrium constant for the reaction at the same temperature. At $25°$ C the constant k_2 is 808 times as large as the constant k_1; that is, when hydrogen and iodine are mixed at the same pressure they react to form hydrogen iodide 808 times as fast as hydrogen iodide gas at this temperature decomposes to hydrogen and iodine. The ratio k_1/k_2 is thus equal to the equilibrium constant:

$$\frac{k_1}{k_2} = \frac{1}{808} = 0.00124 = K$$

Experimental Verification of the Dynamic Nature of Chemical Equilibrium. The fact that the rate of decomposition of pure hydrogen iodide and the rate of interaction of pure hydrogen and pure iodine gas are such that their ratio is equal to the equilibrium constant for the reaction between hydrogen, iodine, and hydriodic acid suggests strongly that at equilibrium both the forward and the reverse reactions are taking place, even though no over-all change in the equilibrium system occurs. However, the skeptic might say that all chemical reaction has ceased in the equilibrium system. It is accordingly very interesting that in recent years it has become possible to verify by experimental methods that the equilibrium state for a chemical reaction is a dynamic steady state.

This has been done by the use of radioactive isotopes. For example, the reaction between arsenious acid, H_3AsO_3, and triiodide ion, I_3^-, to produce arsenic acid, H_3AsO_4, and iodide ion has been studied by chemists for fifty years. It has been shown that when arsenious acid and triiodide ion are mixed in solution they react according to the equation

$$H_3AsO_3 + I_3^- + H_2O \longrightarrow H_3AsO_4 + 3I^- + 2H^+$$

It has also been shown that when arsenic acid, H_3AsO_4, is mixed with iodide ion in acidic solution a reaction occurs, according to the equation

$$H_3AsO_4 + 3I^- + 2H^+ \longrightarrow H_3AsO_3 + I_3^- + H_2O$$

The rates of these reactions have been measured, and also the equilibrium constant has been determined experimentally for the equilibrium mixture obtained either by mixing arsenious acid and triiodide ion or arsenic acid and iodide ion. It was found that the equilibrium constant has the value expected from the rates of the reactions when the pure reactants are mixed.

However, it is still necessary to measure the rates of the reaction in the equilibrium mixture, rather than in a mixture of the pure reactants for the forward direction or the pure reactants for the reverse direction, in order to prove the point in question. This was done a few years ago* by the use of a radioactive isotope of arsenic, made by exposing pure arsenic to a beam of neutrons (see Chapter 32). It was found that arsenious acid made from this radioactive isotope was not converted into radioactive arsenic acid when it was mixed with non-radioactive arsenic acid in solution. When, however, an equilibrium mixture of arsenious acid, arsenic acid, triiodide ion, and iodide ion was made up with the use of radioactive arsenious acid and non-radioactive arsenic acid, it was found that after the passage of a little time there was present some radioactive arsenic acid in the solution, and some non-radioactive arsenious acid. The rates at which radioactive arsenious acid was converted into radioactive arsenic acid, and at which non-radioactive arsenic acid was converted into non-radioactive arsenious acid, were found to be exactly the rates found for the individual reactions when the system was not at the equilibrium state. Accordingly this experiment provides direct evidence that the state of chemical equilibrium is a dynamic state, with the forward reaction and the reverse reaction going on at equal rates.

Illustrative Examples

19-1. In the contact process for making sulfuric acid sulfur dioxide is oxidized to sulfur trioxide. (a) Write the equation for the reaction between sulfur dioxide and oxygen, and write the equilibrium expression. (b) At a certain temperature and concentration of oxygen the value of the equilibrium constant is such that 50% of the SO_2 is converted to SO_3 when the total pressure is 10 atm. Would the fraction converted be increased or decreased by doubling the total pressure?

19-2. In the arc process of fixing nitrogen air is converted in part into nitric oxide, NO, by passing it through an electric arc. Why is this reaction carried out at 1 atm rather than at high pressure?

19-3. Why is the synthesis of ammonia from nitrogen and hydrogen carried out at high pressure?

19-4. The Rates of Homogeneous and Heterogeneous Reactions

A reaction which takes place in a homogeneous system (consisting of a single phase) is called a **homogeneous reaction.** The most important of these reactions are those in gases (such as the formation of nitric oxide in the electric arc, $N_2 + O_2 \rightleftarrows 2NO$) and those in liquid solutions. Some discussion of the rates of homogeneous reactions has been given in the preceding paragraphs, and additional discussion is given below.

A **heterogeneous reaction** is a reaction involving two or more phases. An example is the oxidation of carbon by potassium perchlorate:

$$KClO_4 + 2C \longrightarrow KCl + 2CO_2 \uparrow$$

This is a reaction of two solid phases. This reaction and similar reactions occur when perchlorate propellants are burned. (These propellants,

---

* J. N. Wilson and R. G. Dickinson, *Journal of the American Chemical Society*, **59**, 1358 (1937).

which are used for assisted take-off of airplanes and for propulsion of rockets, consist of intimate mixtures of very fine grains of carbon black and potassium perchlorate held together by a plastic binder.) Another example is the solution of zinc in acid:

$$Zn + 2H^+ \longrightarrow Zn^{++} + H_2 \uparrow$$

In this reaction three phases are involved: the solid zinc phase, the aqueous solution, and the gaseous phase formed by the evolved hydrogen.

The Rate of Homogeneous Reactions.   Most actual chemical processes are very complicated, and the analysis of their rates is very difficult. As a reaction proceeds the reacting substances are used up and new ones are formed; the temperature of the system is changed by the heat evolved or absorbed by the reaction; and other effects may occur which influence the reaction in a complex way. In order to obtain an understanding of the rates of reaction, chemists have attempted to simplify the problem as much as possible. A good understanding has been obtained of homogeneous reactions (in a gaseous or liquid solution) which take place at constant temperature. Experimental studies are made by placing the reaction vessel in a *thermostat*, which is held at a fixed temperature. For example, hydrogen gas and iodine vapor might be mixed, at room temperature, and their conversion into hydrogen iodide followed by observing the change in color of the gas, the iodine vapor having a violet color and the other substances involved in the reaction being colorless. The simple quantitative theory of reaction rate in homogeneous systems has been discussed in the preceding paragraphs.

The *explosion* of a gaseous mixture, such as hydrogen and oxygen, and the *detonation* of a high explosive, such as glyceryl trinitrate (nitroglycerin), are interesting chemical reactions; but the analysis of the rates of these reactions is made very difficult because of the great changes in temperature and pressure which accompany them.

The detonation of a high explosive such as glyceryl trinitrate illustrates the great rate of some chemical reactions. The rate at which a detonation wave moves along a sample of glyceryl trinitrate is about 20,000 feet per second. A specimen of high explosive weighing several grams may accordingly be completely decomposed within a millionth of a second, the time required for the detonation wave to move one quarter of an inch. Another reaction which can occur very rapidly is the fission of the nuclei of heavy atoms. The nuclear fission of several pounds of U^{235} or Pu^{239} may take place in a few millionths of a second in the explosion of an atomic bomb (Chapter 32).

The Rate of Heterogeneous Reactions.   A heterogeneous reaction takes place at the surfaces (the *interfaces*) of the reacting phases, and it can be made to go faster by *increasing the extent of the surfaces.* Thus finely divided zinc reacts more rapidly with acid than does coarse zinc, and the rate of burning of a perchlorate propellant is increased by grinding the potassium perchlorate to a finer crystalline powder.

Sometimes a *reactant is exhausted* in the neighborhood of the interface, and the reaction is slowed down. *Stirring* the mixture then accelerates the reaction, by bringing fresh supplies of the reactant into the reaction region.

Catalysts may accelerate heterogeneous as well as homogeneous reactions.

The rates of nearly all chemical reactions depend greatly on the *temperature.* The effect of temperature is discussed in a later section of this chapter.

Special devices may be utilized to accelerate certain chemical reactions. The formation of a zinc amalgam on the surface of the grains of zinc by treatment with a small amount of mercury increases the speed of the reduction reactions of zinc.

The solution of zinc in acid is retarded somewhat by the bubbles of liberated hydrogen, which prevent the acid from achieving contact with the zinc over its entire surface. This effect can be avoided by bringing a plate of unreactive metal, such as copper or platinum, into electric contact with the zinc (Figure 19-2). The reaction then proceeds as two separate electron reactions. Hydrogen is liberated at the surface of the copper or platinum, and zinc dissolves at the surface of the zinc plate:

$$2H^+ + 2e^- \longrightarrow H_2 \uparrow \text{ at copper surface}$$

$$Zn \longrightarrow Zn^{++} + 2e^- \text{ at zinc surface}$$

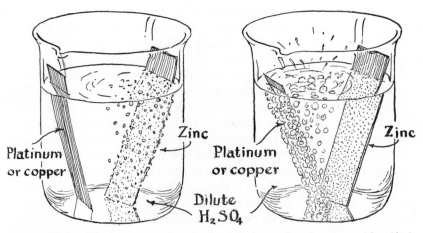

FIGURE 19-2 *The interaction of an inert metal plate and a zinc plate with sulfuric acid, when the plates are not in contact (left) and when the plates are in contact (right).*

The electrons flow from the zinc plate to the copper plate through the electric contact, and electric neutrality in the different regions of the solution is maintained by the migration of ions.

The solution of zinc in acid can be accelerated by adding a small amount of cupric ion to the acid. The probable mechanism of this effect is that zinc replaces cupric ion from the solution, depositing small particles of metallic copper on the surface of the zinc, and these small particles then act in the way described above.

19–5. *Catalysis*

The study of the factors which affect the rate of reaction has become more and more important with the continued great development of chemical industry. A modern method of manufacturing toluene, used for making the explosive trinitrotoluene (TNT) and for other purposes, may be quoted as an example. The substance methylcyclohexane, C_7H_{14}, occurs in large quantities in petroleum. At high temperature and low pressure this substance should decompose into toluene, C_7H_8, and hydrogen. The reaction is so slow, however, that the process could not be carried out commercially until the discovery was made that a certain mixture of metal oxides increases the rate of reaction enough for the process to be put into practice. A substance such as this oxide mixture, which increases the rate of the reaction without being itself changed, is called a catalyst. Many examples of catalysis have already been mentioned, and others are mentioned in later chapters.

Catalysts are of very great practical significance, not only for industrial chemistry but also for life. There exist in the body many catalysts, called *enzymes*, which speed up the various physiological reactions. *Vitamins* are probably needed in part for their use as catalysts—as constituents of enzymes. A discussion of enzymes and vitamins is given in Chapter 31.

It is thought that catalysts speed up reactions by bringing the reacting molecules together and holding them in configurations favorable to reaction. Unfortunately so little is known about the fundamental nature of catalytic activity that the search for suitable catalysts is largely empirical. The test of a catalytic reaction, as of any proposed chemical process, is made by trying it to see if it works.

The Effect of Catalysts on Chemical Equilibrium. It is a consequence of the laws of thermodynamics—the impossibility of perpetual motion—that *a system in equilibrium is not changed by the addition of a catalyst*. The catalyst may increase the rate at which the system approaches its final equilibrium state, but it cannot change the value of the equilibrium constant. Under equilibrium conditions a catalyst has the same effect on the rate of the backward reaction as on that of the corresponding forward reaction.

It is true that a system which has stood unchanged for a long period of time, apparently in equilibrium, may undergo reaction when a small amount of a catalyst is added. Thus a mixture of hydrogen and oxygen at room temperature remains apparently unchanged for a very long period of time; however, if even a minute amount of finely divided platinum (platinum black) is placed in the gas, chemical reaction begins and continues until very little of one of the reacting gases remains. In this case the system in the absence of the catalyst is not in equilibrium with respect to the reaction $2H_2 + O_2 \rightleftarrows 2H_2O$, but only in *metastable equilibrium*, the rate of formation of water being so small that true equilibrium would not be approached in a millennium.

Because of the possibility of metastable equilibrium it is necessary in practice to apply the following **equilibrium criterion:** *a system is considered to have reached equilibrium with respect to a certain reaction when the same final state is reached by approach by the reverse reaction as by the forward reaction.* This true equilibrium is called **stable equilibrium.**

19–6. *The Dependence of Reaction Rate on Temperature*

It is everyday experience that chemical reactions are accelerated by increased temperature. This is true, in fact, for almost all chemical reactions, and the dependence of the reaction rate on temperature is surprisingly similar for reactions of most kinds: **the rate of most reactions is approximately doubled for every 10° C increase in temperature.**

This is a very useful rule. It is only a rough rule—the 10° factor for most reactions is close to 2, but occasionally it is as small as 1.5 or as large as 4. Reactions of very large molecules, such as proteins, may have even larger temperature factors; the rate of denaturation of ovalbumin (the process which occurs when an egg is boiled) increases about fiftyfold for a 10° rise in temperature.

Example 3.   In an experiment a sample of potassium chlorate was 90% decomposed in 20 minutes; about how long would it have taken for this amount of decomposition to occur if the sample had been heated 20° hotter?

   Solution.   It would have taken about one quarter as long; a factor of one half is introduced per 10° rise, giving $\frac{1}{2} \times \frac{1}{2} = \frac{1}{4}$.

Spontaneous Combustion.   Reactions such as the combustion of fuels proceed very rapidly when combustion is begun, but fuels may remain indefinitely in contact with air without burning. In these cases the rate of reaction at room temperature is extremely small. The process of lighting a fire consists in increasing the temperature of part of the fuel until the reaction proceeds rapidly; the exothermic reaction then liberates enough heat to raise another portion of the fuel to the kindling temperature, and in this way the process is continued.

The oxidation of oil-soaked rags or other combustible material may occur rapidly enough at room temperature to produce sufficient heat to increase the temperature somewhat; this accelerates the oxidation, and causes further heating, until the mass bursts into flame. This process is called *spontaneous combustion*.

19–7. *The Effect of Change of Temperature on Chemical Equilibrium*

A reaction that evolves heat as the reaction proceeds is called an *exothermic* reaction, and one that absorbs heat is called an *endothermic* reaction.

From the principle of Le Chatelier we can predict that *increase in temperature will drive a reaction further toward completion (by increasing the equilibrium constant) if the reaction is endothermic and will drive it back (by decreasing the equilibrium constant) if the reaction is exothermic.*

For example, let us consider the NO_2-N_2O_4 equilibrium mixture at room temperature. Heat is absorbed when an N_2O_4 molecule dissociates into two NO_2 molecules. If the reaction mixture were to be increased in temperature by a few degrees, the equilibrium would be changed, according to the principle of Le Chatelier, in such a way as to tend to restore the original temperature, that is, in such a way as to lower the temperature of the system, by using up some of the heat energy. This would be achieved by the decomposition of some additional molecules of dinitrogen tetroxide. Accordingly, in agreement with the statement above, the equilibrium constant would change in such a way as to correspond to the dissociation of more of the N_2O_4 molecules.

This principle is of great practical importance. For example, the synthesis of ammonia from nitrogen and hydrogen is exothermic (the heat evolved is 11.0 kcal per mole of ammonia formed); hence the yield of ammonia is made a maximum by keeping the temperature as low as possible. The commercial process of manufacturing ammonia from the elements became practicable when catalysts were found which caused the reaction to proceed sufficiently rapidly at low temperatures.

19–8. *Photochemistry*

Many chemical reactions are caused to proceed by the effect of light. For example, a dyed cloth may fade when exposed to sunlight, because of the destruction of molecules of the dye under the influence of the sunlight. Reactions of this sort are called *photochemical reactions*. A very important photochemical reaction is the conversion of carbon dioxide and water into carbohydrate and oxygen in the leaves of plants, where the green substance chlorophyll serves as a catalyst.

One law of photochemistry, discovered by Grotthus in 1818, is that *only light which is absorbed is photochemically effective.* Hence a colored substance must be present in a system that shows photochemical reactivity with visible light. In the process of natural photosynthesis this substance is the green chlorophyll.

The second law of photochemistry, formulated in 1912 by Einstein, is that *one molecule of reacting substance may be activated and caused to react by the absorption of one light quantum.* A light quantum is the smallest amount of energy that can be removed from a beam of light by any material system. Its magnitude depends on the frequency of the light: it is equal to $h\nu$, where h is Planck's constant, with value 6.6238×10^{-27} erg sec, and ν is the frequency of the light, equal to c/λ, with c the velocity of light and λ the wavelength of the light. In some systems, such as material containing rather stable dyes, many light quanta are absorbed by the molecules for each molecule that is decomposed; the fading of the dye by light is a slow and inefficient process in these materials. In some simple systems the absorption of one quantum of light results in the reaction or decomposition of one molecule.

There are also chemical systems in which a *chain of reactions* may be set off by one light quantum. An example is the photochemical reaction of hydrogen and chlorine. A mixture of hydrogen and chlorine kept in the dark does not react. When, however, it is illuminated with blue light, reaction immediately begins. Hydrogen is transparent to all visible light; chlorine, which owes its yellow-green color to its strong absorption of blue light, is the photochemically active constituent in the mixture. The absorption of a quantum of blue light by a chlorine molecule splits the molecule into two chlorine atoms:

$$Cl_2 + h\nu \longrightarrow 2Cl$$

The chlorine atoms then react with hydrogen molecules to form hydrogen chloride molecules and hydrogen atoms:

$$Cl + H_2 \longrightarrow HCl + H$$

The hydrogen atoms that are liberated then react with chlorine molecules to form hydrogen chloride molecules and more chlorine atoms:

$$H + Cl_2 \longrightarrow HCl + Cl$$

These new chlorine atoms then react in the same way as did those originally produced by the light, and thus a chain of reactions producing hydrogen chloride may be set up. Thousands of hydrogen chloride molecules may in this way be formed as a result of the absorption of a single quantum of light. It may be observed that the mixture of hydrogen and chlorine explodes when exposed to blue light. The chain of reactions may be broken through the recombination of chlorine atoms to form chlorine molecules; this reaction occurs on the collision of two chlorine atoms with the wall of the vessel containing the gas or with another atom or molecule in the gas.

A photochemical reaction of much geophysical and biological importance is the formation of ozone from oxygen. Oxygen is practically transparent to visible light and to light in the near ultraviolet region, but it strongly absorbs light in the far ultraviolet region—in the region from 1600 Å to 1800 Å. Each light quantum that is absorbed dissociates an oxygen molecule into two oxygen atoms:

$$O_2 + h\nu \longrightarrow 2O$$

A reaction that does not require absorption of a light quantum then follows:

$$O + O_2 \longrightarrow O_3$$

Accordingly there are produced two molecules of ozone, O_3, for each light quantum absorbed. In addition, however, the ozone molecules can be destroyed by combining with oxygen atoms, or by a photochemical reaction. The reaction of combining with oxygen atom is

$$O + O_3 \longrightarrow 2O_2$$

The reactions of photochemical production of ozone and destruction of ozone lead to a photochemical equilibrium, which maintains a small concentration of ozone in the oxygen being irradiated. The layer of the atmosphere in which the major part of the ozone is present is about 15 miles above the earth's surface; it is called the *ozone layer*.

The geophysical and biological importance of the ozone layer results from the absorption of light in the near ultraviolet region, from 2400 Å to 3000 Å, by the ozone. The photochemical reaction is

$$O_3 + h\nu \longrightarrow O + O_2$$

This reaction permits ozone to absorb ultraviolet light so strongly as to remove practically all of the ultraviolet light from the sunlight before it reaches the earth's surface. The ultraviolet light that it absorbs is photochemically destructive toward many of the organic molecules necessary in life processes, and if the ultraviolet light of sunlight were not prevented by the ozone layer from reaching the surface of the earth life in its present form could not exist.

Another interesting photochemical reaction is the darkening of silver halogenide grains in a photographic emulsion. Pure silver halogenides are not very sensitive; adsorbed material and the gelatin of the emulsion increase the sensitivity. After a grain has been in part decomposed by photochemical action, the decomposition can be completed by chemical development (Chapter 28).

Blueprint paper provides another interesting example. Blueprint paper is made by treating paper with a solution of potassium ferricyanide and ferric citrate. Under action of light the citrate ion reduces the ferric ion to ferrous ion, which combines with ferricyanide to form the insoluble blue compound $KFeFe(CN)_6 \cdot H_2O$, Prussian blue. The unreacted substances are then washed out of the paper with water.

Illustrative Exercises

19-4. Why do foods cook faster in a pressure cooker than in an ordinary cooking pot?

19-5. Is the reaction $2NO_2 \longrightarrow N_2O_4$ speeded up more or less than the reverse reaction by an increase in temperature?

Concepts, Facts, and Terms Introduced in This Chapter

Rate of reaction. Factors determining reaction rate. Homogeneous reactions. Heterogeneous reactions. Explosion; detonation; rate of detonation.

Chemical equilibrium the result of equal speeds of opposing reactions. The equilibrium equation. Equilibrium constants.

The effect of change of pressure on reaction rate and on chemical equilibrium.

The equilibrium constant expressed in terms of concentrations and in terms of partial pressures.

The effect of change of temperature on reaction rate and on chemical equilibrium.

Photochemistry. The first law of photochemistry—light must be absorbed to cause a chemical reaction to occur. The second law of photochemistry. Chain reactions. Production of ozone; the ozone layer. The photographic emulsion. Blueprint paper.

Exercises

19-6. If the rate of solution of zinc in hydrochloric acid is proportional to the surface area of the zinc, how much more rapidly will a thousand cubes of zinc each weighing one milligram dissolve in acid than a single cube weighing one gram?

19-7. Write equilibrium expressions for the following reactions:
(a) $2CO_2 \rightleftarrows 2CO + O_2$
(b) $CH_4 + 2O_2 \rightleftarrows CO_2 + 2H_2O(g)$
(c) $N_2 + 3H_2 \rightleftarrows 2NH_3$

19-8. What is the numerical value of the equilibrium constant for the formation of HI (Example 1, this chapter) with partial pressures expressed in millimeters of Hg instead of in atmospheres? What is it in terms of concentrations in moles per liter?

19-9. At temperatures around 800° C iodine vapor is partially dissociated into atoms. If the partial pressure of I_2 is doubled, by what factor is the partial pressure of I changed? By what factor is the degree of dissociation changed?

19-10. It is found by experiment that when hydrogen iodide is heated the degree of dissociation increases. Is the dissociation of hydrogen iodide an exothermic or an endothermic reaction?

19-11. Automobile tires when stored age through oxidation and other reactions of the rubber. By what factor would the safe period of storage be multiplied by lowering the storage temperature by 20° F?

19-12. If it is necessary to store oil-soaked rags, how should this be done?

19-13. Explain the change that takes place in the rate of reaction of permanganate ion and hydrogen peroxide in sulfuric acid solution as the reaction proceeds.

19-14. Does the addition of a catalyst affect the equilibrium constant of a reaction? Explain your answer.

19-15. Producer gas is made by the reduction of carbon dioxide to carbon monoxide by carbon. With the total pressure 1 atmosphere, the equilibrium mixture of the two oxides at 1123° C contains 93.77 percent by volume of carbon monoxide, and 6.23 percent of carbon dioxide. What is the equilibrium constant for this reaction at this temperature? What would be the composition of the mixture in equilibrium at this temperature if the total pressure were 2 atm?

Chapter 20

Acids and Bases

It is useful to give a further discussion of acids and bases after the consideration of the basic principles of chemical equilibrium, because the phenomenon of chemical equilibrium is important in determining many of the properties of acids and bases.

In Chapter 6 an acid was defined as a hydrogen-containing substance which dissociates on solution in water to produce hydrogen ions, and a base was defined as a substance containing the hydroxide ion, OH^-, or the hydroxyl group, $-OH$, which can dissociate in aqueous solution as the hydroxide ion. It was pointed out that acidic solutions have a characteristic sharp taste, due to the hydrogen ion, H^+, or, rather, the hydronium ion, H_3O^+, and that basic solutions have a characteristic brackish taste, due to the hydroxide ion.*

In Chapter 10 it was mentioned that the ordinary mineral acids, (hydrochloric acid, nitric acid, sulfuric acid) are completely ionized (dissociated) in solution, producing one hydrogen ion for every acidic hydrogen atom in the formula of the acid, whereas other acids, such as acetic acid, produce only a smaller number of hydrogen ions. Acids such as acetic acid are called *weak acids*. The reason that a 1 F solution of acetic acid does not have nearly so sharp a taste, and does not react nearly so vigorously with an active metal such as zinc, as a 1 F solution of hydrochloric acid is that the 1 F solution of acetic acid contains a great number of undissociated molecules $HC_2H_3O_2$, and only a relatively small number of ions H^+ (that is, H_3O^+—we shall continue to follow the practice of using the symbol H^+, for convenience) and $C_2H_3O_2^-$. There exists in a solution of acetic acid a steady state, corresponding to the equation

---

* In an acidic solution the concentration of hydrogen ion is greater than that of hydroxide ion, and in a basic solution the concentration of hydroxide ion is greater than that of hydrogen ion; see Section 20–1.

$$HC_2H_3O_2 \rightleftarrows H^+ + C_2H_3O_2^-$$

In order to understand the properties of acetic acid it is necessary to formulate the equilibrium expression for this steady state; by use of this equilibrium expression the properties of acetic acid solutions of different concentrations can be predicted.

The general principles of chemical equilibrium can be similarly used in the discussion of a weak base, such as ammonium hydroxide, and also of salts formed by weak acids and weak bases. In addition, these principles are important in providing an understanding of the behavior of *indicators*, the colored substances that were described in Chapter 6 as useful for determining whether a solution is acidic, neutral, or basic. These principles are of further importance in permitting a discussion of the relation between the concentrations of hydrogen ion and hydroxide ion in the same solution.

20–1. *Hydrogen-ion Concentration*

It was mentioned in the chapter on water (Chapter 17) that pure water does not consist simply of H_2O molecules, but that it also contains hydrogen ions in concentration about 1×10^{-7} moles per liter (at 25° C), and hydroxide ions in the same concentration. These ions are formed by the dissociation of water:

$$H_2O \rightleftarrows H^+ + OH^-$$

The way in which it has been found that pure water contains hydrogen ions and hydroxide ions is the measurement of the electric conductivity of water. The mechanism of the electric conductivity of a solution was discussed in Chapter 10. According to this discussion, electric charge is transferred through the body of the solution by the motion of cations from the region around the anode to the region around the cathode, and anions from the region around the cathode to the region around the anode. If pure water contained no ions whatever its electric conductivity would be zero. When investigators made water as pure as possible, by distilling it over and over again, it was found that the electric conductivity approached a certain small value, about one ten-millionth of that of a $1 F$ solution of hydrochloric acid or sodium hydroxide. This indicates that the ionization of water occurs to such an extent as to give hydrogen ions and hydroxide ions in concentration about one ten-millionth mole per liter. Refined measurements have provided the value 1.00×10^{-7} for $[H^+]$ and $[OH^-]$ in pure water at 25° C.*

---

* The extent of ionization depends somewhat on the temperature. At 0° C $[H^+]$ and $[OH^-]$ are 0.83×10^{-7}, and at 100° C they are 6.9×10^{-7}. When a solution of a strong acid and a solution of a strong base are mixed, a large amount of heat is given off. This shows that the reaction

Instead of saying that the concentration of hydrogen ion in pure water is 1.00×10^{-7}, it is customary to say that the pH of pure water is 7. This new symbol, pH, is defined in the following way: **the pH is the negative common logarithm of the hydrogen-ion concentration:**

$$p\text{H} = -\log [\text{H}^+]$$

or

$$[\text{H}^+] = 10^{-p\text{H}} = \text{antilog} (-p\text{H})$$

We see from this definition of pH that a solution containing 1 mole of hydrogen ions per liter, that is, with a concentration 10^{-0} in H^+, has pH zero. A solution only one tenth as strong in hydrogen ion, containing 0.1 mole of hydrogen ions per liter, has $[\text{H}^+] = 10^{-1}$, and hence has pH 1. The relation between the hydrogen-ion concentration and the pH is shown for simple concentrations along the left side of Figure 20-1.

In science and medicine it is customary to describe the acidity of a solution by saying "The pH of the solution is 3," for example, instead of saying "The hydrogen-ion concentration of the solution is

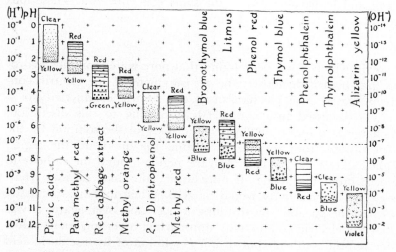

FIGURE 20-1   *Color changes of indicators.*

$$\text{H}^+ + \text{OH}^- \rightarrow \text{H}_2\text{O}$$

gives off heat, and accordingly that the reaction of dissociation of water absorbs heat. In accordance with Le Chatelier's principle, increase in the temperature would shift the equilibrium of dissociation of water in such a way as to tend to restore the original temperature, that is, the reaction would take place in the direction that absorbs heat. This direction is the dissociation of water to hydrogen ions and hydroxide ions, and accordingly the principle requires that increase in temperature cause an increased amount of dissociation of water, as is found experimentally.

10^{-3}." It is evident that the quantity pH is useful, in permitting the exponential expression to be avoided.

The chemical reactions involved in biological processes are often very sensitive to the hydrogen-ion concentration of the medium. In industries such as the fermentation industry the control of the pH of the materials being processed is very important. It is not surprising that the symbol pH was introduced by a Danish biochemist, S. P. L. Sørensen, while he was working on problems connected with the brewing of beer.

Example 1.   What is the pH of a solution with $[H^+] = 0.0200$?

   Solution.   The log of 0.0200 is equal to the log of 2×10^{-2}, which is $0.301 - 2 = -1.699$. The pH of the solution is the negative of the logarithm of the hydrogen-ion concentration. Hence the pH of this solution is **1.699.**

Example 2.   What is the hydrogen-ion concentration of a solution with pH 4.30?

   Solution.   A solution with pH 4.30 has log $[H^+] = -4.30$, or $0.70 - 5$. The antilog of 0.70 is 5.0, and the antilog of -5 is 10^{-5}. Hence the hydrogen-ion concentration in this solution is **5.0×10^{-5}.**

20–2. *The Equilibrium between Hydrogen Ion and Hydroxide Ion in Aqueous Solution*

The equation for the ionic dissociation of water is

$$H_2O \rightleftarrows H^+ + OH^-$$

The expression for the equilibrium constant, in accordance with the principle developed in the preceding chapter, is

$$\frac{[H^+][OH^-]}{[H_2O]} = K_1$$

In this expression the symbol $[H_2O]$ represents the activity (concentration) of water in the solution (see Section 18–11 for the discussion of activity). Since the activity of water in a dilute aqueous solution is nearly the same as that for pure water, it is customary to omit the activity of water in the equilibrium expression for dilute solutions. Accordingly the product of K_1 and $[H_2O]$ may be taken as another constant K_w, and we may write

$$[H^+] \times [OH^-] = K_w$$

This expression states that the product of the hydrogen-ion concentration and the hydroxide-ion concentration in water and in dilute aqueous solutions is a constant, at given temperature. The value of K_w is 1.00×10^{-14} moles^2/l^2 at $25°$ C. *Hence in pure water both H^+ and OH^- have the concentration 1.00×10^{-7} moles per liter at $25°$ C, and in acidic or basic solutions the product of the concentrations of these ions equals 1.00×10^{-14}.* *

Thus a neutral solution contains both hydrogen ions and hydroxide ions at the same concentration, 1.00×10^{-7}. A slightly acidic solution, containing 10 times as many hydrogen ions (concentration 10^{-6}, pH 6), also contains some hydroxide ions, one tenth as many as a neutral solution. A solution containing 100 times as much hydrogen ion as a neutral solution (concentration 10^{-5}, pH 5) contains a smaller amount of hydroxide ion, one one-hundredth as much as a neutral solution; and so on. A solution containing 1 mole of strong acid per liter has hydrogen-ion concentration 1, and pH 0; such a strongly acidic solution also contains some hydroxide ion, the concentration of hydroxide ion being 1×10^{-14}. Although this is a very small number, it still represents a large number of actual ions in unit volume. Avogadro's number is 0.602×10^{24}, and accordingly a concentration of 10^{-14} moles per liter corresponds to 0.602×10^{10} ions per liter, or 0.602×10^7 ions per milliliter; that is, about 6,000,000 hydroxide ions per milliliter.

Illustrative Exercises

20-1.   What is the pH of 1 F HCl solution? Of 1 F NaOH solution? Of the solution obtained by mixing equal volumes of these two solutions?

20-2.   What is the hydrogen-ion concentration of each of the three solutions of the preceding exercise? The hydroxide-ion concentration?

20-3.   A sample of blood is found by experiment to have pH 6.7. What is its $[H^+]$? What is its $[OH^-]$? How many hydrogen ions and how many hydroxide ions (not moles) are there per milliliter?

20-3. Indicators

It was mentioned in Chapter 6 that indicators such as litmus may be used to tell whether a solution is acidic, neutral, or basic. The change in color of an indicator as the pH of the solution changes is not sharp, but extends over a range of one or two pH units. This is the result of the existence of chemical equilibrium between the two differently colored forms of the indicator, and the dependence of the color on the

---

* It must be remembered, in accordance with the discussion given in Section 18–11, that the activities of ions are not exactly equal to the concentrations, except in very dilute solutions; in more concentrated solutions the interaction of the electric charges on ions causes the activities usually to be slightly less than the concentrations. The correct equilibrium expressions are those involving activities of molecular species, rather than concentrations, and the equation for the water equilibrium accordingly also involves activities of hydrogen ion and hydroxide ion. For most of the calculations of interest to us no significant error is made by using concentrations.

hydrogen-ion concentration is due to the participation of hydrogen ion in the equilibrium.

Thus the red form of litmus may be represented by the formula HIn and the blue form by In⁻, resulting from the dissociation reaction

$$\underset{\substack{\text{red} \\ \text{acidic form}}}{\text{HIn}} \rightleftarrows \text{H}^+ + \underset{\substack{\text{blue} \\ \text{basic form}}}{\text{In}^-}$$

In alkaline solutions, with $[\text{H}^+]$ very small, the equilibrium is shifted to the right, and the indicator is converted almost entirely into the basic form (blue for litmus). In acidic solutions, with $[\text{H}^+]$ large, the equilibrium is shifted to the left, and the indicator assumes the acidic form.

Let us calculate the relative amount of the two forms as a function of $[\text{H}^+]$. The equilibrium expression for the indicator reaction written above is

$$\frac{[\text{H}^+][\text{In}^-]}{[\text{HIn}]} = K_{\text{In}}$$

in which K_{In} is the *equilibrium constant for the indicator*. We rewrite this as

$$\frac{[\text{HIn}]}{[\text{In}^-]} = \frac{[\text{H}^+]}{K_{\text{In}}}$$

This equation shows how the ratio of the two forms of the indicator depends on $[\text{H}^+]$. When the two forms are present in equal amounts the ratio of acidic form to alkaline form, $[\text{HIn}]/[\text{In}^-]$, has the value 1, and hence $[\text{H}^+] = K_{\text{In}}$. **The indicator constant K_{In} is thus the value of the hydrogen-ion concentration at which the change in color of the indicator is half completed.** The corresponding pH value is called the pK of the indicator.

Now if the pH is decreased by one unit the value of $[\text{H}^+]$ becomes ten times K_{In} and the ratio $[\text{HIn}]/[\text{In}^-]$ then equals 10. Thus at a pH value 1 less than the pK of the indicator (its midpoint) the acidic form of the indicator predominates over the basic form in the ratio 10 : 1. In this solution 91% of the indicator is in the acidic form, and 9% in the basic form. Over a range of 2 pH units the indicator accordingly changes from 91% acidic form to 91% basic form. For most indicators the color change detectable by the eye occurs over a range of about 1.2 to 1.8 units.

Indicators differ in their pK values; pure water, with pH 7, is neutral to litmus (which has pK equal to 6.8), acidic to phenolphthalein (pK 8.8), and basic to methyl orange (pK 3.7).

A chart showing the color changes and effective pH ranges of several indicators is given in Figure 20-1. The approximate pH of a solution can be found by finding by test the indicator toward which the solution shows a neutral reaction. Test paper, made with a mixture of indicators and showing several color changes, is now available with which the pH of a solution can be estimated to within about 1 unit over the pH range 1 to 13.

In titrating a weak acid or a weak base the indicator must be chosen with care. The way of choosing the proper indicator is described in the following section.

It is seen that an indicator behaves as a weak organic acid; the equilibrium expression for an indicator is the same as that for an ordinary weak acid, as discussed in the following section.

An indicator may be a weak base rather than a weak acid:

$$\underset{\text{basic form}}{\text{InOH}} \rightleftarrows \underset{\text{acidic form}}{\text{In}^+ + \text{OH}^-}$$

The equilibrium expression for this basic dissociation combined with that for the dissociation of water is equivalent to the acidic equilibrium equation given above, which can accordingly be used for all indicators.

By the use of color standards for the indicator, the pH of a solution may be estimated to about 0.1 unit by the indicator method. A more satisfactory general method of determining the pH of a solution is by use of an instrument that measures the hydrogen-ion concentration, making use of a measurement of the electric potential of a cell with cell reaction involving hydrogen ions. Modern glass-electrode pH meters are now available which cover the pH range 0 to 14 with an accuracy approaching 0.01. An instrument of this sort is represented in Figure 20-2.

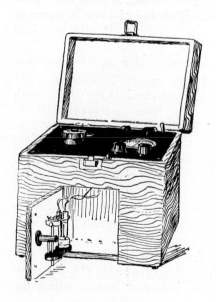

FIGURE 20-2

A modern pH meter.

20–4. *Equivalent Weights of Acids and Bases*

A solution containing one gram formula weight of hydrochloric acid, HCl, per liter is 1 F in hydrogen ion. Similarly a solution containing 0.5 gram formula weight of sulfuric acid, H_2SO_4, per liter is 1 F in replaceable hydrogen. Each of these solutions is neutralized* by an equal volume of a solution containing one gram formula weight of sodium hydroxide, NaOH, per liter, and the weights of the acids are hence equivalent to one gram formula weight of the alkali.

The quotient of the gram formula weight of an acid by the number of hydrogen atoms which are replaceable for the reaction under consideration is called the **equivalent weight of the acid.** Likewise *the quotient of the gram formula weight of a base by the number of hydroyxl groups which are replaceable for the reaction under consideration is called the* **equivalent weight of the base.**

One equivalent weight of an acid neutralizes one equivalent weight

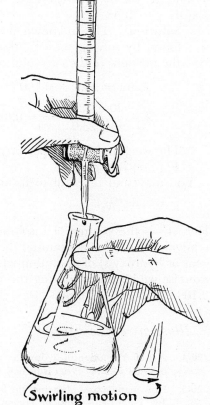

FIGURE 20-3

The process of titration.

* The meaning of "neutralizes" in the case of weak acids or bases is discussed in a later section of this chapter.

of a base. It is important to note that the equivalent weight of a poly-protic acid is not invariant; for H_3PO_4 it may be the gram formula weight, one half this, or one third, depending on whether one, two or three hydrogens are effective in the reaction under consideration.

The *normality* of a solution of an acid or base is the number of equiv-alents of acid or base per liter; a 1 N solution contains 1 equivalent per liter of solution. By determining, with use of an indicator, such as litmus, the relative volumes of acidic and alkaline solutions which are equivalent the normality of one solution can be calculated from the known value of the other. This process of **acid-base titration** (the determination of the *titer* or strength of an unknown solution), with use of special apparatus such as graduated burets and pipets, is an important method of volumetric quantitative analysis (Figure 20-3).

Example 3. It is found by experiment that 25.0 ml of a solution of sodium hydroxide is neutralized by 20.0 ml of a 0.100 N acid solution. What are the normality of the alkaline solution and the weight of NaOH per liter?

Solution. The unknown normality x of the alkaline solution is found by solving the equation which expresses the equivalence of the portions of the two solutions:

$$25.0x = 20.0 \times 0.100$$

$$x = \frac{20.0 \times 0.100}{25.0} = \mathbf{0.080}$$

The weight of NaOH per liter is 0.080 times the equivalent weight, 40.0, or **3.20 g.**

You may find it useful to fix in your mind the following equation:

$$V_1N_1 = V_2N_2$$

Here V_1 is the volume of a solution with normality N_1, and V_2 is the equivalent volume (containing the same number of replaceable hydro-gens or hydroxyls) of a solution with normality N_2. In solving the above exercise we began by writing this equation; 25.0x is V_1N_1, and 20.0 × 0.100 is V_2N_2, in this case.

Illustrative Exercises

20-4. A 1.00 N solution of hydrochloric acid is diluted with water to four times its original volume. What is its new normality?

20-5. How many grams of each of the following substances would be needed to make 1.00 l of 0.100 N solution? The number after each formula is its formula weight. Acids: HBr (81), HNO_3 (63), H_2SO_4 (98), H_3PO_4 (98), $H_2C_2O_4 \cdot 2H_2O$ (oxalic acid dihydrate, 126). Bases: NaOH (40), NH_3 (17), $Ca(OH)_2$ (74).

20-6.   A standard acid solution can be made by dissolving a weighed amount of pure benzoic acid ($HC_7H_5O_2$, one replaceable hydrogen) and making a definite volume of solution with it. How much benzoic acid should be weighed out to make 1000 ml of 0.100 N solution?

20-7.   The volume 50 ml of sodium hydroxide solution is made neutral to litmus by the addition of 60 ml of 0.100 N benzoic acid. What is the normality of the sodium hydroxide solution.

20-8.   In titrating vinegar (a solution of acetic acid, $HC_2H_3O_2$) with 0.120 N sodium hydroxide solution, 10.0 ml of vinegar required 45.0 ml of the alkaline solution to neutralize it. What is the strength of the vinegar, in grams of acetic acid per 100 ml. of vinegar?

20–5. *Weak Acids and Bases*

Ionization of a Weak Acid.   A 0.1 N solution of a strong acid such as hydrochloric acid is 0.1 N in hydrogen ion, since this acid is very nearly completely dissociated into ions except in very concentrated solutions. On the other hand, a 0.1 N solution of acetic acid contains hydrogen ions in much smaller concentration, as is seen by testing with indicators, observing the rate of attack of metals, or simply by tasting. Acetic acid is a weak acid; the acetic acid molecules hold their protons so firmly that not all of them are transferred to water molecules to form hydronium ions. Instead there is an equilibrium reaction,

$$HC_2H_3O_2 + H_2O \rightleftarrows H_3O^+ + C_2H_3O_2^-$$

or, ignoring the hydration of the proton,

$$HC_2H_3O_2 \rightleftarrows H^+ + C_2H_3O_2^-$$

The equilibrium expression for this reaction is

$$\frac{[H^+][C_2H_3O_2^-]}{[HC_2H_3O_2]} = K$$

In general, for an acid HA in equilibrium with ions H^+ and A^- the equilibrium expression is

$$\frac{[H^+][A^-]}{[HA]} = K_a$$

The constant K_a, characteristic of the acid, is called its **acid constant** or **ionization constant.**

Values of acid constants are found experimentally by measuring the pH of solutions of the acids. A table of values is given later in this chapter.

Example 4.   The pH of a 0.100 N solution of acetic acid is found by experiment to be 2.874. What is the acid constant, K_a, of this acid?

Solution. To calculate the acid constant we note that acetic acid added to pure water ionizes to produce hydrogen ions and acetate ions in equal quantities. Moreover, since the amount of hydrogen ion resulting from the dissociation of water is negligible compared with the total amount present, we have

$$[H^+] = [C_2H_3O_2^-] = \text{antilog}\,(-2.874) = 1.34 \times 10^{-3}$$

The concentration $[HC_2H_3O_2]$ is hence $0.100 - 0.001 = 0.099$, and the acid constant has the value

$$K_a = (1.34 \times 10^{-3})^2/0.099 = \mathbf{1.80 \times 10^{-5}}$$

The hydrogen-ion concentration of a weak acid (containing no other electrolytes which react with it or its ions) in $1\,N$ concentration is approximately equal to the square root of its acid constant, as is seen from the following example.

Example 5. What is $[H^+]$ of a $1\,N$ solution of HCN, hydrocyanic acid, which has $K_a = 4 \times 10^{-10}$?
Solution. Let $x = [H^+]$. Then we can write $[CN^-] = x$ (neglecting the amount of hydrogen ion due to ionization of the water), and $[HCN] = 1 - x$. The equilibrium equation is

$$\frac{x^2}{1 - x} = K_a = 4 \times 10^{-10}$$

We know that x is going to be much smaller than 1, since this weak acid is only very slightly ionized. Hence we replace $1 - x$ by 1 (neglecting the small difference between unionized hydrocyanic acid and the total cyanide concentration), obtaining

$$x^2 = 4 \times 10^{-10}$$

$$x = \mathbf{2 \times 10^{-5}} = [H^+]$$

The neglect of the ionization of water is also seen to be justified, since even in this very slightly acidic solution the value of $[H^+]$ is 200 times the value for pure water.

Successive Ionizations of a Polyprotic Acid. A polyprotic acid has several acid constants, corresponding to dissociation of successive hydrogen ions. For phosphoric acid, H_3PO_4, there are three equilibrium expressions:

$$H_3PO_4 \rightleftarrows H^+ + H_2PO_4^-$$

$$K_1 = \frac{[H^+][H_2PO_4^-]}{[H_3PO_4]} = 7.5 \times 10^{-3} = K_{H_3PO_4}$$

$$H_2PO_4^- \rightleftarrows H^+ + HPO_4^{--}$$

$$K_2 = \frac{[H^+][HPO_4^{--}]}{[H_2PO_4^-]} = 6.2 \times 10^{-8} = K_{H_2PO_4^-}$$

$$HPO_4^{--} \rightleftharpoons H^+ + PO_4^{---}$$

$$K_3 = \frac{[H^+][PO_4^{---}]}{[HPO_4^{--}]} = 10^{-12} = K_{HPO_4^{--}}$$

Note that these constants have the dimensions of concentration, mole/l.

The ratio of successive ionization constants for a polybasic acid is usually about 10^{-5}, as in this case. We see that with respect to its first hydrogen phosphoric acid is a moderately strong acid—considerably stronger than acidic acid. With respect to its second hydrogen it is weak, and to its third very weak.

Ionization of a Weak Base. A weak base dissociates in part to produce hydroxide ions:

$$MOH \rightleftharpoons M^+ + OH^-$$

The corresponding equilibrium expression is

$$\frac{[M^+][OH^-]}{[MOH]} = K_b$$

The constant K_b is called the *basic constant* of the base.

Ammonium hydroxide is the only common weak base. Its basic constant has the value 1.81×10^{-5} at $25°$ C. The hydroxides of the alkali metals and the alkaline-earth metals are strong bases.

Example 6. What is the pH of a 0.1 F solution of ammonium hydroxide?

Solution. Our fundamental equation is

$$\frac{[NH_4^+][OH^-]}{[NH_4OH]} = K_b = 1.81 \times 10^{-5}$$

Since the ions NH_4^+ and OH^- are produced in equal amounts by the dissociation of the base and the amount of OH^- from dissociation of water is negligible, we put

$$[NH_4^+] = [OH^-] = x$$

The concentration of NH_4OH is accordingly $0.1 - x$, and we obtain the equation

$$\frac{x^2}{0.1 - x} = 1.81 \times 10^{-5}$$

(Here we have made the calculation as though all the undissociated solute were NH_4OH. Actually there is some dissolved

NH_3 present; however, since the equilibrium $NH_3 + H_2O \rightleftharpoons NH_4OH$ is of such a nature that the ratio $[NH_4OH]/[NH_3]$ is constant, we are at liberty to write the equilibrium expression for the base as shown above, with the symbol $[NH_4OH]$ representing the total concentration of the undissociated solute, including the molecular species NH_3 as well as NH_4OH.)

Solving this equation, we obtain the result

$$x = [OH^-] = [NH_4^+] = 1.34 \times 10^{-3}$$

The solution is hence only slightly alkaline—its hydroxide-ion concentration is the same as that of a $0.00134\ N$ solution of sodium hydroxide.

This value of $[OH^-]$ corresponds to $[H^+] = (1.00 \times 10^{-14})/(1.34 \times 10^{-3}) = 7.46 \times 10^{-12}$, as calculated from the water equilibrium equation

$$[H^+][OH^-] = 1.00 \times 10^{-14}$$

The corresponding pH is **11.13**, which is the answer to the problem.

Very many problems in solution chemistry are solved with use of the acid and base equilibrium equations. The uses of these equations in discussing the titration of weak acids and bases, the hydrolysis of salts, and the properties of buffered solutions are illustrated in the following sections of this chapter.

The student while working a problem should not substitute numbers in the equations in a routine way, but should think carefully about the chemical reactions and equilibria involved and the magnitudes of the concentrations of the different molecular species. Every problem solved should add to his understanding of solution chemistry. *The ultimate goal is such an understanding of the subject that the student can estimate the orders of magnitude of concentrations of the various ionic and molecular species in a solution without having to solve the equilibrium equations.*

Illustrative Exercises

20-9. What is the approximate pH of a $1\ F$ solution of H_3PO_4, which has first acid constant 0.75×10^{-2}? (The ionization of the second and third hydrogens can be neglected in solving this exercise.)

20-10. What is the concentration of SO_4^{--} in a $1\ F$ solution of H_2SO_4? The first ionization is complete, and the ionization constant for the second ionization has the value 1.2×10^{-2}.

20-11. (a) A $0.1\ N$ solution of HCl is diluted tenfold. By how much does the acidity (concentration of hydrogen ion) change? (b) A $0.1\ N$ solution of acetic acid ($K_a = 1.8 \times 10^{-5}$) is diluted tenfold. By how much does the acidity change?

20–6. *The Titration of Weak Acids and Bases.*
The Hydrolysis of Salts

A solution containing say 0.2 mole of a strong acid such as hydrochloric acid in a liter has $[H^+] = 0.2$ and $pH = 0.7$. The addition of strong base, such as $0.2\ N$ NaOH, causes the hydrogen-ion concentration to diminish through neutralization by the added hydroxide ion. When 990 ml of strong base has been added the excess of acid over base is $0.2 \times 10/1000 = 0.002$ mole, and since the total volume is very close to $2\ l$ the value of $[H^+]$ is 0.001, and the pH is 3. When 999 ml has been added, and the neutralization reaction is within 0.1% of completion, the values are $[H^+] = 0.0001$ and $pH = 4$. At $pH = 5$ the reaction is within 0.01% of completion and at pH 6 within 0.001%. Finally pH 7, neutrality, is reached when an amount of strong base has been added exactly equivalent to the amount of strong acid present. A very small excess of strong base causes the pH to increase beyond 7.

We see that to obtain the most accurate results in titrating a strong acid and a strong base an indicator with indicator constant about 10^{-7} ($pK = 7$) should be chosen, such as litmus or bromthymol blue. The titration curve calculated above, and given in Figure 20-4, shows however that the choice of an indicator is in this case not crucial; any indicator with pK between 4 (methyl orange) and 10 (thymolphthalein) could be used with error less than 0.2%.

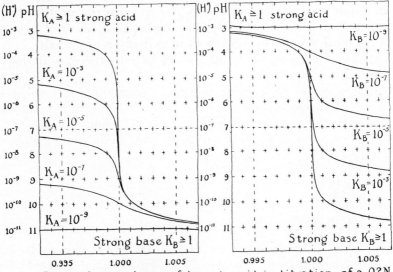

Ratio of equivalents of base to acid in titration of a 0.2N acid with a 0.2N base, either acid or base being strong

FIGURE 20-4   *Acid-base titration curves.*

In titrating a weak acid (with a strong base) or a weak base (with a strong acid) greater care is needed in the selection of an indicator. Let us consider the titration of 0.2 N acetic acid, a moderately weak acid with $K_a = 1.80 \times 10^{-5}$, with 0.2 N sodium hydroxide. When an amount of the alkali equivalent to that of the acid has been added the resultant solution is the same as would be obtained by dissolving 0.1 mole of the salt $NaC_2H_3O_2$ in a liter of water. The solution of this salt is not neutral, with pH 7, however, but is alkaline. Let us consider what happens when $NaC_2H_3O_2$ is dissolved in water. This salt, like most salts, is completely dissociated into ions, Na^+ and $C_2H_3O_2^-$. The acetate ion and hydrogen ion are in equilibrium with undissociated acetic acid, and the reaction

$$H^+ + C_2H_3O_2^- \rightleftharpoons HC_2H_3O_2$$

occurs to some extent. This uses some of the H^+, and reduces $[H^+]$ below 10^{-7}. To retain the water equilibrium

$$[H^+][OH^-] = 10^{-14}$$

some water dissociates:

$$H_2O \rightleftharpoons H^+ + OH^-$$

This increases the OH^- concentration, and the solution becomes basic. The effect can be said to be due to the reaction

$$C_2H_3O_2^- + H_2O \rightleftharpoons HC_2H_3O_2 + OH^-$$

which is the sum of the two reactions given above. **This reaction oi an anion of a weak acid with water to form the undissociated acid and hydroxide ion, which makes a solution of a salt of a strong base and a weak acid basic, is called the hydrolysis of the salt.**

A salt of a strong acid and a weak base hydrolyzes analogously to give an acidic solution.

Our problem of selecting a suitable indicator for acetic acid is to be solved by calculating the pH of a 0.1 N $NaC_2H_3O_2$ solution; a suitable indicator then has pK equal to this pH value.

To make this calculation we use the two equilibrium expressions

$$\frac{[H^+][C_2H_3O_2^-]}{[HC_2H_3O_2]} = 1.80 \times 10^{-5} = K_a$$

and

$$[H^+][OH^-] = 1.00 \times 10^{-14} = K_W$$

Our solution contains Na^+, $C_2H_3O_2^-$, $HC_2H_3O_2$, and OH^- in appreciable concentrations, and H^+ in extremely small concentration (less than 10^{-7}, since the solution is basic). We know that $[Na^+]$ is 0.1, since the solution is 0.1 N $NaC_2H_3O_2$. Moreover, the electrical neutrality of the solution requires that

$$[C_2H_3O_2^-] + [OH^-] = 0.1$$

(neglecting $[H^+]$), and the composition of the solution requires that

$$[HC_2H_3O_2] + [C_2H_3O_2^-] = 0.1$$

From the last two equations we obtain

$$[HC_2H_3O_2] = [OH^-]$$

Now let us put

$$[HC_2H_3O_2] = [OH^-] = x$$

and

$$[C_2H_3O_2^-] = 0.1 - [OH^-] = 0.1 - x$$

We eliminate $[H^+]$ from the equilibrium equations by dividing one by the other, obtaining

$$\frac{[HC_2H_3O_2][OH^-]}{[C_2H_3O_2^-]} = \frac{K_W}{K_a} = \frac{1.00 \times 10^{-14}}{1.80 \times 10^{-5}}$$

or

$$\frac{x^2}{0.1 - x} = 5.56 \times 10^{-10}$$

which on solution gives

$$x = 0.75 \times 10^{-5}$$

Hence

$$[OH^-] = 0.75 \times 10^{-5} \quad \text{and} \quad [H^+] = 1.34 \times 10^{-9}$$

The pH of the solution of sodium acetate is hence 8.87. By reference to Figure 20-1 we see that *phenolphthalein, with* $pK = 9$, *is the best indicator to use for titrating a moderately weak acid such as acetic acid.*

The complete titration curve, showing the pH of the solution as a function of the amount of strong base added, can be calculated in essentially this way. Its course is shown in Figure 20-4 ($K_a = 10^{-5}$). We see that the solution has pH 7 when there is about 1% excess of acid; hence if litmus were used as the indicator an error of about 1% would be made in the titration.

The basic constant of ammonium hydroxide has about the same value as the acid constant of acetic acid. Hence to *titrate a weak base such as ammonium hydroxide with a strong acid methyl orange* (pK 3.8) *may be used as the indicator.*

It is possible by suitable selection of indicators to titrate separately a strong acid and a weak acid or a strong base and a weak base in a mixture of the two. Let us consider, for example, a solution of sodium hydroxide and ammonium hydroxide. If strong acid is added until the

pH is 11.1, which is that of 0.1 N ammonium hydroxide solution, the strong base will be within 1% of neutralization (Figure 20-4). Hence by using alizarine yellow (pK 11) as indicator the concentration of strong base can be determined, and then by a second titration with methyl orange the concentration of ammonium hydroxide can be found.

The Hydrolysis of Salts of Metals Other than the Alkalis and Alkaline Earths.

The metal hydroxides other than the alkalis and alkaline earths are weak bases. Accordingly metal salts of strong acids, such as $FeCl_3$, $CuSO_4$, $KAl(SO_4)_2 \cdot 12H_2O$ (alum), etc., hydrolyze to produce acidic solutions; the sour taste of these salts is characteristic. It is interesting that the hydrolysis of a metal salt need not produce the hydroxide of the metal, but may produce a soluble complex cation; thus the hydrolysis of alum or of aluminum sulfate or nitrate takes place primarily according to the following equation:

$$Al^{+++} + H_2O \rightleftarrows AlOH^{+++} + H^+$$

The complex cation $AlOH^{++}$ is only partially dissociated, and so at equilibrium there exist in the solution in appreciable concentrations all the ions which take part in this reaction, Al^{+++}, $AlOH^{++}$, and H^+. The concentration of hydrogen ion produced in this way is such as to make a solution of any salt of aluminum and a strong acid acidic.

A second hydrolysis reaction

$$AlOH^{++} + H_2O \rightleftarrows Al(OH)_2^+ + H^+$$

and a third

$$Al(OH)_2^+ + H_2O \rightleftarrows Al(OH)_3 + H^+$$

occur to smaller extents. The complex ions $AlOH^{++}$ and $Al(OH)_2^+$ remain in solution, whereas the hydroxide $Al(OH)_3$ is only very slightly soluble and precipitates if more than a very small amount is formed (its solubility is about 10^{-8} moles per liter). This final step in the hydrolysis of aluminum salts leads to precipitation only if the hydrogen-ion concentration of the solution is made small (less than about 10^{-3}) by addition of basic substances.

It will be recalled from the discussion in Chapter 17 that the aluminum ion in aqueous solution is hydrated, having the formula $Al(H_2O)_6^{+++}$, with the six water molecules arranged octahedrally about the aluminum ion. The hydrolysis of aluminum salts may be most accurately represented by the equations

$$Al(H_2O)_6^{+++} \rightleftarrows Al(H_2O)_5OH^{++} + H^+$$

$$Al(H_2O)_5OH^{++} \rightleftarrows Al(H_2O)_4(OH)_2^+ + H^+$$

$$Al(H_2O)_4(OH)_2^+ \rightleftarrows Al(H_2O)_3(OH)_3 + H^+ \rightleftarrows$$

$$Al(OH)_3 \downarrow + 3H_2O + H^+$$

In the process of hydrolysis the hydrated ions of aluminum lose protons, forming successive hydroxide complexes; the final neutral complex then loses water to form the insoluble hydroxide $Al(OH)_3$.

The hydrolysis of ferric salts is so common that the color of ferric ion, $Fe(H_2O)_6^{+++}$, is usually masked by that of the hydroxide complexes. Ferric ion is nearly colorless; it seems to have a very pale violet color, seen in crystals of ferric alum, $KFe(SO_4)_2 \cdot 12H_2O$, and ferric nitrate, $Fe(NO_3)_3 \cdot 9H_2O$, and in ferric solutions strongly acidified with nitric or perchloric acid. Solutions of ferric salts ordinarily have the characteristic yellow to brown color of the hydroxide complexes $Fe(H_2O)_5OH^{++}$ and $Fe(H_2O)_4(OH)_2^+$, or even the red-brown color of colloidal particles of hydrated ferric hydroxide.

Hydrolysis in General. The word hydrolysis is used not only in the above way but also in referring to more general chemical reactions in which a molecule or ion is converted into two or more molecules or ions by reaction with water. The examples discussed above are cases of *anion hydrolysis* and *cation hydrolysis*, such as

$$C_2H_3O_2^- + H_2O \rightleftarrows HC_2H_3O_2 + OH^-$$

$$Al^{+++} + H_2O \rightleftarrows AlOH^{++} + H^+$$

In addition, a reaction such as

$$PCl_5 + 4H_2O \longrightarrow H_3PO_4 + 5HCl$$

or

$$\underset{\text{calcium carbide}}{CaC_2} + 2H_2O \longrightarrow Ca(OH)_2 + \underset{\text{acetylene}}{H_2C_2}$$

is also classed as a hydrolytic reaction. From the more general concepts of acids and bases discussed later a relation can be seen between such reactions as these and the hydrolysis of anions and cations.

Not all reactions involving water are classed as hydrolytic reactions. Thus the reaction of water with a molecule or ion such as calcium oxide

$$CaO + H_2O \rightleftarrows Ca(OH)_2$$

is usually called *hydration*.

20–7. *Buffered Solutions*

Very small amounts of strong acid or base suffice to change the hydrogen-ion concentration of water in the slightly acidic to slightly basic region; one drop of strong concentrated acid added to a liter of water makes it appreciably acidic, increasing the hydrogen-ion concentration by a factor of 5000, and two drops of strong alkali would then make it basic, decreasing the hydrogen-ion concentration by a factor of over a million. Yet there are solutions to which large amounts of strong acid or base can be added with only very small resultant change in hydrogen-ion concentration. Such solutions are called **buffered solutions.**

Blood and other physiological solutions are buffered; the pH of blood changes only slowly from its normal value (about 7.4) on addition of acid or base. Important among the buffering substances in blood are the serum proteins (Chapter 31), which contain basic and acidic groups that can combine with the added acid or base.

A drop of concentrated acid, which when added to a liter of pure water increases [H⁺] 5000-fold (from 10^{-7} to 5×10^{-4}), produces an increase of [H⁺] of less than 1% (from 1.00×10^{-7} to 1.01×10^{-7}, for example) when added to a liter of buffered solution such as the phosphate buffer made by dissolving 0.2 gram formula weight of phosphoric acid in a liter of water and adding 0.3 gram formula weight of sodium hydroxide.

This is a half-neutralized phosphoric acid solution; its principal ionic constituents and their concentrations are Na⁺, 0.3 M; HPO₄⁻⁻, 0.1 M; H₂PO₄⁻, 0.1 M; H⁺, about 10^{-7} M. From the titration curve of Figure 20-5 we see that this solution is a good buffer; to change its pH from 7 to 6.5 (tripling the hydrogen ion or hydroxide ion concen-

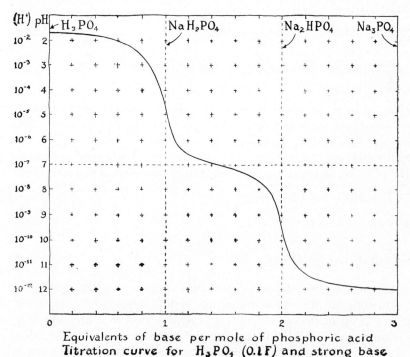

Equivalents of base per mole of phosphoric acid
Titration curve for H_3PO_4 (0.1F) and strong base

FIGURE 20-5   *Titration curve for phosphoric acid and a strong base.*

tration) about one twentieth of an equivalent of strong acid or base is needed per liter, whereas this amount of acid or base in water would cause a change of 5.7 pH units (an increase or decrease of $[H^+]$ by the factor 500,000). Such a solution, usually made by dissolving the two well-crystallized salts KH_2PO_4 and $Na_2HPO_4 \cdot 2H_2O$ in water, is widely used for buffering in the neutral region (pH 5.3 to 8.0).* Other useful buffers are sodium citrate-hydrochloric acid (pH 1 to 3.5), acetic acid-sodium acetate (pH 3.6 to 5.6), boric acid-sodium hydroxide (pH 7.8 to 10.0), and glycine-sodium hydroxide (pH 8.5 to 13).

The behavior of a buffer can be understood from the equilibrium equation for the acid dissociation. Let us consider the case of acetic acid-sodium acetate. The solution contains $HC_2H_3O_2$ and $C_2H_3O_2^-$ in equal or comparable concentrations. The equilibrium expression

$$\frac{[H^+][C_2H_3O_2^-]}{[HC_2H_3O_2]} = K_a$$

may be written as

$$[H^+] = \frac{[HC_2H_3O_2]}{[C_2H_3O_2^-]} K_a$$

This shows that when $[C_2H_3O_2^-]$ and $[HC_2H_3O_2]$ are equal, as in an equimolal mixed solution of $HC_2H_3O_2$ and $NaC_2H_3O_2$, the value of $[H^+]$ is just that of K_a, 1.80×10^{-5}, and hence the pH is 4.7. A 1 : 5 mixture of $HC_2H_3O_2$ and $NaC_2H_3O_2$ has $[H^+] = \frac{1}{5}K_a$ and pH 5.4, and a 5 : 1 mixture has $[H^+] = 5K_a$ and pH 4.0. By choosing a suitable ratio of $HC_2H_3O_2$ to $NaC_2H_3O_2$ any desired hydrogen-ion concentration in this neighborhood can be obtained.

It is seen from the equilibrium expressions that *the effectiveness of a buffer depends on the concentrations of the buffering substances;* a tenfold dilution of the buffer decreases by the factor 10 the amount of acid or base per liter which can be added without causing the pH to change more than the desired amount.

For the phosphate buffer in the pH 7 region the equilibrium constant of interest is that for the reaction

$$H_2PO_4^- \rightleftharpoons HPO_4^{--} + H^+$$

The value of $K_{H_2PO_4^{--}}$ is 6.2×10^{-8}; this is accordingly the value of $[H^+]$ expected for a solution with $[H_2PO_4^-] = [HPO_4^{--}]$.

If the buffered solution is dilute, this is its hydrogen-ion concentration. Because the activities of ions are affected by other ions, however, there is appreciable deviation from the calculated values in salt solutions as concentrated as 0.1 M. This fact accounts for the small

---

* A concentrated neutral buffer solution containing one half gram formula weight of each salt per liter may be kept in the laboratory to neutralize either acid or base spilled on the body.

discrepancies between the pH values calculated from equilibrium constants and those given in the buffer tables.

20–8. *The Strengths of the Oxygen Acids*

The oxygen acids, which consist of oxygen atoms O and hydroxide groups OH attached to a central atom ($HClO_4 = ClO_3(OH)$, $H_2SO_4 = SO_2(OH)_2$, etc.), vary widely in strength, from very strong acids such as perchloric acid, $HClO_4$, to very weak ones such as boric acid, H_3BO_3. It is often useful to know the approximate strengths of these acids. Fortunately there have been formulated some simple and easily remembered rules regarding these acid strengths.

The Rules Expressing the Strengths of the Oxygen Acids. The strengths of these oxygen acids are expressed approximately by the following two rules:

Rule 1. The successive acid constants K_1, K_2, K_3, $\cdots$ are in the ratios $1 : 10^{-5}$: We have already noted the examples of phosphoric acid

$$K_{H_3PO_4} = 7.5 \times 10^{-3} \qquad K_{H_2PO_4^-} = 6.2 \times 10^{-8} \qquad K_{HPO_4^{--}} = 10^{-12}$$

and sulfurous acid

$$K_{H_2SO_3} = 1.2 \times 10^{-2} \qquad K_{HSO_3^-} = 1 \times 10^{-7}$$

The rule holds well for all the acids of the class under consideration.

Rule 2. The value of the first ionization constant is determined by the value of m in the formula $XO_m(OH)_n$: if m is zero (no excess of oxygen atoms over hydrogen atoms, as in $B(OH)_3$) the acid is very weak, with $K_1 \leq 10^{-7}$; for m = 1 the acid is weak, with $K_1 \cong 10^{-2}$; for m = 2 ($K_1 \cong 10^{-3}$) or m = 3 ($K_1 \cong 10^8$) the acid is strong.

Note the occurrence here of the facter 10^{-5}. The applicability of this rule is shown by the tables at the end of this section.

The second rule can be understood in the following way. The force attracting H^+ to ClO^- to form $ClOH$ (hypochlorous acid) is that of an O—H valence bond. But the force between H^+ and either one of the two oxygen atoms of the ion ClO_2^- to form $ClOOH$ (chlorous acid) may be smaller than that for an O—H valence bond because the total attraction for the proton is divided between the two oxygen atoms, and hence this acid (of the second class) may well be expected to be more highly dissociated than hypochlorous acid. An acid of the third class would be still more highly dissociated, since the total attraction for the proton would be divided among three oxygen atoms.

With use of these rules we can answer questions as to the hydrolysis of salts or the choice of indicators for titration without referring to tables of acid constants.

Example 7.   What reaction to litmus would be expected of solutions of the following salts: NaClO, NaClO₂, NaClO₃, NaClO₄?

   Solution.   The corresponding acids are shown by the rule to be very weak, weak, strong, and very strong, respectively. Hence NaClO and NaClO₂ would through hydrolysis give basic solutions, and the other two salts would give neutral solutions.

Example 8.   What indicator could be used for titrating periodic acid, H_5IO_6?

   Solution.   This acid has one extra oxygen atom, and is hence of the second class, as is phosphoric acid. We accordingly refer to Figures 20-5 and 20-1, and see that methyl orange should be satisfactory for titrating the first hydrogen or phenolphthalein for titrating the first two hydrogens.

First class; Very weak acids $X(OH)_n$ or H_nXO_n
First acid constant about 10^{-7} or less

	K_1
Hypochlorous acid, HClO	3.2×10^{-8}
Hypobromous acid, HBrO	2×10^{-9}
Hypoiodous acid, HIO	1×10^{-11}
Silicic acid, H_4SiO_4	1×10^{-10}
Germanic acid, H_4GeO_4	3×10^{-9}
Boric acid, H_3BO_3	5.8×10^{-10}
Arsenious acid, H_3AsO_3	6×10^{-10}
Antimonous acid, H_3SbO_3	10^{-11}

Second class; Weak acids $XO(OH)_n$ or H_nXO_{n+1}
First acid constant about 10^{-2}

	K_1
Chlorous acid, HClO₂	1.1×10^{-2}
Sulfurous acid, H_2SO_3	1.2×10^{-2}
Selenious acid, H_2SeO_3	0.3×10^{-2}
Phosphoric acid, H_3PO_4	0.75×10^{-2}
Phosphorous acid,* H_2HPO_3	1.6×10^{-2}
Hypophosphorous acid,* HH_2PO_2	1×10^{-2}
Arsenic acid, H_3AsO_4	0.5×10^{-2}
Periodic acid, H_5IO_6	1×10^{-3}
Nitrous acid, HNO_2	0.45×10^{-3}
Acetic acid, $HC_2H_3O_2$	1.80×10^{-5}
Carbonic acid,† H_2CO_3	0.45×10^{-6}

* It is known that phosphorous acid has the structure H—P—OH with a double-bonded O and an OH group on the phosphorus, and hypophosphorous acid the structure H—P—OH with a double-bonded O and an H on the phosphorus; the hydrogen atoms which are bonded to the phosphorus atom are not counted in applying the rule.

† The low value for K_1 for carbonic acid is due in part to the existence of some of the unionized acid in the form of dissolved CO_2 molecules rather than H_2CO_3. The proton dissociation constant for the molecular species H_2CO_3 is about 2×10^{-4}.

Third class; Strong acids $XO_2(OH)_n$ or H_nXO_{n+2}
  First acid constant about 10^3
  Second acid constant about 10^{-2}

	K_1	K_2
Chloric acid, $HClO_3$	Large	
Sulfuric acid, H_2SO_4	Large	1.2×10^{-2}
Selenic acid, H_2SeO_4	Large	1×10^{-2}

Fourth class; Very strong acids $XO_3(OH)_n$ or H_nXO_{n+3}
  First acid constant about 10^8

Perchloric acid, $HClO_4$	Very strong
Permanganic acid, $HMnO_4$	Very strong

Other Acids. There is no simple way of remembering the strengths of acids other than those discussed above. HCl, HBr, and HI are strong, but HF is weak, with $K_a = 7.2 \times 10^{-4}$. The homologs of water are weak acids, with the following reported acid constants:

	K_1	K_2
Hydrosulfuric acid, H_2S	1.1×10^{-7}	1.0×10^{-14}
Hydroselenic acid, H_2Se	1.7×10^{-4}	1×10^{-12}
Hydrotelluric acid, H_2Te	2.3×10^{-3}	1×10^{-11}

The hydrides NH_3, PH_3, etc., function as bases by adding protons rather than as acids by losing them.

Oxygen acids which do not contain a single central atom have strengths corresponding to reasonable extensions of our rules, as shown by the following examples:

Very weak acids: $K_1 = 10^{-7}$ or less

	K_1	K_2
Hydrogen peroxide, HO—OH	2.4×10^{-12}	
Hyponitrous acid, HON—NOH	9×10^{-8}	1×10^{-11}

Weak acids: $K_1 = 10^{-2}$

	K_1	K_2
Oxalic acid, HOOC—COOH	5.9×10^{-2}	6.4×10^{-5}

The following acids are not easily classified:

	K_1
Hydrocyanic acid, HCN	4×10^{-10}
Cyanic acid, HOCN	Strong
Thiocyanic acid, HSCN	Strong
Hydrazoic acid, HN_3	1.8×10^{-5}

20–9. *More General Concepts of Acids and Bases*

In recent years several more general concepts of acids and bases have been introduced. They are useful for some purposes, such as the discussion of non-aqueous solutions. One of these concepts, due to the

Danish chemist J. N. Brönsted, is that an acid is any molecular or ionic species which can give up a proton (which is a *proton donor*), and a base is any one which can take up a proton (which is a *proton acceptor*). Thus NH_4^+ is called an acid, since it can give up a proton:

$$NH_4^+ \rightleftarrows NH_3 + H^+$$

and NH_3 is called a base, since this reaction can be reversed. Any acid anion, such as the acetate ion, could be called a base from this point of view.

The Brönsted concept provides a simple way of discussing hydrolysis, as is illustrated by the following example. The acetate ion is a base of significant strength, since the equilibrium

$$C_2H_3O_2^- + H^+ \rightleftarrows HC_2H_3O_2$$

favors the product $HC_2H_3O_2$. Hence a solution of sodium acetate is expected to be basic in reaction. This explanation of hydrolysis is an interesting alternative to that given in an earlier section of this chapter.

Another still more general concept was introduced by G. N. Lewis. He called a base anything which has available an unshared pair of electrons (such as NH_3, :N(—H) with H above and H below) and an acid anything which could attach itself to such a pair of electrons (such as H^+, to form NH_4^+, or BF_3, to form

$$F-B-N-H$$

with F, F, F on boron and H, H on nitrogen).

This concept explains many phenomena, such as the effect of certain substances other than hydrogen ion in changing the color of indicators. Another interesting application of the concept is its explanation of salt formation by reaction of acidic oxides and basic oxides.

Acid Strength and Condensation. It is observed that the tendency of oxygen acids to condense to larger molecules is correlated with their acid strengths. Very strong acids, such as $HClO_4$ and $HMnO_4$, condense only with difficulty, and the substances formed, Cl_2O_7 and Mn_2O_7, are very unstable. Less strong acids, such as H_2SO_4, form condensation products such as $H_2S_2O_7$, pyrosulfuric acid, on strong heating, but these products are not stable in aqueous solution. Phosphoric acid forms pyrophosphate ion and other condensed ions in aqueous solution, but these ions easily hydrolyze to the orthophosphate ion; other weak acids behave similarly. The very weak oxygen acids, including silicic acid (Chapter 24) and boric acid, condense very readily, and their condensation products are very stable substances.

This correlation is reasonable. The unionized acids contain oxygen atoms bonded to hydrogen atoms, and the condensed acids contain oxygen atoms bonded to two central atoms:

$$
\begin{array}{ccc}
\text{H}-\overset{\cdot\cdot}{\text{O}}: & & :\overset{\cdot\cdot}{\text{O}}-\text{H} \\
\diagdown & & \diagup \\
& \text{Si} & \\
\diagup & & \diagdown \\
\text{H}-\overset{\cdot\cdot}{\underset{\cdot\cdot}{\text{O}}}: & & :\underset{\cdot\cdot}{\text{O}}-\text{H}
\end{array}
$$

$$
\begin{array}{ccccc}
\text{H}-\overset{\cdot\cdot}{\text{O}}: & & \overset{\cdot\,\cdot}{\text{O}} & & :\overset{\cdot\cdot}{\text{O}}-\text{H} \\
\diagdown & & & & \diagup \\
\text{Si} & & & & \text{Si} \\
\diagup \diagdown & & & & \diagup \diagdown \\
\text{H}-\underset{\cdot\cdot}{\text{O}}: \quad :\underset{\cdot\cdot}{\text{O}}-\text{H} & & & & \text{H}-\underset{\cdot\cdot}{\text{O}}: \quad :\underset{\cdot\cdot}{\text{O}}-\text{H}
\end{array}
$$

It is hence not surprising that stability of the unionized acid (low acid strength) should be correlated with stability of the condensed molecules.

Concepts and Terms Introduced in This Chapter

Hydrogen-ion concentration. pH. Equilibrium between H^+ and OH^-. Indicators. Equivalent weights of acids and bases. Normality Ionization equilibria of weak acids and bases. Acid constant; basic constant. Titration of weak acids and bases. Choice of suitable indicator.

Hydrolysis of salts. Anion hydrolysis; cation hydrolysis; hydrolysis in general. Buffered solutions. Strengths of the oxygen acids. Simple rules. General concepts of acids and bases. Proton donors and acceptors. Acid strength and tendency to undergo condensation.

Exercises

20-12. Define indicator, and explain why most indicators undergo their color change within a range of about 2 pH units.

20-13. Which of these oxides are acid anhydrides and which basic anhydrides? Write an equation for each representing its reaction with water.

P_2O_3	Fe_2O_3	Na_2O	Mn_2O_7	RaO
Cl_2O	B_2O_3	Al_2O_3	MnO	SO_2
Cl_2O_7	CO_2	I_2O_5	TeO_3	SO_3
N_2O_5	Cu_2O	MgO	SiO_2	As_2O_3

20-14. How many grams of each of the following substances would be needed to make up 1 l of 0.1 N acid or base?

NaOH   CaO $NaHC_2O_4 \cdot H_2O$
H_2SO_4 $KHSO_4$ I_2O_5

20-15. What is the pH to 1 pH unit of 1 N HCl? of 0.1 N HCl? of 10 N HCl? of 0.1 N NaOH? of 10 N NaOH?

20-16. What is the normality of a solution of a strong acid 25.00 ml of which is rendered neutral by 33.35 ml of 0.1122 N NaOH solution?

20-17. A patent medicine for stomach ulcers contains 2.1 g of $Al(OH)_3$ per 100 ml. How far wrong is the statement on the label that the preparation is "capable of combining with 16 times its volume of $N/10$ HCl"?

20-18. Boric acid loses only one hydrogen ion. In 0.1 M H_3BO_3, $[H^+] = 1.05 \times 10^{-5}$. Calculate the ionization constant for boric acid.

20-19. What indicators should be used in titrating the following acids:

K_a

HNO$_2$ 4.5×10^{-4}
H_2S (first hydrogen) 1.1×10^{-7}
HCN $4 \ \ \times 10^{-10}$

20-20. With what indicators could you titrate separately for HCl and $HC_2H_3O_2$ in a solution containing both acids?

20-21. Calculate the pH of a solution that is 0.1 F in HNO_2 and 0.1 F in HCl.

20-22. What ionic and molecular species would be present in a solution prepared by mixing equal volumes of 1 N NaOH and 0.5 N NH_4OH? Estimate their concentrations.

20-23. Which of these substances form acidic solutions, which neutral, and which basic? Write equations for the reactions which give excess H^+ or OH^-.

NaCl $(NH_4)_2SO_4$ $CuSO_4$
NaCN $NaHSO_4$ $FeCl_2$
Na_3PO_4 NaH_2PO_4 $KAl(SO_4)_2$
NH_4Cl Na_2HPO_4 $Zn(ClO_4)_2$
NH_4CN $KClO_4$ BaO

20-24. Approximately how much acetic acid must be added to a 0.1 N solution of sodium acetate to make the solution neutral?

20-25. What relative weights of KH_2PO_4 and $Na_2HPO_4 \cdot 2H_2O$ should be taken to make a buffered solution with pH 6.0?

20-26. Calculate the pH of a solution that is prepared from
(a) 10 ml 1 F HCN, 10 ml 1 F NaOH
(b) 10 ml 1 F NH_4OH, 10 ml 1 F HCl
(c) 10 ml 1 F NH_4OH, 10 ml 1 F NH_4Cl

20-27. Calculate the pH of a solution that is
(a) 0.1 F in NH_4Cl, 0.1 F in NH_4OH
(b) 0.05 F in NH_4Cl, 0.15 F in NH_4OH
(c) 1.0 F in $HC_2H_3O_2$, 0.3 F in $NaC_2H_3O_2$
(d) prepared by mixing 10 ml of 1 F $HC_2H_3O_2$ with 90 ml 0.05 F NaOH.
Which of these would be good buffers?

20-28.   Calculate the hydrogen-ion concentration in the following solutions:
    (a) 1 M $HC_2H_3O_2$, $K = 1.8 \times 10^{-5}$
    (b) 0.06 M HNO_2, $K = 0.45 \times 10^{-3}$
    (c) 0.004 M NH_4OH, $K_b = 1.8 \times 10^{-5}$
    (d) 0.1 M HF, $K = 7.2 \times 10^{-4}$
    What are the pH values of the solutions?

20-29.   Carbon dioxide, produced by oxidation of substances in the tissues, is carried by the blood to the lungs. Part of it is in solution as carbonic acid, and part as hydrogen carbonate ion, HCO_3^-. If the pH of the blood is 7.4, what fraction is carried as the ion?

20-30.   Estimate the acid constants of H_2SeO_4, H_3AsO_4, H_5IO_6, HOCl, and H_3AsO_3, without reference to the text, by using the simple rule given in this chapter.

20-31.   Calculate the concentration of the various ionic and molecular species in a solution that is
    (a) 0.3 F in HCl, and 0.1 F in H_2S
    (b) buffered to a pH of 4, and 0.1 F in H_2S
    (c) 0.2 F in KHS
    (d) 0.2 F in K_2S

20-32.   The poisonous *botulinus* organism does not grow in canned vegetables if the pH is less than 4.5. Some investigators (*Journal of Chemical Education*, **22**, 409, [1945]) have recommended that in home canning of non-acid foods, such as beans, without a pressure canner a quantity of hydrochloric acid be added. The amount of hydrochloric acid recommended is 25 ml of 0.5 N hydrochloric acid per pint jar.

    Calculate the pH that this solution would have, assuming it originally to be neutral, and neglecting the buffering action of the organic material. Also calculate the amount of baking soda ($NaHCO_3$), measured in teaspoonfuls, that would be required to neutralize the acid after the jar is open. One teaspoonful equals 4 grams of baking soda.

Chapter 21

Solubility Product
and Precipitation

In the preceding chapter we have discussed the properties of acids and bases in relation to the theory of chemical equilibrium. Another important application of the theory of chemical equilibrium is that to the solubility of substances.

Often the success or failure of a chemical process depends upon the value of the solubility of a substance in a particular solvent. The ammonia-soda process for making sodium carbonate (Chapter 7) is an example. In general chemists have to resort to experiment to find the solubility of a substance in which they are interested. Many experimental values have been determined during the past hundred years, and can be found by looking in the tables of solubility in handbooks or reference books. There are certain circumstances, however, under which the effect of a change in the nature of the solvent on the solubility of a substance can be calculated from theoretical considerations. This is the question that we shall discuss in the present chapter.

In many cases the solubility of a substance is not changed very much by the addition of small amounts of other substances to the solution. Ordinarily, for example, the presence of a non-ionizing solute, such as sugar or iodine, has very little effect on the solubility of a salt in water, and conversely the presence of a salt such as sodium nitrate has little effect on the solubility of iodine or other non-ionizing substances in water. Also the presence of a salt that has no ion in common with another salt whose solubility is under consideration ordinarily produces only a rather small effect on the solubility of the second salt, usually a small increase.

Sometimes, however, the solubility of a substance in a particular solvent is greatly changed by the presence of other solutes. For example, iodine is very much more soluble in a solution containing iodide ion than it is in pure water. The reason for the increase in solubility is that iodine, I_2, combines with iodide ion, I^-, to form the complex *tri-iodide ion*, I_3^-:

$$I_2 + I^- \longrightarrow I_3^-$$

This phenomenon of *increase in solubility through the formation of a complex ion* is very important in many chemical processes. It will be discussed in the following chapter, which deals with the nature of complex ions.

Another important effect is the *decrease* in solubility of a salt because of the presence of another salt that has a *common ion* with the first salt. For example, it is found by experiment that 1.8 mg of silver chloride, AgCl, will dissolve in 1 liter of water at 20° C, but that only 0.0002 mg will dissolve in a liter of water containing 0.1 gfw of potassium chloride in solution. Thus the presence of the potassium chloride reduces the solubility of silver chloride to about 0.01 percent of its value in pure water. This effect is especially striking when it is remembered that most other salts, such as lead sulfate, $PbSO_4$, have the same solubility, to within 5 or 10 percent, in a 0.1 F solution of potassium chloride as in pure water.

The explanation of this effect is given in the following paragraphs.

21–1. *The Solubility-Product Principle*

Let us consider a system in which there is an aqueous solution containing silver ion, Ag^+, chloride ion, Cl^-, and perhaps other ions, in equilibrium with crystals of silver chloride. A crystal must be essentially electrically neutral, and because of this requirement a crystal grows by adding one silver ion and one chloride ion at nearly the same time. We may consider that the process of growth involves the combination of one silver ion with one chloride ion in solution to form an unionized AgCl molecule, which then attaches itself to the surface of the growing crystal. Similarly we may consider the process of solution of the crystal as involving the separation of an AgCl molecule from the surface of the crystal, and then its dissociation into the ions Ag^+ and Cl^- in the solution.

The solution is in equilibrium with the crystal when the number of molecules leaving the surface of the crystal in unit time is exactly equal to the number of molecules attaching themselves to the surface of the crystal in the same time; this represents the steady state characteristic of chemical equilibrium. Accordingly at saturation there would be present in the solution a certain concentration of undissociated silver chloride molecules, which we may represent by the symbol $[AgCl]_{maximum}$. If the concentration of silver chloride molecules in the solution has this value, $[AgCl]_{maximum}$, the solution is saturated with respect to silver chloride crystals. If, however, the concentration of silver chloride molecules is less than $[AgCl]_{maximum}$, the solution is an unsaturated solution, and more silver chloride would dissolve in it.

Now let us consider the equilibrium between the undissociated molecules AgCl and the ions. The reaction of dissociation of the molecules is

$$AgCl \rightleftharpoons Ag^+ + Cl^-$$

In accordance with the general discussion of chemical equilibrium given in Chapter 19, we may write the following equilibrium expression for this reaction:

$$\frac{[Ag^+][Cl^-]}{[AgCl]} = K \tag{1}$$

Here K is the equilibrium constant for the reaction of dissociation of silver chloride molecules into ions. We may rewrite this equation by multiplying through by $[AgCl]$:

$$[Ag^+][Cl^-] = [AgCl]K$$

Now in any saturated solution of silver chloride the value of $[AgCl]$ is the value corresponding to equilibrium with the crystal, that is, $[AgCl]_{maximum}$. This value is, at a given temperature, a constant for all solutions saturated with silver chloride. We may accordingly combine it with the dissociation constant K to produce a new constant K_{SP}, which is equal to $[AgCl]_{maximum}K$. The equilibrium expression then becomes, for a saturated solution,

$$[Ag^+][Cl^-] = K_{SF} \tag{2}$$

This equation is the equilibrium expression which holds for all solutions that are saturated with silver chloride. We see that the product of the concentration of the silver ion and the concentration of the chloride ion is equal to a constant, K_{SP}. This constant (which has a constant value at a given temperature, but in general will change somewhat with the temperature) is called the *solubility product* of silver chloride. The solubility-product equation may be used to calculate the solubility of silver chloride in solutions containing extra silver ions or extra chloride ions.

Let us first consider the effect of the chloride solution in a qualitative way, with the use of Le Chatelier's principle. Suppose that we have a saturated solution of silver chloride in pure water, and we then add some potassium chloride to the solution. The potassium chloride will ionize to produce potassium ions, K^+, and chloride ions, Cl^-. Accordingly the concentration of chloride ion in the solution is increased by the addition of potassium chloride. This increase in the concentration of chloride ion will have the effect of changing the equilibrium represented by Equation 1.

According to the principle of Le Chatelier, the equilibrium will shift in such a way as to tend to restore the original conditions; that is, as to tend to decrease the concentration of chloride ion toward the original value. This is done by the combination of silver ions and chloride ions to form silver chloride molecules, which will then attach themselves to the silver chloride crystal in order to preserve the equilibrium between the silver chloride crystal and the silver chloride molecules. Accordingly, by this argument, the addition of potassium chloride to a saturated solution of silver chloride would cause some of the silver chloride to crystallize out. This is a restatement of the fact mentioned above that silver chloride dissolves to a smaller extent in potassium chloride solution than in pure water.

The quantitative discussion of the solubility is described in the following examples.

Example 1. What is the value of the solubility product of silver chloride at 20° C?

    Solution. The solubility of silver chloride is 0.0018 g per liter at 20° C. The formula weight of AgCl is 143, and hence the solubility is equal to $\dfrac{0.0018}{143}$ or 1.27×10^{-5} gfw per liter. Silver chloride ionizes nearly completely to form silver ion and chloride ion, in dilute solution. We see that this solution contains 1.27×10^{-5} moles of silver ion per liter, and the same amount of chloride ion per liter:

$$[Ag^+] = 1.27 \times 10^{-5} \text{ mole/l}$$
$$[Cl^-] = 1.27 \times 10^{-5} \text{ mole/l}$$

The solubility product, K_{SP}, is equal to $[Ag^+][Cl^-]$. The numerical value of the solubility product is then found by use of Equation 2:

$$K_{SP} = [Ag^+][Cl^-] = 1.27 \times 10^{-5} \times 1.27 \times 10^{-5}$$
$$= 1.6 \times 10^{-10} \text{ mole}^2/l^2$$

Note that the units of this solubility product are mole^2/l^2 because the expression for the solubility product in this case involves a product of two ion concentrations.

The use of the solubility product in calculating solubility in the presence of a common ion is illustrated in the following example.

Example 2. Calculate the solubility of silver chloride in a 0.1 *F* solution of potassium chloride at 20° C.

    Solution. We know that the solubility of silver chloride is less in a solution containing chloride ion than in pure water, because of the common-ion effect, discussed above. Let us solve this problem by introducing the symbol x, equal to the solubility, in gfw per liter, of silver chloride in 1 F potassium chloride solution. Each molecule of silver chloride introduces one silver ion and one chloride ion: accordingly x gfw of AgCl in a liter of solution would produce x mole/l of silver ion and x mole/l of chloride ion. However, the solution already contains 0.1 mole per liter of chloride ion, resulting from the ionization of the 0.1 gfw/l of potassium chloride present. Hence we see that the total concentration of silver ion in the saturated solution is x, and the total concentration of chloride ion is $x + 0.1$.

$$[Ag^+] = x$$
$$[Cl^-] = x + 0.1$$

The product of the ion concentrations is equal to the solubility product, for every saturated solution of silver chloride. Using the numerical value of K_{SP}, from Example 1, we may accordingly write

$$x(x + 0.1) = K_{SP} = 1.6 \times 10^{-10}$$

The solution of this equation will give the answer to the problem.

It will be noted that this equation is a quadratic equation in x. If, in working one of the examples given at the end of this chapter, you obtain a cubic equation, or even a more complex algebraic equation, you must not give up. It is often possible to obtain an approximate solution of an equation of this sort without much effort. Let us consider the factors in the above equation. The first factor is x, the unknown quantity; there is nothing that we can do to change this factor—we want only to find its value. The second factor is $(x + 0.1)$. It is easy to simplify this factor. We know that the solubility of silver chloride in pure water is 1.27×10^{-5} (Example 1), and, from the foregoing discussion, that its solubility in the solution that we are now discussing is smaller. Thus we know that x is small compared with 0.1, and that, as an approximation, we could replace $x + 0.1$ simply by 0.1. If we do this, our equation becomes

$$0.1x = 1.6 \times 10^{-10}$$

or

$$x = 1.6 \times 10^{-9} \text{ mole/l.}$$

The value obtained for x in this way is so small compared with 1 that we see that the approximation that has been made was justified, and that this value, 1.6×10^{-9} mole/l, is the value of the concentration of silver ion in the saturated solution. Each silver ion resulted from the solution of 1 molecule of silver chloride; accordingly the solubility of silver chloride in this solution is **1.6 × 10⁻⁹ gfw per liter.** If we multiply this by the gram formula weight, 143, we obtain **2.3 × 10⁻⁷ g/l** as the calculated solubility of silver chloride in 0.1 F potassium chloride solution. This is about 0.01% of the solubility in pure water.

Whenever the problem arises of finding the solubility of a sparingly soluble salt in a solution in which there are already present either anions or cations of the salt itself, the solubility-product principle can be used. You must remember that *the solubility-product principle applies only to saturated solutions of the salt.* The product of the ion concentrations can of course have any value less than K_{SP} for an unsaturated solution.

The approximation of actual ionic solutions to ideal solutions is such that calculations made with use of the solubility-product principle are usually good to within 10% if the ionic concentrations are less than about 0.01 M, and to within 20% if they are less than about 0.1 M.

Illustrative Exercises

21-1. Silver chloride is about $1.3 \times 10^{-5} F$ soluble in water. Would you expect its solubility in 0.1 F NaNO₃ solution to be much less, about the same, or much greater? What would you expect its solubility in 0.1 F NaCl solution to be? In 0.1 F AgNO₃ solution.

21-2. How much AgBr would you predict to dissolve in 1 l of 1 F NaBr solution? The solubility product of AgBr is 4×10^{-13}.

21-3. The solubility product of AgI is 1×10^{-16}, and that of AgCl is 1.6×10^{-10}. What do you think would happen if 1 gram formula weight of AgCl, as a fine powder, were to be stirred into 1 l of 1 F KI solution? (Hint: Consider the reaction of Ag⁺ and I⁻ when some of the silver chloride dissolves.)

21–2. The Solubility of Carbonate in Acid. Hard Water

Effect of pH on Solubility. The solubility of many substances is strongly dependent on the acidity or basicity of the solution in which the substances are dissolved. An ordinary salt of a strong acid and a strong base, such as sodium chloride, is soluble to almost the same extent in an acidic or basic solution (not containing sodium ion or chloride ion) as in pure water. However, the solubility of an acid or a base in a solution which is not neutral would be expected to be changed because of the common-ion effect. This may be illustrated by the following example.

Hard Water. In Chapter 17 it was mentioned that hard water sometimes contains a large amount of dissolved calcium carbonate. Ordinarily we think of calcium carbonate as an insoluble substance, and the question about its occurrence in hard water is an interesting one.

Usually hard water (with temporary hardness, which can be removed by boiling) is described as containing calcium hydrogen carbonate, $Ca(HCO_3)_2$, in solution. There is in fact an equilibrium between various forms of carbonic acid in solution, molecules of unionized carbonic acid, H_2CO_3, being present, as well as hydrogen carbonate ions, HCO_3^-, and carbonate ions, CO_3^{--}. A solution is saturated with respect to calcium carbonate when the product of the concentration of calcium ion and the concentration of carbonate ion, CO_3^{--}, becomes equal to the solubility product of calcium carbonate.

In a basic solution only a very small amount of calcium carbonate needs to dissolve in order to saturate the solution with this substance. Accordingly ground water that is basic in reaction does not dissolve any significant amount of calcium carbonate as it filters through limestone. On the other hand, an acidic solution can dissolve a large amount of calcium carbonate, the increase of solubility being due to the conversion of the dissolved carbonate ion into hydrogen carbonate ion and unionized carbonic acid. Acidic ground water in a limestone district usually contains a large amount of calcium ion.

The following calculation shows that the solubility of calcium carbonate in neutral or slightly acidic water is many times greater than that in alkaline water.

The solubility product of calcium carbonate is 4.8×10^{-9}:

$$[Ca^{++}][CO_3^{--}] = 4.8 \times 10^{-9} \text{ mole}^2/l^2$$

In a solution sufficiently alkaline for all the carbonate to exist as the carbonate ion, CO_3^{--}, the solubility of calcium carbonate is just the square root of this solubility product. If 7×10^{-5} gfw of $CaCO_3$ is dissolved in a liter of water to form 7×10^{-5} mole/l of calcium ion and 7×10^{-5} mole/l of carbonate ion, CO_3^{--}, the product of these two concentrations is 49×10^{-10}, or 4.9×10^{-9}, which is thus equal to the solubility product. The gfw of calcium carbonate is 100, and accordingly the solubility of calcium carbonate in alkaline water is only 0.007 g/l. This is only 7 parts per million. As was stated in Chapter 17, domestic water with hardness less than 100 ppm is considered to be good, and accordingly we would not expect trouble from temporary hardness in a basic water.

Now let us consider an acidic ground water, perhaps with pH 6.3 after it has passed through the limestone. At pH 6.3 the hydrogen-ion concentration, $[H^+]$, is 5×10^{-7}. This hydrogen-ion concentration is so great that most of the carbonate present in the solution has been converted into hydrogen carbonate ion, HCO_3^-, or undissociated carbonic acid, H_2CO_3, by the reactions

$$CO_3^{--} + H^+ \rightleftarrows HCO_3^-$$

and

$$HCO_3^- + H^+ \rightleftarrows H_2CO_3$$

The equilibrium expression for the dissociation of HCO_3^- is

$$\frac{[H^+][CO_3^{--}]}{HCO_3^-} = K_{HCO_3^-} = 4.7 \times 10^{-11}$$

The above value for the acid constant for HCO_3^- has been given in Chapter 21. We can rewrite this equation by dividing through by $[H^+]$. It then becomes

$$\frac{[CO_3^{--}]}{[HCO_3^-]} = \frac{4.7 \times 10^{-11}}{[H^+]}$$

When the hydrogen ion concentration is 5×10^{-7}, we obtain the equation

$$\frac{[CO_3^{--}]}{[HCO_3^-]} = \frac{4.7 \times 10^{-11}}{5 \times 10^{-7}} = 0.94 \times 10^{-4}$$

Accordingly the concentration ratio of carbonate ion to hydrogen carbonate ion is approximately 1 : 10,000; there is about 10,000 times as much hydrogen carbonate ion present in the solution as carbonate ion.

The amount of unionized carbonic acid in the solution can be calculated in the same way. The equilibrium expression for the ionization of carbonic acid, H_2CO_3, into hydrogen ion and hydrogen carbonate ion is

$$\frac{[H^+][HCO_3^-]}{[H_2CO_3]} = K_{H_2CO_3} = 4.3 \times 10^{-7}$$

This may be rewritten as

$$\frac{[HCO_3^-]}{[H_2CO_3]} = \frac{4.3 \times 10^{-7}}{[H^+]}$$

Since the value of $[H^+]$ is 5×10^{-7} at pH 6.3, the ratio on the right is practically equal to unity. Accordingly we have found that at this pH the concentration of unionized carbonic acid is roughly equal to the concentration of hydrogen carbonate ion. The ratios of $[CO_3^{--}]$, $[HCO_3^-]$, and $[H_2CO_3]$ have thus been found to be 1 : 10,000 : 10,000. The total carbonate concentration, in all three forms, is accordingly 20,000 times the concentration of the carbonate ion, CO_3^{--}.

The equilibrium expression for a saturated solution of calcium carbonate

$$[Ca^{++}][CO_3^{--}] = K_{SP} = 4.8 \times 10^{-9}$$

can accordingly be written for a solution at pH 6.3 as

$$[Ca^{++}][\text{total carbonate in solution}] = 4.8 \times 10^{-9} \times 20,000$$
$$= 0.96 \times 10^{-4}$$

If no calcium ion or carbonate was present in the original water, the solution of calcium carbonate from the limestone would cause the two concentrations $[Ca^{++}]$ and [total carbonate in solution] to be equal. Each of these concentrations would then be equal to the square root of the number on the right-hand side of the above equation, and hence equal to 1×10^{-2} or 0.01 mole/l. This corresponds to just 1 g/l of calcium carbonate, or 1,000 parts per million, which would make the water too hard for domestic use.

21-3. *The Precipitation of Sulfides*

In most of the systems of qualitative analysis for the metal ions use is made of the procedure of *sulfide precipitation*. This involves the treatment of the solution with hydrogen sulfide, leading to the precipitation of about fifteen of the twenty-three or twenty-four metals that are commonly tested for.

The great usefulness of the sulfides in qualitative analysis depends on two factors—the great range of the solubilities of the sulfides, and the great range of the concentrations of the sulfide ion, S^{--}, which can be obtained by varying the acidity of the solutions. The range of concentrations of sulfide ions is determined by the pH of the solution in exactly the same way as described in the preceding paragraph for the dependence of carbonate-ion concentration on pH.

Some of the solubility products are the following:

	K_{SP}		K_{SP}
HgS	10^{-54}	ZnS	10^{-24}
CuS	10^{-40}	FeS	10^{-22}
CdS	10^{-28}	CoS*	10^{-21}
PbS	10^{-28}	NiS*	10^{-21}
SnS	10^{-28}	MnS*	10^{-16}

It is seen that these solubility products vary over a wide range, from 10^{-16} to 10^{-54}.

The acid constants for hydrogen sulfide are

$$K_{H_2S} = \frac{[H^+][HS^-]}{[H_2S]} = 9.1 \times 10^{-8}$$

$$K_{HS^-} = \frac{[H^+][S^{--}]}{[HS^-]} = 1.2 \times 10^{-15}$$

* CoS and NiS are probably dimorphous; the less soluble forms, with K_{SP} about 10^{-27}, are not easily precipitated from acid solutions. MnS is dimorphous; the value given is for the usual flesh-colored form, the green form having $K_{sp} = 10^{-22}$.

By multiplying these equations together we obtain

$$\frac{[H^+]^2[S^{--}]}{[H_2S]} = 9.1 \times 10^{-8} \times 1.2 \times 10^{-15} = 1.1 \times 10^{-22}$$

or

$$[S^{--}] = \frac{1.1 \times 10^{-22}[H_2S]}{[H^+]^2}$$

In the system of qualitative analysis part of the procedure consists in saturating a solution of suitable hydrogen-ion concentration with hydrogen sulfide. In a solution that is saturated with hydrogen sulfide gas at 1 atm the value of $[H_2S]$ is about 0.1 M. The foregoing equation then becomes

$$[S^{--}] = \frac{1.1 \times 10^{-23}}{[H^+]^2}$$

We see that by changing the pH from 0, corresponding to a 1 N solution of strong acid, to 12, corresponding to a moderately strongly basic solution, the sulfide-ion concentration can be varied throughout the great range from 10^{-23} mole/l to over 1 mole/l.

If the various metals are present in a solution which has been acidified with 0.3 N hydrochloric acid, some of the metal ions precipitate as sulfides and others do not. The metal ions that precipitate as sulfides under these conditions are Hg^{++}, Cu^{++}, Cd^{++}, Pb^{++}, Sn^{++}, Sn^{++++}, As^{+++}, As^{+++++}, Sb^{+++}, Sb^{+++++}, and Bi^{+++}. The solubility products for the corresponding sulfides, HgS, CuS, CdS, PbS, SnS, SnS_2, As_2S_3, As_2S_5, Sb_2S_3, Sb_2S_5, and Bi_2S_3, have values corresponding to precipitation under these conditions. These metals are said to constitute the *hydrogen sulfide group* in the system of qualitative analysis.

After the precipitate of these sulfides has been separated by filtration, the filtrate may be made neutral or basic by adding ammonium hydroxide. In a neutral or basic solution, with hydrogen-ion concentration less than 10^{-7}, the sulfide-ion concentration becomes greater than 10^{-9}, as is shown by the above equation. Under these conditions any sulfide MS with K_{SP} less than 10^{-13} would precipitate. This class includes the sulfides of Zn^{++}, Fe^{++}, Co^{++}, Ni^{++}, and Mn^{++}.

21–4. *Values of Solubility Products*

In Table 21-1 there are given values of the solubility-product constants at room temperature for many substances. More complete tables of values of these constants may be found in the handbooks and reference books mentioned at the end of Chapter 1.

TABLE 21-1   *Solubility-Product Constants at Room Temperature (18° to 25° C)*

HALIDES	K_{SP}	HALIDES	K_{SP}
AgCl	1.6×10^{-10}	Hg$_2$I$_2$*	1×10^{-28}
AgBr	4×10^{-13}	MgF$_2$	6×10^{-9}
AgI	1×10^{-16}	PbF$_2$	3.2×10^{-8}
BaF$_2$	1.7×10^{-6}	PbCl$_2$	1.7×10^{-5}
CaF$_2$	3.4×10^{-11}	PbBr$_2$	6.3×10^{-6}
CuCl	1×10^{-7}	PbI$_2$	9×10^{-9}
CuBr	1×10^{-8}	SrF$_2$	3×10^{-9}
CuI	1×10^{-12}	TlCl	2.0×10^{-4}
Hg$_2$Cl$_2$*	1×10^{-18}	TlBr	4×10^{-6}
Hg$_2$Br$_2$*	5×10^{-23}	TlI	6×10^{-8}

CARBONATES	K_{SP}	CARBONATES	K_{SP}
Ag$_2$CO$_3$	8×10^{-12}	FeCO$_3$	2×10^{-11}
BaCO$_3$	5×10^{-9}	MnCO$_3$	9×10^{-11}
CaCO$_3$	4.8×10^{-9}	PbCO$_3$	1×10^{-13}
CuCO$_3$	1×10^{-10}	SrCO$_3$	1×10^{-9}

CHROMATES	K_{SP}	CHROMATES	K_{SP}
Ag$_2$CrO$_4$	1×10^{-12}	PbCrO$_4$	2×10^{-14}
BaCrO$_4$	2×10^{-10}	SrCrO$_4$	3.6×10^{-5}

HYDROXIDES	K_{SP}	HYDROXIDES	K_{SP}
Al(OH)$_3$	1×10^{-33}	Fe(OH)$_3$	1×10^{-38}
Ca(OH)$_2$	8×10^{-6}	Mg(OH)$_2$	6×10^{-12}
Cd(OH)$_2$	1×10^{-14}	Mn(OH)$_2$	1×10^{-14}
Co(OH)$_2$	2×10^{-16}	Ni(OH)$_2$	1×10^{-14}
Cr(OH)$_3$	1×10^{-30}	Pb(OH)$_2$	1×10^{-16}
Cu(OH)$_2$	6×10^{-20}	Sn(OH)$_2$	1×10^{-26}
Fe(OH)$_2$	1×10^{-15}	Zn(OH)$_2$	1×10^{-17}

| SULFIDES: see Section 21-3 | | | |

SULFATES	K_{SP}	SULFATES	K_{SP}
Ag$_2$SO$_4$	1.2×10^{-5}	Hg$_2$SO$_4$*	6×10^{-7}
BaSO$_4$	1×10^{-10}	PbSO$_4$	2×10^{-8}
CaSO$_4 \cdot$ 2H$_2$O	2.4×10^{-5}	SrSO$_4$	2.8×10^{-7}

* The solubility-product expressions for mercurous salts involve the concentration $[Hg_2^{++}]$.

Concepts, Facts, and Terms Introduced in This Chapter

Decrease in solubility of a salt because of common-ion effects. The solubility product—a kind of equilibrium constant. Quantitative treatment of the common-ion effect.

Effect of pH on the solubility of acidic and basic substances. Solubility of calcium carbonate in water. Sulfide precipitation. Values of solubility products.

Exercises

21-4. State whether you would expect the solubility of lead chloride, $PbCl_2$, in a 1 F solution of each of the following salts to be much greater than, approximately equal to, or much less than that in pure water: Na_2SO_4, KCl, $KClO_4$, $Pb(C_2H_3O_2)_2$, $NaNO_3$.

21-5. Would you predict the solubility of lead chloride in a 1 F solution of lead acetate to be greater than or less than that in a 1 F solution of sodium chloride?

21-6. Making use of the solubility-product principle, explain why a metal hydroxide such as ferric hydroxide, $Fe(OH)_3$, is much more soluble in an acidic solution than it is in a basic solution.

21-7. The mineral gypsum has the formula $CaSO_4 \cdot 2H_2O$, its solubility product being 2.4×10^{-5} mole^2/l^2. Calculate the solubility of calcium sulfate in grams of anhydrous $CaSO_4$ per liter. Would you expect ground water which has filtered through a deposit of gypsum to be hard?

21-8. Would you predict acidic ground water which has filtered through a deposit of gypsum to have greater hardness, the same hardness, or smaller hardness than basic ground water that has filtered through a deposit of gypsum? Explain your answer.

21-9. Discuss the hardness of ground water in a limestone region, in terms of the pH of the water. Describe and explain the method of softening hard water with temporary hardness by the use of calcium hydroxide.

21-10. Discuss the principles involved in the separation of heavy metals into two groups by precipitation of their sulfides.

21-11. The value of K_{sp} for silver iodide, AgI, is 1×10^{-16}. What is the solubility of this salt in water, in gfw/l and g/l?

21-12. What would you expect to happen if 1 g of finely powdered silver iodide were stirred into a 1 F solution of sodium chloride? The solubility-product constants are given in Table 22-1.

21-13. Would lead chloride or lead iodide precipitate first if a solution of lead acetate were added drop by drop to a solution 1 M in chloride ion and 1 M in iodide ion? What would be the composition of the solution when the second salt began to precipitate? The solubility products are given in Table 22-1.

21-14. (a) Would silver acetate, $AgC_2H_3O_2$, be more soluble or less soluble in a buffered solution at pH 4.7 than in a basic solution, with pH greater than 7? Be sure to consider the equilibrium between hydrogen ion, acetate ion, and acetic acid in solving this problem. (b) After answering the foregoing question qualitatively, calculate the ratio of solubilities in these two solutions.

21-15. Using the solubility product of silver acetate, 3.6×10^{-3}, and the ionization constant of acetic acid, calculate the solubility of silver acetate in a basic solution, a solution with pH 4.7, and a solution with pH 3.4.

21-16. The value of the solubility product for barium carbonate is 5×10^{-9}. What is the solubility of this salt in solutions buffered at pH 12, 8, 7, and 6? How would you describe ground water which has been filtered through a deposit of barite, $BaCO_3$. and had these pH values?

Chapter 22

Complex Ions

22–1. The Nature of Complex Ions

An ion which contains several atoms, such as the sulfate ion, SO_4^{--}, is called a *complex ion*. Familiar examples of complex ions other than those of the oxygen acids are the deep blue cupric ammonia complex ion, $Cu(NH_3)_4^{++}$, which is formed by adding ammonium hydroxide to a solution of cupric salt, the ferrocyanide ion, $Fe(CN)_6^{----}$, the ferricyanide ion, $Fe(CN)_6^{---}$, and the triiodide ion, I_3^-. Even the hydrated metal ions such as $Al(H_2O)_6^{+++}$ are properly considered to be complex ions.

Complex ions are important in the methods of separation used in qualitative and quantitative chemical analysis and in various industrial processes. Their structure and properties are discussed in detail in this chapter.

22–2. Ammonia Complexes

A solution of a cupric salt is blue in color. This blue color is due to the absorption of yellow and red light, and consequent preferential transmission of blue light. The molecular species which absorbs the light is the *hydrated copper ion*, probably $Cu(H_2O)_4^{++}$. Crystalline hydrated cupric salts such as $CuSO_4 \cdot 5H_2O$ are blue, like the aqueous solution, whereas anhydrous $CuSO_4$ is white.*

When a few drops of sodium hydroxide solution are added to a cupric solution a blue precipitate is formed. This is cupric hydroxide, $Cu(OH)_2$, which precipitates when the ion concentration product $|Cu^{++}||OH^-|^2$ reaches the solubility product of the hydroxide. (Here the

---

* The crystal structure of $CuSO_4 \cdot 5H_2O$ shows that in the crystal four water molecules are attached closely to the cupric ion, and the fifth is more distant.

symbol Cu^{++} is used, as is conventional, for the ion species $Cu(H_2O)_4^{++}$.)
Addition of more sodium hydroxide solution leads to no further change.

If ammonium hydroxide is added in place of sodium hydroxide the same precipitate of $Cu(OH)_2$ is formed. On addition of more ammonium hydroxide, however, the precipitate dissolves, giving a clear solution with a deeper and more intense blue color than the original cupric solution.*

The solution of the precipitate cannot be attributed to increase in hydroxide-ion concentration, because sodium hydroxide does not cause it, nor to ammonium ion, because ammonium salts do not cause it. There remains undissociated NH_4OH or NH_3, which might combine with the cupric ion. It has in fact been found that the new deep blue ion species formed by addition of an excess of ammonium hydroxide is the **cupric ammonia complex** $Cu(NH_3)_4^{++}$, similar to the hydrated cupric ion except that the four water molecules have been replaced by ammonia molecules. This complex is sometimes called the *cupric tetrammine complex*, the word *ammine* meaning an attached ammonia molecule.

Salts of this complex ion can be crystallized from ammonia solution. The best known one is **cupric tetrammine sulfate monohydrate,** $Cu(NH_3)_4SO_4 \cdot H_2O$, which has the same deep blue color as the solution.

The reason that the precipitate of cupric hydroxide dissolves in an excess of ammonium hydroxide can be given in the following way. A precipitate of cupric hydroxide is formed because the concentration of cupric ion and the concentration of hydroxide ion are greater than the values corresponding to the solubility product of cupric hydroxide. If there were some way for copper to be present in the solution without exceeding the solubility product of cupric hydroxide then precipitation would not occur. In the presence of ammonia, copper exists in the solution not as the cupric ion (that is, the hydrated cupric ion), but principally as the cupric ammonia complex $Cu(NH_3)_4^{++}$. This complex is far more stable than the hydrated cupric ion. The reaction of formation of the cupric ammonia complex is

$$Cu^{++} + 4NH_3 \rightleftharpoons Cu(NH_3)_4^{++}$$

We see from the equation for the reaction that the addition of ammonia to the solution causes the equilibrium to shift to the right, more of the cupric ion being converted into cupric ammonia complex as more and more ammonia is added to the solution. When sufficient ammonia is present a large amount of copper may exist in the solution as cupric ammonia complex, at the same time that the cupric ion concentration is less than that required to cause precipitation of cupric hydroxide. When ammonia is added to a solution in contact with the precipitate of cupric hydroxide, the cupric ion in the solution is con-

---

* In describing color the adjective deep refers not to intensity but to shade; deep blue tends toward indigo.

verted to cupric ammonia complex, causing the solution to be unsaturated with respect to cupric hydroxide. The cupric hydroxide precipitate then dissolves, and if enough ammonia is present the process continues until the precipitate has dissolved completely.

This process of **solution of a slightly soluble substance through formation of a complex by one of its ions** is the basis of some of the most important practical applications of complex formation. Several examples are mentioned later in this chapter.

The nickel ion forms two rather stable ammonia complexes. When a small amount of ammonium hydroxide solution is added to a solution of a nickel salt (green in color) a pale green precipitate of nickel hydroxide, $Ni(OH)_2$, is formed. On addition of more ammonium hydroxide solution this dissolves to give a blue solution, which with still more ammonium hydroxide changes color to light blue-violet.

The light blue-violet complex is shown to be the **nickel hexammine ion**, $Ni(NH_3)_6^{++}$, by the facts that the same color is shown by crystalline $Ni(NH_3)_6Cl_2$ and other crystals containing six ammonia molecules per nickel ion, and that x-ray studies have revealed the presence in these crystals of octahedral complexes in which the six ammonia molecules are situated about the nickel ion at the corners of a regular octahedron. The structure of crystalline $Ni(NH_3)_6Cl_2$ is shown in Figure 22-1.

The blue complex is probably the **nickel tetramminedihydrate ion,** $Ni(NH_3)_4(H_2O)_2^{++}$. Careful studies of the change in color with in-

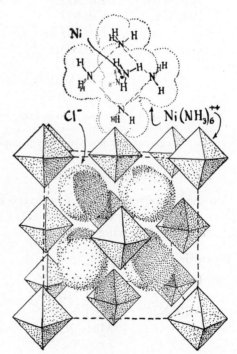

FIGURE 22-1

The structure of crystalline nickel hexammine chloride, $Ni(NH_3)_6Cl_2$. The crystal contains octahedral nickel hexammine ions and chloride ions.

creasing ammonia concentration indicate that the ammonia molecules are added one by one, and that all the complexes $Ni(H_2O)_6^{++}$, $Ni(H_2O)_5NH_3^{++}$, $Ni(H_2O)_4(NH_3)_2^{++}$, $Ni(H_2O)_3(NH_3)_3^{++}$, $Ni(H_2O)_2$ $(NH_3)_4^{++}$, $Ni(H_2O)(NH_3)_5^{++}$, and $Ni(NH_3)_6^{++}$ exist.

Several metal ions form ammonia complexes with sufficient stability to put the hydroxides into solution. Others, such as aluminum and iron, do not. The formulas of the stable complexes are given below. There is no great apparent order about the stability or composition of the complexes, except that often the unipositive ions add two, the bipositive ions four, and the terpositive ions six ammonia molecules.

The **silver ammonia complex,** $Ag(NH_3)_2^+$, is sufficiently stable for ammonium hydroxide to dissolve precipitated silver chloride by reducing the concentration of silver ion, $[Ag^+]$, below the value required for precipitation by the solubility product of AgCl. A satisfactory test for silver ion is the formation with chloride ion of a precipitate which is soluble in ammonium hydroxide. Ammonia complexes in general are decomposed by acid, because of formation of ammonium ion; for example, as in the reaction

$$Ag(NH_3)_2^+ + Cl^- + 2H^+ \longrightarrow AgCl \downarrow + 2NH_4^+$$

Stable Ammonia Complexes

$Cu(NH_3)_2^+$	$Cu(NH_3)_4^{++}$	$Co(NH_3)_6^{+++}$
$Ag(NH_3)_2^+$	$Zn(NH_3)_4^{++}$	$Cr(NH_3)_6^{+++}$
$Au(NH_3)_2^+$	$Cd(NH_3)_4^{++}$	
	$Hg(NH_3)_2^{++}$	
	$Hg(NH_3)_4^{++}$	
	$Ni(NH_3)_4^{++}$	
	$Ni(NH_3)_6^{++}$	
	$Co(NH_3)_6^{++}$	

Notes: 1. Cobaltous ammonia ion is easily oxidized by air to cobaltic ammonia ion.
2. Chromic ammonia ion forms only slowly, and is decomposed by boiling, to give chromium hydroxide precipitate.

22–3. Cyanide Complexes

Another important class of complex ions includes those formed by the metal ions with cyanide ion. The common cyanide complexes are given in the following table.

Cyanide Complexes

$Cu(CN)_2^-$	$Zn(CN)_4^{--}$	$Fe(CN)_6^{---}$
$Ag(CN)_2^-$	$Cd(CN)_4^{--}$	$Co(CN)_6^{---}$
$Au(CN)_2^-$	$Hg(CN)_4^{--}$	
	$Mn(CN)_6^{----}$	
	$Fe(CN)_6^{----}$	$Au(CN)_4^-$
	$Co(CN)_6^{----}$	

Some of these complexes are very stable—the stability of the **argentocyanide ion,** $Ag(CN)_2{}^-$, for example, is so great that addition of iodide ion does not cause silver iodide to precipitate, even though the solubility product of silver iodide is very small. The **ferrocyanide ion,** $Fe(CN)_6{}^{----}$, **ferricyanide ion,** $Fe(CN)_6{}^{---}$, and **cobalticyanide ion,** $Co(CN)_6{}^{---}$, are so stable that they are not appreciably decomposed by strong acid. The others are decomposed by strong acid, with the formation of hydrocyanic acid, HCN.

An illustration of the stability of the ferrocyanide complex is provided by the old method of making potassium ferrocyanide, $K_4Fe(CN)_6$, by strongly heating nitrogenous organic material (such as dried blood and hides) with potassium hydroxide and iron filings.

The **cobaltocyanide ion,** $Co(CN)_6{}^{----}$, is, like the cobaltous ammonia complex, a very strong reducing agent; it is able to decompose water, liberating hydrogen, as it changes into cobalticyanide ion.

Cyanide solutions are used in the **electroplating** of gold, silver, zinc, cadmium, and other metals. In these solutions the concentrations of uncomplexed metal ions are very small, and this favors the production of a uniform fine-grained deposit. Other complex-forming anions (tartrate, citrate, chloride, hydroxide) are also used in plating solutions.

22–4. *Complex Halogenides and Other Complex Ions*

Nearly all anions can enter into complex formation with metal ions. Thus stannic chloride, $SnCl_4$, forms with chloride ion the stable **hexachlorostannate ion,** $SnCl_6{}^{--}$, which with cations crystallizes in an extensive series of salts. Various complexes of this kind are discussed below.

Chloride Complexes. Many chloride complexes are known; representative are the following:

$CuCl_2(H_2O)_2, CuCl_3(H_2O)^-, CuCl_4{}^{--}$
$AgCl_2{}^-, AuCl_2{}^-$
$HgCl_4{}^{--}$
$CdCl_4{}^{--}, CdCl_6{}^{----}$
$SnCl_6{}^{--}$
$PtCl_6{}^{--}$
$AuCl_4{}^-$

The cupric chloride complexes are recognizable in strong hydrochloric acid solutions by their green color. The crystal $CuCl_2 \cdot 2H_2O$ is bright green, and x-ray studies have shown that it contains the complex molecule $CuCl_2(H_2O)_2$. The ion $CuCl_3(H_2O)^-$ is usually written $CuCl_3{}^-$; it is highly probable that the indicated water molecule is present, and, indeed, the ion $Cu(H_2O)_3Cl^+$ very probably also exists in solution.

The stability of the **tetrachloroaurate ion** $AuCl_4^-$ is responsible for the ability of aqua regia, a mixture of nitric and hydrochloric acids, to dissolve gold, which is not significantly soluble in the acids separately. Nitric acid serves as the oxidizing agent which oxidizes gold to the terpositive state, and the chloride ions provided by the hydrochloric acid further the reaction by combining with the auric ion to form the stable complex:

$$Au + 4HCl + 3HNO_3 \longrightarrow HAuCl_4 + 3NO_2 \uparrow + 3H_2O$$

The solution of platinum in aqua regia likewise results in the stable **hexachloroplatinate ion,** $PtCl_6^{--}$.

Other Halogenide Complexes. The bromide and iodide complexes closely resemble the chloride complexes, and usually have similar formulas.

Fluoride ion is more effective than the other halogenide ions in forming complexes. Important examples are the **tetrafluoroborate ion,** BF_4^-, the **hexafluorosilicate ion,** SiF_6^{--}, the **hexafluoroaluminate ion,** AlF_6^{---}, and the **ferric hexafluoride ion,** FeF_6^{---}.

The **triiodide ion,** I_3^-, is formed by dissolving iodine in an iodide solution. Other similar complexes exist, including the **dibromoiodide** and **dichloroiodide ions,** IBr_2^- and ICl_2^-.

Complexes with Thiosulfate, Nitrite, etc. A useful complex is that formed by thiosulfate ion, $S_2O_3^{--}$, and silver ion. Its formula is $Ag(S_2O_3)_2^{---}$, and its structure is

This complex ion is sufficiently stable to cause silver chloride and bromide to be soluble in thiosulfate solutions, and this is the reason that sodium thiosulfate solution ("hypo") is used after development of a photographic film or paper to dissolve away the unreduced silver halide, which if allowed to remain in the emulsion would in the course of time darken through long exposure to light.

Of the nitrite complexes that with cobaltic ion, $Co(NO_2)_6^{---}$, called the **cobaltinitrite ion** or **hexanitritocobaltic ion,** is the most familiar. **Potassium cobaltinitrite,** $K_3Co(NO_2)_6$, is one of the least soluble potassium salts, and its precipitation on addition of sodium cobaltinitrite reagent is commonly used as a test for potassium ion.

Ferric ion and thiocyanate ion combine to give a product with an intense red color; this reaction is used as a test for ferric ion. The red color seems to be due to various complexes, ranging from $Fe(H_2O)_5NCS^{++}$ to $Fe(NCS)_6^{---}$. The azide ion, NNN^-, gives a similar color with ferric ion.

The Chromic and Cobaltic Complexes.   Terpositive chromium and cobalt combine with cyanide ion, nitrite ion, chloride ion, sulfate ion, oxalate ion, water, ammonia, and many other ions and molecules to form a very great number of complexes, with a wide range of colors, which are nearly the same for corresponding chromic and cobaltic complexes. Most of these complexes are stable, and are formed and decomposed slowly. Representative are the members of the series

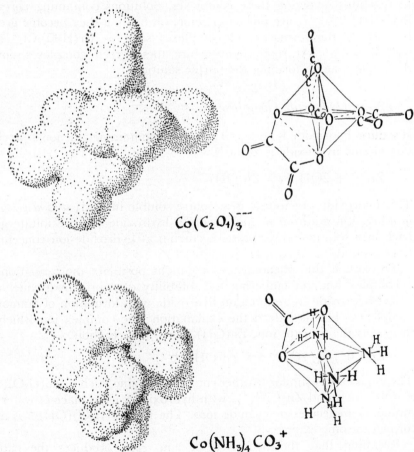

$Co(C_2O_4)_3^{---}$

$Co(NH_3)_4CO_3^+$

FIGURE 22-2   *The structure of the cobaltic trioxalate ion, $Co(C_2O_4)_3^{---}$, and the cobaltic tetrammine carbonate ion, $Co(NH_3)_4CO_3^+$. Two oxygen atoms of each oxalate group or carbonate group are bonded to cobalt, and occupy two of the six corners of the octahedron. These corners must be adjacent, connected by an edge of the octahedron.*

$$Cr(NH_3)_6^{+++} \qquad\qquad Cr(NH_3)_5Cl^{++} \qquad\qquad Cr(NH_3)_4Cl_2^{+}$$
$$\text{yellow} \qquad\qquad\qquad\qquad \text{purple} \qquad\qquad\qquad\qquad \text{green}$$

$$Cr(NH_3)_3Cl_3 \qquad\qquad\qquad Cr(NH_3)_2Cl_4^{-}$$
$$\text{violet} \qquad\qquad\qquad\qquad \text{orange-red}$$

and

$$Co(NH_3)_6^{+++} \qquad\qquad Co(NH_3)_5H_2O^{+++} \quad \cdot\cdot \quad Co(H_2O)_6^{+++}$$
$$\text{yellow} \qquad\qquad\qquad\qquad \text{rose-red} \qquad\qquad\qquad \text{purple}$$

A group such as oxalate ion, $C_2O_4^{--}$, or carbonate ion, CO_3^{--}, may occupy two of the six coordination places in an octahedral complex; examples are $Co(NH_3)_4CO_3^{+}$ and $Cr(C_2O_4)_3^{---}$. The structure of these complexes is shown in Figure 22-2.

The often puzzling color changes shown by chromic solutions are due to reactions involving these complexes. Solutions containing chromic ion, $Cr(H_2O)_6^{+++}$, are purple in color; on heating they become green, because of the formation of complexes such as $Cr(H_2O)_4Cl_2^{+}$ and $Cr(H_2O)_5SO_4^{+}$. At room temperature these green complexes slowly decompose, again forming the purple solution.

22–5. *Hydroxide Complexes*

If sodium hydroxide is added to a solution containing zinc ion a precipitate of zinc hydroxide is formed:

$$Zn^{++} + 2OH^- \rightleftarrows Zn(OH)_2$$

This hydroxide precipitate is of course soluble in acid; *it is also soluble in alkali*. On addition of more sodium hydroxide the precipitate goes back into solution, this process occurring at hydroxide-ion concentrations around 0.1 M to 1 M.

To explain this phenomenon we might postulate the formation of a complex ion, remembering the solubility of cupric hydroxide and nickel hydroxide in ammonium hydroxide with formation of ammonia complexes. This is indeed the explanation; the complex ion which is formed is the **zincate ion**, $Zn(OH)_4^{--}$, by the reaction

$$Zn(OH)_2 + 2OH^- \rightleftarrows Zn(OH)_4^{--}$$

The ion is closely similar to other complexes of zinc, such as $Zn(H_2O)_4^{++}$, $Zn(NH_3)_4^{++}$, and $Zn(CN)_4^{--}$, with hydroxide ions in place of water or ammonia molecules or cyanide ions. The ion $Zn(H_2O)(OH)_3^-$ is also formed to some extent.

Recalling that the hydrolysis of zinc salts produces the cation $Zn(H_2O)_3OH^+$, we see that the molecular species which exist in zinc solutions of different pH values are the following:

Acidic solution $\qquad \begin{cases} Zn(H_2O)_4^{++} \\ Zn(H_2O)_3(OH)^{+} \end{cases}$

Neutral solution $Zn(H_2O)_2(OH)_2 \rightleftharpoons Zn(OH)_2 \downarrow$

Basic solution $\begin{cases} Zn(H_2O)(OH)_3^- \\ Zn(OH)_4^{--} \end{cases}$

The conversion of each complex into the following one occurs by removal of a proton from one of the four water molecules of the tetrahydrated zinc ion. The precipitate of zinc hydroxide is formed by loss of water from the neutral complex $Zn(H_2O)_2(OH)_2$.

The precipitate $Zn(OH)_2$ also fits into the system of complexes, despite the difference of its formula from the general expression ZnX_4. Two molecules of $Zn(H_2O)_2(OH)_2$ can combine with loss of one molecule of water to form the larger complex

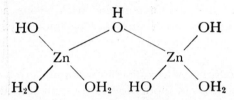

In this complex, $Zn_2(H_2O)_3(OH)_4$, each zinc ion is surrounded by four oxygen atoms (of OH^- or H_2O), exactly as in the hydrated zinc cation or the zincate anion; the loss of water without decrease in ligancy is achieved by the dual role played by one hydroxide oxygen atom, which serves as part of the coordination tetrahedron for both zinc ions. By continuing this process all of the tetrahedra can be linked together into an infinite framework, in which each tetrahedron shares its corners with four other tetrahedra. This is the structure of the $Zn(OH)_2$ precipitate.

Amphoteric Hydroxides. A hydroxide, such as zinc hydroxide, which can combine with acids to form salts and also with bases to form salts is called an *amphoteric hydroxide*. The amphoteric properties of a metal hydroxide are determined by the stability of the hydroxide complex of the metal.

The principal common amphoteric hydroxides and their anions* are the following:

$Zn(OH)_2$	$Zn(OH)_4^{--}$,	zincate ion
$Al(OH)_3$	$Al(OH)_4^-$,	aluminate ion
$Cr(OH)_3$	$Cr(OH)_4^-$,	chromite ion
$Pb(OH)_2$	$Pb(OH)_3^-$,	plumbite ion
$Sn(OH)_2$	$Sn(OH)_3^-$,	stannite ion

* Because of the difficulty of determining the amount of hydration of an ion in aqueous solutions, chemists have been slow to accept these formulas; the older formulas are ZnO_2^{--}, AlO_2^-, etc.

It is possible that plumbite ion and stannite ion contain more hydroxide groups than indicated.

In addition the following hydroxides evidence acidic properties by combining with hydroxide ion to form complex anions:

$Sn(OH)_4$	$Sn(OH)_6^{--}$,	stannate ion
$As(OH)_3$	$As(OH)_4^-$,	arsenite ion
$As(OH)_5$	AsO_4^{---},	arsenate ion
$Sb(OH)_3$	$Sb(OH)_4^-$,	antimonite ion
$Sb(OH)_5$	$Sb(OH)_6^-$,	antimonate ion

Except for arsenate ion, and possibly arsenite ion, the anions are hydroxide complexes as indicated.

The hydroxides of this second set are not properly described as amphoteric, despite their acidic properties, because they do not have basic properties. These hydroxides do not combine with strong acids in general, but dissolve in acid only in the presence of anions such as chloride ion with which they can form complexes, such as the chlorostannate ion, $SnCl_6^{--}$.

The hydroxides listed above form hydroxide complex anions to a sufficient extent to make them soluble in moderately strong alkali. Other common hydroxides have weaker acidic properties: $Cu(OH)_2$ and $Co(OH)_2$ are only slightly soluble in very strong alkali, and $Cd(OH)_2$, $Fe(OH)_3$, $Mn(OH)_2$, and $Ni(OH)_2$ are effectively insoluble. The common analytical method of separation of Al^{+++}, Cr^{+++}, and Zn^{++} from Fe^{+++}, Mn^{++}, Co^{++}, and Ni^{++} with use of sodium hydroxide is based on these facts.

22–6. Sulfide Complexes

Sulfur, which is directly below oxygen in the periodic table of the elements, has many similar properties with it. One of these is the property of combining with another atom to form complexes; there exist *sulfo acids* (thio acids) of many elements similar to the oxygen acids. An example is **sulfophosphoric acid,** H_3PS_4, which corresponds exactly in formula to phosphoric acid, H_3PO_4. This sulfo acid is not of much importance; it is unstable, and hydrolyzes in water to phosphoric acid and hydrogen sulfide:

$$H_3PS_4 + 4H_2O \longrightarrow H_3PO_4 + 4H_2S$$

But other sulfo acids, such as **sulfarsenic acid,** H_3AsS_4, are stable, and are of use in analytical chemistry and in chemical industry.

All of the following arsenic acids are known:

$$H_3AsO_4 \quad H_3AsO_3S \quad H_3AsO_2S_2 \quad H_3AsOS_3 \quad H_3AsS_4$$

The structure of the five complex anions AsO_4^{---}, AsO_3S^{---}, $AsO_2S_2^{---}$, $AsOS_3^{---}$, and AsS_4^{---} is the same: an arsenic atom surrounded tetrahedrally by four other atoms, oxygen or sulfur.

Some metal sulfides are soluble in solutions of sodium sulfide or ammonium sulfide because of formation of a complex sulfo anion. The important members of this class are HgS, As_2S_3, Sb_2S_3, As_2S_5, Sb_2S_5, and SnS_2, which react with sulfide ion in the following ways:

$$HgS + S^{--} \rightleftarrows HgS_2^{--}$$
$$As_2S_3 + 3S^{--} \rightleftarrows 2AsS_3^{---}$$
$$Sb_2S_3 + 3S^{--} \rightleftarrows 2SbS_3^{---}$$
$$As_2S_5 + 3S^{--} \rightleftarrows 2AsS_4^{---}$$
$$Sb_2S_5 + 3S^{--} \rightleftarrows 2SbS_4^{---}$$
$$SnS_2 + S^{--} \rightleftarrows SnS_3^{--}$$

Mercuric sulfide is soluble in a solution of sodium sulfide and sodium hydroxide (to repress hydrolysis of the sulfide, which would decrease the sulfide ion concentration), but not in a solution of ammonium sulfide and ammonium hydroxide, in which the sulfide-ion concentration is smaller. The other sulfides listed are soluble in both solutions. CuS, Ag_2S, Bi_2S_3, CdS, PbS, ZnS, CoS, NiS, FeS, MnS, and SnS are not soluble in sulfide solutions, but most of these form complex sulfides by fusion with Na_2S or K_2S. Although SnS is not soluble in Na_2S or $(NH_4)_2S$ solutions, it dissolves in solutions containing both sulfide and disulfide, Na_2S_2 or $(NH_4)_2S_2$, or sulfide and peroxide. The disulfide ion, S_2^{--}, or peroxide oxidizes the tin to the stannic level, and the sulfostannate ion is then formed:

$$SnS + S_2^{--} \rightleftarrows SnS_3^{--}$$

Many schemes of qualitative analysis involve separation of the copper-group sulfides (PbS, Bi_2S_3, CuS, CdS) from the tin-group sulfides (HgS, As_2S_3, As_2S_5, Sb_2S_3, Sb_2S_5, SnS, SnS_2) by treatment with Na_2S-Na_2S_2 solution, which dissolves only the tin-group sulfides.

22–7. The Quantitative Treatment of Complex Formation

The quantitative theory of chemical equilibrium, as discussed in earlier chapters, can be applied in a straightforward manner to problems involving the formation of complexes. Some of the ways in which this can be done are exemplified in the following paragraphs.

Example 1. Ammonium hydroxide is added to a cupric solution until a precipitate is formed, and the addition is continued until part of the precipitate has dissolved to give a deep blue solution. What would be the effect of dissolving some ammonium chloride in the solution?

Solution. The weak base NH_4OH is partially ionized and is in equilibrium with dissolved ammonia:

$$NH_3 + H_2O \rightleftarrows NH_4OH \rightleftarrows NH_4^+ + OH^-$$

Addition of NH_4Cl would increase $[NH_4]^+$, which would shift the equilibrium to the left, producing more NH_3 and decreasing the hydroxide-ion concentration. The precipitate $Cu(OH)_2$ is in equilibrium with the solution according to the reaction

$$Cu(OH)_2 + 4NH_3 \rightleftharpoons Cu(NH_3)_4^{++} + 2OH^-$$

Both the increase of $[NH_3]$ and the decrease of $[OH^-]$ caused by addition of NH_4Cl to the solution would shift this reaction to the right; hence more of the precipitate would dissolve.

Example 2. Would a precipitate of AgCl be formed if 1 ml of 1 F $AgNO_3$ were added to 100 ml of a solution 1 M in CN^- and 1 M in Cl^-? The solubility product of AgCl is 1×10^{-10} and the complex formation constant of $Ag(CN)_2^-$ is

$$\frac{[Ag(CN)_2^-]}{[Ag^+][CN^-]^2} = 1 \times 10^{21}$$

Solution. With $[CN^-] = 1$, the ratio $[Ag^+]/[Ag(CN)_2^-]$ has the value 1×10^{-21}. Hence if all the added silver ion were in solution the value of $[Ag(CN)_2^-]$ would be 10^{-2} (since except for a minute amount the total silver present would be in the form of this complex), and the value of $[Ag^+]$ would be $10^{-2} \times 10^{-21} = 10^{-23}$. Now the product $[Ag^+][Cl^-]$ equals 10^{-23} if $[Ag^+] = 10^{-23}$ and $[Cl^-] = 1$; the product of these values is very much smaller than the solubility product 10^{-10}, so that the solution is far from saturated with respect to AgCl, and no precipitate would form.

TABLE 22-1   *Ammonia Concentrations Producing 50% Conversion of Metal Ions to Complexes*

METAL ION	COMPLEX ION	AMMONIA CONCENTRATION
Cu^+	$Cu(NH_3)_2^+$	5×10^{-6}
Ag^+	$Ag(NH_3)_2^+$	2×10^{-4}
Zn^{++}	$Zn(NH_3)_4^{++}$	5×10^{-3}
Cd^{++}	$Cd(NH_3)_4^{++}$	5×10^{-2}
	$Cd(NH_3)_6^{++}$	10
Hg^{++}	$Hg(NH_3)_2^{++}$	2×10^{-9}
	$Hg(NH_3)_4^{++}$	2×10^{-1}
Cu^{++}	$Cu(NH_3)_4^{++}$	5×10^{-4}
Ni^{++}	$Ni(NH_3)_4^{++}$	5×10^{-2}
	$Ni(NH_3)_6^{++}$	5×10^{-1}
Co^{++}	$Co(NH_3)_6^{++}$	1×10^{-1}
Co^{+++}	$Co(NH_3)_6^{+++}$	1×10^{-6}

In Tables 22-1 and 22-2 there are given values of equilibrium constants or equivalent constants for the reactions of formation of some complexes. The values of equilibrium constants must be used with some caution in making calculations. Thus for the reaction

$$Cu^{++} + 4NH_3 \rightleftharpoons Cu(NH_3)_4^{++}$$

we would write $K = \dfrac{[Cu(NH_3)_4^{++}]}{[Cu^{++}][NH_3]^4}$ as the equilibrium constant, and

expect the concentration ratio $[Cu(NH_3)_4^{++}]/[Cu^{++}]$ to vary with the fourth power of the ammonia concentration. This is true, however, only as an approximation, because of the fact that the reaction is more complicated than this. Actually the ammonia molecules attach themselves to the copper ion one at a time (replacing water molecules), and an accurate treatment would require that there be considered the four successive equilibria

$$Cu(H_2O)_4^{++} + NH_3 \rightleftharpoons Cu(H_2O)_3NH_3^{++} + H_2O$$
$$Cu(H_2O)_3NH_3^{++} + NH_3 \rightleftharpoons Cu(H_2O)_2(NH_3)_2^{++} + H_2O$$
$$Cu(H_2O)_2(NH_3)_2^{++} + NH_3 \rightleftharpoons CuH_2O(NH_3)_3^{++} + H_2O$$
$$CuH_2O(NH_3)_3^{++} + NH_3 \rightleftharpoons Cu(NH_3)_4^{++} + H_2O$$

The consequence of the existence of these intermediate complexes is that the formation of the final product takes place over a larger range of values of the ammonia concentration than it would otherwise. If the complex were formed in one step the change from 1% to 99% conversion would require only a ten-fold increase in $[NH_3]$; it is found by experiment, however, that the ammonia concentration must be increased 10,000-fold to produce this conversion, as followed by the color change.

TABLE 22-2   *Ion Concentrations Producing 50% Conversion of Metal Ions to Complexes*

METAL ION	COMPLEX ION	ION CONCENTRATION
Cu^+	$Cu(CN)_2^-$	1×10^{-8}
	$CuCl_2^-$	4×10^{-3}
Ag^+	$Ag(CN)_2^-$	3×10^{-11}
	$AgCl_2^-$	3×10^{-3}
	$Ag(NO_2)_2^-$	4×10^{-2}
	$Ag(S_2O_3)_2^{---}$	3×10^{-7}
Zn^{++}	$Zn(CN)_4^{--}$	1×10^{-4}
Cd^{++}	$Cd(CN)_4^{--}$	6×10^{-5}
	CdI_4^{--}	3×10^{-2}
Hg^{++}	$Hg(CN)_4^{--}$	5×10^{-11}
	$HgCl_4^{--}$	9×10^{-5}
	$HgBr_4^{--}$	4×10^{-6}
	HgI_4^{--}	1×10^{-8}
	$Hg(SCN)_4^{--}$	3×10^{-6}

22–8. *The Structural Chemistry of Complexes*

The concept of the coordination of ions or groups in a definite geometric arrangement about a central ion was developed shortly after the beginning of the present century by the Swiss chemist A. Werner to account for the existence and properties of compounds such as K_2SnCl_6, $Co(NH_3)_6I_3$, etc. Before Werner's work these compounds had been assigned formulas such as $SnCl_4 \cdot 2KCl$ and $CoI_3 \cdot 6NH_3$, and had been classed as "molecular compounds," of unknown nature. Werner showed that the properties of the complexes of Cr^{+++}, Co^{+++}, Sn^{++++}, and other atoms with ligancy 6 could be explained by the postulate that the six attached groups are arranged about the central atom at the corners of a circumscribed regular octahedron.

One important property which Werner explained in this way is the existence of *isomers of inorganic complexes*. For example, there are two complexes with the formula $Co(NH_3)_4Cl_2^+$, one violet in color and one green. Werner identified these two complexes with the cis and trans structures shown in Figure 22-3. In the cis form the chloride ions are

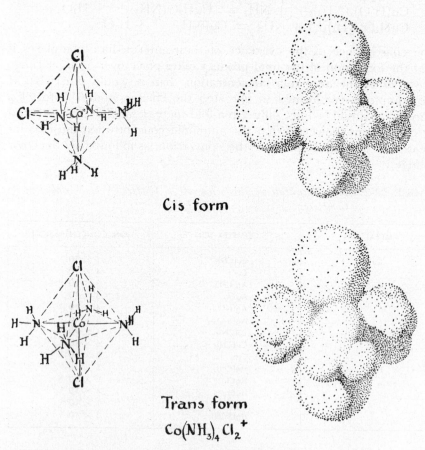

Cis form

Trans form

$Co(NH_3)_4\,Cl_2^+$

FIGURE 22-3   *The cis and trans isomers of the cobaltic tetrammine dichloride ion, $Co(NH_3)_4Cl_2^+$. In the cis form the two chlorine atoms occupy adjacent corners of the coordination octahedron about the cobalt atom, and in the trans form the two chlorine atoms occupy opposite corners.*

in adjacent positions, and in the trans form in opposite positions. Werner identified the violet complex with the cis configuration through the observation that it could be made easily from the carbonate-ammonia complex $Co(NH_3)_4CO_3^+$, for which only the cis form is possible (Fig. 22-2).

Complexes MX_4 are sometimes tetrahedral in configuration ($Zn(CN)_4^{--}$, $Zn(NH_3)_4^{++}$), and sometimes square and planar ($Ni(CN)_4^{--}$, $Cu(NH_3)_4^{++}$, $PdCl_4^{--}$).

It is interesting that in many complexes the number of electrons about the central atom, including two electrons for each bond to the attached atoms, is equal to the number in a noble gas. Thus in the zinc-ammonia complex

$$\left[\begin{array}{c} NH_3 \\ \cdot\cdot \\ H_3N : Zn : NH_3 \\ \cdot\cdot \\ NH_3 \end{array} \right]^{++}$$

the 28 electrons of the zinc ion Zn^{++} and the 8 electrons of the four bonds total 36, the number in krypton; in this complex the zinc atom has achieved the krypton electronic structure. Similarly in the ferro-cyanide ion, $Fe(CN)_6^{----}$, the iron atom has the krypton comple-ment of 36 electrons. In some other complexes there is a deficiency of electrons about the central atom: $Cu(NH_3)_4^{++}$, 35; $Ni(CN)_4^{--}$, 34; $Fe(CN)_6^{---}$, 35; $Cr(NH_3)_6^{+++}$, 33. Only rarely is there an excess, and this leads to instability; thus although cobaltous ion Co^{++} is stable, its complexes such as $Co(CN)_6^{----}$ and $Co(NH_3)_6^{++}$, with 37 elec-trons about the cobalt atom, are so unstable that they are very easily oxidized by atmospheric oxygen to the corresponding cobaltic com-plexes, and in the absence of oxygen they reduce water, liberating hydrogen.

In recent years a great amount of information about the structure of complexes has been gathered by use of x-rays, magnetic measure-ments, and other modern methods. This information about the con-figuration of the atoms in the complexes has been correlated with their chemical properties in such a way as to bring reasonable order into this field of chemistry.

Concepts, Facts, and Terms Introduced in This Chapter

Ammonia complexes. Effect of complex formation on solubility. Cyanide complexes. Complex halides and other complexes. Sodium thiosulfate as photographic fixer. Hydroxide complexes. Amphoteric hydroxides. Sulfide complexes. Equilibrium ex-pressions for complex formation. Structural chemistry—tetrahedral, octahedral, square complexes. Existence of isomers.

Exercises

22-1.   Discuss the effects of adding to three portions of a cupric solution (a) NH_4OH, (b) NaOH, (c) NH_4Cl. Write equations for reactions.

22-2.   To three portions of a solution containing Ni^{++} and Al^{+++} there are added (a) NaOH, (b) NH_4OH, (c) $NaOH + NH_4OH$. What happens in each case?

22-3.   Is silver chloride more or less soluble in $1 F NH_4OH$ than in a solution $1 F$ in NH_4Cl and $1 F$ in NH_4OH? Why? (Note that there are two opposing effects— one resulting from the change in degree of ionization of NH_4OH and the other from the increase in concentration of chloride ion. Which of these effects is the larger?)

22-4.   Write the equation for the principal chemical reaction involved in fixing a photographic film.

22-5.   For each of the following cases state in which of the two solutions the substance is more soluble, and why. Write equations for reactions.

$KClO_4$	in	$1 F K_2SO_4$	or	$1 F Na_2SO_4$
$AgC_2H_3O_2$	in	$0.1 F NaC_2H_3O_2$	or	$0.1 F HC_2H_3O_2$
$Al(OH)_3$	in	$1 F NaOH$	or	$1 F NH_4OH$
$Cu(OH)_2$	in	$1 F NaOH$	or	$1 F NH_4OH$
$Cu(OH)_2$	in	$1 F NH_4OH$	or	$1 F NH_4OH + 1 F NH_4Cl$

22-6.   From the complex constant of $Ag(S_2O_3)_2^{---}$ (obtained from Table 22-2) and the solubility product of AgBr calculate the thiosulfate-ion concentration needed to dissolve 5 g AgBr per liter.

22-7.   Arrange the following solutions in order of ability to dissolve AgCl, using data from Tables 22-1 and 22-2: $0.1 F NaNO_2$, $0.1 F Na_2S_2O_3$, $0.1 F NaCN$.

22-8.   Will 0.1 g AgBr dissolve in 100 ml of $1 F NH_4OH$ solution? (K_{SP} for AgBr = 4×10^{-13}.)

22-9.   Write the chemical equation for the solution of platinum in aqua regia. Explain why platinum dissolves in aqua regia but not in either hydrochloric acid or nitric acid alone.

22-10. Would sodium cyanide be an effective and satisfactory substitute for sodium thiosulfate as a fixer? See Table 22-2 for data.

22-11. Perchlorate ion is generally found to be the weakest complexing reagent of the common anions. Which solution will be more acidic, $0.1 F Zn(ClO_4)_2$ or $0.1 F ZnCl_2$?

22-12. How many structural isomers of the octahedral complex $Co(NH_3)_3Cl_3$ are there?

22-13. How many isomers of the tetrahedral complex $Zn(NH_3)_2Cl_2$ are there? Of the planar, square complex $Pt(NH_3)_2Cl_2$?

22-14. If each CO molecule donates two electrons to the nickel atom in $Ni(CO)_4$, what is the electron configuration of the nickel atom in this molecule? Predict the probable formula for iron carbonyl, remembering that the atomic number of iron is 2 less than that of nickel.

22-15. What concentration of NH_3 is there in a solution that is $1 F$ in NH_4Cl? Is much $Hg(NH_3)_2^{++}$ formed when $1 F NH_4Cl$ is added to an Hg^{++} solution?

Chapter 23

Energy and Chemical Change

In earlier chapters mention has been made that some chemical reactions take place with the evolution of heat, and some with the absorption of heat. The reactions that take place with the evolution of heat are called exothermic reactions, and those that take place with the absorption of heat are called endothermic reactions. Of course, any reaction that is exothermic when it takes place in one direction is endothermic when it takes place in the reverse direction.

The relation of energy to chemical change is important both in the science of chemistry and in its industrial applications. For example, in the construction of very large concrete dams the heat that is evolved during the setting of Portland cement may cause the concrete to crack, and it is accordingly necessary to include a system of pipes in the mass of concrete, in order to allow the concrete to be cooled by a stream of water. We can see that it would be useful if a method could be devised to permit this reaction, the setting of Portland cement, to occur without the evolution of heat; but unfortunately the nature of the relation between energy and chemical change is such that it is not possible to achieve this result.

In the present chapter we shall give a detailed discussion of the heat evolved or absorbed in chemical reactions, and of related questions, including also the question of the relation of energy change to chemical equilibrium.

The branch of chemistry dealing with heats of reaction and closely related subjects is called *thermochemistry*. The more general study of the relations between energy and chemical change, including such questions as the electric potential that can be obtained from an electrolytic cell and the amount of work that can be done by chemical means, is called *thermodynamic chemistry*. Thermochemistry and thermodynamic chemistry are a part of physical chemistry.

23–1. *Heat of Reaction*

The heat of a chemical reaction is the quantity of heat that is evolved when the reaction takes place at constant temperature and constant pressure. The symbol Q may be used to represent the heat of reaction. If heat is evolved, that is, if the reaction is exothermic, Q is a positive quantity, and if heat is absorbed by the reaction, the reaction being endothermic, Q is a negative quantity.

We can tell whether a chemical reaction is exothermic or endothermic by causing the reactants, at room temperature, say, to undergo reaction, and then by determining the temperature of the products. If the products are warmer than the reactants were, the reaction is exothermic, and if they are colder, the reaction is endothermic. For example, we know that when a fuel burns in air the products are very hot. This reaction, the combustion of a fuel, is a strongly exothermic reaction. On the other hand, when common salt is dissolved in water the solution is cooled somewhat below room temperature. This reaction, the solution of salt in water, is endothermic.

Measuring the Heat of a Reaction.   An instrument used to measure the heat of a reaction is called a *calorimeter*. Calorimeters are made of various designs, corresponding to the nature of the reaction to be studied. A calorimeter of simple design is shown in Figure 23-1. This calorimeter consists of a reaction vessel, which may be built to withstand considerable pressure, in the center of a larger vessel filled with water, and provided with a stirrer and a sensitive thermometer. The larger vessel is surrounded by insulating material.

If it is desired to obtain the heat of a reaction such as the combustion of carbon, a weighed quantity of carbon is placed in the reaction vessel, and oxygen gas is forced into the vessel under pressure. A reaction vessel for this purpose is strongly built of steel, to stand high pressure; it is called a *combustion bomb*. The temperature of the surrounding water is recorded, and the sample of carbon is ignited by passing an electric current through a wire embedded in it. The heat liberated by the reaction causes the entire system inside of the insulating material to increase in temperature. After enough time has elapsed to permit the temperature of this material to become uniform, the temperature is again recorded. From the rise in temperature and the total water equivalent of the calorimeter (that is, the weight of water that would require the same amount of heat to cause the temperature to rise one degree as is required to cause a rise in temperature of one degree

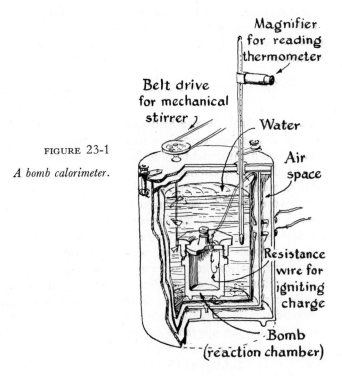

Magnifier for reading thermometer

Belt drive for mechanical stirrer

Water

Air space

Resistance wire for igniting charge

Bomb (reaction chamber)

FIGURE 23-1

A bomb calorimeter.

of the total material of the calorimeter inside of the insulation), the amount of heat liberated in the reaction can be calculated. A correction must of course be made for the amount of heat introduced by the electric current that produced the ignition.

It has been found by experiments of this sort that the heat of combustion of carbon in the form of graphite to carbon dioxide is 94,230 calories per gram atom of carbon. That is, the value of Q for the reaction

$$C_{gr} + O_2 \longrightarrow CO_2$$

is 94,230 cal. The heat of the reaction may be expressed by including the value of Q in the equation:

$$C_{gr} + O_2 \longrightarrow CO_2 + 94,230 \text{ cal}$$

The heat of solution of sodium chloride in water might be determined by use of a calorimeter similar to that shown in Figure 23-1, but provided with a central container in which water is placed, with a little bucket of salt crystals arranged in such a way as to permit the bucket to be dropped into the water during the experiment. A stirrer for the salt solution would also be needed in order to cause the salt to dissolve sufficiently rapidly. When this experiment is carried out, it is found that the process of solution of 1 gfw of sodium chloride in water is accompanied by the absorption of approximately 1,200 cal. The heat of the reaction depends slightly on the concentration of the solution that is produced. We may express this heat effect by the following equation:

$$NaCl(s) + aq \longrightarrow Na^+(aq) + Cl^-(aq) - 1,200 \text{ cal}$$

The Heat Content of a Substance. It has been found by experiment that it is possible to assign to every chemical substance at standard conditions a numerical value of its *heat content*, such that the heat liberated during a chemical reaction can be found by subtracting the heat contents of the products from the heat contents of the reactants. (The word *enthalpy* is often used for heat content.) *It is customary to place the heat contents of the elements equal to zero.* The heat content of carbon dioxide is then $-94,230$ calories per mole, since the amount of heat 94,230 calories is liberated when 1 gram atom of carbon combines with 1 mole of oxygen to form 1 mole of carbon dioxide. We see that the heat content of a compound is just equal to the heat of formation of the compound from its elements, but with opposite sign. Thus *a compound such as carbon dioxide which is formed from the elements by an exothermic reaction has a negative heat content.*

It is evident that it is not necessary to determine the heat of a particular reaction by experiment. If the heat of formation of every compound involved in the reaction is known, the heat of the reaction can be calculated. Values of heats of formation of compounds from elements in their standard states are given in the chemical handbooks and other reference books. The standard reference books are F. R. Bichowsky and F. D. Rossini, *The Thermochemistry of Chemical Substances*, Reinhold Publishing Corp., New York, 1936, and *Selected Values of Chemical Thermodynamic Properties*, Circular of the Bureau of Standards 500, **1952**.

For example, suppose that we want to know the heat of reaction of carbon monoxide and oxygen to form carbon dioxide. The heat of formation of carbon dioxide from carbon in its standard state (diamond) and oxygen has been found by experiment to be 94,450 cal/mole:

$$C + O_2 \longrightarrow CO_2 + 94,450 \text{ cal}$$

The heat of formation of carbon monoxide from carbon and oxygen is 26,840 calories per mole of carbon monoxide. We may express this by the following equation:

$$C + \tfrac{1}{2}O_2 \longrightarrow CO + 26,840 \text{ cal}$$

In this equation we have written $\tfrac{1}{2}O_2$, instead of multiplying by 2 throughout the equation, in order that the product should be 1 mole of carbon monoxide. The heats of formation given in tables always refer to 1 mole of the compound.

By subtracting the second equation from the first, we obtain the result

$$CO + \tfrac{1}{2}O_2 \longrightarrow CO_2 + 67{,}610 \text{ cal}$$

Hence we have found that the heat of reaction of carbon monoxide (1 mole) with oxygen to form carbon dioxide is 67,610 calories.

23–2. Heat Capacity. Heats of Fusion, Vaporization, and Transition

The amount of heat required to raise the temperature of unit quantity (1 mole or 1 gram) of a substance by 1° C without change in phase is called the *heat capacity* (sometimes called *specific heat*) of the substance. Values of the heat capacity of substances are given in tables which may be found in reference books.

Some general rules exist, such as that the molar heat capacity (at constant pressure) of any monatomic gas is approximately 5 cal/deg mole, except at very low temperatures. The most useful rule (*Kopp's rule*) is that *the molar heat capacity of a solid substance is the sum of its atomic heat capacities, with the value about 6.2 for all atoms except the light ones*, for which values used are

H	C	N	O	F
2.5	2.0	3.0	4.0	5.0

The following examples illustrate the agreement of this rule with experiment; the experimental values are for room temperature.

SUBSTANCE	HEAT CAPACITY CAL/DEG G	EXPERIMENTAL MOLAR HEAT CAPACITY	CALCULATED SUM OF ATOMIC VALUES FROM RULE
C, graphite	0.160	1.9	2.0 cal/deg mole
Pb	.0305	6.3	6.2
CuI	.066	12.5	12.4
NH_4Br	.210	20.6	19.2
$CaSO_4 \cdot 2H_2O$	.265	45.7	46.4
H_2O (ice)	.50	9.0	9.0

The *rule of Dulong and Petit*, dealing with the relation between the heat capacity of an element and its atomic weight, has been mentioned in Chapter 9. It is closely related to Kopp's rule.

The heat capacity of a liquid substance is usually somewhat larger than that of a solid. Water has an unusually large heat capacity.

Heat of Fusion.   A definite amount of heat is required to convert a crystal into the liquid at the melting point; this is called the *heat of fusion*. The heat of fusion of ice is 79.7 cal/g or 1,436 cal/mole.

Heat of Vaporization. The heat absorbed on vaporization at the boiling point is the *heat of vaporization;* for water its value is 539.6 cal/g or 9,710 cal/mole.

For most substances a rough value of the heat of vaporization can be predicted from *Trouton's rule,* which states that the quotient of the molar heat of vaporization by the absolute boiling point has a constant value, about 21. For example, this rule predicts that the molar heat of vaporization of carbon disulfide, b.p. 319.3° A, is $21 \times 319.8 = 6,700$ cal; the experimental value is 6,391 cal. The heats of vaporization of water and alcohol are larger than expected from Trouton's rule, apparently because of the strong intermolecular forces in the liquids, due to the action of hydrogen bonds.

Heat of Transition. The transition of a substance from one crystalline modification to another crystalline modification stable in a higher temperature range is accompanied by the absorption of the *heat of transition.* The value of this quantity for the transition of red phosphorus to white phosphorus, for example, is 3,700 cal/mole, and for red mercuric iodide to yellow mercuric iodide it is 3,000 cal/mole.

The use of these thermal quantities in calculations is illustrated below.

Example 1. What product would result from adding 100 ml of water to 56 g of powdered lime, CaO, in an insulated vessel of small heat capacity? The heat of the reaction $CaO + H_2O$ (l) $\longrightarrow Ca(OH)_2$ is 16.0 kcal/mole.

> **Solution.** The product is one mole of $Ca(OH)_2$, with heat capacity (Kopp's rule) 19.2 cal/deg, and 82 ml of water, with heat capacity 82 cal/deg. The heat required to raise this system from 20° (room temperature) to 100° is $80 \times 101.2 = 8,096$ cal., approximately 8.1 kcal. There remains available $16.0 - 8.1 = 7.9$ kcal. The heat of vaporization of water, given above as 540 cal/g, is 0.54 kcal/g; hence about $7.9/0.54 = 14.6$ g of water will be boiled away, leaving as the product a mixture of 74 g of slaked lime and 67 g of water at 100° C.
>
> In working this problem we have assumed that the vessel is open, and that the reaction is taking place under atmospheric pressure.

23–3. *Heats of Formation and Relative Electronegativity of Atoms*

In Chapter 11 it was pointed out that in general strong bonds are formed between atoms which differ greatly in electronegativity, and weaker bonds between atoms with a smaller electronegativity difference.

The most electronegative element is fluorine, in the upper right corner of the periodic table, and the electronegativity of elements decreases toward the left and toward the bottom of the table. Hydrogen and iodine, although quite different in general, are approximately equal in electronegativity. In the molecule H—I⬩⬩ the two atoms attract the shared electron pair which constitutes the covalent bond between them about equally. This bond is accordingly much like the covalent bonds in the elementary molecules H—H and ⬩⬩I—I⬩⬩. It is hence not surprising that the energy of the H—I bond is very nearly the average of the energies of the H—H bond and the I—I bond. The heat of formation of HI is only 1.5 kcal/mole:

$$\tfrac{1}{2}H_2 + \tfrac{1}{2}I_2 \rightleftharpoons HI + 1.5 \text{ kcal/mole}$$

On the other hand, hydrogen and chlorine differ considerably in electronegativity, and we may assume the covalent bond in HCl to have considerable ionic character, with the chlorine attracting the bonding electrons (resonance between H ⬩ Cl ⬩ and H⁺ ⬩ Cl ⬩ ⁻). This *partial ionic character* of the bond stabilizes the molecule, and causes hydrogen and chlorine to unite vigorously to form hydrogen chloride, which has the value 22 kcal/mole for its heat of formation:

$$\tfrac{1}{2}H_2 + \tfrac{1}{2}Cl_2 \longrightarrow HCl + 22 \text{ kcal/mole}$$

The following statement may be repeated from Chapter 11: *The greater the separation of two elements on the electronegativity scale, the greater is the strength of the bond between them.* The electronegativity scale of the elements, given in Figure 11-9, was formulated largely from the observed heats of formation of substances.

The electronegativity scale is useful mainly in drawing roughly quantitative conclusions. Compounds between elements close together on the scale have small heats of formation, and tend to be unstable. Examples are NCl_3, CI_4, SI_2, PH_3, AsH_3, SiH_4. Compounds between metals and non-metals, which are far apart on the scale, are in general stable, and have large heats of formation. The heats of formation of the alkali halides, such as NaCl, lie between 70 and 150 kcal/mole.

The quantitative relation between bond energy and electronegativity difference may be expressed by an equation. For a single covalent bond between two atoms A and B the extra energy due to the partial ionic character is approximately $23(x_A - x_B)^2$ kcal/mole; that is, it is proportional to the square of the difference in electronegativity

TABLE 23-1 *Values of the Electronegativity of Elements*

	x		x		x		x
H	2.1	Na	0.9	K	0.8	Rb	0.8
Li	1.0	Mg	1.2	Ca	1.0	Sr	1.0
Be	1.5	Al	1.5	Sc	1.3	Y	1.3
B	2.0	Si	1.8	Ti	1.6	Zr	1.6
C	2.5	P	2.1	Ge	1.7	Sn	1.7
N	3.0	S	2.5	As	2.0	Sb	1.8
O	3.5	Cl	3.0	Se	2.4	Te	2.1
F	4.0			Br	2.8	I	2.4

of the two atoms, and the proportionality constant has the value 23 kcal/mole. For example, chlorine and fluorine have electronegativity values differing by 1 (Table 23-1); hence the heat of formation of ClF (containing one Cl—F bond) is predicted to be 23 kcal/mole. The observed heat of formation of ClF is 25.7 kcal/mole. The agreement between the predicted and observed heat of formation is only approximate. There seem to be other factors than electronegativity affecting the heats of formation of substances, and it is for this reason that the values of the electronegativity are given only to one decimal place in Table 23-1.

Heats of formation calculated in this way would refer to elements in states in which the atoms formed single bonds, as they do in the molecules P_4 and S_8. Nitrogen (N_2) and oxygen (O_2) contain multiple bonds, and the nitrogen and oxygen molecules are more stable, by 110 kcal/mole and 48 kcal/mole, respectively, than they would be if the molecules contained single bonds (as in P_4 and S_8). Hence we must correct for this extra stability, by using the equation

$$Q = \text{heat of formation (in kcal/mole)} = 23 \, \Sigma(x_A - x_B)^2 - 55 n_N - 24 n_O$$

Here the summation indicated by Σ is to be taken over all the bonds represented by the formula of the compound. The symbol n_N means the number of nitrogen atoms in the formula, and n_O the number of oxygen atoms.

As an example, we may consider the substance nitrogen trichloride, $N\diagdown{}^{\displaystyle Cl}_{\displaystyle Cl}\!\!-Cl$ (NCl_3).

Nitrogen and chlorine have the same electronegativity; hence the first term contributes nothing. There is one nitrogen atom in the molecule. Hence $Q = -55$ kcal/mole. The minus sign shows that the substance is unstable, and that heat is liberated when it decomposes. Nitrogen trichloride is in fact an oil which explodes easily, with great violence:

$$2NCl_3 \longrightarrow N_2 + 3Cl_2 + 110 \text{ kcal}$$

23–4. Heats of Combustion

Thermochemical data for organic substances are usually obtained experimentally by burning the substances in oxygen and measuring the amounts of heat evolved. These *heats of combustion* of the substances are reported in tables in the standard reference books.

The method of determining heats of combustion has been described above, for carbon. This method, with use of a bomb calorimeter, is the customary basis for determining the value of a fuel, such as coal or oil. A weighed sample of the fuel is placed in the bomb calorimeter, the bomb is filled with oxygen, and the fuel is burned. The fuel value or calorific value of the fuel is considered to be measured by its heat of combustion, and when large amounts of fuel are purchased the price may be determined by the result of tests in a bomb calorimeter.

In reporting the calorific value of fuels it is customary to use the *British thermal unit* (B.T.U.) instead of the calorie as the unit of heat. The British thermal unit is the amount of heat required to raise the temperature of 1 pound of water by 1 degree Fahrenheit. Since a pound is 453 g, and 1 degree F is $\frac{5}{9}$ degrees C, the British thermal unit is equal to $\frac{5}{9} \times 453 = 252$ cal. The calorific value of a fuel expressed in B.T.U. per pound of fuel has a numerical value $\frac{9}{5}$ as great as that expressed in calories per gram.

Example 2. The heat of combustion of ethylene, C_2H_4, is 331.6 kcal/mole, and that of ethane, C_2H_6, is 368.4 kcal/mole. What is the heat of hydrogenation of ethylene to ethane?

Solution. We are given the equations

$$C_2H_4 + 3O_2 \longrightarrow 2CO_2 + 2H_2O(l) + 331.6 \text{ kcal}$$

$$C_2H_6 + 3\tfrac{1}{2}O_2 \longrightarrow 2CO_2 + 3H_2O(l) + 368.4 \text{ kcal}$$

By subtracting the second equation from the first, we obtain

$$C_2H_4 + H_2O(l) \longrightarrow C_2H_6 + \tfrac{1}{2}O_2 - 36.8 \text{ kcal}$$

It is necessary to know the value of the heat of formation of water (given in the handbooks) in order to solve this problem:

$$H_2 + \tfrac{1}{2}O_2 \longrightarrow H_2O(l) + 68.4 \text{ kcal}$$

By adding this equation to the previous one we obtain the result

$$C_2H_4 + H_2 \longrightarrow C_2H_6 + 31.6 \text{ kcal}$$

Accordingly the reaction of combination of ethylene with hydrogen to form ethane must be exothermic, the molar heat of hydrogenation of ethylene being **31.6 kcal.**

It is interesting to note that the heat of this reduction can be found without having to carry out the particular reaction at all—it can be obtained, as shown by the calculation we have just made, from measurement of the heat of combustion of ethylene, the heat of combustion of ethane, and the heat of combustion of hydrogen. Heats of combustion are ordinarily reliable to about 0.5 percent. The molar heat of hydrogenation of ethylene has been determined directly by carrying out the hydrogenation reaction (in the presence of a catalyst) in a calorimeter. The value 32.8 ± 0.1 kcal was obtained by this direct method.

Heat of Reaction and the Tendency of the Reaction to Take Place. It has been pointed out in earlier paragraphs that some reactions that take place are exothermic, and some are endothermic. A reaction that reaches a measurable equilibrium may be caused to go in either direction, by starting with one set of reactants or another. For example, the reaction involving the red gas nitrogen dioxide and the colorless gas dinitrogen tetroxide has a heat effect shown by the following equation:

$$2NO_2 \longrightarrow N_2O_4 + 15,000 \text{ cal/mole}$$
red   colorless

If we had a sample of pure NO_2, it would react to produce some molecules of N_2O_4, liberating 15,000 cal of heat for every mole of N_2O_4 formed. On the other hand, if we had some pure N_2O_4 (obtained perhaps by allowing some crystals of dinitrogen tetroxide to evaporate) some of the molecules of the substance would decompose to form NO_2, and this reaction would be endothermic, 15,000 cal of heat being absorbed by the system for every mole of N_2O_4 decomposed.

However, even though it is possible for endothermic reactions, as well as exothermic reactions, to take place, most reactions that take place with the conversion of the reacting substances almost completely into the products are exothermic. We are accordingly reasonably safe in assuming that the equilibrium state for a system involving the emission of a large amount of heat when the reaction proceeds from left to right favors very much the products, written on the right side of the equation. The fact that the heat of formation of water is 68.4 kcal/mole suggests that it would be useless to attempt to dissociate water into hydrogen and oxygen by heating it, unless it were heated to an extremely high temperature. The heat of formation of hydrogen fluoride, HF, is 64.0 kcal/mole; we would accordingly predict that this substance too would be stable and would not break down into its elements very readily. On the other hand, the heat of formation of hydrogen iodide, HI, from gaseous hydrogen and gaseous iodine is only 1.5 kcal/mole, and it is accordingly not surprising that hydrogen iodide decomposes in part into hydrogen and iodine vapor.

A further discussion of this general question is given in a later section of this chapter.

Heat Values of Foods.   One important use of foods is to serve as a source of energy, permitting work to be done, and of heat, keeping the body warm. Foods serve in this way through their oxidation within the body by oxygen which is extracted from the air in the lungs and is carried to the tissues by the hemoglobin of the blood. The ultimate products of oxidation of most of the hydrogen and carbon in foods are water and carbon dioxide. The nitrogen is for the most part converted into urea, $CO(NH_2)_2$, which is eliminated in the urine.

Heats of combustion of foods and their relation to dietary requirements have been thoroughly studied. The food ingested daily by a healthy man of average size doing a moderate amount of muscular work should have a total heat of combustion of about 3,000 kcal. About 90% of this is made available as work and heat by digestion and metabolism of the food.

Fats and carbohydrates are the principal sources of energy in foods. Pure fat has a caloric value (heat of combustion) of 4,080 kcal per pound, and pure carbohydrate (sugar) a caloric value of about 1,860 kcal per pound. The caloric values of foods are obtained by use of a bomb calorimeter, just as was described above for fuels. The third main constituent of food, protein, is needed primarily for growth and for the repair of tissues. About 50 g of protein is the daily requirement for an adult of average size. Usually about twice this amount of protein is ingested. This amount, 100 g, has a caloric value of only about 400 kcal, the heat of combustion of protein being about 2,000 kcal per pound. Accordingly fat and carbohydrate must provide about 2,600 kcal of the 3,000 kcal required daily.

23–5. *Heat and Work*

The relation between heat and work is treated in courses in physics, and may be briefly reviewed here. Work is done by a directed force acting through a distance; the amount of work done by a force of one dyne acting through a distance of one centimeter is called one *erg*. If this amount of work is done in putting an object initially at rest into motion, we say that the moving object has a *kinetic energy* of 1 erg. All of this kinetic energy may be used to do work, as the moving object is slowed down to rest; for example, a string attached to the moving object might serve to lift a small weight to a certain height above its original position.

Another way in which the moving object can be slowed down to rest is through *friction*. The process which then occurs is that the kinetic energy of the directed motion of the moving body is converted into energy of randomly directed motion of the molecules of the bodies between which friction occurs. This increase in vigor of molecular motion corresponds to an increase in temperature of the bodies. We say that heat has been added to the bodies, causing their temperatures to rise. Thus if one of the bodies was 1 g of water, and if its temperature rose by 1 deg, we would say that 1 cal of heat had entered it.

The question at once arises as to how much work must be done to produce this much heat. This question was answered by experiments carried out in Manchester, England, between 1840 and 1878 by James Prescott Joule (1818–1889), after Count Rumford (Benjamin Thompson, 1753–1814, an American Tory) had shown in 1798 that the friction of a blunt borer in a cannon caused an increase in temperature of the cannon. Joule's work led to essentially the value now accepted for the mechanical equivalent of heat, that is, the relation between heat and work:

1 cal = 4.185 joule = 4.185 × 10⁷ erg

The large unit of energy introduced here, the **joule**, is 1×10^7 ergs. One joule is equal to the work done by the flow of one coulomb of electricity through a potential difference of one volt, and hence it is also equal to 1 watt-second:

1 joule = 1 volt-coulomb = 1 watt-sec.

It is interesting to note that 1 cal is a large amount of energy. Since the force of gravity on 1 g of water is 980 dynes, the water would have to fall through a height of $4.185 \times 10^7/980 = 42,690$ cm, or 1,400 feet, to get enough kinetic energy to raise its temperature by 1° C when converted into heat.

The Production of Low Temperatures. It is not very hard to achieve high temperatures. A strongly exothermic chemical reaction can be made to take place rapidly, in such a way as to allow the energy that is given out to be used to heat a system that it is desired to have at a high temperature. Temperatures as high as 2,800° C can be reached by use of the oxy-hydrogen torch and as high as 3,500° C by use of the oxy-acetylene torch. Still higher temperatures can be reached by pouring electric energy into a system. The temperature in an electric arc is between 5,000° and 6,000° C. The highest temperature that has been produced by man except by the detonation of an atomic bomb is about 20,000° C. This very high temperature was obtained by passing the electricity stored in a large electric condenser through a fine wire; the great amount of electric energy passing through the wire causes it to explode, and heats the metallic vapor to about 20,000°. The temperature at the center of a detonating atomic bomb is extremely high—of the order of magnitude of 50,000,000°.

The problem of removing energy from a portion of matter, and taking it to a lower temperature, is not so easy. It would be fine if some strongly endothermic reaction could be found which would proceed rapidly, and would thus cool a system to lower and lower temperatures. However, it is difficult to find a reaction of this kind.

The usual method of achieving low temperatures involves the evaporation of a liquid. This process, the change of a substance from the liquid state at the boiling point to the gaseous state at the boiling point, is an endothermic reaction. An amount of heat equal to the heat of vaporization is absorbed in the process. For example, the heat of vaporization of water is 10,571 calories per mole. When 18 grams of water is made to evaporate at room temperature, by blowing a current of air over it in order to carry away the water vapor, 10,571 calories of heat is absorbed, and the system is cooled by this amount. Water is not so effective for use in this way as are some other substances, such as diethyl ether, $(C_2H_5)_2O$, and ethyl chloride, C_2H_5Cl. These substances are sometimes used to freeze a small portion of the body for a minor surgical operation.

Ammonia, NH_3, is usually used as the refrigerant in the manufacture of ice. The way in which a commercial ice plant operates is indicated by Figure 23-2. Ammonia gas, which can be made to condense to a

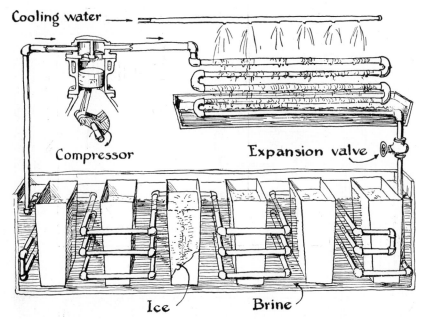

FIGURE 23-2   *The manufacture of ice with ammonia as the refrigerant.*

liquid at room temperature by compressing it, is passed through a mechanical compressor, indicated at the left of the figure. The compressed gas liquefies, giving out a quantity of heat equal to the heat of vaporization. This causes the liquid ammonia to be at a temperature considerably above room temperature. The warm liquid is passed through cooling coils, and heat is transferred to the cooling water, reducing the temperature of the liquid ammonia to room temperature. The liquid is then allowed to pass through an expansion valve, into a region of low pressure. The liquid evaporates in this region of low pressure, forming ammonia gas, and absorbing an amount of heat equal to the heat of vaporization. This absorption of heat cools a brine bath in which the tanks of water to be frozen to blocks of ice are contained, and the gaseous ammonia is then ready to be compressed again.

Ordinary domestic refrigerators operate in the same way. A diagram of a domestic refrigerator operated by electricity is shown in Figure 23-3. Instead of ammonia, other substances are usually used in domestic refrigerators; methyl chloride (CH_3Cl) and dichlorodifluoromethane (CCl_2F_2) are the common ones. The last of these substances, dichlorodifluoromethane, is a popular refrigerant, because it is not toxic, and there is little danger in case that some of it escapes from the refrigerating system.

It is interesting to ask why the evaporation of the liquid takes place, even though this reaction is endothermic. The explanation of this phenomenon is given by the con-

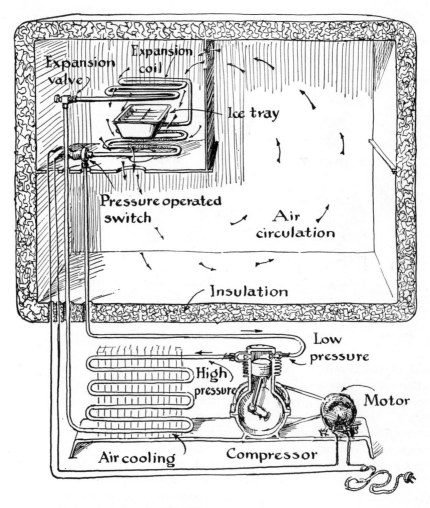

FIGURE 23-3   *A modern electric refrigerator.*

sideration of *probability*. Let us consider a large flask, with volume 10 liters, into which some water molecules are introduced. We might well think that it would be equally probable that a particular water molecule would be in any place in the flask—that the probability would be 1 in 10,000 that the molecule would occupy any particular milliliter of volume within the flask. If enough water has been introduced into the flask, however, some of the water will liquefy, the rest remaining as water vapor. Let us suppose that there is 1 ml of liquid water present in a little puddle at the bottom of the flask. At room temperature most of the water-substance present in the flask will be in this puddle of liquid water, only a fraction of the water molecules being present as water vapor. Now, although it seems very improbable that a water molecule should stay in the small volume, 1 milliliter, occupied by the liquid water, instead of occupying the remaining 9,999 milliliters of space, we know that the reason that the water vapor condenses to liquid water is that liquid water is the more stable state, and that condensation proceeds until the rate at which gas molecules strike the surface of the liquid and stick is just equal to the rate at which molecules of the liquid leave the surface and escape into the gas. This is the equilibrium state. We see that the equilibrium state involves a balance between the effect of *energy*, which tends to concentrate the molecules into the liquid phase, and the effect of *probability*, which tends to change the liquid into the gas. If the volume of the flask were five times as great, making the probability for the gas phase 49,999 to 1 instead of 9,999 to 1, five times as many molecules would leave the liquid phase and move to the gaseous phase.

Accordingly we see that this effect of probability can be made to cause more of the liquid to evaporate, simply by increasing the volume of the system. This is the explanation of the process of refrigeration described above. When the total volume is reduced, by use of a compressor, more of the substance changes to the liquid phase; and when the volume is increased, by allowing the substance to pass through the reducing valve from the region of high pressure to the region of low pressure, more of the substance evaporates.

In the branch of science called thermodynamic chemistry a more detailed consideration is given to the relative effects of energy and probability. It has been found that the effect of probability can be described quantitatively by a new property of substances. This new property, which represents the probability of a substance in various states, is called *entropy*.

23–6. *The Driving Force of Chemical Reactions*

What makes a chemical reaction go? This is a question that chemists and students have asked ever since chemical reactions began to be investigated. At the beginning of the nineteenth century the question was answered by saying that two substances react if they have a "chemical affinity" for each other. This answer, of course, had no real value until some quantitative meaning was given to "chemical affinity," and some way was found for measuring or predicting it.

It might be thought that the heat of a reaction is its driving force, and that a reaction will proceed if it evolves heat, and not proceed if it would absorb heat. This idea, however, is wrong; many reactions proceed even though they absorb heat. We have mentioned some of these reactions in the preceding sections of this chapter; another example is that when mercuric oxide is heated it decomposes into mercury and oxygen, with absorption of heat.

In the preceding section we have pointed out that, in addition to the energy change taking place during a reaction, there is another important factor involved, the *probability* of the states represented by the reactants and the products. This probability factor is described by the quantity called the *entropy*. Whereas the energy change that accompanies a chemical reaction does not depend very much on the pressures of the gases or the concentrations of the solutes involved in the reaction, the entropy change does depend on these partial pressures and concentrations. In general a system held at constant temperature will reach a steady state, called the state of equilibrium. In this state of the system the reaction has no preferential tendency to proceed either forward or backward; it has no driving force in either direction. If, however, the concentration of one of the reactants (a solute or a gas) is increased, a driving force comes into existence, which causes the reaction to go in the forward direction, until the equilibrium expression, involving the concentrations or partial pressures of reactants and products, again becomes equal to the equilibrium constant for the reaction.

It is clear from these considerations that *the driving force of a reaction depends not only on the chemical formulas of the reactants, and the structure of their molecules, but also on the concentrations of the reactants and of the products.*

A great step forward was made around the end of the last century when it was found that an energy quantity called its **free energy** can be assigned to each substance, such that a reaction in a system held at constant temperature tends to proceed if it is accompanied by a decrease in free energy; that is, if the free energy of the reactants is greater than that of the products. *The free energy of a substance is a property that expresses the resultant of the energy (heat content) of the substance and its inherent probability (entropy).* If the substances whose formulas are written on the left of the double arrow in a chemical equation and those whose formulas are written on the right have the same entropy (probability), the reaction will proceed in the direction that leads to the evolution of heat, that is, in the exothermic direction. If the substances on the left and those on the right have the same energy, the reaction will proceed from the substances with the smaller probability (entropy) toward the substances with the greater probability (entropy). At equilibrium, when a reaction has no preferential tendency to go in either the forward or backward direction, the free energy of the substances on the left side is exactly equal to that of the substances on the right side. *At equilibrium the driving force of the heat-content change (enthalpy change) accompanying a reaction is exactly balanced by the driving force of the probability change (entropy change).*

The discovery of the relation between equilibrium constant and free energy has simplified the task of systematizing chemical reactions. Chemists might determine, at 25° C, say, the value of the equilibrium constant of each reaction in which they are interested. This would be a great task. It would be far simpler to determine the standard free energy values at 25° C for each of a large number of chemical substances. Then, by combining these values, the free energy change for any chemical reaction involving these substances as reactants and products could be calculated, and from it the equilibrium constant for this reaction could be found.

The great simplification introduced by this procedure can be seen by examining Table 23-2, given in the next section. This table contains only 57 entries, which correspond to 57 different electron reactions. By combining any two of these electron reactions the equation for an ordinary oxidation-reduction reaction can be written. There are $57 \times 56/2$, or 1596, of these oxidation-reduction reactions which can be formed from the 57 electron reactions. The 57 numbers in the table can be combined in such a way as to give the 1596 values of their equilibrium constants; accordingly this small table permits a prediction to be made as to whether any one of these 1596 reactions will tend to go in the forward direction or the reverse direction.

A similar table given in the book on oxidation potentials written by W. M. Latimer occupies eight pages; the information given on these eight pages permits one to calculate values of the equilibrium constants for about 85,000 reactions. A table giving the equilibrium constants for these 85,000 reactions would occupy 1750 pages of the same size as the pages in Professor Latimer's book; and, moreover, it is evident that if the equilibrium constants were independent of one another, and had to be determined by separate experiments, we would not have been able to gather nearly so much information about these reactions.

The study of the free energy of substances constitutes a complex subject and only a bare introduction to it can be given in a course in general chemistry. The following section deals with free-energy changes accompanying oxidation-reduction reactions; a similar treatment can also be given to other reactions.

23–7. *The Table of Standard Oxidation-Reduction Potentials*

In the discussion of oxidation-reduction reactions in Chapter 12 a brief table was given of oxidation-reduction couples arranged according to strength, the couple with the strongest reducing agent being at the top of the table and that with the strongest oxidizing agent at the bottom.

Table 23-2 is a more extensive table of this kind.

From this table we see that of the substances listed lithium metal is the strongest reducing agent, and fluoride ion is the weakest; and conversely fluorine is the strongest oxidizing agent and lithium ion the weakest.

There is given for each couple the value of the standard potential E^0. This is the potential developed by the electric cell formed by the couple under consideration and the standard hydrogen couple $\frac{1}{2}H_2 \rightleftarrows H^+ + e^-$; this standard hydrogen couple has been selected as the reference point, with $E^0 = 0$.

For example, a cell made with a strip of zinc as one electrode, in contact with a solution 1 M in Zn^{++}, and a piece of platinum over which bubbles of hydrogen are passing as the other electrode (Figure 12-6) would develop the potential 0.762 volts, this being the value given in the table for the couple $\frac{1}{2}Zn = \frac{1}{2}Zn^{++} + e^-$.

The potential of a cell depends on the concentrations or partial pressures of the reacting substances. The standard concentrations of the dissolved substances in Table 23-2 are taken to be approximately 1 M (more accurately, unit activity, correction being made for deviation from the perfect-solution law), and the standard pressure for gases is 1 atm (corrected in very accurate work for deviation from the perfect-gas law).

23–8. *Equilibrium Constants for Oxidation-Reduction Couples*

The zinc-hydrogen cell develops a large electrical potential, 0.762 v, because the over-all reaction

$$\frac{1}{2}Zn + H^+ \rightleftarrows \frac{1}{2}Zn^{++} + \frac{1}{2}H_2$$

which represents the reduction of hydrogen ion by zinc metal, has a strong tendency to go to the right, and in a cell so built that the electron reactions occur at separate electrodes this tendency results in electrons being forced into one electrode by the electrode reaction and pulled out of the other. It is clear that the equilibrium constant

$$K = \frac{[Zn^{++}]^{\frac{1}{2}}p_{H_2}^{\frac{1}{2}}}{[H^+]}$$

for the over-all reaction must have a large numerical value, corresponding to the tendency of the reaction to proceed to the right.

Half a century ago it was shown by physical chemists from the laws of thermodynamics that the equilibrium constant of the over-all cell reaction can be calculated from the potential of the cell. In fact, we can calculate from standard potentials of the couples as given in Table 23-2 values of equilibrium constants for the couples. These values are also given in the table.

TABLE 23-2 *Standard Oxidation-Reduction Potentials and Equilibrium Constants*

The values apply to temperature 25° C, with standard concentration
for aqueous solutions 1 M and standard pressure of gases 1 atm.

	E^0	K
$Li \rightleftarrows Li^+ + e^-$.............................	3.05	4×10^{50}
$Cs \rightleftarrows Cs^+ + e^-$.............................	2.92	1×10^{49}
$Rb \rightleftarrows Rb^+ + e^-$.............................	2.92	1×10^{49}
$K \rightleftarrows K^+ + e^-$.............................	2.92	1×10^{49}
$\frac{1}{2}Ba \rightleftarrows \frac{1}{2}Ba^{++} + e^-$.............................	2.90	5×10^{48}
$\frac{1}{2}Sr \rightleftarrows \frac{1}{2}Sr^{++} + e^-$.............................	2.89	4×10^{48}
$\frac{1}{2}Ca \rightleftarrows \frac{1}{2}Ca^{++} + e^-$.............................	2.87	2×10^{48}
$Na \rightleftarrows Na^+ + e^-$.............................	2.712	4.0×10^{45}
$\frac{1}{3}Al + \frac{4}{3}OH^- \rightleftarrows \frac{1}{3}Al(OH)_4^- + e^-$.............	2.35	3×10^{39}
$\frac{1}{2}Mg \rightleftarrows \frac{1}{2}Mg^{++} + e^-$.............................	2.34	2×10^{39}
$\frac{1}{2}Be \rightleftarrows \frac{1}{2}Be^{++} + e^-$.............................	1.85	1×10^{31}
$\frac{1}{3}Al \rightleftarrows \frac{1}{3}Al^{+++} + e^-$.............................	1.67	1×10^{28}
$\frac{1}{2}Zn + 2OH^- \rightleftarrows \frac{1}{2}Zn(OH)_4^{--} + e^-$.............	1.216	2.7×10^{20}
$\frac{1}{2}Mn \rightleftarrows \frac{1}{2}Mn^{++} + e^-$.............................	1.18	7×10^{19}
$\frac{1}{2}Zn + 2NH_3 \rightleftarrows \frac{1}{2}Zn(NH_3)_4^{++} + e^-$........	1.03	2×10^{17}
$Co(CN)_6^{----} \rightleftarrows Co(CN)_6^{---} + e^-$.........	0.83	1×10^{14}
$\frac{1}{2}Zn \rightleftarrows \frac{1}{2}Zn^{++} + e^-$.............................	.762	6.5×10^{12}
$\frac{1}{3}Cr \rightleftarrows \frac{1}{3}Cr^{+++} + e^-$.............................	.74	3×10^{12}
$\frac{1}{2}H_2C_2O_4(aq) \rightleftarrows CO_2 + H^+ + e^-$.............	.49	2×10^8
$\frac{1}{2}Fe \rightleftarrows \frac{1}{2}Fe^{++} + e^-$.............................	.440	2.5×10^7
$\frac{1}{2}Cd \rightleftarrows \frac{1}{2}Cd^{++} + e^-$.............................	.402	5.7×10^6
$\frac{1}{2}Co \rightleftarrows \frac{1}{2}Co^{++} + e^-$.............................	.277	4.5×10^4
$\frac{1}{2}Ni \rightleftarrows \frac{1}{2}Ni^{++} + e^-$.............................	.250	1.6×10^4
$I^- + Cu \rightleftarrows CuI(s) + e^-$.............................	.187	1.4×10^3
$\frac{1}{2}Sn \rightleftarrows \frac{1}{2}Sn^{++} + e^-$.............................	.136	1.9×10^2
$\frac{1}{2}Pb \rightleftarrows \frac{1}{2}Pb^{++} + e^-$.............................	.126	1.3×10^2
$\frac{1}{2}H_2 \rightleftarrows H^+ + e^-$.............................	.000	1
$\frac{1}{2}H_2S \rightleftarrows \frac{1}{2}S + H^+ + e^-$.............................	-0.141	4.3×10^{-3}
$Cu^+ \rightleftarrows Cu^{++} + e^-$.............................	-0.153	2.7×10^{-3}
$\frac{1}{2}H_2O + \frac{1}{2}H_2SO_3 \rightleftarrows \frac{1}{2}SO_4^{--} + 2H^+ + e^-$.........	-0.17	1×10^{-3}
$\frac{1}{2}Cu \rightleftarrows \frac{1}{2}Cu^{++} + e^-$.............................	-0.345	1.6×10^{-6}
$Fe(CN)_6^{----} \rightleftarrows Fe(CN)_6^{---} + e^-$.........	-0.36	9×10^{-7}
$I^- \rightleftarrows \frac{1}{2}I_2(s) + e^-$.............................	-0.53	1×10^{-9}
$MnO_4^{--} \rightleftarrows MnO_4^- + e^-$.............................	-0.54	1×10^{-9}
$\frac{4}{3}OH^- + \frac{1}{3}MnO_2 \rightleftarrows \frac{1}{3}MnO_4^- + \frac{2}{3}H_2O + e^-$......	-0.57	3×10^{-10}
$\frac{1}{2}H_2O_2 \rightleftarrows \frac{1}{2}O_2 + H^+ + e^-$.............................	-0.682	3.5×10^{-12}
$Fe^{++} \rightleftarrows Fe^{+++} + e^-$.............................	-0.771	1.1×10^{-13}
$Hg \rightleftarrows \frac{1}{2}Hg_2^{++} + e^-$.............................	-0.799	3.7×10^{-14}
$Ag \rightleftarrows Ag^+ + e^-$.............................	-0.800	3.5×10^{-14}
$H_2O + NO_2 \rightleftarrows NO_3^- + 2H^+ + e^-$.............	-0.81	3×10^{-14}
$\frac{1}{2}Hg \rightleftarrows \frac{1}{2}Hg^{++} + e^-$.............................	-0.854	4.5×10^{-15}
$\frac{1}{2}Hg_2^{++} \rightleftarrows Hg^{++} + e^-$.............................	-0.910	5.0×10^{-16}
$\frac{1}{2}HNO_2 + \frac{1}{2}H_2O \rightleftarrows \frac{1}{2}NO_3^- + H^+ + e^-$.........	-0.94	2×10^{-16}
$NO + H_2O \rightleftarrows HNO_2 + H^+ + e^-$.............	-0.99	2×10^{-17}
$\frac{1}{2}ClO_3^- + \frac{1}{2}H_2O \rightleftarrows \frac{1}{2}ClO_4^- + H^+ + e^-$.........	-1.00	2×10^{-17}
$Br^- \rightleftarrows \frac{1}{2}Br_2(l) + e^-$.............................	-1.065	1.3×10^{-18}
$H_2O + \frac{1}{2}Mn^{++} \rightleftarrows \frac{1}{2}MnO_2 + 2H^+ + e^-$.........	-1.23	2×10^{-21}
$Cl^- \rightleftarrows \frac{1}{2}Cl_2 + e^-$.............................	-1.358	1.5×10^{-23}
$\frac{7}{6}H_2O + \frac{1}{3}Cr^{+++} \rightleftarrows \frac{1}{6}Cr_2O_7^{--} + \frac{7}{3}H^+ + e^-$......	-1.36	1×10^{-23}
$\frac{1}{2}H_2O + \frac{1}{6}Cl^- \rightleftarrows \frac{1}{6}ClO_3^- + H^+ + e^-$.........	-1.45	4×10^{-25}
$\frac{1}{3}Au \rightleftarrows \frac{1}{3}Au^{+++} + e^-$.............................	-1.50	6×10^{-26}
$\frac{4}{5}H_2O + \frac{1}{5}Mn^{++} \rightleftarrows \frac{1}{5}MnO_4^- + \frac{8}{5}H^+ + e^-$.........	-1.52	3×10^{-26}
$\frac{1}{2}Cl_2 + H_2O \rightleftarrows HClO + H^+ + e^-$.............	-1.63	4×10^{-28}
$H_2O \rightleftarrows \frac{1}{2}H_2O_2 + H^+ + e^-$.............................	-1.77	2×10^{-30}
$Co^{++} \rightleftarrows Co^{+++} + e^-$.............................	-1.84	1×10^{-31}
$F^- \rightleftarrows \frac{1}{2}F_2 + e^-$.............................	-2.65	4×10^{-44}

The meaning of the equilibrium constants of the oxidation-reduction couples can be made clear by the discussion of some examples. For the couple

$$\tfrac{1}{2}Zn \rightleftharpoons \tfrac{1}{2}Zn^{++} + e^-$$

the constant is given as $K = 6.5 \times 10^{12}$. For this reaction the equilibrium expression is written according to the convention adopted in Chapter 20 as

$$K = [Zn^{++}]^{\frac{1}{2}}[e^-]$$

(The term [Zn] does not appear in the denominator because the activity of a crystalline substance is constant, at a given temperature, and is conventionally taken equal to unity.) It is this product which has the value 6.5×10^{12}.

This is, however, not of use until the quantity $[e^-]$, the electron concentration, has been evaluated or eliminated. It can be eliminated by combining the couple with another couple. Thus for the reaction

$$\tfrac{1}{2}H_2 \rightleftharpoons H^+ + e^-$$

we have K given in the table as 1 (corresponding to $E^0 = 0$), which leads to

$$\frac{[H^+][e^-]}{p_{H_2}^{\frac{1}{2}}} = 1$$

By dividing this into the above equation we obtain

$$\frac{[Zn^{++}]^{\frac{1}{2}}[e^-]}{[H^+][e^-]/p_{H_2}^{\frac{1}{2}}} = \frac{6.5 \times 10^{12}}{1}$$

We now cancel the term $[e^-]$ and obtain the result

$$\frac{[Zn^{++}]^{\frac{1}{2}}p_{H_2}^{\frac{1}{2}}}{[H^+]} = 6.5 \times 10^{12}$$

This is the equilibrium equation corresponding to the reaction

$$\tfrac{1}{2}Zn + H^+ \rightleftharpoons \tfrac{1}{2}Zn^{++} + \tfrac{1}{2}H_2$$

We may for convenience square the equilibrium expression, obtaining

$$\frac{[Zn^{++}]p_{H_2}}{[H^+]^2} = 42 \times 10^{24}$$

corresponding to the reaction

$$Zn + 2H^+ \rightleftharpoons Zn^{++} + H_2$$

This tells us that the equilibrium pressure of hydrogen for the reaction of zinc with acid is extremely great; the reaction cannot be stopped by increasing the pressure of hydrogen, but will proceed until all of the zinc is dissolved.

On the other hand, for tin the equilibrium expression is

$$\frac{[Sn^{++}]p_{H_2}}{[H^+]^2} = (2 \times 10^2)^2 = 4 \times 10^4$$

Hence equilibrium would be reached, for example, by having $[Sn^{++}] = 1$, $p_{H_2} = 4$ atm, and $[H^+] = 0.01$.

Additional illustrations of the use of the table are given in the following sections.

You will have noticed that the electron reactions are all written in Table 23-2 so as to produce one electron. This is done for convenience; with this convention the ratio of two values of K gives the equilibrium constant for the reaction obtained by subtracting the equation for one couple from that for another. It is sometimes desirable to clear the equation of fractions by multiplying by a suitable factor; as we have seen from the examples given above, and as we know from the definition of equilibrium constant, this involves raising the equilibrium constant to the power equal to this factor.

23–9. Examples Illustrating the Use of Standard Oxidation-Reduction Potentials

Many questions about chemical reactions can be answered by reference to a table of standard oxidation-reduction potentials. In particular it can be determined whether or not a given oxidizing agent and a given reducing agent can possibly react to an appreciable extent, and the extent of possible reaction can be predicted. It cannot be said, however, that the reaction will necessarily proceed at a significant rate under given conditions; *the table gives information only about the state of chemical equilibrium and not about the rate at which equilibrium is approached.* For this reason the most valuable use of the table is in connection with reactions which are known to take place, to answer questions as to the extent of reaction; but the table is also valuable in telling whether or not it is worth while to try to make a reaction go by changing conditions.

Some ways in which the table can be used are illustrated below.

Example 1.   Is ferricyanide ion a stronger or a weaker oxidizing agent than ferric ion?

  Solution.   We see from the table that the ferrocyanide-ferricyanide potential is larger than the ferrous-ferric potential; hence ferrocyanide ion is a stronger reducing agent than ferrous ion, and ferricyanide ion is a weaker oxidizing agent than ferric ion.

Example 2. Would you expect reaction to occur on mixing solutions of ferrous sulfate and mercuric sulfate?

    Solution. The ferrous-ferric couple has potential -0.771 v and the mercurous-mercuric couple -0.910 v; hence the latter couple is the stronger oxidizing of the two, and the reaction

$$2Fe^{++} + 2Hg^{++} \longrightarrow 2Fe^{+++} + Hg_2^{++}$$

would occur, and proceed well toward completion.

Example 3. What would you expect to occur on mixing solutions of ferrous sulfate and mercuric chloride?

    Solution. The above oxidation-reduction reaction would take place; in addition when the solubility product of the very slightly soluble salt Hg_2Cl_2 is reached this substance would precipitate, keeping the concentration $[Hg_2^{++}]$ low and causing the oxidation-reduction reaction to go further toward completion than in the previous case.

Example 4. In the manufacture of potassium permanganate a solution containing manganate ion is oxidized by chlorine. Would bromine or iodine be as good?

    Solution. From the table we see that the values of E^0 and K are the following:

		E^0	K
$MnO_4^{--} \rightleftarrows MnO_4^- + e^-$		-0.54	1×10^{-9}
$Cl^- \rightleftarrows \frac{1}{2}Cl_2 + e^-$		-1.358	2×10^{-23}
$Br^- \rightleftarrows \frac{1}{2}Br_2(l) + e^-$		-1.065	1×10^{-18}
$I^- \rightleftarrows \frac{1}{2}I_2(s) + e^-$		-0.535	1×10^{-9}

The value for iodine is so close to that for manganate-permanganate that effective oxidation by iodine (approaching completion) would not occur; hence iodine would be unsatisfactory. Bromine would produce essentially complete reaction, and in this respect would be as good as chlorine; but it costs ten times as much, and so should not be used.

Concepts, Facts, and Terms Introduced in This Chapter

Heat accompanying a chemical change. Thermochemistry, exothermic reaction, endothermic reaction. Definition of heat of reaction. Heat content. Heat of formation. Heat of combustion. Heat values of foods. Heat of neutralization. Heats of formation and relative electronegativity of atoms. The production of high temperatures and low temperatures.

The energy factor (enthalpy) and the probability factor (entropy) in chemical reactions. The driving force of chemical reactions—free energy. Oxidation-reduction potentials and their uses.

Exercises

23-1. A 3% solution (by weight) of hydrogen peroxide in an insulated bottle is caused to decompose by adding a small amount of a catalyst (MnO_2). How warm does the solution become? The heat of formation of $H_2O_2(aq)$ is 45.65 kcal/mole.

23-2. The molar heats of formation of NO and NO_2 are -21.5 kcal and -7.43 kcal, respectively. Is the reaction $2NO + \frac{1}{2}O_2 \longrightarrow 2NO_2$ exothermic or endothermic? What is the heat of the reaction?

23-3. From data given in this chapter and the following table of composition of foods, calculate the caloric value of the foods:

| | PERCENT BY WEIGHT | | |
	PROTEIN	FAT	CARBOHYDRATE
American cheese	28.8	35.9	9.3
Whole milk	3.3	4.0	5.0
White bread	9.3	1.2	52.2
Butter	1.0	85.0	
Potatoes	2.5	0.1	20.3

23-4. What is the heat of hydrogenation of methyl alcohol to methane? The heats of combustion of methyl alcohol and methane are 182.6 and 213.0 kcal/mole, respectively.

23-5. What oxidizing agents might be selected to oxidize manganous ion to permanganate ion?

23-6. Calculate the equilibrium constant for the reaction

$$Ni + Cd^{++} \longrightarrow Ni^{++} + Cd$$

23-7. Calculate the equilibrium constant for the decomposition of hydrogen peroxide into oxygen and water.

23-8. Do you think that cadmium could replace zinc for reducing ferric ion to the ferrous state preliminary to permanganate titration? Could metallic iron itself be used as the reducing agent for this purpose?

23-9. Is aluminum a stronger or a weaker reducing agent in use with basic solution (pH 14) than with acidic solution (pH 0)?

23-10. Would chlorine be liberated if a solution of hypochlorous acid and one of hydrochloric acid were mixed? If a solution of sodium hypochlorite and one of sodium chloride were mixed? Explain.

23-11. Can H_2S reduce ferric ion in acid solution? Cupric ion? Mercuric ion?

23-12. What would be the ratio of concentrations of bromide ion and iodide ion in an aqueous solution saturated with bromine and iodide?

23-13. Assuming that all of the heat energy given out by food on combustion could be used for doing work, calculate the amount of food (fat, say) which would be used by a 200-lb. man in climbing a 6000-ft. hill.

23-14. A person with a distaste for exercise and dieting decided to lose weight by drinking a gallon of ice water a day. His normal daily diet had a caloric value of

3000 kcal. What fraction of this did he use up in warming the ice water to body temperature, 37° C?

23-15. The heat of formation of $H_2O(g)$ is 57.80 kcal/mole, and the heat capacity of steam is about 0.50 cal/g. What is the maximum temperature that could be expected from an oxygen-hydrogen flame? One reason that this temperature is not reached in practice is that water dissociates partially to hydrogen and oxygen at very high temperatures.

23-16. Calculate the exact atomic weight of an element which has, as the solid elementary substance, a heat capacity of 0.092 cal/g and whose oxide contains 11.18% oxygen. You will need to make use of the law of Dulong and Petit.

23-17. A piece of metal weighing 100 g and at temperature 120° C was dropped into a liter of water at temperature 20.00° C. The final temperature was 20.53° C. What is the approximate atomic weight of the metal?

23-18. Without referring to tables, estimate the heat capacity of aluminum, iron, and lead.

Reference Books

F. R. Bichowsky and F. D. Rossini, *The Thermochemistry of Chemical Substances*, Reinhold Publishing Corp., New York, **1936.**

F. D. Rossini and others, *Selected Values of Chemical Thermodynamic Properties*, Circular of the Bureau of Standards 500, **1952.**

W. M. Latimer and J. H. Hildebrand, *The Reference Book of Inorganic Chemistry*, The Macmillan Company, New York, **1951.**

W. M. Latimer, *The Oxidation States of the Elements and Their Potentials in Aqueous Solutions*, Prentice-Hall, Inc., New York, **1952**; a very valuable and useful survey of oxidation potentials and equilibrium constants.

PART FIVE

Metals and Alloys and the Compounds of Metals

The six chapters, Chapters 24 to 29, that constitute Part V of our book deal with the properties of many substances.

Chapter 24 deals with the nature of metals and alloys. This part of chemistry has great practical importance. The development of automobiles, airplanes, jet motors, skyscrapers, and other objects characteristic of our civilization has been determined by the properties of the known alloys, and general progress in technology has often resulted from progress in the science of metals. The rate of progress has been limited by the fact that the chemistry of metals and alloys has lagged behind other branches of chemistry. The general theory of valence, in its modern electronic form, can be used with great power in the discussion of the compounds of metals with non-metals and of non-metals with non-metals, but the compounds of metals with metals, which are present in many alloys, have not yet been satisfactorily encompassed by this theory. The discussion of the nature of metals and alloys in Chapter 24 is accordingly incomplete; nevertheless, despite its incompleteness the science of metals in its present state is of great value in the fields of engineering which depend upon metallic materials.

Ores are the source of metals in nature. The winning of metals from their ores and their refining constitute the field of metallurgy. The chemical aspects of metallurgy are presented in Chapter 25.

The subject of Chapter 26 is the chemistry of the elements of groups I, II, III, and IV. It is interesting that the central group of the periodic system, group IV, is uniquely important to both the organic world and the inorganic world. Carbon, the first element of this group, is present in practically all of the many thousands of substances that are characteristic of living organisms, and silicon, the second element in this group, is present in most of the substances that make up the earth's crust. Most of the rocks and minerals are silicates, compounds of silicon that also contain oxygen and one or more metallic elements. The nature of silicates and of other compounds of silicon is discussed in this chapter. A discussion is also given of other silicate materials of practical importance, including glass and cement.

The chemistry of some of the transition metals is taken up in Chapters 27, 28, and 29. Chapter 27 deals with iron, cobalt, nickel, and the platinum metals, Chapter 28 with copper, zinc, and gallium and their congeners, and Chapter 29 with titanium, vanadium, chromium, and manganese and related metals.

Chapter 24

The Nature of
Metals and Alloys

24–1. *The Metallic Elements*

About seventy-six of the one hundred elementary substances are metals. A metal may be defined as a substance which has large conductivity of electricity and of heat, has a characteristic luster, called metallic luster, and can be hammered into sheets (is malleable) and drawn into wire (is ductile); in addition, the electric conductivity increases with decrease in temperature.*

The metallic elements may be taken to include lithium and beryllium in the first short period of the periodic table, sodium, magnesium, and aluminum in the second short period, the thirteen elements from potassium to gallium in the first long period, the fifteen from rubidium to antimony in the second long period, the twenty-nine from cesium to bismuth in the first very long period (including the fourteen rare-earth metals), and the twelve from francium to element 100.

The metals themselves and their alloys are of great usefulness to man, because of the properties characteristic of metals. Our modern civilization is based upon iron and steel, and valuable alloy steels are made that involve the incorporation with iron of vanadium, chromium, manganese, cobalt, nickel, molybdenum, tungsten, and other metals. The importance of these alloys is due primarily to their hardness and

---

* Sometimes there is difficulty in classifying an element as a metal, a metalloid, or a nonmetal. For example, the element tin can exist in two forms, one of which, the common form, called white tin, is metallic, whereas the other, gray tin, has the properties of a metalloid. The next element in the periodic table, antimony, exists in only one crystalline form, with the electric and thermal properties of a metal, and with metallic luster, but very brittle, rather than malleable and ductile. We shall consider both tin and antimony to be metals, although antimony is sometimes classed with the metalloids.

strength. These properties are a consequence of the presence in the metals of very strong bonds between the atoms. For this reason it is of especial interest to us to understand the nature of the forces that hold the metal atoms together in metals and alloys.

24–2. *The Structure of Metals*

In a non-metal or metalloid the number of atoms that each atom has as its nearest neighbors is determined by its covalence. For example, the iodine atom, which is univalent, has only one other iodine atom close to it in a crystal of iodine: the crystal, like liquid iodine and iodine vapor, is composed of diatomic molecules. In a crystal of sulfur there are S_8 molecules, in which each sulfur atom has two nearest neighbors, to each of which it is attached by one of its two covalent bonds. In diamond the quadrivalent carbon atom has four nearest neighbors. On the other hand, the potassium atom in potassium metal, the calcium atom in calcium metal, and the titanium atom in titanium metal, which have one, two, and four outer electrons, respectively, do not have only one, two, and four nearest neighbors, but have, instead, eight or twelve nearest neighbors. We may state that one of the characteristic features of a metal is that each atom has a large number of neighbors; the num-

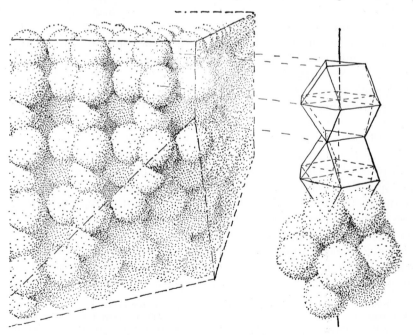

FIGURE 24-1   *The hexagonal close-packed arrangement of spheres. Many metals crystallize with this structure.*

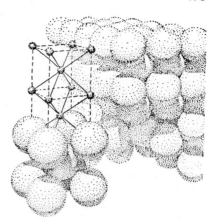

FIGURE 24-2

The atomic arrangement in α-iron (body-centered arrangement).

ber of small interatomic distances is greater than the number of valence electrons.

Most metals crystallize with an atomic arrangement in which each atom has surrounded itself with the maximum number of atoms that is geometrically possible. There are two common metallic structures that correspond to the closest possible packing of spheres of constant size. One of these structures, called the cubic closest-packed structure, has been described in Chapter 2. The other structure, called hexagonal closest packing, is represented in Figure 24-1. It is closely similar to the cubic closest-packed structure; each atom is surrounded by twelve equidistant neighbors, with, however, the arrangement of these neighbors slightly different from that in cubic closest packing. About fifty of the seventy-six metals have the cubic closest-packed structure or the hexagonal closest-packed structure, or both.

Another common structure, assumed by about twenty metals, is the body-centered cubic structure. In this structure, shown as Figure 24-2, each atom has eight nearest neighbors, and six next-nearest neighbors. These six next-nearest neighbors are 15% more distant than the eight nearest neighbors; in discussing the structure it is difficult to decide whether to describe each atom as having ligancy 8 or ligancy 14.

The periodicity of properties of the elements, as functions of the atomic number, is illustrated by the observed values of the interatomic distances in the metals, as shown in Figure 24-3. These values are half of the directly determined interatomic distances for the metals with a cubic closest-packed or hexagonal closest-packed structure. For other metals a small correction has been made; it has been observed, for example, that a metal such as iron, which crystallizes in a modification with a closest-packed structure and also a modification with the body-centered cubic structure, has contact interatomic distances about 3% less in the latter structure than in the former, and accordingly a correction of 3% can

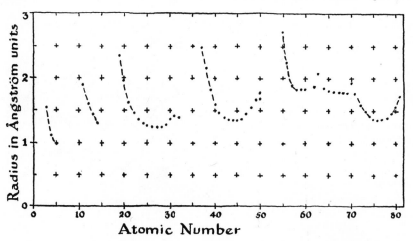

FIGURE 24-3   *The atomic radii of metals, plotted against atomic number.*

be made for body-centered cubic structures, to convert the interatomic distances to ligancy 12.

We may well expect that the strongest bonds would have the shortest interatomic distances, and it is accordingly not surprising that the large interatomic distances shown in Figure 24-3 are those for soft metals, such as potassium; the smallest ones, for chromium, iron, nickel, etc., refer to the hard, strong metals.

24–3. The Nature of the Transition Metals

The long periods of the periodic system can be described as short periods with ten additional elements inserted. The first three elements of the long period between argon and krypton, which are the metals potassium, calcium, and scandium, resemble their congeners of the preceding short period, sodium, magnesium, and aluminum, respectively. Similarly the last four elements in the sequence, germanium, arsenic, selenium, and bromine, resemble their preceding congeners, silicon, phosphorus, sulfur, and chlorine, respectively. The remaining elements of the long period, titanium, vanadium, chromium, manganese, iron, cobalt, nickel, copper, zinc, and gallium, have no lighter congeners; they are not closely similar in their properties to any lighter elements.

The properties of these elements accordingly suggest that the long period can be described as involving the introduction of ten elements in the center of the series. The introduction of these elements is correlated with the insertion of ten additional electrons into the M shell, converting it from a shell of 8 electrons, as in the argon atom, to a shell of 18 electrons. It is convenient to describe the long period as involving ten *transition metals*, corresponding to the ten electrons. We shall consider the ten elements from titanium, group IVa, to gallium, group IIIb, as constituting the ten transition elements in the first long period, and shall take the heavier congeners of these elements as the transition elements in the later series.

The chemical properties of the transition elements do not change so strikingly with change in atomic number as do those of the other elements. In the series potassium, calcium, scandium the normal salts of the elements correspond to the maximum oxidation numbers given by the positions of the elements in the periodic system, 1 for potassium, 2 for calcium, and 3 for scandium; the sulfates, for example, of these elements are K_2SO_4, $CaSO_4$, and $Sc_2(SO_4)_3$. The fourth element, titanium, tends to form salts representing a lower oxidation number than its maximum, 4; although compounds such as titanium dioxide, TiO_2, and titanium tetrachloride, $TiCl_4$, can be prepared, most of the compounds of titanium represent lower oxidation states, $+2$ or $+3$. The same tendency is shown by the succeeding elements. The compounds of vanadium, chromium, and manganese representing the maximum oxidation numbers $+5$, $+6$, and $+7$, respectively, are strong oxidizing agents, and are easily reduced to compounds in which these elements have oxidation numbers $+2$ or $+3$. The oxidation numbers $+2$ and $+3$ continue to be the important ones for the succeeding elements, iron, cobalt, nickel, copper, and zinc.

A striking characteristic of most of the compounds of the transition metals is their *color*. Nearly every compound formed by vanadium, chromium, manganese, iron, cobalt, nickel, and copper is strongly colored, the color depending not only on the atomic number of the metallic element but also on its state of oxidation, and, to some extent, on the nature of the non-metallic element or anion with which the metal is combined. It seems clear that the color of these compounds is associated with the presence of an incomplete M shell of electrons; that is, with an M shell containing less than its maximum number of electrons, 18. When the M shell is completed, as in the compounds of bipositive zinc ($ZnSO_4$, etc.) and of unipositive copper ($CuCl$, etc.), the substances are in general colorless. Another property characteristic of incompleted inner shells is *paramagnetism*, the property of a substance of being attracted into a strong magnetic field. Nearly all of the compounds of the transition elements in oxidation states corresponding to the presence of incompleted inner shells are strongly paramagnetic.

24–4. *The Metallic State*

The characteristic properties of hardness and strength of the transition metals and their alloys are a consequence of the presence in the metals of very strong bonds between the atoms. For this reason it is of especial

interest to us to understand the nature of the forces that hold the metal
atoms together in these metals and alloys.

Let us consider the first six metals of the first long period, potassium,
calcium, scandium, titanium, vanadium, and chromium. The first of
these metals, potassium, is a soft, light metal, with low melting point.
The second metal, calcium, is much harder and denser, and has a much
higher melting point. Similarly, the third metal, scandium, is still harder,
still denser, and melts at a still higher temperature, and this change in
properties continues through titanium, vanadium, and chromium. It is
well illustrated in Figure 24-4, which shows a quantity called the ideal

density, equal to $\dfrac{50}{\text{gram-atomic volume}}$. This ideal density, which is in-

versely proportional to the gram-atomic volume of the metal, is the
density that these metals would have if they all had the same atomic
weight, 50. It is an inverse measure of the interatomic distances in the
metals. We see that the ideal density increases steadily from its minimum
value of about 1 for potassium to a value of about 7 for chromium,
and many other properties of the metals, including hardness and tensile
strength, show a similar steady increase through this series of six metals.

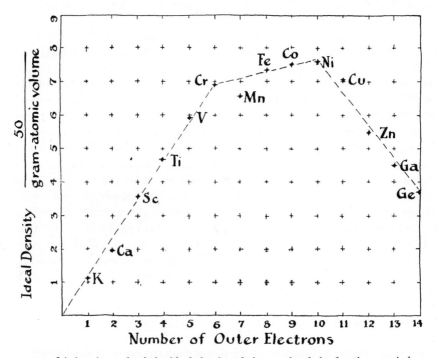

FIGURE 24-4   *A graph of the ideal density of the metals of the first long period.
The ideal density is defined here as the density that these metals would have in
case that their atomic weights were all equal to 50.*

There is a simple explanation of this change in properties in terms of the electronic structure of the metals. The potassium atom has only one electron outside of its completed argon shell. It could use this electron to form a single covalent bond with another potassium atom, as in the diatomic molecules K_2 that are present, together with monatomic molecules K, in potassium vapor. In the crystal of metallic potassium each potassium atom has a number of neighboring atoms, at the same distance. It is held to these neighbors by its single covalent bond, which resonates among the neighbors. In metallic calcium there are *two* valence electrons per calcium atom, permitting each atom to form two bonds with its neighbors. These two bonds resonate among the calcium-calcium positions, giving a total bonding power in the metal twice as great as that in potassium. Similarly in scandium, with *three* valence electrons, the bonding is three times as great as in potassium, and so on to chromium, where, with *six* valence electrons, the bonding is six times as great.

This increase does not continue in the same way beyond chromium. Instead, the strength, hardness, and other properties of the transition metals remain essentially constant for the five elements chromium, manganese, iron, cobalt, and nickel, as is indicated by the small change in ideal density in Figure 24-4. (The low value for manganese is due to the existence of this metal with an unusual crystal structure, shown by no other element.) We can conclude that the metallic valence does not continue to increase, but remains at the value six for these elements. Then, after nickel, the metallic valence again decreases, through the series copper, zinc, gallium, and germanium, as is indicated by the rapid decrease in ideal density in Figure 24-4, and by a corresponding decrease in hardness, melting point, and other properties.

It is interesting to note that in the metallic state chromium has metallic valence 6, corresponding to the oxidation number +6 characteristic of the chromates and dichromates, rather than to the lower oxidation number +3 shown in the chromium salts, and that the metals manganese, iron, cobalt, and nickel also have metallic valence 6, although nearly all of their compounds represent the oxidation state +2 or +3. *The valuable physical properties of the transition metals are the result of the high metallic valence of the elements.*

A discussion of the structure of some alloys is given in the following sections of this chapter.

24–5. *The Nature of Alloys*

An *alloy* is a metallic material containing two or more elements. It may be homogeneous, consisting of a single phase, or heterogeneous, being a mixture of phases. An example of a homogeneous alloy is coinage silver. An ordinary sample of coinage silver consists of small crystal

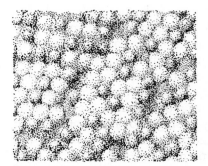

FIGURE 24-5

An alloy of gold and copper. The alloy consists of small crystals, each crystal being made of gold atoms and copper atoms in an orderly array, but with the atoms of the two different kinds distributed essentially at random among the atomic positions.

grains, each of which is a solid solution of copper and silver, with structure of the sort represented in Figure 24-5. Another example of a homogeneous alloy is the very hard metallic substance tantalum carbide, TaC. It is a compound, with the same structure as sodium chloride, Figure 4-6. Each tantalum atom has twelve tantalum atoms as neighbors. In addition, carbon atoms, which are relatively small, are present in the interstices between the tantalum atoms, and serve to bind them together. Each carbon atom is bonded to the six tantalum atoms that surround it. The bonds are $\frac{2}{3}$ bonds—the four covalent bonds resonate among the six positions about the carbon atom. Each tantalum atom is bonded not only to the adjacent carbon atoms but also to the twelve tantalum atoms surrounding it. The large number of bonds (nine valence electrons per TaC, as compared with five per Ta, occupying, in metallic tantalum, nearly the same volume) explains the greater hardness of the compound than of tantalum itself.

A discussion of the structure of some alloys will be given in later sections of this chapter and in the following chapters. Before entering upon this discussion we shall consider a general principle which has been found to have great value, not only in this field but also in many other fields of chemistry.

The Phase Rule—a Method of Classifying All Systems in Equilibrium. We have so far discussed a number of examples of systems in equilibrium. These examples include, among others, a crystal or a liquid in equilibrium with its vapor (Chapter 2), a crystal and its liquid in equilibrium with its vapor at its melting point (Chapter 2), a solution in equilibrium with the vapor of the solvent and with the frozen solvent (Chapter 8), and a precipitate in equilibrium with ions in solution (Chapter 21).

These systems appear to be quite different from one another. However, it was discovered by a great American theoretical physicist, Professor J. Willard Gibbs of Yale University (1839–1903), that a simple, unifying principle holds for all systems in equilibrium. This principle is called the *phase rule*.

The phase rule is a relation among the number of independent *components*, the number of *phases*, and the *variance* of a system in equilibrium. The independent components (or, briefly, the components) of a system are the substances that must be added to realize the system. The word phase has been defined earlier (Chapter 18). Thus a system containing ice, water, and water vapor consists of three phases but only one component (water-substance), since any two of the phases can be formed from the third. The variance of the system is the number of independent ways in which the system can be varied; these ways may include varying the temperature and the pressure, and also varying the composition of any solutions (gaseous, liquid, or crystalline) which exist as phases in the system.

The nature of the phase rule can be induced from some simple examples. Consider the system represented in Figure 24-6. It is made of water-substance (water in its various forms), in a cylinder with movable piston (to permit the pressure to be changed), placed in a thermostat with changeable temperature. If only one phase is present both the pressure and the temperature can be arbitrarily varied over wide ranges: the variance is 2. For example, liquid water can be held at any temperature from its freezing point to its boiling point under any applied pressure. But if two phases are present the pressure is automatically

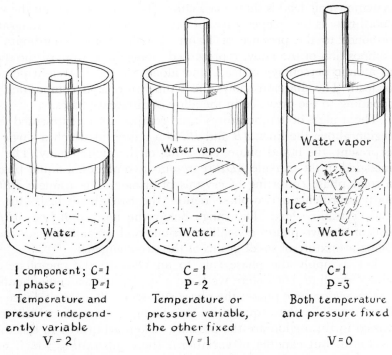

FIGURE 24-6   *A simple system illustrating the phase rule.*

determined by the temperature, and hence the variance is reduced to 1. For example, pure water vapor in equilibrium with water at a given temperature has a definite pressure, the vapor pressure of water at that temperature. And if three phases are present in equilibrium, ice, water, and water vapor, both the temperature and the pressure are exactly fixed; the variance is then 0. This condition is called the *triple point* of ice, water, and water vapor. It occurs at temperature $+0.0099°$ C and pressure 4.58 mm of mercury.

We see that for this simple system, with one component, the sum of the number of phases and the variance is equal to 3. It was discovered by Gibbs that for every system in equilibrium the sum of the number of phases and the variance is 2 greater than the number of components:

Number of phases + Variance = Number of components + 2 or, using the abbreviations P, V, and C,

$$P + V = C + 2$$

This is the **phase rule.**

Examples of application of the phase rule are given in the following discussion of some alloy systems.

The Binary System Arsenic-Lead.   The phase diagram for the binary system arsenic-lead is shown as Figure 24-7. In this diagram the vertical coordinate is the temperature, in degrees centigrade. The diagram corresponds to the pressure of 1 atm. The horizontal coordinate is the composition of the alloy, represented along the bottom of the diagram in atomic percentage of lead, and along the top in weight percentage of lead. The diagram shows the temperature and composition corresponding to the presence in the alloy of different phases.

The range of temperatures and compositions represented by the region above the lines AB and BC is a region in which a single phase is present, the liquid phase, consisting of the molten alloy. The region included in the triangle ADB represents two phases, a liquid phase and a solid phase consisting of crystals of arsenic. The triangle BEC similarly represents a two-phase region, the two phases being the liquid and crystalline lead. The range below the horizontal line DBE consists of the two phases crystalline arsenic and crystalline lead, the alloy being a mixture of small grains of the two elements.

Let us apply the phase rule to an alloy in the one-phase region above the line ABC. Here we have a system of two components, and, in this region, one phase; the phase rule states that the variance should be three. The three quantities describing the system which may be varied in this region are the pressure (taken arbitrarily in this diagram as 1 atm, but capable of variation), the temperature, which may be varied through the range permitted by the boundaries of the region,

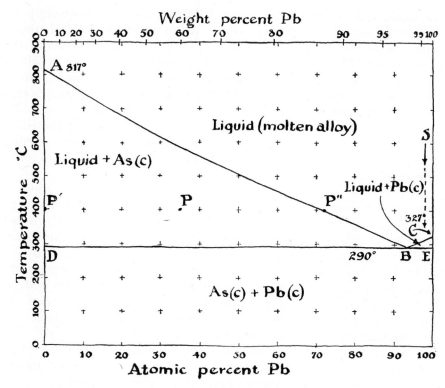

FIGURE 24-7   *Phase diagram for the binary system arsenic-lead.*

and the composition of the molten alloy, which may similarly be varied through the range of compositions permitted by the boundaries of the region.

An alloy in the region *ADB*, such as that represented by the point *P*, at 35 atomic percent lead and 400° C, lies in a two-phase region, and the variance is accordingly stated by the phase rule to be two. The pressure and the temperature are the two variables; the phase rule hence states that it is not possible to vary the composition of the phases present in the alloy. The phases are crystalline arsenic, represented by the point *P'* directly to the left of *P*, and the molten alloy, with the composition *P''* directly to the right of *P*. The composition of the molten alloy in equilibrium with crystalline arsenic at 400° C and 1 atm pressure is definitely fixed at *P''*; it cannot be varied.

The only conditions under which three phases can be in equilibrium with one another at the arbitrary pressure 1 atm are represented by the point *B*. With three phases in equilibrium with one another for this two-component system, the phase rule requires that there be only one arbitrary variable, which we have used in fixing the pressure arbitrarily at 1 atm. Correspondingly we see that the composition of the liquid is fixed at that represented by the point *B*, 93 atomic percent lead, and the composition of the two solid phases is fixed, these phases being pure arsenic and pure lead. The temperature is also fixed, at the value 290° C, corresponding to the point *B*. This point is called the *eutectic point*, and the corresponding alloy is called the *eutectic alloy*, or simply the *eutectic*. The word eutectic means melting easily; the eutectic has a sharp melting point. When a liquid alloy with the eutectic composition is cooled, it crystallizes completely on reaching the temperature 290°, forming a mixture of very small grains of pure arsenic and pure lead, with a fine texture. When this alloy is slowly heated, it melts sharply at the temperature 290°.

The lines in the phase diagram are the boundaries separating a region in which one group of phases are present from a region in which another group of phases are present. These boundary lines can be located by various experimental methods, including the measurement of the temperature at which transitions occur from one phase to another. If a crucible filled with pure arsenic is heated to a temperature above the melting point of the arsenic, 817° C, and the system is then allowed to cool, it would be noted, by means of a thermometer or thermocouple in the molten arsenic, that the temperature decreases steadily with time until the value 817° C is reached, and then remains constant at that value for several minutes, while the arsenic is freezing. After all of the molten arsenic has frozen, the temperature will again begin to decrease steadily, until room temperature is reached.

If, however, a mixture of 35 atomic percent lead and 65 atomic percent arsenic is heated to make the molten alloy with this composition, and this melt is allowed to cool, a somewhat different behavior is observed. The cooling will proceed uniformly until a temperature of about 590° C is reached. At this temperature the rate of cooling will be decreased somewhat, because arsenic will begin to crystallize out of the melt, and the energy of crystallization liberated by the arsenic will help to keep the system warm. The reason that the alloy begins to freeze at a lower temperature than pure arsenic is the same as the reason that a salt solution or sugar solution freezes at a temperature lower than the freezing point of pure water, as discussed in Chapter 18. The slope of the line *AB* is a measure of the *freezing point depression* of molten arsenic by dissolved lead. As arsenic begins to crystallize out of the molten alloy, the composition of the melt changes, and a lower temperature is required to cause more arsenic to crystallize out. The crystallization of arsenic alone continues until the temperature reaches the eutectic temperature, 290° C, and the composition of the melt reaches the eutectic value, represented by point *B*. When this state is reached the temperature of the crystallizing alloy stays constant until the eutectic melt has completely crystallized into a fine-grained mixture of crystalline arsenic and crystalline lead. The solid alloy then consists of large

primary crystals of arsenic embedded in a fine-grained eutectic mixture of arsenic crystals and lead crystals.

If a molten alloy of arsenic and lead with the eutectic composition
is cooled, the temperature drops at a regular rate until the eutectic
temperature, 290° C, is reached; the liquid then crystallizes into the
solid eutectic alloy, the temperature remaining constant until crystallization is complete. The cooling curves obtained for the eutectic composition are accordingly similar to those of the pure metal. The eutectic
has a constant melting point, just as has either one of the pure elementary substances.

The effect of the phenomenon of depression of the freezing point
in causing the eutectic melting point to be lower than the melting
point of the pure metals can be intensified by the use of additional
components. Thus an alloy with eutectic melting point 70° C can be
made by melting together 50 weight percent bismuth (m.p. 271° C),
27 percent lead (m.p. 327.5° C), 13 percent tin (m.p. 232° C), and 10
percent cadmium (m.p. 321° C), and the melting point can be reduced
still further, to 47° C, by the incorporation in this alloy of 18 percent
of its weight of indium (m.p. 155° C).

It is now possible, in terms of this phase diagram, to discuss a phenomenon mentioned in Chapter 16. It was stated there that a small
amount, about $\frac{1}{2}$ percent by weight, of arsenic is added to lead used to
make lead shot, in order to increase the hardness of the shot and also to
improve the properties of the molten material. Lead shot is made by
dripping the molten alloy through a sieve. The fine droplets freeze
during their passage through the air, and are caught in a tank of water
after they have solidified. If pure lead were used the falling drops would
solidify rather suddenly on reaching the temperature 327° C. A falling
drop tends not to be perfectly spherical, but to oscillate between pro-
late and oblate ellipsoidal shapes, as you may have noticed by observing drops of water dripping from a faucet; and hence the shot made
of pure lead might be expected not to be perfectly spherical in shape.
But the alloy containing $\frac{1}{2}$ percent arsenic by weight, represented by
the arrow S, would begin to freeze on reaching the temperature 320° C,
and would continue to freeze, forming small crystals of pure lead, until
the eutectic temperature 290° C is reached. During this stage of its
history the drop would consist of a sludge of lead crystals in the molten
alloy, and this sluggish sludge would be expected to be drawn into
good spherical shape by the action of the surface-tension forces of the
liquid.

The Binary System Lead-Tin. The phase diagram for the lead-tin
system of alloys is shown as Figure 24-8. This system rather closely
resembles the system arsenic-lead, except for the fact that there is an
appreciable solubility of tin in crystalline lead and a small solubility

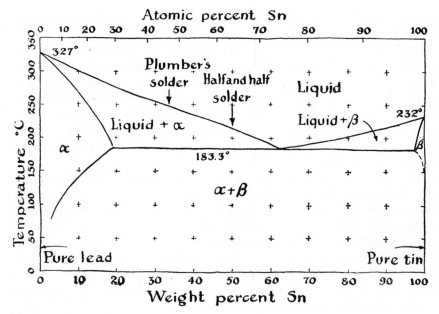

FIGURE 24-8   *Phase diagram for the binary system lead-tin.*

of lead in crystalline tin. The phase designated α (alpha) is a solid solution of tin in lead, the solubility being 19.5 weight percent at the eutectic temperature and dropping to 2 percent at room temperature. The phase β (beta) is a solid solution of lead in tin, the solubility being about 2 percent at the eutectic temperature and extremely small at room temperature. The eutectic composition is about 62 weight percent tin, 38 weight percent lead.

The composition of *solder* is indicated by the two arrows, corresponding to ordinary plumbers' solder and to half-and-half solder. The properties of solder are explained by the phase diagram. The useful property of solder is that it permits a wiped-joint to be made. As the solder cools it forms a sludge of crystals of the α phase in the liquid alloy, and the mechanical properties of this sludge are such as to permit it to be handled by the plumber in an effective way. The sludge corresponds to transition through the region of the phase diagram in which liquid and the α phase are present together. For plumbers' solder the temperature range involved is about 70°, from 250° C to 183° C, the eutectic temperature.

The Binary System Silver-Gold.   The metals silver and gold are completely miscible with one another not only in the liquid state but also in the crystalline state. A solid alloy of silver and gold consists of a single phase, homogeneous crystals with the cubic closest packed structure, described for copper in Chapter 2, with gold and silver

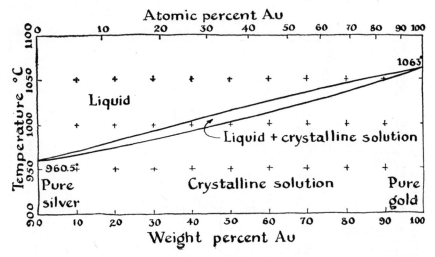

FIGURE 24-9   *Phase diagram for the binary system silver-gold, showing the formation of a complete series of crystalline solutions.*

atoms occupying the positions in this lattice essentially at random (Figure 24-5). The phase diagram shown as Figure 24-9 represents this situation. It is seen that the addition of a small amount of gold to pure silver does not depress the freezing point, in the normal way, but instead causes an increase in the temperature of crystallization.

The alloys of silver and gold, usually containing some copper, are used in jewelry, in dentistry, and as a gold solder.

The Binary System Silver-Strontium. A somewhat more complicated binary system, that formed by silver and strontium, is represented in Figure 24-10. It is seen that four intermetallic compounds are formed, their formulas being Ag_4Sr, Ag_5Sr_3, $AgSr$, and Ag_2Sr_3. These compounds and the pure elements form a series of eutectics; for example, the alloy containing 25 weight percent strontium is the eutectic mixture of Ag_4Sr and Ag_5Sr_3.

Some other binary systems are far more complicated than this one. As many as a dozen different phases may be present, and these phases may involve variation in composition, resulting from the formation of solid solutions. Ternary alloys (formed from three components), and alloys involving four or more components are of course still more complex.

It is seen that the formulas of intermetallic compounds, such as Ag_4Sr, do not correspond in any simple way to the usually accepted valences of the element. Compounds such as Ag_4Sr can be described by saying that the strontium atom uses its two valence electrons in forming bonds with the silver atoms which surround it, and that the silver

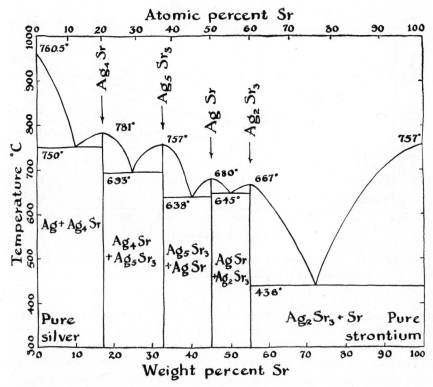

FIGURE 24-10 *Phase diagram for the binary system silver-strontium, showing the formation of four intermetallic compounds.*

atoms then use their remaining electrons in forming bonds with other silver atoms. Some progress has been made in developing a valence theory of the structure and properties of intermetallic compounds and of alloys in general, but this field of chemistry is still far from its final form.

Concepts, Facts, and Terms Introduced in This Chapter

The metallic elements and their properties. The structure of metals: cubic closest packing, hexagonal closest packing, the body-centered structure.

Transition metals: position in periodic table, electronic structure, color and paramagnetism of compounds.

The metallic state; importance of metals and alloys; the nature of the metallic bond; metallic valence in relation to hardness, strength, and other properties.

The nature of alloys. Homogeneous and heterogeneous alloys. Solid solutions, intermetallic compounds. The phase rule, $P + V = C + 2$; number of phases, variance, number of components of a system in equilibrium; triple point. Phase diagrams of binary systems; eutectic mixture; eutectic point. The systems As-Pb, Pb-Sn, Ag-Au, Ag-Sr as examples.

Exercises

24-1. Aluminum crystallizes in cubic closest packing. How many nearest neighbors does each atom have? Predict its metallic valence from its position in the periodic table. Would you predict it to have greater or less tensile strength than magnesium? Why?

24-2. Discuss the metallic valence of the elements rubidium, strontium, and yttrium. What would you predict about change in hardness, density, strength, and melting point in this series of elements?

24-3. How many nearest neighbors does an atom have in a cubic closest-packed structure (example, copper)? In a hexagonal closest-packed structure (example, magnesium)? In a body-centered structure (example, iron)?

24-4. Compare the metallic valences of chromium and iron with their oxidation numbers in their principal compounds.

24-5. Describe the structure of tantalum carbide. Can you explain its much greater strength and hardness than of tantalum itself?

24-6. Define alloy, intermetallic compound, phase, variance, eutectic, triple point.

24-7. State the phase rule, and give an application of it.

24-8. Cadmium (m.p. 321° C) and bismuth (m.p. 271° C) do not form solid solutions nor compounds with one another. Their eutectic point lies at 61 weight percent bismuth and 146° C. Sketch their phase diagram, and label each region to show what phases are present.

24-9. Describe the structure of the alloy that would be obtained by cooling a melt of silver containing 10 atomic percent strontium (see Figure 24-10).

24-10. What is plumbers' solder? Would the alloy with 60 weight % tin and 40 weight % lead be satisfactory as solder?

Chapter 25

Metallurgy

Metals are obtained from ores. *An* **ore** *is a mineral or other natural material that may be profitably treated for the extraction of one or more metals.*

The process of extracting a metal from the ore is called *winning* the metal. *Refining* is the purification of the metal that has been extracted from the ore. *Metallurgy* is the science and art of winning and refining metals, and preparing them for use.

Processes of many different kinds are used for winning metals. The simplest processes are those used to obtain the metals that occur in nature in the elementary state. Thus nuggets of gold and of the platinum metals may be picked up by hand, in some deposits, or may be separated by a hydraulic process (use of a stream of water), when the nuggets occur mixed with lighter materials in a placer deposit.* A quartz vein containing native gold may be treated by mining it, pulverizing the quartz in a stamp mill, and then mixing the rock powder with mercury. The gold dissolves in the mercury, which is easily separated from the rock powder because of its great density, and the gold can be recovered from the amalgam (its alloy with mercury) by distilling off the mercury.

The chemical processes involved in the winning of metals are mainly the reduction of a compound of the metal (usually oxide or sulfide). The principal reducing agent that is used is carbon, often in the form of coke. An example is the reduction of tin dioxide, SnO_2, with carbon, as described in Section 25–4. Another example is the reduction of ion oxide with coke in a blast furnace (Chapter 27). Occasionally other reducing agents than carbon are used; thus antimony is won from stibnite, Sb_2S_3, by heating it with iron:

$$Sb_2S_3 + 3Fe \longrightarrow 3FeS + 2Sb$$

* A placer deposit is a glacial deposit or alluvial deposit (made by a river, lake, or arm of the sea), as of sand or gravel, containing gold or other valuable material.

The strongly electropositive metals, such as the alkali metals, the alkaline-earth metals, and aluminum, are won by electrolysis (Chapter 10, Section 25–6). Some metals are won by reduction of their oxides by a more electropositive metal (Section 25–5).

The principal methods of winning metals are discussed in the following sections of this chapter. The metallurgy of iron and its congeners is taken up in Chapter 27.

Impure metals are purified in various ways. Distillation is used for mercury, and sublimation for zinc, cadmium, tin, and antimony. Copper and some other metals are refined electrolytically (Section 25–7). An unusual method of refining a metal is the Mond process for nickel (Section 27–5).

25–1. *The Metallurgy of Copper*

Copper occurs in nature as *native copper;* that is, in the free state. Other ores of copper include *cuprite*, Cu_2O; *chalcocite*, Cu_2S; *chalcopyrite*, $CuFeS_2$; *malachite*, $Cu_2CO_3(OH)_2$; and *azurite*, $Cu_3(CO_3)_2(OH)_2$. Malachite, a beautiful green mineral, is sometimes polished and used in jewelry.

An ore containing native copper may be treated by grinding and then washing away the gangue (the associated rock or earthy material), and melting and casting the copper. Oxide or carbonate ores may be leached with dilute sulfuric acid, to produce a cupric solution from which the copper can be deposited by electrolysis (Chapter 10). High-grade oxide and carbonate ores may be reduced by heating with coke mixed with a suitable flux. (A flux is a material, such as limestone, that combines with the silicate minerals of the gangue to form a slag that is liquid at the temperature of the furnace, and can be easily separated from the metal.)

Sulfide ores are smelted by a complex process. Low-grade ores are first concentrated, by a process such as *flotation*. The finely ground ore is treated with a mixture of water and a suitable oil. The oil wets the sulfide minerals, and the water wets the silicate minerals of the gangue. Air is then blown through to produce a froth, which contains the oil and the sulfide minerals; the silicate minerals sink to the bottom.

The concentrate or the rich sulfide ore is then roasted in a furnace through which air is passing. This removes some of the sulfur as sulfur dioxide, and leaves a mixture of Cu_2S, FeO, SiO_2, and other substances. This roasted ore is then mixed with limestone to serve as a flux, and is heated in a furnace. The iron oxide and silica combine with the limestone to form a slag, and the cuprous sulfide melts and can be drawn off. This impure cuprous sulfide is called *matte*. It is then reduced by blowing air through the molten material:

$$Cu_2S + O_2 \longrightarrow SO_2 + 2Cu$$

Some copper oxide is also formed by the blast of air, and this is reduced by stirring the molten metal with poles of green wood. The copper obtained in this way has a characteristic appearance, and is called *blister copper*. It contains about 1% of iron, gold, silver, and other impurities, and is usually refined electrolytically, as described in Section 25–7.

25–2. *The Metallurgy of Silver and Gold*

The principal ores of silver are *native silver*, Ag; *argentite*, Ag_2S; and *cerargyrite* or *horn-silver*, AgCl. The **cyanide process** of winning the metal from these ores is widely used. This process involves treating the crushed ore with a solution of sodium cyanide, NaCN, for about two weeks, with thorough aeration to oxidize the native silver. The reactions producing the soluble complex ion $Ag(CN)_2^-$ may be written in the following way:

$$4Ag + 8CN^- + O_2 + 2H_2O \longrightarrow 4Ag(CN)_2^- + 4OH^-$$
$$AgCl + 2CN^- \longrightarrow Ag(CN)_2^- + Cl^-$$
$$Ag_2S + 4CN^- \longrightarrow 2Ag(CN)_2^- + S^{--}$$

The silver is then obtained from the solution by reduction with metallic zinc:

$$Zn + 2Ag(CN)_2^- \longrightarrow 2Ag + Zn(CN)_4^{--}$$

The **amalgamation process** is used for native silver. The ore is treated with mercury, which dissolves the silver. The liquid amalgam is then separated from the gangue and distilled, the mercury collecting in the receiver and the silver remaining in the retort.

Silver is obtained as a by-product in the refining of copper and lead. The sludge from the electrolytic refining of copper may be treated by simple chemical methods to obtain its content of silver and gold. The small amount of silver in lead is obtained by an ingenious method, the *Parkes process*. This involves stirring a small amount (about 1%) of zinc into the molten lead. Liquid zinc is insoluble in liquid lead, and the solubility of silver in liquid zinc is about 3000 times as great as in liquid lead. Hence most of the silver dissolves in the zinc. The zinc-silver phase comes to the top, solidifies as the crucible cools, and is lifted off. The zinc can then be distilled away, leaving the silver. Gold present in the lead is also obtained by this process.

Gold is obtained from its ores, such as gold-bearing quartz, by pulverizing the ore and washing it over plates of copper coated with a layer of amalgam. The gold dissolves in the amalgam, which is then scraped off and separated by distillation. The tailings may then be treated with cyanide solution, and the gold be won from the cyanide solution by electrolysis or treatment with zinc:

$$4Au + 8CN^- + O_2 + 2H_2O \longrightarrow 4Au(CN)_2^- + 4OH^-$$

$$2Au(CN)_2^- + Zn \longrightarrow 2Au + Zn(CN)_4^{--}$$

25-3. *The Metallurgy of Zinc, Cadmium, and Mercury*

The principal ore of zinc is *sphalerite* or *zinc blende*, ZnS. Less important ores include *zincite*, ZnO; *smithsonite*, $ZnCO_3$; *willemite*, Zn_2SiO_4; *calamine*, $Zn_2SiO_3(OH)_2$; and *franklinite*, Fe_2ZnO_4.

Many ores of zinc are concentrated by flotation before smelting. Sulfide ores and carbonate ores are then converted to oxide by roasting:

$$2ZnS + 3O_2 \longrightarrow 2ZnO + 2SO_2$$

$$ZnCO_3 \longrightarrow ZnO + CO_2$$

The zinc oxide is mixed with carbon and heated in a fire-clay retort to a temperature high enough to vaporize the zinc:

$$ZnO + C \longrightarrow Zn \uparrow + CO \uparrow$$

The zinc vapor is condensed in fire-clay receivers. At first the zinc is condensed in the cool condenser as a fine powder, called *zinc dust*, which contains some zinc oxide. After the receiver becomes hot the vapor condenses to a liquid, which is cast in ingots called *spelter*. Spelter contains small amounts of cadmium, iron, lead, and arsenic. It can be purified by careful redistillation.

The zinc oxide can also be reduced by electrolysis. It is dissolved in sulfuric acid, and electrolyzed with aluminum sheets as cathodes. The deposited zinc, which is about 99.95% pure, is stripped off the cathodes, melted, and cast into ingots, for use where pure zinc is needed, as in the production of brass. The sulfuric acid is regenerated in the process, as is seen from the reactions:

Solution of zinc oxide: $\quad ZnO + 2H^+ \longrightarrow Zn^{++} + H_2O$

Cathode reaction: $\quad\quad\quad Zn^{++} + 2e^- \longrightarrow Zn$

Anode reaction: $\quad\quad\quad\quad H_2O \longrightarrow \frac{1}{2}O_2 \uparrow + 2H^+ + 2e^-$

Over-all reaction: $\quad\quad\quad ZnO \longrightarrow Zn + \frac{1}{2}O_2$

Cadmium is obtained mainly as a by-product in the smelting and refining of zinc; it occurs to the amount of about one percent in many zinc ores. The sulfide of cadmium, CdS, is called *greenockite*. Cadmium is more volatile than zinc, and in the reduction of zinc oxide containing cadmium oxide it is concentrated in the first portions of dust collected in the receivers.

Mercury occurs as the native metal, in small globules of pure mercury and as crystalline silver amalgam. Its most important ore is the red

mineral *cinnabar*, HgS. Cinnabar is smelted simply by heating it in a
retort in a stream of air, and condensing the mercury vapor in a receiver:

$$HgS + O_2 \longrightarrow Hg\uparrow + SO_2\uparrow$$

25–4. *The Metallurgy of Tin and Lead*

The principal ore of tin is *cassiterite*, SnO_2, the main deposits of which
are in Colombia and the East Indies. The crude ore is ground and
washed in a stream of water, which separates the lighter gangue from
the heavy cassiterite. The ore is then roasted, to oxidize the sulfides of
iron and copper to products which are removed by leaching with
water. The purified ore is then mixed with carbon and reduced in a
reverberatory furnace. The crude tin produced in this way is resmelted
at a gentle heat, and the pure metal flows away from the higher-melting
impurities, chiefly compounds of iron and arsenic. Some tin is purified
by electrolysis.

The principal ore of lead is *galena*, PbS, which occurs, often in beautiful cubic crystals, in large deposits in the United States, Spain, and
Mexico. The ore is first roasted until part of it has been converted into
lead oxide, PbO, and lead sulfate, $PbSO_4$. The supply of air to the furnace is then cut off, and the temperature is raised. Metallic lead is then
produced by the reactions

$$PbS + 2PbO \longrightarrow 3Pb + SO_2$$
and
$$PbS + PbSO_4 \longrightarrow 2Pb + 2SO_2$$

Some lead is also made by heating galena with scrap iron:

$$PbS + Fe \longrightarrow Pb + FeS$$

Silver is often removed from lead by the Parkes process, described
in Section 25–2. Some pure lead is made by electrolytic refining.

25–5. *Reduction of Metal Oxides or Halogenides by*
Strongly Electropositive Metals

Some metals, including titanium, zirconium, hafnium, lanthanum,
and the lanthanons, are most conveniently obtained by reaction of
their oxides or halogenides with a more electropositive metal. Sodium,
potassium, calcium, and aluminum are often used for this purpose.
Thus titanium may be made by reduction of titanium tetrachloride
by calcium:

$$TiCl_4 + 2Ca \longrightarrow Ti + 2CaCl_2$$

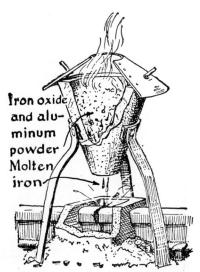

FIGURE 25-1

The preparation of a metal (in this case iron) by the aluminothermic process.

Iron oxide
and alu-
minum
powder
Molten
iron

Titanium, zirconium, and hafnium are purified by the decomposition of their tetraiodides on a hot wire. The impure metal is heated with iodine in an evacuated flask, to produce the tetraiodide as a gas:

$$Zr + 2I_2 \longrightarrow ZrI_4$$

The gas comes into contact with a hot filament, where it is decomposed, forming a wire of the purified metal:

$$ZrI_4 \longrightarrow Zr + 2I_2$$

The process of preparing a metal by reduction of its oxide by aluminum is called the *aluminothermic process*. For example, chromium can be prepared by igniting a mixture of powdered chromium(III) oxide and powdered aluminum:

$$Cr_2O_3 + 2Al \longrightarrow Al_2O_3 + 2Cr$$

The heat liberated by this reaction is so great as to produce molten chromium. The aluminothermic process is a convenient way of obtaining a small amount of liquid metal, such as iron for welding (Figure 25-1).

25–6. *The Electrolytic Production of Aluminum*

All commercial aluminum is made electrolytically, by a process discovered in 1886 by a young American, Charles M. Hall (1863–1914), and independently, in the same year, by a young Frenchman, P. L. T. Héroult (1863–1914). A carbon-lined iron box, which serves as cathode, contains the electrolyte, which is the molten mineral cryolite, Na_3AlF_6

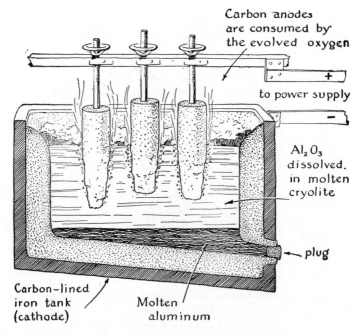

Carbon anodes
are consumed by
the evolved oxygen

to power supply

Al_2O_3
dissolved.
in molten
cryolite

plug

Carbon-lined
iron tank
(cathode)   Molten
                 aluminum

FIGURE 25-2   *The electrolytic production of aluminum.*

(or a mixture of AlF_3, NaF, and sometimes CaF_2, to lower the melting point), in which aluminum oxide, Al_2O_3, is dissolved (Figure 25-2). The aluminum oxide is obtained from the ore *bauxite* by a process of purification, which is described below. The anodes in the cell are made of carbon. The passage of the current provides heat enough to keep the electrolyte molten, at about 1000° C. The aluminum metal that is produced by the process of electrolysis sinks to the bottom of the cell, and is tapped off. The cathode reaction is

$$Al^{+++} + 3e^- \longrightarrow Al$$

The anode reaction involves the carbon of the electrodes, which is converted into carbon dioxide:

$$C + 2O^{--} \longrightarrow CO_2\uparrow + 4e^-$$

The cells operate at about 5 volts potential difference between the electrodes.

Bauxite is a mixture of aluminum minerals ($AlHO_2$, $Al(OH)_3$), which contains some ion oxide. It is purified by treatment with sodium hydroxide solution, which dissolves hydrated aluminum oxide, as the aluminate ion, $Al(OH)_4^-$, but does not dissolve iron oxide:

$$Al(OH)_3 + OH^- \longrightarrow Al(OH)_4^-$$

The solution is filtered, and is then acidified with carbon dioxide, which reverses the above reaction, by forming hydrogen carbonate ion, HCO_3^-:

$$Al(OH)_4^- + CO_2 \longrightarrow HCO_3^- + Al(OH)_3$$

The precipitated aluminum hydroxide is then dehydrated by ignition (heating to a high temperature), and the purified aluminum oxide is ready for addition to the electrolyte.

25-7. *The Electrolytic Refining of Metals*

Several metals, won from their ores by either chemical or electrochemical processes, are further refined by electrolytic methods.

Metallic copper is sometimes obtained by leaching a copper ore with sulfuric acid and then depositing the metal by electrolysis of the copper sulfate solution obtained in this way. Most copper ores, however, are converted into crude copper by chemical reduction, with carbon as the reducing agent. This crude copper is cast into anode plates about $\frac{3}{4}$ in. thick, and is then refined electrolytically.

The process of electrolytic refining of copper is a simple one (Figure 25-3). The anodes of crude copper alternate with cathodes of thin sheets of pure copper coated with graphite, which makes it possible to strip off the deposit. The electrolyte is copper sulfate. As the current passes through, crude copper dissolves from the anodes and a purer copper deposits on the cathodes. Metals below copper in the electromotive-force series, such as gold, silver, and platinum, remain undis-

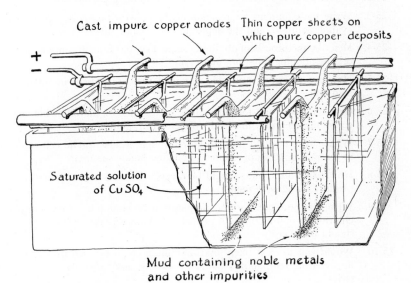

FIGURE 25-3   *The electrolytic refining of copper.*

solved, and fall to the bottom of the tank as a sludge, from which they can be recovered. More active metals, such as iron, remain in the solution.

Concepts, Facts, and Terms Introduced in This Chapter

Ores. Metallurgy—the winning and refining of metals.

Ores of copper: native copper, cuprite, chalcocite, chalcopyrite, malachite, azurite. Concentration of ore by flotation. Roasting of sulfide ore to Cu_2S, matte. Oxidation to blister copper. Electrolytic refining of copper.

Ores of silver: native silver, argentite, cerargyrite. The amalgamation process; the cyanide process; the Parkes process. The similar metallurgy of gold.

Ores of zinc: sphalerite, zincite, smithsonite, willemite, calamine, franklinite. Reduction of zinc oxide with carbon or of zinc ion by electrolysis.

Greenockite, CdS. Cadmium metal as a by-product of zinc.

Cinnabar, HgS. Production of mercury by oxidation.

Cassiterite, SnO_2. Reduction by carbon.

Galena, PbS. Production of lead by roasting or by reduction by iron.

Reduction of metal oxides or halogenides by sodium, potassium, calcium, or aluminum. The aluminothermic process.

Bauxite, $AlHO_2$ and $Al(OH)_3$. Electrolytic production of aluminum.

Exercises

25-1. What is a mineral? What is an ore?

25-2. Describe the amalgamation process of winning gold and silver.

25-3. Write the equations for reaction of the mineral bromyrite, AgBr, with sodium cyanide solution, and the deposition of metallic silver.

25-4. Describe the process of obtaining refined copper from an impure copper sulfide ore, mentioning flotation, matte, and blister copper.

25-5. How are the silver and gold obtained that are present in small amounts in lead ore?

25-6. Give the name and formula of one ore of each of the following metals: zinc, cadmium, mercury, tin, lead, copper, silver, gold.

25-7. What current would need to flow through an electrolytic cell to deposit zinc at the rate of 10 kg per hour from a zinc sulfate solution?

25-8. How much aluminum should be mixed with 1 kg of manganese(IV) oxide to produce manganese metal?

25-9. Write the equation for the preparation of lanthanum from lanthanum(III) chloride by reduction with potassium. What relative weights of the reactants should be taken?

25-10. Would you think it likely that aluminum could be used instead of potassium in preparing lanthanum? Could calcium be used? (See the electromotive-force series.)

Chapter 26

Lithium, Beryllium, Boron, and Silicon and Their Congeners

In this chapter we shall discuss the metals and metalloids of groups I, II, III, and IV of the periodic table, and their compounds.

The alkali metals, group I, are the most strongly electropositive elements—the most strikingly metallic. Many of their compounds have been mentioned in earlier chapters. The alkaline-earth metals are also strongly electropositive.

Boron, silicon, and germanium are metalloids, with properties intermediate between those of metals and those of non-metals. The electric conductivity* of boron, for example, is 1×10^{-6} mho/cm; this value is intermediate between the values for metals (4×10^5 mho/cm for aluminum, for example), and those for non-metals (2×10^{-13} for diamond, for example). They have a corresponding tendency to form oxygen acids, rather than to serve as cations in salts.

Silicon (from Latin *silex*, flint) is the second element in group IV, and is hence a congener of carbon. Silicon plays an important part in the inorganic world, similar to that played by carbon in the organic world. Most of the rocks that constitute the earth's crust are composed of the silicate minerals, of which silicon is the most important elementary constituent.

The importance of carbon in organic chemistry results from its ability to form carbon-carbon bonds, permitting complex molecules, with the

* The electric conductivity, in mho/cm, is the current in amperes flowing through a rod with cross-section 1 cm² when there is an electric potential difference between the ends of the rod of 1 volt per cm length of the rod.

most varied properties, to exist. The importance of silicon in the inorganic world results from a different property of the element—a few compounds are known in which silicon atoms are connected to one another by covalent bonds, but these compounds are relatively unimportant. The characteristic feature of the silicate minerals is the existence of chains and more complex structures (layers, three-dimensional frameworks) in which the silicon atoms are not bonded directly to one another but are connected by oxygen atoms. The nature of these structures is described briefly in later sections of this chapter.

26–1. *The Electronic Structures of Lithium, Beryllium, Boron, and Silicon and Their Congeners*

The electronic structures of the elements of groups I, II, III, and IV are given in Table 26-1. The distribution of the electrons among the

TABLE 26-1   *The Electronic Structures of the Elements of Groups I, II, III, and IV*

Z	ELEMENT	K	L		M			N				O			P	
		1s	2s	2p	3s	3p	3d	4s	4p	4d	4f	5s	5p	5d	6s	6p
3	Li	2	1													
4	Be	2	2													
5	B	2	2	1												
6	C	2	2	2												
11	Na	2	2	6	1											
12	Mg	2	2	6	2											
13	Al	2	2	6	2	1										
14	Si	2	2	6	2	2										
19	K	2	2	6	2	6		1								
20	Ca	2	2	6	2	6		2								
21	Sc	2	2	6	2	6	1	2								
32	Ge	2	2	6	2	6	10	2	2							
37	Rb	2	2	6	2	6	10	2	6			1				
38	Sr	2	2	6	2	6	10	2	6			2				
39	Y	2	2	6	2	6	10	2	6	1		2				
50	Sn	2	2	6	2	6	10	2	6	10		2	2			
55	Cs	2	2	6	2	6	10	2	6	10		2	6		1	
56	Ba	2	2	6	2	6	10	2	6	10		2	6		2	
57	La	2	2	6	2	6	10	2	6	10		2	6	1	2	
82	Pb	2	2	6	2	6	10	2	6	10	14	2	6	10	2	2

orbitals is the same in this table as in the energy-level chart, Figure 5-6, with one exception: the normal state of the lanthanum atom has been found by the study of the spectrum of lanthanum to correspond to the presence of one electron in the 5d orbital, rather than in the 4f orbital, as indicated in the energy-level chart.

The elements of group I have one more electron than the preceding noble gas, those of group II have two more, and those of group III have three more. The outermost shell of each of these noble-gas atoms is an octet of electrons, two electrons in the s orbital and six in the three p orbitals of the shell. The one, two, or three outermost electrons of the metallic elements are easily removed, with formation of the cations Li^+, Na^+, K^+, Rb^+, Cs^+, Be^{++}, Mg^{++}, Ca^{++}, Sr^{++}, Ba^{++}, Al^{+++}, Sc^{+++}, Y^{+++}, and La^{+++}. Each of these elements forms only one principal series of compounds, in which it has oxidation number $+1$ for group I, $+2$ for group II, or $+3$ for group III. The metalloid boron also forms compounds in which its oxidation number is $+3$, but the cation B^{+++} is not stable.

Whereas carbon is adjacent to boron in the sequence of the elements, and also silicon to aluminum, the succeeding elements of group IV of the periodic table, germanium, tin, and lead, are widely separated from the corresponding elements of group III, scandium, yttrium, and lanthanum. Germanium is separated from scandium by the ten elements of the iron transition series, tin from yttrium by the ten elements of the palladium transition series, and lead from lanthanum by the ten elements of the platinum transition series, and also the fourteen lanthanons.*

Each of the elements of group IV has four valence electrons, which occupy s and p orbitals of the outermost shell. The maximum oxidation number of these elements is $+4$. All of the compounds of silicon correspond to this oxidation number. Germanium, tin, and lead form two series of compounds, representing oxidation number $+4$ and oxidation number $+2$, the latter being more important than the former for lead.

26–2. *The Alkali Metals and Their Compounds*

The elements of the first group, lithium, sodium, potassium, rubidium, and cesium,† are soft, silvery-white metals with great chemical reactivity. These metals are excellent conductors of electricity. Some of their physical properties are given in Table 26-2. It can be seen from the table that they melt at low temperatures—four of the five metals melt below the boiling point of water. Lithium, sodium, and potassium are lighter than water. The vapors of the alkali metals are mainly monatomic, with a small concentration of diatomic molecules (Li_2, etc.), in which the two atoms are held together by a covalent bond.

* There is some disagreement among chemists about nomenclature of the groups of the periodic system. We have described the transition elements as coming between groups III and IV in the long periods of the periodic table. An alternative that has found about as wide acceptance is to place them between groups II and III.

† The sixth alkali metal, francium (Fr), element 87, has been obtained only in minute quantities, and no information has been published about its properties.

TABLE 26-2 *Some Properties of the Alkali Metals*

	SYMBOL	ATOMIC NUMBER	ATOMIC WEIGHT	MELTING POINT	BOILING POINT	DENSITY	METALLIC RADIUS*	IONIC RADIUS†
Lithium	Li	3	6.940	186° C	1336° C	0.530 g/cm³	1.55Å	0.60Å
Sodium	Na	11	22.991	97.5°	880°	.963	1.90	.95
Potassium	K	19	39.100	62.3°	760°	.857	2.35	1.33
Rubidium	Rb	37	85.48	38.5°	700°	1.594	2.48	1.48
Cesium	Cs	55	132.91	28.5°	670°	1.992	2.67	1.69

* For ligancy 12.

† For singly charged cation (Na^+, for example), with ligancy 6, as in the sodium chloride crystal.

The alkali metals are made by electrolysis of the molten hydroxides or chlorides (Chapter 10). Because of their reactivity, the metals must be kept in an inert atmosphere or under oil. The metals are useful chemical reagents in the laboratory, and they find industrial use (especially sodium) in the manufacture of organic chemicals, dyestuffs, and lead tetraethyl (a constituent of "ethyl gasoline"). Sodium is used in sodium-vapor lamps, and, because of its large heat conductivity, in the stems of valves of airplane engines, to conduct heat away from the valve heads. Cesium is used in vacuum tubes, to increase electron emission from filaments.

Compounds of sodium are readily identified by the yellow color that they give to a flame. Lithium causes a carmine coloration of the flame, and potassium, rubidium, and cesium cause a violet coloration. These elements may be tested for in the presence of sodium by use of a blue filter of cobalt glass.

The Discovery of the Alkali Metals. The alchemists had recognized many compounds of sodium and potassium. The metals themselves were isolated by Sir Humphry Davy in 1807 by electrolyzing their hydroxides. Compounds of lithium were recognized as containing a new element by the Swedish chemist Johan August Arfwedson, in 1817. The metal itself was first isolated in 1855. Rubidium and cesium were discovered in 1860 by the German chemist Robert Wilhelm Bunsen (1811–1899), by use of the spectroscope. Bunsen and the physicist Kirchhoff had invented the spectroscope just the year before, and cesium was the first element to be discovered by the use of this instrument. The spectrum of cesium contains two bright lines in the blue region and the spectrum of rubidium contains two bright lines in the extreme red (Section 28–5).

Compounds of Lithium. Lithium occurs in the minerals* *spodumene,* $LiAlSi_2O_6$, *amblygonite,* $LiAlPO_4F$, and *lepidolite,* $K_2Li_3Al_5Si_6O_{20}F_4$. Lithium chloride, LiCl, is made by fusing (melting) a mineral containing lithium with barium chloride, $BaCl_2$, and extracting the fusion with water. It is used in the preparation of other compounds of lithium.

Compounds of lithium have found use in the manufacture of glass and of glazes for dishes and porcelain objects.

* Only specialists try to remember complicated formulas, such as that of lepidolite

Compounds of Sodium.   The most important compound of sodium is sodium chloride (common salt), NaCl. It crystallizes as colorless cubes, with melting point $801°$ C, and it has a characteristic salty taste. It occurs in sea water to the extent of 3%, and in solid deposits and concentrated brines (salt solutions) that are pumped from wells. Many million tons of the substance are obtained from these sources every year. It is used mainly for the preparation of other compounds of sodium and of chlorine, as well as of sodium metal and chlorine gas. Blood plasma and other body fluids contain about 0.9 g of sodium chloride per 100 ml.

Sodium hydroxide (caustic soda), NaOH, is a white hygroscopic (water-attracting) solid, which dissolves readily in water. Its solutions have a smooth, soapy feeling, and are very corrosive to the skin (this is the meaning of "caustic" in the name caustic soda). Sodium hydroxide is made either by the electrolysis of sodium chloride solution or by the action of calcium hydroxide, $Ca(OH)_2$, on sodium carbonate, Na_2CO_3:

$$Na_2CO_3 + Ca(OH)_2 \longrightarrow CaCO_3 \downarrow + 2NaOH$$

Calcium carbonate is insoluble, and precipitates out during this reaction, leaving the sodium hydroxide in solution. Sodium hydroxide is a useful laboratory reagent and a very important industrial chemical. It is used in industry in the manufacture of soap, the refining of petroleum, and the manufacture of paper, textiles, rayon and cellulose film, and many other products. The sodium carbonates have been discussed in Chapter 7, and many other sodium salts have been mentioned in other chapters.

Compounds of Potassium.   Potassium chloride, KCl, forms colorless cubic crystals, resembling those of sodium chloride. There are very large deposits of potassium chloride, together with other salts, at Stassfurt, Germany, and near Carlsbad, New Mexico. Potassium chloride is also obtained from Searles Lake in the Mojave Desert in California.

Potassium hydroxide, KOH, is a strongly alkaline substance, with properties similar to those of sodium hydroxide. Other important salts of potassium, which resemble the corresponding salts of sodium, are potassium sulfate, K_2SO_4, potassium carbonate, K_2CO_3, and potassium hydrogen carbonate, $KHCO_3$.

Potassium hydrogen tartrate (*cream of tartar*), $KHC_4H_4O_6$, is a constituent of grape juice; sometimes crystals of the substance are formed in grape jelly. It is used in making baking powder, as mentioned in Section 7–5.

The principal use of potassium compounds is in *fertilizers*. Plant fluids contain large amounts of potassium ion, concentrated from the soil, and potassium salts must be present in the soil in order for plants to grow. A fertilizer containing potassium sulfate or some other salt of potassium must be used if the soil becomes depleted in this element.

The compounds of rubidium and cesium resemble those of potassium closely. They do not have any important uses.

26–3. *The Alkaline-earth Metals and Their Compounds*

The metals of group II of the periodic table, beryllium, magnesium, calcium, strontium, barium, and radium, are called the alkaline-earth metals. Some of their properties are listed in Table 26-3. These metals

TABLE 26-3   *Some Properties of the Alkaline-earth Metals*

	SYMBOL	ATOMIC NUMBER	ATOMIC WEIGHT	MELTING POINT*	DENSITY	METALLIC RADIUS	IONIC RADIUS†
Beryllium	Be	4	9.013	1350° C	1.86 g/cm³	1.12 Å	0.31 Å
Magnesium	Mg	12	24.32	651°	1.75	1.60	.65
Calcium	Ca	20	40.08	810°	1.55	1.97	.99
Strontium	Sr	38	87.63	800°	2.60	2.15	1.13
Barium	Ba	56	137.36	850°	3.61	2.22	1.35
Radium	Ra	88	226.05	960°	(4.45)	(2.46)‡	

* The boiling points of these metals are uncertain; they are about 600° higher than the melting points.
† For doubly charged cation with ligancy 6.
‡ Estimated.

are much harder and less reactive than the alkali metals. The compounds of all the alkaline-earth metals are similar in composition; they all form oxides MO, hydroxides $M(OH)_2$, carbonates MCO_3, sulfates MSO_4, etc. (M = Be, Mg, Ca, Sr, Ba, or Ra).

A Note on the Alkaline-earth Family.   The early chemists gave the name "earth" to many non-metallic substances. Magnesium oxide and calcium oxide were found to have an alkaline reaction, and hence were called the *alkaline earths*. The metals themselves (magnesium, calcium, strontium, and barium) were isolated in 1808 by Humphry Davy. Beryllium was discovered in the mineral beryl ($Be_3Al_2Si_6O_{18}$) in 1798 and was isolated in 1828.

Beryllium.   Beryllium is a light, silvery white metal, which can be made by electrolysis of a fused mixture of beryllium chloride, $BeCl_2$, and sodium chloride. The metal is used for making windows for x-ray tubes (x-rays readily penetrate elements with low atomic number, and beryllium metal has the best mechanical properties of the very light elements). It is also used as a constituent of special alloys. About 2% of beryllium in copper produces a hard alloy especially suited for use in springs.

The principal ore of beryllium is *beryl*, $Be_3Al_2Si_6O_{18}$. *Emeralds* are beryl crystals containing traces of chromium, which give them a green color. *Aquamarine* is a bluish-green variety of beryl.

The compounds of beryllium have little special value, except that beryllium oxide, BeO, is used in the uranium piles in which plutonium is made from uranium (Chapter 32).

Compounds of beryllium are very poisonous. Even the dust of the powdered metal or its oxides may cause very serious illness.

Magnesium.   Magnesium metal is made by electrolysis of fused magnesium chloride, and also by the reduction of magnesium oxide by carbon or by ferrosilicon (an alloy of iron and silicon). Except for calcium and the alkali metals, magnesium is the lightest metal known; and it finds use in lightweight alloys, such as *magnalium* (10% magnesium, 90% aluminum).

Magnesium reacts with boiling water, to form magnesium hydroxide, $Mg(OH)_2$, an alkaline substance:

$$Mg + 2H_2O \longrightarrow Mg(OH)_2 + H_2 \uparrow$$

The metal burns in air with a bright white light, to form magnesium oxide, MgO, the old name of which is *magnesia:*

$$2Mg + O_2 \longrightarrow 2MgO$$

Flashlight powder is a mixture of magnesium powder and an oxidizing agent.

Magnesium oxide suspended in water is used in medicine (as "milk of magnesia"), for neutralizing excess acid in the stomach and as a laxative. Magnesium sulfate, "Epsom salt," $MgSO_4 \cdot 7H_2O$, is used as a cathartic.

Magnesium carbonate, $MgCO_3$, occurs in nature as the mineral *magnesite*. It is used as a basic lining for copper convertors and open-hearth steel furnaces (Chapter 27).

Calcium.   Metallic calcium is made by the electrolysis of fused calcium chloride, $CaCl_2$. The metal is silvery white in color, and is somewhat harder than lead. It reacts with water, and burns in air when ignited, forming a mixture of calcium oxide, CaO, and calcium nitride, Ca_3N_2.

Calcium has a number of practical uses—as a deoxidizer (substance removing oxygen) for iron and steel and for copper and copper alloys, as a constituent of lead alloys (metal for bearings, or the sheath for electric cables) and of aluminum alloys, and as a reducing agent for making other metals from their oxides.

Calcium reacts with cold water to form calcium hydroxide, $Ca(OH)_2$, and burns readily in air, when ignited, to produce calcium oxide, CaO.

Calcium sulfate occurs in nature as the mineral *gypsum*, $CaSO_4 \cdot 2H_2O$. Gypsum is a white substance, which is used commercially for fabrication into wallboard, and conversion into *plaster of Paris*. When gypsum is heated a little above 100° C it loses three quarters of its water of crystallization, forming the powdered substance $CaSO_4 \cdot \frac{1}{2}H_2O$, which is called plaster of Paris. (Heating to a higher temperature produces anhydrous $CaSO_4$, which reacts more slowly with water.) When mixed with water the small crystals of plaster of Paris dissolve and then crystallize as long needles of $CaSO_4 \cdot 2H_2O$. These needles grow together, and form a solid mass, with the shape into which the wet powder was molded.

Strontium.   The principal minerals of strontium are strontium sulfate, *celestite*, $SrSO_4$, and strontium carbonate, *strontianite*, $SrCO_3$.

Strontium nitrate, $Sr(NO_3)_2$, is made by dissolving strontium carbonate in nitric acid. It is mixed with carbon and sulfur to make red fire for use in fireworks, signal shells, and railroad flares. Strontium chlorate, $Sr(ClO_3)_2$, is used for the same purpose. The other compounds of strontium are similar to the corresponding compounds of calcium. Strontium metal has no practical uses.

Barium.   The metal barium has no significant use. Its principal compounds are barium sulfate, $BaSO_4$, which is only very slightly soluble in water and dilute acids, and barium chloride, $BaCl_2 \, 2H_2O$, which is soluble in water. Barium sulfate occurs in nature as the mineral *barite*.

Barium, like all elements with large atomic number, absorbs x-rays strongly, and a thin paste of barium sulfate and water is swallowed as a "barium meal" to obtain contrasting x-ray photographs and fluoroscopic views of the alimentary tract. The solubility of the substance is so small that the poisonous action of most barium compounds is avoided.

Barium nitrate, $Ba(NO_3)_2$, and barium chlorate, $Ba(ClO_3)_2$, are used for producing green fire in fireworks.

Radium.   Compounds of radium are closely similar to those of barium. The only important property of radium and its compounds is its radioactivity, which has been mentioned in Chapter 3, and will be discussed further in Chapter 32.

26–4. *Boron*

Boron can be made by heating potassium tetrafluoroborate, KBF_4, with sodium in a crucible lined with magnesium oxide:

$$KBF_4 + 3Na \longrightarrow KF + 3NaF + B$$

The element can also be made by heating boric oxide, B_2O_3, with powdered magnesium:

$$B_2O_3 + 3Mg \longrightarrow 3MgO + 2B$$

Boron forms brilliant transparent crystals, nearly as hard as diamond.

Boron forms a compound with carbon, B_4C. This substance, **boron carbide,** is the hardest substance known next to diamond, and it has found extensive use as an abrasive and for the manufacture of small mortars and pestles for grinding very hard substances.

Boric acid, H_3BO_3, occurs in the volcanic steam jets of central Italy. The substance is a white crystalline solid, which is sufficiently volatile to be carried along with a stream of steam. Boric acid can be made by treating borax with an acid. It is a very weak acid, and is used in medicine as a mild antiseptic.

The principal source of compounds of boron is the complex borate minerals, including *borax*, sodium tetraborate decahydrate, $Na_2B_4O_7 \cdot 10H_2O$; *kernite*, sodium tetraborate tetrahydrate, $Na_2B_4O_7 \cdot 4H_2O$ (which gives borax when water is added); and *colemanite*, calcium hexaborate pentahydrate, $Ca_2B_6O_{11} \cdot 5H_2O$. The main deposits of these minerals are in California.

Borax is used in making certain types of enamels and glass (such as Pyrex glass, which contains about 12% of B_2O_3), for softening water, as a household cleanser, and as a flux* in welding metals. The last of these uses depends upon the power of molten borax to dissolve metallic oxides, forming borates.

26–5. *Aluminum*

Some of the physical properties of aluminum and its congeners are given in Table 26-4. Aluminum is only about one third as dense as

TABLE 26-4   *Some Physical Properties of Elements of Groups III and IV*

	ATOMIC NUMBER	ATOMIC WEIGHT	DENSITY (g/cm^3)	MELTING POINT	ATOMIC RADIUS*
B	5	10.82	2.54	2,300° C	0.80 Å
Al	13	26.98	2.71	660°	1.43
Sc	21	44.96	3.18	1,200°	1.62
Y	39	88.92	4.51	1,490°	1.80
La	57	138.92	6.17	826°	1.87
C†	6	12.011	3.52	3,500°	0.77
Si	14	28.09	2.36	1,440°	1.17
Ge	32	72.60	5.35	959°	1.22
Sn	50	118.70	7.30	232°	1.62
Pb	82	207.21	11.40	327°	1.75

* Single-bond covalent radius for B, C, Si, and Ge, metallic radius (ligancy 12) for the others.
† Diamond.

iron, and some of its alloys, such as duralumin (described below), are as strong as mild steel; it is this combination of lightness and strength,

* A flux is a material that forms a melt when heated with metal oxides.

together with low cost, that has led to the extensive use of aluminum alloys in airplane construction. Aluminum is also used, in place of copper, as a conductor of electricity; its electric conductivity is about 80% of that of copper.* Its metallurgy has been discussed in Chapter 25.

The metal is reactive (note its position in the electromotive-force series, Section 12–5), and when strongly heated it burns rapidly in air or oxygen. Aluminum dust forms an explosive mixture with air. Under ordinary conditions, however, aluminum rapidly becomes coated with a thin, tough layer of aluminum oxide, which protects it against further corrosion.

Some of the **alloys of aluminum** are very useful. *Duralumin* or *dural* is an alloy (containing about 94.3% aluminum, 4% copper, 0.5% manganese, 0.5% magnesium, and 0.7% silicon) which is stronger and tougher than pure aluminum. It is less resistant to corrosion, however, and often is protected by a coating of pure aluminum. Plate made by rolling a billet of dural sandwiched between and welded to two pieces of pure aluminum is called alclad plate (Figure 26-1).

Aluminum oxide (*alumina*), Al_2O_3, occurs in nature as the mineral *corundum*. Corundum and impure corundum (*emery*) are used as abrasives. Pure corundum is colorless. The precious stones *ruby* (red) and *sapphire* (blue or other colors) are transparent crystalline corundum containing small amounts of other metallic oxides (chromic oxide, titanium oxide). Artificial rubies and sapphires can be made by melting aluminum oxide (m.p. 2,050° C) with small admixtures of other oxides, and cooling the melt in such a way as to produce large crystals. These stones are indistinguishable from natural stones, except for the presence of characteristic rounded microscopic air bubbles. They are used as gems, as

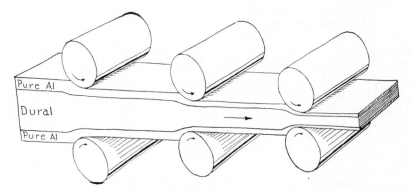

FIGURE 26-1   *Rolling aluminum-clad plate.*

---

* The conductivity refers to the conductance of electricity by a wire of unit cross-sectional area. The density of aluminum is only 30% of that of copper; accordingly an aluminum wire with the same weight as a copper wire with the same length conducts 2.7 times as much electricity as the copper wire.

bearings ("jewels") in watches and other instruments, and as dies through which wires are drawn.

Aluminum sulfate, $Al_2(SO_4)_3 \cdot 18H_2O$, may be made by dissolving aluminum hydroxide in sulfuric acid:

$$2Al(OH)_3 + 3H_2SO_4 + 12H_2O \longrightarrow Al_2(SO_4)_3 \cdot 18H_2O$$

It is used in water purification and as a mordant in dyeing and printing cloth (a *mordant* is a substance which fixes the dye to the cloth, rendering it insoluble). Both of these uses depend upon its property of producing a gelatinous precipitate of aluminum hydroxide, $Al(OH)_3$, when it is dissolved in a large amount of neutral or slightly alkaline water. The reaction which occurs (hydrolysis) is the reverse of the above reaction (Chapter 20). In dyeing and printing cloth the gelatinous precipitate aids in holding the dye onto the cloth. In water purification it adsorbs dissolved and suspended impurities, which are removed as it settles to the bottom of the reservoir.

A solution containing aluminum sulfate and potassium sulfate, K_2SO_4, forms, on evaporation, beautiful colorless cubic (octahedral) crystals of **alum,** $KAl(SO_4)_2 \cdot 12H_2O$. Similar crystals of ammonium alum, $NH_4Al(SO_4)_2 \cdot 12H_2O$, are formed with ammonium sulfate. The alums also are used as mordants in dyeing cloth, in water purification, and in weighting and sizing paper (by precipitating aluminum hydroxide in the meshes of the cellulose fibers).

Aluminum chloride, $AlCl_3$, is made by passing dry chlorine or hydrogen chloride over heated aluminum:

$$2Al + 3Cl_2 \longrightarrow 2AlCl_3$$
$$2Al + 6HCl \longrightarrow 2AlCl_3 + 3H_2$$

The anhydrous salt is used in many chemical processes, including a cracking process for making gasoline.

26–6. *Scandium, Yttrium, Lanthanum, and the Lanthanons*

Scandium, yttrium, and lanthanum,* the congeners of boron and aluminum, form colorless compounds similar to those of aluminum, their oxides having the formulas Sc_2O_3, Y_2O_3, and La_2O_3. These elements and their compounds have not yet found any important use.

Scandium, yttrium, and lanthanum usually occur in nature with the fourteen lanthanons, cerium (atomic number 58) to lutetium (atomic number 71).† All of these elements except promethium (which is

---

* Actinium, the heaviest member of group III, is a radioactive element which occurs in minute quantities in uranium ores (Chapter 32).

† Lanthanum is often considered as one of the rare-earth elements (lanthanons). For convenience, the convention is adopted here of including lanthanum as a member of group III, leaving fourteen elements in the lanthanon group.

made artificially) occur in nature in very small quantities, the principal source being the mineral *monazite*, a mixture of phosphates containing also some thorium phosphate (Section 29–2).

The metals themselves are very electropositive, and are accordingly difficult to prepare. Electrolytic reduction of a fused oxide-fluoride mixture may be used. An alloy containing about 70% cerium and smaller amounts of other lanthanons and iron gives sparks when scratched. This alloy is widely used for cigarette lighters and gas lighters.

These elements are usually terpositive, forming salts such as $La(NO_3)_3 \cdot 6H_2O$. Cerium forms also a well-defined series of salts in which it is quadripositive. This oxidation state corresponds to its atomic number, 4 greater than that of xenon. Praseodymium, neodymium, and terbium form dioxides, but not the corresponding salts.

The bipositive europium(II) ion is stable, and europium forms a series of europium(II) salts as well as of europium(III) salts. Ytterbium and samarium have a somewhat smaller tendency to form salts representing the +2 state of oxidation.

The ions of several of the lanthanons have characteristic colors. A special glass containing lanthanon ions is used in glassblowers' goggles.

Many of the lanthanon compounds are strongly paramagnetic. Crystalline compounds of gadolinium, especially gadolinium sulfate octahydrate, $Gd_2(SO_4)_3 \cdot 8H_2O$, are used in the magnetic method of obtaining extremely low temperatures.

The sulfides cerium monosulfide, CeS, and thorium monosulfide, ThS, and related sulfides have been found valuable as refractory substances. The melting point of cerium monosulfide is 2,450° C.

26–7. Silicon and Its Simpler Compounds

Elementary Silicon and Silicon Alloys.   Silicon is a brittle steel-gray metalloid. Some of its physical properties are given in Table 26–4. It can be made by the reduction of silicon tetrachloride by sodium:

$$SiCl_4 + 4Na \longrightarrow Si + 4NaCl$$

The element has the same crystal structure as diamond, each silicon atom forming single covalent bonds with four adjacent silicon atoms which surround it tetrahedrally.

Silicon contaminated with carbon can be obtained by reduction of silica, SiO_2, with carbon in an electric furnace. An alloy of iron and silicon, called *ferrosilicon*, is obtained by reducing a mixture of iron oxide and silica with carbon.

Ferrosilicon, which has composition approximately FeSi, is used in the manufacture of acid-resisting alloys, such as *duriron*, which contains about 15% silicon. Duriron is used in chemical laboratories and manufacturing plants. A mild steel containing a few percent of silicon may be made which has a high magnetic permeability, and is used for the cores of electric transformers.

Silicides. Many metals form compounds with silicon, called silicides. These compounds include Mg_2Si, Fe_2Si, $FeSi$, $CoSi$, $NiSi$, $CaSi_2$, $Cu_{15}Si_4$, and $CoSi_2$. Ferrosilicon consists largely of the compound $FeSi$. Calcium silicide, $CaSi_2$, is made by heating a mixture of lime, silica, and carbon in an electric furnace. It is a powerful reducing agent, and is used for removing oxygen from molten steel in the process of manufacture of steel.

Silicon Carbide. Silicon carbide, SiC, is made by heating a mixture of carbon and sand in a special electric furnace:

$$SiO_2 + 3C \longrightarrow SiC + 2CO \uparrow$$

The structure of this substance is similar to that of diamond (Figure 11-11), with carbon and silicon atoms alternating; each carbon atom is surrounded by a tetrahedron of silicon atoms, and each silicon atom by a tetrahedron of carbon atoms. The covalent bonds connecting all of the atoms in this structure make silicon carbide very hard. The substance is used as an abrasive.

26–8. *Silicon Dioxide*

Silicon dioxide (*silica*), SiO_2, occurs in nature in three different crystal forms, as the minerals *quartz* (hexagonal), *cristobalite* (cubic), and *tridymite* (hexagonal). Quartz is the most widespread of these minerals; it occurs in many deposits as well-formed crystals, and also as a crystalline constituent of many rocks, such as granite. It is a hard, colorless substance. Its crystals may be identified as right-handed or left-handed, by their face development (Figure 26-2), and also by the direction in which they rotate the plane of polarization of polarized light.

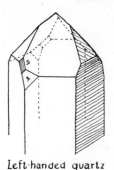

If face ˘x˘ is absent striae on face ˘s˘ will identify its position

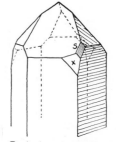

Left-handed quartz   Right-handed quartz

FIGURE 26-2 *Two kinds of quartz crystals.*

The structure of quartz is closely related to that of silicic acid, H_4SiO_4. In silicic acid silicon has ligancy 4, the silicon atom being surrounded by a tetrahedron of four oxygen atoms, with one hydrogen atom attached to each oxygen atom. Silicic acid, which is a very weak acid, has the property of undergoing condensation very readily, with elimination of water (Section 20–9). If each of the four hydroxyl groups of a silicic acid molecule condenses with a similar hydroxyl group of an adjacent molecule, eliminating water, a structure is obtained in which the silicon atom is bonded to four surrounding silicon atoms by silicon-oxygen-silicon bonds. This process leads to a condensation product with formula SiO_2, since each silicon atom is surrounded by four oxygen

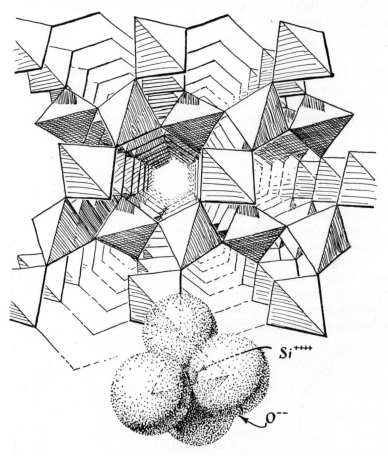

FIGURE 26-3   *The crystal structure of quartz. Each silicon atom is bonded to four oxygen atoms, which are arranged about it at the corners of a tetrahedron, and each oxygen atom serves as a corner of two silicon tetrahedra. In this diagram most of these SiO₄ groups are represented by tetrahedra; only one group is represented by showing the spherical atoms.*

atoms, and each oxygen atom serves as a neighbor to two silicon atoms (Figure 26-3). The structure of quartz and of the other forms of silica may be described as consisting of SiO_4 tetrahedra, with each oxygen atom serving as the corner of two of these tetrahedra. In order to break a crystal of quartz it is necessary to break some silicon-oxygen bonds. In this way the structure of quartz accounts for the hardness of the mineral.

Cristobalite and tridymite are similarly made from SiO_4 tetrahedra fused together by sharing oxygen atoms, with, however, different arrangements of the tetrahedra in space than that of quartz.

Silica Glass.   If any of the forms of silica is melted (m.p. about 1,600° C) and the molten material is then cooled, it usually does not crystallize at the original melting point, but the liquid becomes more viscous as the temperature is lowered, until, at about 1,500° C, it is so stiff that it cannot flow. The material obtained in this way is not crystalline, but is a super-cooled liquid, or glass. It is called *silica glass* (or sometimes *quartz glass* or *fused quartz*). Silica glass does not have the properties of a crystal—it does not cleave, nor form crystal faces, nor show other differences in properties in different directions. The reason for this is that the atoms which constitute it are not arranged in a completely regular manner in space, but show a randomness in arrangement similar to that of the liquid.

The structure of silica glass is very similar in its general nature to that of quartz and the other crystalline forms of silica. Nearly every silicon atom is surrounded by a tetrahedron of four oxygen atoms, and nearly every oxygen atom serves as the common element of two of these tetrahedra. However, the arrangement of the framework of tetrahedra in the glass is not regular, as it is in the crystalline forms of silica, but is irregular, so that a very small region may resemble quartz, and an adjacent region may resemble cristobalite or tridymite, in the same way that liquid silica, above the melting point of the crystalline forms, would show some resemblance to the structures of the crystals.

Silica glass is used for making chemical apparatus and scientific instruments. The coefficient of thermal expansion of silica glass is very small, so that vessels made of the material do not break readily on sudden heating or cooling. Silica is transparent to ultraviolet light, and because of this property it is used in making mercury-vapor ultraviolet lamps and optical instruments for use with ultraviolet light.

26–9. *Sodium Silicate and Other Silicates*

Silicic acid (orthosilicic acid), H_4SiO_4, cannot be made by the hydration of silica. The sodium and potassium salts of silicic acid are soluble in water, however, and can be made by boiling silica with a solution of sodium hydroxide or potassium hydroxide, in which it slowly dissolves. A concentrated solution of **sodium silicate**, called *water glass*, is available commercially and is used for fireproofing wood and cloth, as an adhesive, and for preserving eggs. This solution is not sodium orthosilicate, Na_4SiO_4, but is a mixture of the sodium salts of various condensed silicic acids, such as $H_6Si_2O_7$, $H_4Si_3O_8$, and $(H_2SiO_3)_\infty$.

A gelatinous precipitate of condensed silicic acids $(SiO_2 \cdot xH_2O)$ is obtained when an ordinary acid, such as hydrochloric acid, is added to a solution of sodium silicate. When this precipitate is partially dehydrated it forms a porous product called *silica gel*. This material has great powers of adsorption for water and other molecules and is used as a drying agent and decolorizing agent.

Except for the alkali silicates, most silicates are insoluble in water. Many occur in nature, as ores and minerals.

26–10. *The Silicate Minerals*

Most of the minerals that constitute rocks and soil are silicates, which usually also contain aluminum. Many of these minerals have complex formulas, corresponding to the complex condensed silicic acids from which they are derived. These minerals can be divided into three principal classes, the *framework minerals* (hard minerals similar in their properties to quartz), the *layer minerals* (such as mica), and the *fibrous minerals* (such as asbestos).

The Framework Minerals. Many silicate minerals have tetrahedral framework structures in which some of the tetrahedra are AlO_4 tetrahedra instead of SiO_4 tetrahedra. These minerals have structures somewhat resembling that of quartz, with additional ions, usually alkali or alkaline-earth ions, introduced in the larger openings in the framework structure. Ordinary *feldspar* (*orthoclase*), $KAlSi_3O_8$, is an example of a tetrahedral aluminosilicate mineral. The aluminosilicate tetrahedral framework, $(AlSi_3O_8{}^-)_\infty$, extends throughout the entire crystal, giving it hardness nearly as great as that of quartz. Some other aluminosilicate minerals with tetrahedral framework structures are the following:

Kaliophilite	$KAlSiO_4$	Analcite	$NaAlSi_2O_6 \cdot H_2O$
Leucite	$KAlSi_2O_6$	Natrolite	$Na_2Al_2Si_3O_{10} \cdot 2H_2O$
Albite	$NaAlSi_3O_8$	Chabazite	$CaAl_2Si_4O_{12} \cdot 6H_2O$
Anorthite	$CaAl_2Si_2O_8$	Sodalite	$Na_4Al_3Si_3O_{12}Cl$

A characteristic feature of these tetrahedral framework minerals is that the number of oxygen atoms is just twice the sum of the number of aluminum and silicon atoms. In some of these minerals the framework is an open one, through which corridors run which are sufficiently large to permit ions to move in and out. The *zeolite minerals*, used for softening water, are of this nature. As the hard water, containing Ca^{++} and Fe^{+++} ions, passes around the grains of the mineral, these cations enter the mineral, replacing an equivalent number of sodium ions (Section 17–1).

Some of the zeolite minerals contain water molecules in the corridors and chambers within the aluminosilicate framework, as well as alkali and alkaline-earth ions. When a crystal of one of these minerals, such as chabazite, $CaAl_2Si_4O_{12} \cdot 6H_2O$, is heated, the water molecules are driven out of the structure. The crystal does not collapse, however, but retains essentially its original size and shape, the spaces within the framework formerly occupied by water molecules remaining unoccupied. This dehydrated chabazite has a strong attraction for water molecules, and for molecules of other vapors, and can be used as a drying agent or absorbing agent for them. The structure of silica gel, mentioned above as a drying agent, is similar in nature.

Some of the important minerals in soil are aluminosilicate minerals which have the property of base exchange, and which, because of this property, serve a useful function in the nutrition of the plant.

An interesting framework mineral is *lazulite*, or *lapis lazuli*, a mineral with a beautiful blue color. When ground into a powder, this mineral constitutes the pigment called *ultramarine*. Lazulite has the formula $Na_8Al_6Si_6O_{24}(S_x)$. It consists of an aluminosilicate framework in which

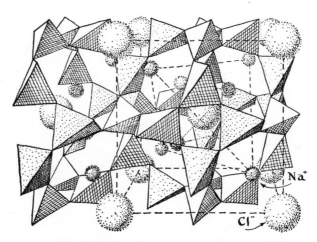

FIGURE 26-4   *The structure of the mineral sodalite, $Na_4Al_3Si_3O_{12}Cl$. The framework consists of AlO_4 tetrahedra and SiO_4 tetrahedra, which share corners with one another. In the spaces formed by this framework there are large chloride ions and the smaller sodium ions, represented in the drawing by spheres. The mineral lazulite has the same structure, except that the chloride ions are replaced by polysulfide groups.*

there are sodium ions (some of which neutralize the charge of the framework) and anions S_x^{--}, such as S_2^{--} and S_3^{--} (Figure 26-4). These polysulfide ions are responsible for the color of the pigment. It was discovered at the beginning of the eighteenth century that a synthetic ultramarine can be made by melting together a suitable sodium aluminosilicate mixture with sulfur. Similar stable pigments with different colors can also be made by replacing the sulfur by selenium and the sodium ion by other cations.

Minerals with Layer Structures. By a condensation reaction involving three of the four hydroxyl groups of each silicic acid molecule, a condensed silicic acid can be made, with composition $(H_2Si_2O_5)_\infty$, which has the form of an infinite layer, as shown in Figure 26-5. The mineral *hydrargillite*, $Al(OH)_3$, has a similar layer structure, which involves AlO_6 octahedra (Figure 26-6). More complex layers, involving both tetrahedra and octahedra, are present in other layer minerals, such as *talc*, *kaolinite* (clay), and *mica*.

In talc and kaolinite, with formulas $Mg_3Si_4O_{10}(OH)_2$ and $Al_2Si_2O_5(OH)_4$, respectively, the layers are electrically neutral, and they are loosely superimposed on one another to form the crystalline material. These layers slide over one another very readily, which gives to these minerals their characteristic properties (softness, easy cleavage, soapy feel). In mica, $KAl_3Si_3O_{10}(OH)_2$, the aluminosilicate layers are

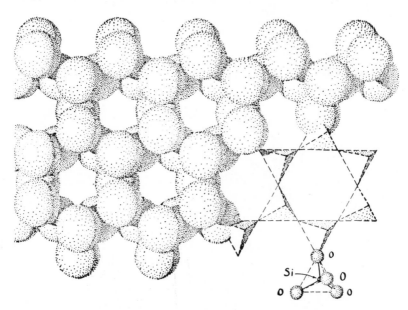

FIGURE 26-5   *A portion of an infinite layer of silicate tetrahedra, as present in talc and other minerals with layer structures.*

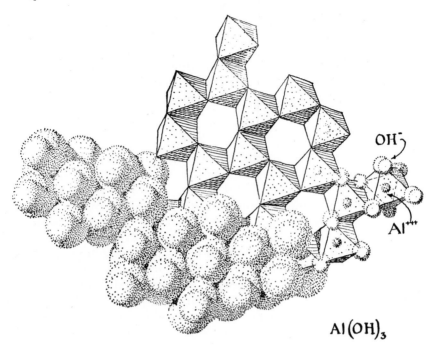

FIGURE 26-6   *The crystal structure of aluminum hydroxide, Al(OH)₃. This sub-stance crystallizes in layers, consisting of octahedra of oxygen atoms (hydroxide ions) about the aluminum atom. Each oxygen atom serves as a corner for two aluminum octahedra.*

negatively charged, and positive ions, usually potassium ions, must be present between the layers in order to give the mineral electric neutrality. The electrostatic forces between these positive ions and the negatively charged layers make mica considerably harder than kaolinite and talc, but its layer structure is still evident in its perfect basic cleavage, which permits the mineral to be split into very thin sheets. These sheets of mica are used for windows in stoves and furnaces, and for electric insulation in machines and instruments.

Other layer minerals, such as *montmorillonite*, with formula approximately $AlSi_2O_5(OH)\cdot xH_2O$, are important constituents of soils, and have also found industrial uses, as catalysts in the conversion of long-chain hydrocarbons into branched-chain hydrocarbons (to make high-octane gasoline), and for other special purposes.

The Fibrous Minerals.   The fibrous minerals contain very long silicate ions in the form of tetrahedra condensed into a chain. These crystals can be cleaved readily in directions parallel to the silicate chains, but not in the directions which cut the chains. Accordingly crystals of these minerals show the extraordinary property of being easily unravelled into fibers. The principal minerals of this sort, *tremolite*, $Ca_2Mg_5Si_8O_{22}(OH)_2$, and *chrysotile*, $Mg_6Si_4O_{11}(OH)_6 \cdot H_2O$, are called *asbestos*. Deposits of these minerals are found, especially in South Africa, in layers several inches thick. These minerals are shredded into fibers, which are then spun or felted into asbestos yarn, fabric and board for use for thermal insulation and as a heat-resistant structural material.

26–11. *Glass*

Silicate materials with important uses include glass, porcelain, glazes and enamels, and cement. Ordinary glass is a mixture of silicates in the form of a supercooled liquid. It is made by melting a mixture of sodium carbonate (or sodium sulfate), limestone, and sand, usually with some scrap glass of the same grade to serve as a flux. After the bubbles of gas have been expelled, the clear melt is poured into molds or stamped with dies, to produce pressed glass ware, or a lump of the semifluid material on the end of a hollow tube is blown, sometimes in a mold, to produce hollow ware, such as bottles and flasks. *Plate glass* is made by pouring liquid glass onto a flat table and rolling it into a sheet. The sheet is then ground flat and polished on both sides. *Safety glass* consists of a sheet of tough plastic sandwiched between two sheets of glass.

Ordinary glass (soda-lime glass, soft glass) contains about 10% sodium, 5% calcium, and 1% aluminum, the remainder being silicon and oxygen. It consists of an aluminosilicate tetrahedral framework, within which are embedded sodium ions and calcium ions and some smaller complex anions. Soda-lime glass softens over a range of temperatures beginning at a dull-red heat, and can be conveniently worked in this temperature range.

Boric acid easily forms highly condensed acids, similar to those of silicic acid, and borate glasses are similar to silicate glasses in their properties. *Pyrex glass*, used for chemical glassware and baking dishes, is a boro-alumino-silicate glass containing only about 4% of alkali and alkaline-earth metal ions. This glass is not so soluble in water as is soft glass, and it also has a smaller coefficient of thermal expansion than soft glass, so that it does not break readily when it is suddenly heated or cooled.

Glazes on chinaware and pottery and *enamels* on iron kitchen utensils and bathtubs consist of easily fusible glass containing pigments or white fillers such as titanium dioxide and tin dioxide.

26–12. *Cement*

Portland cement is an aluminosilicate powder which sets to a solid mass on treatment with water. It is usually manufactured by grinding limestone and clay to a fine powder, mixing with water to form a slurry, and burning the mixture, with a flame of gas, oil, or coal dust, in a long rotary kiln. At the hot end of the kiln, where the temperature is about 1,500° C, the aluminosilicate mixture is sintered together into small round marbles, called "clinker." The clinker is ground to a fine powder in a ball mill (a rotating cylindrical mill filled with steel balls), to produce the final product.

Portland cement before treatment with water consists of a mixture of calcium silicates, mainly Ca_2SiO_4 and Ca_3SiO_5, and calcium aluminate, $Ca_3Al_2O_6$. When treated with water the calcium aluminate hydrolyzes, forming calcium hydroxide and aluminum hydroxide, and these substances react further with the calcium silicates to produce calcium aluminosilicates, in the form of intermeshed crystals.

Ordinary *mortar* for laying bricks is made by mixing sand with slacked lime. This mortar slowly becomes hard through reaction with carbon dioxide of the air, forming calcium carbonate. A stronger mortar is made by mixing sand with Portland cement. The amount of cement needed for a construction job is greatly reduced by mixing sand and crushed stone or gravel with the cement, forming the material called *concrete*. Concrete is a very valuable building material. It does not require carbon dioxide from the air in order to harden, and it will set under water or in very large masses.

26–13. *The Silicones*

When we consider the variety of structures represented by the silicate minerals, and their resultant characteristic and useful properties, we might well expect chemists to synthesize many new and valuable silicon compounds. In recent years this has been done; many silicon compounds, of the class called *silicones*, have been found to have valuable properties.

The simplest silicones are the methyl silicones. These substances exist as oils, resins, and elastomers (rubber-like substances). Methyl silicone oil consists of long molecules, each of which is a silicon-oxygen chain with methyl groups attached to the silicon atoms. A short silicone molecule would have the following structure:

A *silicone oil* for use as a lubricating oil or in hydraulic systems contains molecules with an average of about 10 silicon atoms per molecule.

The valuable properties of the silicone oils are their very low coefficient of viscosity with temperature, ability to withstand high temperature without decomposition, and chemical inertness to metals and most reagents. A typical silicone oil increases only about sevenfold in viscosity on cooling from $100°$ F to $-35°$ F, whereas a hydrocarbon oil with the same viscosity at $100°$ F increases in viscosity about 1,800-fold at $-35°$ F.

Resinous silicones can be made by polymerizing silicones into cross-linked molecules. These resinous materials are used for electric insulation. They have excellent dielectric properties and are stable at operating temperatures at which the usual organic insulating materials decompose rapidly. The use of these materials permits electric machines to be operated with increased loads.

Silicones may be polymerized to molecules containing 2,000 or more $(CH_3)_2SiO$ units, and then milled with inorganic fillers (such as zinc oxide or carbon black, used also for ordinary rubber), and vulcanized, by heating to cause cross-links to form between the molecules, bonding them into an insoluble, infusible three-dimensional framework.

Similar silicones with ethyl groups or other organic groups in place of the methyl groups are also used.

The coating of materials with a water-repellent film has been achieved by use of the *methylchlorosilanes*. A piece of cotton cloth exposed for a second or two to the vapor of trimethylchlorosilane, $(CH_3)_3SiCl$, be-

comes coated with a layer of

$$
\begin{array}{c}
CH_3 \\
H_3C \quad | \quad CH_3 \\
\diagdown | \diagup \\
Si \\
| \\
O \\
\diagup \\
R
\end{array}
$$

groups, through reaction

with hydroxyl groups of the cellulose:

$$(CH_3)_3SiCl + HOR \longrightarrow (CH_3)_3SiOR + HCl \uparrow$$

The exposed methyl groups repel water in the way that a hydrocarbon film such as lubricating oil would. Paper, wool, silk, glass, porcelain, and other materials can be treated in this way. The treatment has been found especially useful for ceramic insulators.

26–14. *Germanium*

The chemistry of germanium, a moderately rare and unimportant element, is similar to that of silicon. Most of the compounds of germanium correspond to oxidation number $+4$; examples are germanium tetrachloride, $GeCl_4$, a colorless liquid with boiling point $83°$ C, and germanium dioxide, GeO_2, a colorless crystalline substance melting at 1,086° C.

The compounds of germanium have found little use. The element itself, a gray metalloid, is a poor conductor of electricity. It has the property, when alloyed with very small amounts of other elements, of permitting an electric current to pass only one way through its surface, in contact with a small metal wire. This rectifying power, which is superior to that of other crystals, has caused the substance to find much use in recent years in special pieces of apparatus, such as radar. It is also the basis of the transistor, a simple apparatus for amplifying minute currents of electricity, which can replace the ordinary vacuum tube for such purposes.

26–15. *Tin*

Tin is a silvery-white metal, with great malleability, permitting it to be hammered into thin sheets, called tin foil. Ordinary *white tin*, which has metallic properties, slowly changes at temperatures below 18° C to a non-metallic allotropic modification, *gray tin*, which has the diamond structure. (The physical properties given in Table 26-2 pertain to white tin.) At very low temperatures, around −50° C, the speed of this conversion is sufficiently great so that metallic tin objects sometimes fall into a powder of gray tin. This phenomenon has been called the "tin pest."

Tin finds extensive use as a protective layer for mild steel. Tin plating is done by dipping clean sheets of mild steel into molten tin, or by electrolytic deposition. Copper and other metals are sometimes also coated with tin.

The principal alloys of tin are *bronze* (tin and copper), *soft solder* (50% tin and 50% lead), *pewter* (75% tin and 25% lead), and *britannia metal* (tin with small amounts of antimony and copper).

Bearing metals, used as the bearing surfaces of sliding-contact bearings, are usually alloys of tin, lead, antimony, and copper. They contain small, hard crystals of a compound such as SnSb embedded in a soft matrix of tin or lead. The good bearing properties result from orientation of the hard crystals to present flat faces at the bearing surface.

Tin is reactive enough to displace hydrogen from dilute acids, but it does not tarnish in moist air. It reacts with warm hydrochloric acid to produce stannous chloride, $SnCl_2$, and hydrogen, and with hot concentrated sulfuric acid to produce stannous sulfate, $SnSO_4$, and sulfur dioxide, the equations for these reactions being

$$Sn + 2HCl \longrightarrow SnCl_2 + H_2 \uparrow$$

and

$$Sn + 2H_2SO_4 \longrightarrow SnSO_4 + SO_2 \uparrow + 2H_2O$$

With cold dilute nitric acid it forms stannous nitrate, and with concentrated nitric acid it is oxidized to a hydrated stannic acid, H_2SnO_3.

Compounds of Tin. Stannous chloride, made by solution of tin in hydrochloric acid, forms colorless crystals $SnCl_2 \cdot H_2O$ on evaporation of the solution. In neutral solution the substance hydrolyzes, forming a precipitate of stannous hydroxychloride, $Sn(OH)Cl$. The hydrolysis in solution may be prevented by the presence of an excess of acid. Stannous chloride solution is used as a mordant in dyeing cloth.

The stannous ion is an active reducing agent, which is easily oxidized to stannic chloride, $SnCl_4$, or, in the presence of excess chloride ion, to the complex chlorostannate ion, $SnCl_6^{--}$.

Stannic chloride, $SnCl_4$, is a colorless liquid (boiling point 114°), which fumes very strongly in moist air, producing hydrochloric acid and stannic acid, $H_2Sn(OH)_6$. Sodium stannate, $Na_2Sn(OH)_6$, contains the octahedral hexahydroxystannate ion (stannate ion). This complex ion is similar in structure to the chlorostannate ion. Sodium stannate is used as a mordant, and in preparing fireproof cotton cloth and weighting silk. The cloth is soaked in the sodium stannate solution, dried, and treated with ammonium sulfate solution. This treatment causes hydrated stannic oxide to be deposited in the fibers.

Stannous hydroxide, $Sn(OH)_2$, is formed by adding dilute sodium hydroxide solution to stannous chloride. It is readily soluble in excess alkali, producing the stannite ion, $Sn(OH)_3^-$.

Stannous sulfide, SnS, is obtained as a dark brown precipitate by addition of hydrogen sulfide or sulfide ion to a solution of a stannous salt. Stannic sulfide, SnS_2, is formed in the same way from stannic solution; it is yellow in color. Stannic sulfide is soluble in solutions of ammonium sulfide or sodium sulfide, producing the sulfostannate ion, SnS_4^{----}. Stannous sulfide is not soluble in sulfide solution, but is easily oxidized in the presence of polysulfide solutions to the sulfostannate ion. These properties are used in some schemes of qualitative analysis.

26–16. *Lead*

Lead is a soft, heavy, dull gray metal with low tensile strength. It is used in making type, for covering electric cables, and in many alloys. The organic lead compound lead tetraethyl, $Pb(C_2H_5)_4$, is added to gasoline to prevent knock in automobile engines.

Lead forms a thin surface layer of oxide in air. This oxide slowly changes to a basic carbonate. Hard water forms a similar coating on lead, which protects the water from contamination with soluble lead compounds. Soft water dissolves appreciable amounts of lead, which is poisonous; for this reason lead pipes should not be used to carry drinking water.

There are several oxides of lead, of which the most important are lead monoxide (*litharge*), PbO, minium or red lead, Pb_3O_4, and lead dioxide, PbO_2.

Litharge is made by heating lead in air. It is a yellow powder or yellowish-red crystalline material, used in making lead glass and for preparing compounds of lead. It is amphoteric, dissolving in warm sodium hydroxide solution to produce the plumbite ion, $Pb(OH)_4^{--}$. Red lead, Pb_3O_4, can be made by heating lead in oxygen. It is used in glass making, and for making a red paint for protecting iron and steel structures. Lead dioxide, PbO_2, is a brown substance made by oxidizing a solution of sodium plumbite, $Na_2Pb(OH)_4$, with hypochlorite ion, or by anodic oxidation of lead sulfate. It is soluble in sodium hydroxide and potassium hydroxide, forming the hexahydroxyplumbate ion, $Pb(OH)_6^{--}$. The principal use of lead dioxide is in the lead storage battery (Chapter 12).

Lead nitrate, $Pb(NO_3)_2$, is a white crystalline substance made by dissolving lead, lead monoxide, or lead carbonate in nitric acid. Lead carbonate, $PbCO_3$, occurs in nature as the mineral *cerussite*. It appears as a precipitate when a solution containing the hydrogen carbonate ion, HCO_3^-, is added to lead nitrate solution. With a more basic carbonate solution a basic carbonate of lead, $Pb_3(OH)_2(CO_3)_2$, is deposited. This basic salt, called *white lead*, is used as a white pigment in paint. For this use it is manufactured by methods involving the oxidation of lead by air, the formation of a basic acetate by interaction with vinegar or acetic acid, and the decomposition of this salt by carbon dioxide. Lead chromate, $PbCrO_4$, is also used as a pigment, under the name *chrome yellow*.

Lead sulfate, $PbSO_4$, is a white, nearly insoluble substance. Its precipitation is used as a test for either lead ion or sulfate ion in analytical chemistry.

Concepts, Facts, and Terms Introduced in This Chapter

The electronic structures of elements of groups I, II, III, and IV.

The alkali and alkaline-earth metals. Their compounds. Boron, boron carbide, boric acid.

Aluminum and its alloys. Duralumin, aluminum-clad plate. Corundum, ruby, sapphire. Aluminum sulfate, alum. Precipitation of aluminum hydroxide. Aluminum chloride.

Scandium, yttrium, lanthanum, and the lanthanons.

Importance of silicon in the inorganic world. Characteristic feature of silicate minerals—the existence of structures consisting of silicon atoms bonded together by oxygen atoms.

Elementary silicon. Alloys of silicon: ferrosilicon, duriron, alloys for transformer cores, with oriented crystal grains. Silicides. Silanes. Silicon carbide. Silicon dioxide—

silica, quartz, cristobalite, tridymite. Right-handed and left-handed quartz. The structure of quartz-silicate tetrahedra sharing corners with surrounding tetrahedra. Silica glass (quartz glass, fused quartz). The nature of glass. Silicic acid, sodium silicate, silica gel. The silicate minerals—framework minerals, layer minerals, fibrous minerals. Feldspar, zeolite minerals, lazulite, ultramarine, and other framework minerals. Talc, kaolinite (clay), mica, montmorillonite, and other layer minerals. Asbestos (tremolite, chrysotile) and other fibrous minerals. Glass: window glass, plate glass. Pyrex glass, glazes. Portland cement. Concrete. Mortar. The silicones—silicone oil, silicone rubber. The methylchlorosilanes; the coating of materials with a water-repellent film.

Germanium, a gray metalloid used in the transistor.

White tin, gray tin. Tin plate. Alloys of tin—bronze, soft solder, pewter, britannia metal. Compounds of tin(II) and tin(IV).

Lead, lead tetraethyl, PbO_2, white lead, lead chromate, lead sulfate.

Exercises

26-1.   Would you predict that the alkali metals could be prepared by the aluminothermic method (reduction of the oxide with metallic aluminum)? Why?

26-2.   Outline the process of manufacture of sodium hydroxide from sodium chloride by way of sodium carbonate, prepared by ammonia-soda process. Write equations for all reactions.

26-3.   Compare the properties of elements of groups I, II, III, and IV with their electronegativities (Table 11-8). What electronegativity value separates the metals from the metalloids?

26-4.   State the name and formula of one mineral of each of the following elements: lithium, sodium, potassium, beryllium, magnesium, calcium, strontium, barium.

26-5.   Discuss the significance to the chemical properties of the first, second, and third ionization potentials (Table 5-5) of sodium and magnesium.

26-6.   Aluminum hydroxide is soluble in both dilute hydrochloric acid and dilute sodium hydroxide solution. Write equations for the two reactions.

26-7.   Compare the electronic structures of the aluminate ion and the orthosilicate ion.

26-8.   Beryllium hydroxide is essentially insoluble in water, but is soluble both in acids and in alkalis. What do you think the products of its reaction with sodium hydroxide solution are? Discuss these properties of the substance in relation to the position of beryllium in the periodic table and the electronegativity scale.

26-9.   Discuss the electronic structure of potassium fluoroborate, KBF_4. Its solution in water contains the complex ion BF_4^-.

26-10.   How much lithium is there in spodumene, $LiAlSi_2O_6$?

26-11.   What is the electronic structure of the aluminum atom? How does it explain the fact that all compounds of aluminum correspond to oxidation number $+3$?

26-12.   Assuming bauxite to contain equal amounts by weight of $AlHO_2$ and $Al(OH)_3$, calculate the weight of aluminum that might be obtained from 100 tons of bauxite.

26-13.   What is the crystal structure of elementary silicon? Of silicon carbide? In what way are these structures related to the electronic structures of the atoms?

26-14. What is the oxidation number of Si in Mg_2Si? In $CaSi_2$?

26-15. Write a chemical equation for the preparation of calcium silicide in the electric furnace.

26-16. Write the chemical equation underlying the use of calcium silicide in the steel industry?

26-17. Write the structural formulas of the simpler silicanes. How are these substances prepared?

26-18. Compare the properties of silica glass and crystalline quartz. What properties of a glass, as distinct from a crystal, are important in the uses of glass?

26-19. To how many silicon or aluminum atoms is each oxygen atom bonded in a framework crystal, such as feldspar?

26-20. Write a general formula for an anhydrous sodium aluminosilicate which is a framework mineral, containing only tetrahedrally coordinated aluminum and silicon.

26-21. Can you suggest an explanation of the fact that silicon dioxide does not form a fibrous mineral with the structure shown below?

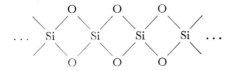

Silicon disulfide does form fibrous crystals of this sort.

26-22. Compare the properties of talc and mica, and explain their differences in terms of their structure.

26-23. What is Portland cement? What happens when it sets?

26-24. What is the formula of a simple silicone? What is the difference in structure of silicone oil, silicone resin, and silicone rubber?

26-25. Describe the process for preparing a "silicone rubber."

26-26. What elements are present in bronze? In soft solder?

26-27. Write the equation for the reaction of stannic chloride and moist air.

26-28. What are the principal uses of lead, lead tetraethyl, lead dioxide, and white lead?

References

Chapter 10 of *The Nature of the Chemical Bond*, Linus Pauling, Cornell University Press, Ithaca, **1940**.

E. G. Rochow, *An Introduction to the Chemistry of the Silicones*, John Wiley and Sons, Inc., New York, **1951**.

Morgan Sparks, "The Junction Transistor," *Scientific American*, **187**, 28 (July 1952).

F. H. Spedding, "The Rare Earths" (the Lanthanons), *Scientific American*, **185**, 26 (November 1951).

Chapter 27

Iron, Cobalt,
Nickel, and the
Platinum Metals

In this chapter and in the two following chapters we shall discuss the chemistry of the transition metals—the elements that occur in the central region of the periodic table (Section 24–3). These elements and their compounds have great practical importance. Their chemical properties are complex and interesting.

We shall begin the discussion of the transition metals with iron, cobalt, nickel, and the platinum metals, which lie in the center of the transition-metal region in the periodic table. The following chapter will be devoted to the elements that lie to the right of these metals; these are copper, zinc, and gallium and their congeners. Chapter 29 will deal with the chemistry of titanium, vanadium, chromium, and manganese and other elements of groups IVa, Va, VIa, and VIIa of the periodic table.

27–1. *The Electronic Structures and Oxidation States of Iron,*
Cobalt, Nickel, and the Platinum Metals

The electronic structures of iron, cobalt, nickel, and the platinum metals are given in Table 27-1, as represented in the energy-level diagram of Figure 5-6. It is seen that each of the atoms has two outermost electrons, in the $4s$ orbital for iron, cobalt, and nickel, the $5s$ orbital for ruthenium, rhodium, and palladium, and the $6s$ orbital for osmium, iridium, and

TABLE 27-1   *The Electronic Structures of Iron, Cobalt, Nickel, and the Platinum Metals*

Z	ELEMENT	K	L		M			N				O			P
		1s	2s	2p	3s	3p	3d	4s	4p	4d	4f	5s	5p	5d	6s
26	Fe	2	2	6	2	6	6	2							
27	Co	2	2	6	2	6	7	2							
28	Ni	2	2	6	2	6	8	2							
44	Ru	2	2	6	2	6	10	2	6	6		2			
45	Rh	2	2	6	2	6	10	2	6	7		2			
46	Pd	2	2	6	2	6	10	2	6	8		2			
76	Os	2	2	6	2	6	10	2	6	10	14	2	6	6	2
77	Ir	2	2	6	2	6	10	2	6	10	14	2	6	7	2
78	Pt	2	2	6	2	6	10	2	6	10	14	2	6	8	2

platinum. The next inner shell is incomplete, the $3d$ orbital (or $4d$, or $5d$) contains only six, seven, or eight electrons, instead of the full complement of ten.

It might be expected that the two outermost electrons would be easily removed, to form a bipositive ion. In fact, iron, cobalt, and nickel all form important series of compounds in which the metal is bipositive. These metals also have one or more higher oxidation states. The platinum metals form covalent compounds representing various oxidation states between +2 and +8.

Iron can assume the oxidation states +2, +3, and +6, the last being rare, and represented by only a few compounds, such as potassium ferrate, K_2FeO_4. The oxidation states +2 and +3 correspond to the ferrous ion, Fe^{++}, and ferric ion, Fe^{+++}, respectively. The ferrous ion has six electrons in the incomplete $3d$ orbital, and the ferric ion has five electrons in this orbital. The magnetic properties of the compounds of iron and other transition elements are due to the presence of a smaller number of electrons in the $3d$ orbital than required to fill this orbital. For example, ferric ion can have all five of its $3d$ electrons with spins oriented in the same direction, because there are five $3d$ orbitals in the $3d$ subshell, and the Pauli principle permits parallel orientation of the spins of electrons so long as there is only one electron per orbital. The ferrous ion is easily oxidized to ferric ion, by air or other oxidizing agents. Both bipositive and terpositive iron form complexes, such as the ferrocyanide ion, $Fe(CN)_6^{----}$, and the ferricyanide ion, $Fe(CN)_6^{---}$, but they do not form complexes with ammonia.

Cobalt(II) and cobalt(III) compounds are known; the cobalt(II) ion, Co^{++}, is more stable than the cobalt(III) ion, Co^{+++}, which is a sufficiently powerful oxidizing agent to oxidize water, liberating oxygen. On the other hand, the covalent cobalt(III) complexes, such as the cobalticyanide ion, $Co(CN)_6^{---}$, are very stable, and the cobalt(II) complexes, such as the cobaltocyanide ion, $Co(CN)_6^{----}$, are unstable, being strong reducing agents.

Nickel forms only one series of salts, containing the nickel ion, Ni^{++}. A few compounds of nickel with higher oxidation number are known; of these the nickel(IV) oxide, NiO_2, is important.

As was mentioned in Chapter 24, iron, cobalt, and nickel are sexivalent in the metals and their alloys. This high metallic valence causes the bonds to be especially strong, and confers valuable properties of strength and hardness on the alloys.

27–2. Iron

Pure iron is a bright silvery-white metal which tarnishes (rusts rapidly) in moist air or in water containing dissolved oxygen. It is soft, malleable, and ductile, and is strongly magnetic ("ferromagnetic"). Its melting point is 1,535° C, and its boiling point 3,000°. Ordinary iron (alpha-

TABLE 27-2   *Some Physical Properties of Iron, Cobalt, and Nickel*

	ATOMIC NUMBER	ATOMIC WEIGHT	DENSITY	MELTING POINT	BOILING POINT	METALLIC RADIUS*
Iron	26	55.85	7.86 g/cm³	1,535° C	3,000° C	1.26 Å
Cobalt	27	58.94	8.93	1,480	2,900	1.25
Nickel	28	58.71	8.89	1,452	2,900	1.24

* For ligancy 12.

iron) has the atomic arrangement shown in Figure 24-2 (the body-centered arrangement—each atom is in the center of a cube formed by the eight surrounding atoms). At 912° C alpha-iron undergoes a transition to another allotropic form, gamma-iron, which has the face-centered arrangement described for copper in Chapter 2 (Figures 2-4 and 2-5). At 1,400° C another transition occurs, to delta-iron, which has the same body-centered structure as alpha-iron.

Pure iron, containing only about 0.01% of impurities, can be made by electrolytic reduction of iron salts. It has little use; a small amount is used in analytical chemistry, and a small amount in the treatment of anemia.*

Metallic iron is greatly strengthened by the presence of a small amount of carbon, and its mechanical and chemical properties are also improved by moderate amounts of other elements, especially other transition metals. Wrought iron, cast iron, and steel are described in the following sections.

* See hemoglobin, Chapter 31.

The Ores of Iron.   The chief ores of iron are its oxides *hematite*, Fe_2O_3, and *magnetite*, Fe_3O_4, and its carbonate *siderite*, $FeCO_3$. The hydrated ferric oxides such as *limonite* are also important. The sulfide *pyrite*, FeS_2, is used as a source of sulfur dioxide, but the impure iron oxide left from its roasting is not satisfactory for smelting iron, because the remaining sulfur is a troublesome impurity.

The Metallurgy of Iron.   The ores of iron are usually first roasted, in order to remove water, to decompose carbonates, and to oxidize sulfides. They are then reduced with coke, in a structure called a *blast furnace* (Figure 27-1). Ores containing limestone or magnesium carbonate are mixed with an acidic flux (containing an excess of silica), such as sand or clay, in order to make a liquid *slag*. Limestone is used as flux for ores containing an excess of silica. The mixture of ore, flux, and coke is introduced at the top of the blast furnace, and preheated air is blown in at the bottom through *tuyeres*.* As the solid materials slowly descend they are converted completely into gases, which escape at the top, and two liquids, molten iron and slag, which are tapped off at the bottom. The parts of the blast furnace where the temperature is highest are water-cooled, to keep the lining from melting.

The important reactions which occur in the blast furnace are the combustion of coke to carbon monoxide, the reduction of iron oxide by the carbon monoxide, and the combination of acidic and basic oxides (the impurities of the ore and the added flux) to form slag:

$$2C + O_2 \longrightarrow 2CO$$
$$3CO + Fe_2O_3 \longrightarrow 2Fe + 3CO_2$$
$$CaCO_3 \longrightarrow CaO + CO_2$$
$$CaO + SiO_2 \longrightarrow CaSiO_3$$

The slag is a glassy silicate mixture of complex composition, idealized as calcium metasilicate, $CaSiO_3$, in the above equation.

The hot exhaust gases, which contain some unoxidized carbon monoxide, are cleaned of dust and then are mixed with air and burned in large steel structures filled with fire brick. When one of these structures, which are called *stoves*, has thus been heated to a high temperature the burning exhaust gas is shifted to another stove and the heated stove is used to pre-heat the air for the blast furnace.

Cast Iron.   The molten iron from the blast furnace, having been in contact with coke in the lower part of the furnace, contains several percent of dissolved carbon (usually about 3 or 4%), together with silicon, manganese, phosphorus, and sulfur in smaller amounts. These

---

* A tuyere is a nozzle through which an air-blast is delivered to a furnace, forge, or converter.

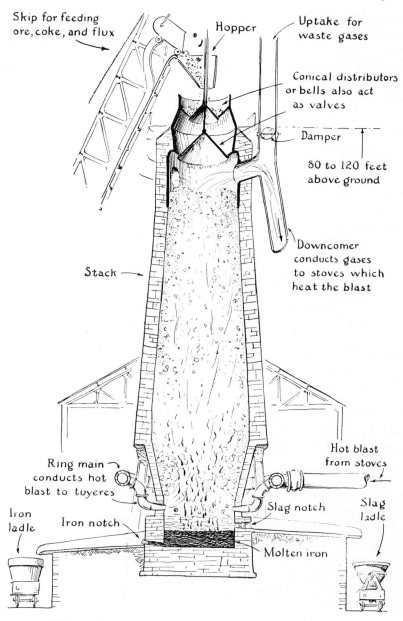

FIGURE 27-1   *A blast furnace for smelting iron ore.*

FIGURE 27-2

A photomicrograph of white cast iron, consisting largely of the compound cementite, Fe₃C. Magnification 100 ×. (From Malleable Founders' Society.)

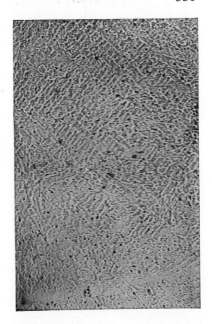

impurities lower its melting point from 1,535° C, that of pure iron, to about 1,200° C. This iron is often cast into bars called *pigs;* the cast iron itself is called *pig iron*.

When cast iron is made by sudden cooling from the liquid state it is white in color, and is called **white cast iron.** It consists largely of the compound *cementite*, Fe_3C, a hard, brittle substance (Figure 27-2).

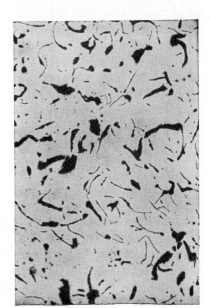

FIGURE 27-3

A photomicrograph of gray cast iron, unetched. The white background is ferrite, and the black particles are flakes of graphite. Magnification 100 ×. (From Malleable Founders' Society.)

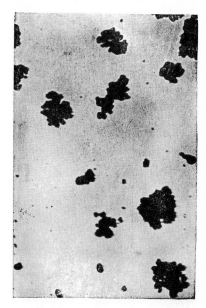

FIGURE 27-4

A photomicrograph of malleable cast iron, show-ing ferrite (background) and globular particles of graphite. Unetched. Magnification 100 ×. (From Malleable Founders' Society.)

Gray cast iron, made by slow cooling, consists of crystalline grains of pure iron (called *ferrite*) and flakes of graphite (Figure 27-3). Both white cast iron and gray cast iron are brittle, the former because its principal constituent, cementite, is brittle, and the latter because the tougher fer-rite in it is weakened by the soft flakes of graphite distributed through it.

Malleable cast iron, which is tougher and less brittle than either white or ordinary gray cast iron, is made by heat treatment of gray cast iron of suitable composition. Under this treatment the flakes of graphite coalesce into globular particles, which, because of their small cross-sectional area, weaken the ferrite less than do the flakes (Figure 27-4).

Cast iron is the cheapest form of iron, but its usefulness is limited by its low strength. A great amount is converted into steel, and a smaller amount into wrought iron.

Wrought Iron.   Wrought iron is nearly pure iron, with only 0.1% or 0.2% carbon and less than 0.5% of all impurities. It is made by melting cast iron on a bed of iron oxide in a reverberatory furnace (Figure 27-5). As the molten cast iron is stirred the iron oxide oxidizes the dissolved carbon to carbon monoxide, and the sulfur, phosphorus, and silicon are also oxidized and pass into the slag. As the impurities are removed the melting point of the iron rises, and the mass becomes pasty. It is then taken out of the furnace and beaten under steam hammers to force out the slag.

Wrought iron is a strong, tough metal which can be readily welded and forged. In past years it was extensively used for making chains,

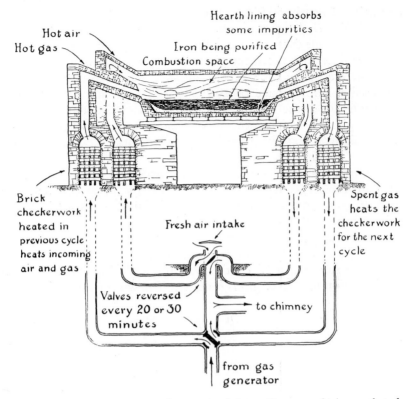

Hearth lining absorbs
some impurities

Hot air
Hot gas

Iron being purified
Combustion space

Brick
checkerwork
heated in
previous cycle
heats incoming
air and gas

Fresh air intake

Spent gas
heats the
checkerwork
for the next
cycle

Valves reversed
every 20 or 30
minutes

to chimney

from gas
generator

FIGURE 27-5 *Reverberatory furnace, used for making wrought iron and steel.*

wire, and similar objects. It has now been largely displaced by mild steel.

27–3. *Steel*

Steel is a purified alloy of iron, carbon, and other elements which is manufactured in the liquid state. Most steels are almost free from phosphorus, sulfur, and silicon, and contain between 0.1 and 1.5% of carbon. *Mild steels* are low-carbon steels (less than 0.2%). They are malleable and ductile, and are used in place of wrought iron. They are not hardened by being quenched (suddenly cooled) from a red heat. *Medium steels*, containing from 0.2 to 0.6% carbon, are used for making rails and structural elements (beams, girders, etc.). Mild steels and medium steels can be forged and welded. *High-carbon steels* (0.75 to 1.50% carbon) are used for making razors, surgical instruments, drills, and other tools. Medium steels and high-carbon steels can be hardened and tempered (see a following section).

At the end of World War I the United States had a steel-making capacity of nearly 50,000,000 tons of steel per year, and by the end of World War II this capacity had been nearly doubled.

Steel is made from pig iron chiefly by the *open-hearth process* (by which over 90% of that produced in the United States is made) and by the *Bessemer process*. In each process either a basic or an acidic lining may be used in the furnace or converter. A basic lining (lime, magnesia, or a mixture of the two) is used if the pig iron contains elements, such as phosphorus, which form acidic oxides, and an acidic lining (silica) if the pig iron contains base-forming elements.

The Open-Hearth Process.   Open-hearth steel is made in a reverberatory furnace; that is, a furnace in which the flame is reflected by the roof onto the material to be heated (Figure 27-5). Cast iron is melted with scrap steel and some hematite in a furnace heated with gas or oil fuel. The fuel and air are preheated by passage through a checkerwork of hot brick at one side of the furnace, and a similar checkerwork on the other side is heated by the hot outgoing gases. From time to time the direction of flow of gas is reversed. The carbon and other impurities

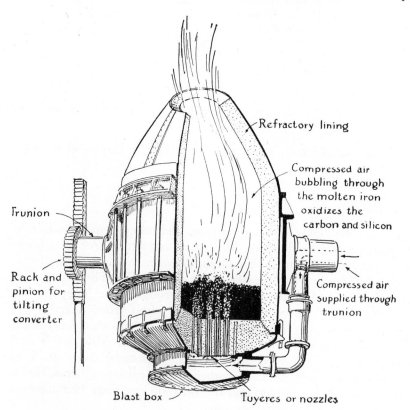

FIGURE 27-6   *Bessemer converter, used for making steel from pig iron.*

in the molten iron are oxidized by the hematite and by excess air in the furnace gas. Analyses are made during the run, which requires about 8 hours, and when almost all the carbon is oxidized the amount desired for the steel is added as coke or as a high-carbon alloy, usually ferro-manganese or spiegeleisen. The molten steel is then cast into billets. Open-hearth steel of very uniform quality can be made, because the process can be closely checked by analyses during the several hours of the run.

The Bessemer Process. The Bessemer process of making steel was invented by an American, William Kelly, in 1852 and independently by an Englishman, Henry Bessemer, in 1855. Molten pig iron is poured into an egg-shaped converter (Figure 27-6). Air is blown up through the liquid from tuyeres in the bottom, oxidizing silicon, manganese, and other impurities and finally the carbon. In about ten minutes the reaction is nearly complete, as is seen from the change in character of the flame of burning carbon monoxide from the mouth of the converter. High-carbon alloy is then added, and the steel is poured.

The Bessemer process is inexpensive, but the steel is not so good as open-hearth steel.

The Properties of Steel. When high-carbon steel is heated to bright redness and slowly cooled, it is comparatively soft. However, if it is rapidly cooled, by quenching in water, oil, or mercury, it becomes harder than glass, and brittle instead of tough. This hardened steel can be "tempered" by suitable reheating, to give a product with the

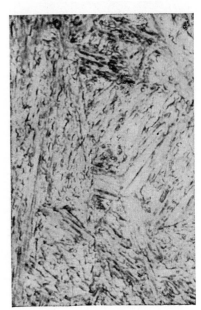

FIGURE 27-7

A photomicrograph of martensite, a constituent of hardened steel. Magnification 2000 ×. (From Dr. D. S. Clark.)

desired combination of hardness and toughness. Often the tempering is carried out in such a way as to leave a very hard cutting edge backed up by softer, tougher metal.

The amount of tempering can be estimated roughly by the interference colors of the thin film of oxide formed on a polished surface of the steel during reheating: a straw color (230° C) corresponds to a satisfactory temper for razors, yellow (250° C) for pocket knives, brown (260° C) for scissors and chisels, purple (270°) for butcher knives, blue (290°) for watch springs, and blue-black (320°) for saws.

These processes of hardening and tempering can be understood by consideration of the phases which can be formed by iron and carbon. Carbon is soluble in gamma-iron, the form stable above 912° C. If the steel is quenched from above this temperature there is obtained a solid solution of carbon in gamma-iron. This material, called *martensite*, is very hard and brittle (Figure 27-7). It confers hardness and brittleness upon hardened high-carbon steel. Martensite is not stable at room temperature, but its rate of conversion to more stable phases is so small at room temperature as to be negligible, and hardened steel containing martensite remains hard as long as it is not reheated.

When hardened steel is tempered by mild reheating the martensite undergoes transformation to more stable phases. The changes which it undergoes are complex, but result ultimately in a mixture of grains of alpha-iron (ferrite) and the hard carbide Fe_3C, cementite. Steel containing 0.9% carbon (*eutectoid steel*) changes on tempering into *pearlite*, which is composed of extremely thin alternating layers of ferrite and

FIGURE 27-8

A photomicrograph of pearlite, showing lamellae of ferrite and cementite. Magnification 1000 × (From Dr. D. S. Clark.)

FIGURE 27-9

A photomicrograph of hypo-eutectoid steel, showing grains of pearlite. Carbon content of steel 0.38%. Magnification 500 ×. (From Dr. D. S. Clark.)

cementite (Figure 27-8). Pearlite is strong and tough. Steel containing less than 0.9% carbon (*hypo-eutectoid steel*) changes on tempering into a microcrystalline metal consisting of grains of ferrite and grains of pearlite (Figure 27-9), whereas that containing more than 0.9% carbon (*hyper-eutectoid steel*) on tempering yields grains of cementite and grains of pearlite.

Steel intended to withstand both shock and wear must be tough and strong and must also present a very hard surface. Steel objects with these properties are made by a process called *case-hardening*. Medium-carbon steel objects are heated in contact with carbon or sodium cyanide until a thin surface layer is converted into high-carbon steel, which can be hardened by suitable heat treatment. Some alloy steels are case-hardened by formation of a surface layer of metal nitrides, by heating the objects in an atmosphere of ammonia.

Alloy Steels. Many alloy steels, steel containing considerable amounts of metals other than iron, have valuable properties and extensive industrial uses. Manganese steel (12 to 14% Mn) is extraordinarily hard, and crushing and grinding machines and safes are made of it. Nickel steels have many special uses. Chromium-vanadium steel (5 to 10% Cr, 0.15% V) is tough and elastic, and is used for automobile axles, frames, and other parts. Stainless steels usually contain chromium; a common composition is 18% Cr, 8% Ni. Molybdenum and tungsten steels are used for high-speed cutting tools.

27–4. *Compounds of Iron*

Iron is an active metal, which displaces hydrogen easily from dilute acids. It burns in oxygen to produce ferrous-ferric oxide, Fe_3O_4. This oxide is also made by interaction with superheated steam. One method of preventing rusting involves the production of an adherent surface layer of this oxide on iron.

Iron becomes *passive* when it is dipped in very concentrated nitric acid. It then no longer displaces hydrogen from dilute acids. However, a sharp blow on the metal produces a change which spreads over the surface from the point struck, the metal once more becoming active. This production of passivity is due to the formation of a protective layer of oxide, and the passivity is lost when the layer is broken. Passivity is also produced by other oxidizing agents, such as chromate ion; safety razor blades kept in a solution of potassium chromate remain sharp much longer than blades kept in air.

When exposed to moist air iron becomes oxidized, forming a loose coating of rust, which is a partially hydrated ferric oxide.

Ferrous Compounds. The ferrous compounds, containing bipositive iron, are usually green in color. Most of the ferrous salts are easily oxidized to the corresponding ferric salts through the action of atmospheric oxygen.

Ferrous sulfate, $FeSO_4 \cdot 7H_2O$, is made by dissolving iron in sulfuric acid, or by allowing pyrite to oxidize in air. The green crystals of the substance are efflorescent, and often have a brown coating of a ferric hydroxide-sulfate, produced by atmospheric oxidation. Ferrous sulfate is used in dyeing and in making ink. To make ink a solution of tannic acid, a complex organic acid obtained by extraction of nut-galls, is mixed with ferrous sulfate, producing ferrous tannate. On oxidation by the air a fine black insoluble pigment is produced.

Ferrous chloride, $FeCl_2 \cdot 4H_2O$, is made by dissolving iron in hydrochloric acid. It is pale green in color. **Ferrous hydroxide,** $Fe(OH)_2$, is formed as a nearly white precipitate on addition of alkali to a ferrous solution. The precipitate rapidly becomes a dirty green, and finally brown, by oxidation by air. **Ferrous sulfide,** FeS, is a black compound made by heating iron filings with sulfur. It is used in making hydrogen sulfide. Ferrous sulfide is also obtained as a black precipitate by the action of sulfide ion on a ferrous salt in solution.

Ferrous carbonate, $FeCO_3$, occurs in nature as a mineral, and can be obtained as a white precipitate by the action of carbonate ion on ferrous ion in the absence of dissolved oxygen. Like calcium carbonate, ferrous carbonate is soluble in acidic waters. Hard waters often contain ferrous or ferric ion.

Ferric Compounds. The hydrated ferric ion, $Fe(H_2O)_6^{+++}$, is pale violet in color. The ion loses protons readily, however, and ferric salts in solution usually are yellow or brown, because of the formation of hydroxide complexes. **Ferric nitrate,** $Fe(NO_3)_3 \cdot 6H_2O$, exists as pale violet deliquescent crystals. Anhydrous **ferric sulfate,** $Fe_2(SO_4)_3$, is obtained as a white powder by evaporation of a ferric sulfate solution. A well-crystallized ferric sulfate is **iron alum,** $KFe(SO_4)_2 \cdot 12H_2O$, which forms pale violet octahedral crystals.

Ferric chloride, $FeCl_3 \cdot 6H_2O$, is obtained as yellow deliquescent crystals by evaporation of a solution made by oxidation of ferrous chloride with chlorine. Solutions of ferric ion containing chloride ion are more intensely colored, yellow or brown, than nitrate or sulfate solutions because of the formation of ferric chloride complexes. Anhydrous ferric chloride, Fe_2Cl_6, can be made by passing chlorine over heated iron.

Ferric ion in solution can be reduced to ferrous ion by treatment with metallic iron or by reduction with hydrogen sulfide or stannous ion.

Ferric hydroxide, $Fe(OH)_3$, is formed as a brown precipitate when alkali is added to a solution of ferric ion. When it is strongly heated ferric hydroxide is converted into **ferric oxide,** Fe_2O_3, which, as a fine powder, is called *rouge* and, as a pigment, *Venetian red.*

Complex Cyanides of Iron. Cyanide ion added to a solution of ferrous or ferric ion forms precipitates, which dissolve in excess cyanide to produce complex ions. Yellow crystals of **potassium ferrocyanide,** $K_4Fe(CN)_6 \cdot 3H_2O$, are made by heating organic material, such as dried blood, with iron filings and potassium carbonate. The mass produced by the heating is extracted with warm water, and the crystals are made by evaporation of the solution. **Potassium ferricyanide,** $K_3Fe(CN)_6$, is made as red crystals by oxidation of ferrocyanide.

These substances contain the complexes *ferrocyanide ion*, $Fe(CN)_6^{----}$, and *ferricyanide ion*, $Fe(CN)_6^{---}$, respectively, and the ferrocyanides and ferricyanides of other metals are easily made from them.

The pigments *Turnbull's blue* and *Prussian blue* are made by addition of ferrous ion to a ferricyanide solution or ferric ion to a ferrocyanide solution. The pigments which precipitate have the approximate composition $KFeFe(CN)_6 \cdot H_2O$. They have a brilliant blue color. Ferrous ion and ferrocyanide ion produce a white precipitate of $K_2FeFe(CN)_6$, whereas ferric ion and ferricyanide ion form only a brown solution.

27–5. Cobalt

Cobalt occurs in nature in the minerals *smaltite*, $CoAs_2$, and *cobaltite*, $CoAsS$, usually associated with nickel. The metal is obtained by reducing the oxide with aluminum.

Metallic cobalt is silvery-white, with a slight reddish tinge. It is less reactive than iron, and displaces hydrogen slowly from dilute acids. It is used in special alloys, including *Alnico*, a strongly ferromagnetic alloy of aluminum, nickel, cobalt, and iron which is used for making permanent magnets.

Cobalt ion, $Co(H_2O)_6^{++}$, in solution and in hydrated salts is red or pink in color. **Cobalt chloride,** $CoCl_2 \cdot 6H_2O$, forms red crystals, which when dehydrated change into a deep blue powder. Writing made with a dilute solution of cobalt chloride is almost invisible, but becomes blue when the paper is warmed, dehydrating the salt. **Cobalt oxide,** CoO, is a black substance which dissolves in molten glass, to give it a blue color (*cobalt glass*).

Terpositive cobalt ion is unstable, and an attempt to oxidize Co^{++} usually leads to the precipitation of **cobalt(III) hydroxide,** $Co(OH)_3$. The covalent compounds of cobalt(III) are very stable. The most important of these are **potassium cobaltinitrite,** $K_2Co(NO_2)_6$, and **potassium cobalticyanide,** $K_3Co(CN)_6$.

27–6. Nickel

Nickel occurs, with iron, in meteorites. Its principal ores are *nickelite*, $NiAs$, *millerite*, NiS, and *pentlandite*, $(Ni,Fe)S$. The metal is produced, as an alloy containing iron and other elements, by roasting the ore and reducing with carbon. In the purification of nickel by the Mond process the compound **nickel carbonyl,** $Ni(CO)_4$, is manufactured and then decomposed. The ore is reduced with hydrogen to metallic nickel under conditions such that the iron oxide is not reduced. Carbon monoxide is then passed through the reduced ore at room temperature; it combines with the nickel to form nickel carbonyl:

$$Ni + 4CO \longrightarrow Ni(CO)_4$$

Nickel carbonyl is a gas. It is passed into a decomposer heated to 150° C; the gas decomposes, depositing pure metallic nickel, and the liberated carbon monoxide is returned to be used again.

Nickel is a white metal, with a faint tinge of yellow. It is used in making alloys, including the copper-nickel alloy (75% Cu, 25% Ni) used in coinage. Iron objects are plated with nickel by electrolysis from an ammoniacal solution. The metal is still less reactive than cobalt, and displaces hydrogen only very slowly from acids.

The hydrated salts of nickel such as **nickel sulfate,** $NiSO_4 \cdot 6H_2O$, and **nickel chloride,** $NiCl_2 \cdot 6H_2O$, are green in color. **Nickel(II) hydroxide,** $Ni(OH)_2$, is formed as an apple-green precipitate by addition of alkali to a solution containing nickel ion. When heated it produces the insoluble green substance **nickel(II) oxide,** NiO. Nickel(II) hydroxide is soluble in ammonium hydroxide, forming ammonia complexes such as $Ni(NH_3)_4(H_2O)_2^{++}$ and $Ni(NH_3)_6^{++}$.

In alkaline solution nickel(II) hydroxide can be oxidized to a hydrated **nickel(IV) oxide**, $NiO_2 \cdot xH_2O$. This reaction is used in the *Edison storage cell*. The electrodes of this cell are plates coated with $NiO_2 \cdot xH_2O$ and metallic iron, which are converted on discharge of the cell into nickel(II) hydroxide and ferrous hydroxide, respectively. The electrolyte in this cell is a solution of sodium hydroxide.

27-7. The Platinum Metals

The congeners of iron, cobalt, and nickel are the *platinum metals*, ruthenium, rhodium, palladium, osmium, iridium, and platinum. Some properties of these elements are given in Table 27-3.

The platinum metals are noble metals, chemically unreactive, which are found in nature as native alloys, consisting mainly of platinum.

TABLE 27-3   *Some Physical Properties of the Platinum Metals*

	ATOMIC NUMBER	ATOMIC WEIGHT	DENSITY	MELTING POINT
Ru	44	101.1	12.36 g/cm³	2,450° C
Rh	45	102.91	12.48	1,985°
Pd	46	106.4	12.09	1,555°
Os	76	190.2	22.69	2,700°
Ir	77	192.2	22.82	2,440°
Pt	78	195.09	21.60	1,755°

Ruthenium and **osmium** are iron-gray metals, the other four elements being whiter in color. Ruthenium can be oxidized to RuO_2, and even to the octavalent compound RuO_4. Osmium unites with oxygen to form osmium tetroxide, "osmic acid," OsO_4, a white crystalline substance melting at 40° C and boiling at about 100° C. Osmium tetroxide has an irritating odor similar to that of chlorine. It is a very poisonous substance. Its aqueous solution is used in histology (the study of the tissues of plants and animals); it stains tissues through its reduction by organic matter to metallic osmium, and also hardens the material without distorting it.

Ruthenium and osmium form compounds corresponding to various states of oxidation, such as the following: $RuCl_3$, K_2RuO_4, Os_2O_3, $OsCl_4$, K_2OsO_4.

Rhodium and **iridium** are very unreactive metals, not being attacked by aqua regia (a mixture of nitric acid and hydrochloric acid). Iridium is alloyed with platinum to produce a very hard alloy, which is used for the tips of gold pens, surgical tools, and scientific apparatus. Representative compounds are Rh_2O_3, K_3RhCl_6, Ir_2O_3, K_3IrCl_6, and K_2IrCl_6.

Palladium is the only one of the platinum metals which is attacked by nitric acid. Metallic palladium has an unusual ability to absorb hydrogen. At 1,000° C it absorbs enough hydrogen to correspond to the formula $PdH_{0.6}$.

The principal compounds of palladium are the salts of chloropalladous acid, H_2PdCl_4, and chloropalladic acid, H_2PdCl_6. The chloropalladite ion, $PdCl_4^{--}$, is a planar ion, consisting of the palladium atom with four coplanar chlorine atoms arranged about it at the corners of a square. The chloropalladate ion, $PdCl_6^{--}$, is an octahedral covalent complex ion.

Platinum is the most important of the palladium and platinum metals. It is grayish-white in color, and is very ductile. It can be welded at a red heat, and melted in an oxyhydrogen flame. Because of its very small chemical activity it is used in electrical apparatus and in making crucibles and other apparatus for use in the laboratory. Platinum is attacked by chlorine and dissolves in a mixture of nitric and hydrochloric acids. It also interacts with fused alkalis, such as potassium hydroxide, but not with alkali carbonates.

The principal compounds of platinum are the salts of chloroplatinous acid, H_2PtCl_4, and chloroplatinic acid, H_2PtCl_6. These salts are similar in structure to the corresponding palladium salts. Both palladium and platinum form many other covalent complexes, such as the platinum(II) ammonia complex ion, $Pt(NH_3)_4^{++}$.

A finely divided form of metallic platinum, called *platinum sponge*, is made by strongly heating ammonium chloroplatinate, $(NH_4)_2PtCl_6$. *Platinum black* is a fine powder of metallic platinum made by adding zinc to chloroplatinic acid. These substances have very strong catalytic activity, and are used as catalysts in commercial processes, such as the oxidation of sulfur dioxide to sulfur trioxide. Platinum black causes the ignition of a mixture of illuminating gas and air or hydrogen and air as a result of the heat developed by the rapid chemical combination of the gases in contact with the surface of the metal.

Concepts, Facts, and Terms Introduced in This Chapter

Physical properties and oxidation states of iron, cobalt, and nickel.

Hematite, magnetite, siderite, limonite, pyrite. Metallurgy of iron: blast furnace, slag, tuyere, stove, pig iron, white cast iron, cementite, gray cast iron, ferrite, malleable cast iron, wrought iron. Mild steel, medium steel, high-carbon steel. Open-hearth process, Bessemer process. Acidic lining, basic lining. The hardening and tempering of steel. Martensite, pearlite, eutectoid steel, hypo-eutectoid steel, hyper-eutectoid steel. Case-hardening. Alloy steels.

Chemical properties of iron. Passivity. Ferrous compounds: ferrous sulfate, ferrous ammonium sulfate, ferrous chloride, ferrous hydroxide, ferrous sulfide, ferrous carbonate. Ferric compounds: ferric nitrate, ferric sulfate, iron alum, ferric chloride, ferric hydroxide, ferric oxide (rouge, Venetian red). Potassium ferrocyanide, potassium ferricyanide, Prussian blue.

Properties of cobalt. Ores—smaltite, cobaltite. Alnico and other alloys. Cobalt chloride, cobalt oxide, cobalt(III) hydroxide, potassium cobaltinitrite, potassium cobalticyanide. Cobalt glass.

Nickel. Nickelite, millerite, pentlandite. Metallurgy of nickel. Mond process, nickel carbonyl. Nickel plating from ammoniacal solution. Nickel sulfate, nickel(II) hydroxide, nickel chloride, nickel(II) oxide. Nickel(IV) oxide, Edison storage cell.

Properties of the palladium metals and platinum. Ruthenium, osmium, rhodium, iridium, palladium, platinum. Osmium tetroxide. Chloropalladous acid, chloropalladic acid, chloroplatinous acid, chloroplatinic acid. Platinum sponge, platinum black. Uses of the palladium and platinum metals.

Exercises

27-1. Make a list of the known oxidation states of iron, cobalt, and nickel, naming the free ion, a complex ion, and a solid compound for each state, if they exist.

27-2. Compare the stability of the free cobalt(III) ion, Co^{+++}, with that of the cobalticyanide ion, $Co(CN)_6^{---}$, and explain in terms of electronic structure.

27-3. What happens to the acidity of a ferrous sulfate solution when air is bubbled through it? Write the equation.

27-4. What are the oxidation states of iron in hematite, magnetite, and siderite?

27-5. What are the chemical reactions for the conversion of hematite to cast iron?

27-6. Calculate the percentage of carbon in cementite.

27-7. What can you say about the equilibrium in the following chemical reaction, from your knowledge of the properties of steel and cast iron?

$$3Fe + C \rightleftarrows Fe_3C$$

27-8. What are the chemical reactions in the open-hearth process of making steel? In the Bessemer process?

27-9. What is the composition of stainless steel?

27-10. What is the normality of a permanganate solution, 48.0 ml of which is required to titrate 0.400 g of $(NH_4)_2Fe(SO_4)_2 \cdot 6H_2O$?

27-11. In which direction does the following chemical reaction mainly proceed?

$$Cu + Fe^{++} \rightleftarrows Fe + Cu^{++}$$

27-12. What chemical reaction do you think would take place between siderite and carbonated water?

27-13. Which do you predict would have the lower pH, an aqueous solution of ferric nitrate, or an aqueous solution of ferric chloride?

27-14. What compounds of the $Fe(CN)_6^{---}$ ion are the most strongly colored?

27-15. Write a chemical equation for the preparation of metallic cobalt. Why is not cobalt made by the same method as is used for the commercial preparation of iron?

27-16. What are the names and formulas of an ore of cobalt and an ore of nickel?

27-17   What chemical reactions take place when acidic solutions of bipositive nickel, cobalt, and iron are treated with aqueous ammonia?

27-18. Name compounds of the important oxidation states of palladium and platinum.

27-19. Devise a simple method for the separation of osmium in qualitative analysis.

27-20. What are the most important properties of platinum?

27-21. Devise a method of converting pyrite into ferrous sulfate, and write equations for the chemical reactions.

27-22. Write formulas for the following compounds:

ferrous chloride	ferrous sulfate	ferric nitrate
Prussian blue	iron alum	potassium ferrocyanide
potassium chloroplatinate	potassium chloropalladite	nickel hydroxide
osmium tetroxide	nickel(IV) oxide	potassium cobaltinitrite

27-23. Write an electronic structural formula for nickel carbonyl, and discuss the arrangement of the electrons around the nickel atoms in relation to the structure of krypton. Iron forms a carbonyl $Fe(CO)_5$, and chromium a carbonyl $Cr(CO)_6$; discuss the electronic structures of these substances.

27-24. What substances are used for making acidic linings and for making basic linings of furnaces and converters? What conditions determine the choice between acidic linings and basic linings?

Chapter 28

Copper, Zinc, and Gallium and Their Congeners

In the preceding chapter we have begun the discussion of the chemistry of the transition metals through the consideration of iron, cobalt, nickel, and their congeners, the palladium and platinum metals. We shall now take up the chemistry of the elements that lie to the right of these elements in the periodic table.

The three metals copper, silver, and gold comprise group Ib of the periodic table. These metals all form compounds representing oxidation state +1, as do the alkali metals, but aside from this they show very little similarity in properties to the alkali metals. The alkali metals are very soft and light, and very reactive chemically, whereas the metals of the copper group are much harder and heavier and are rather inert, sufficiently so to occur in the free state in nature and to be easily obtainable by reducing their compounds, sometimes simply by heating. The metals zinc, cadmium, and mercury (group IIb) are also much different from the alkaline-earth metals (group II), and gallium and its congeners (group IIIb) from the elements of group III.

In this chapter, in connection with the discussion of the compounds of silver, there is also a section on photography, including color photography (Section 28–6).

28–1. Electronic Structures and Oxidation States of Copper, Silver, and Gold

The electronic structures of copper, silver, and gold, as well as those of zinc and gallium and their congeners, are given in Table 28-1.

It is seen that copper has one outer electron, in the $4s$ orbital of the M shell, zinc has two outer electrons, in the $4s$ orbital, and gallium has three outer electrons, two in the $4s$ orbital and one in the $4p$ orbital. The congeners of these elements also have one, two, or three electrons in the outermost shell. The shell next to the outermost shell in each case contains 18 electrons; this is the M shell for copper, zinc, and gallium, the N shell for silver, cadmium, and indium, and the O shell for gold, mercury, and thallium. This shell is called an *eighteen-electron shell*.

The electrons in the outermost shell are held loosely, and can be easily removed. The resulting ions, Cu^+, Zn^{++}, Ga^{+++}, etc., have an outer shell of eighteen electrons, and are called *eighteen-shell ions*. If these elements either lose their outermost electrons, forming eighteen-shell ions, or share the outermost electrons with other atoms, the resulting oxidation state is $+1$ for copper, silver, and gold, $+2$ for zinc, cadmium, and mercury, and $+3$ for gallium, indium, and thallium.

TABLE 28-1   *Electronic Structures of Copper, Zinc, and Gallium and Their Congeners*

Z	ELEMENT	K	L		M			N				O			P	
		1s	2s	2p	3s	3p	3d	4s	4p	4d	4f	5s	5p	5d	6s	6p
29	Cu	2	2	6	2	6	10	1								
30	Zn	2	2	6	2	6	10	2								
31	Ga	2	2	6	2	6	10	2	1							
47	Ag	2	2	6	2	6	10	2	6	10		1				
48	Cd	2	2	6	2	6	10	2	6	10		2				
49	In	2	2	6	2	6	10	2	6	10		2	1			
79	Au	2	2	6	2	6	10	2	6	10	14	2	6	10	1	
80	Hg	2	2	6	2	6	10	2	6	10	14	2	6	10	2	
81	Tl	2	2	6	2	6	10	2	6	10	14	2	6	10	2	1

These are important oxidation states for all of these elements; there are, however, also some other important oxidation states. The cuprous ion, Cu^+, is unstable, and the cuprous compounds, except the very insoluble ones, are easily oxidized. The cupric ion, Cu^{++} (hydrated to $Cu(H_2O)_4^{++}$), occurs in many copper salts, and the cupric compounds are the principal compounds of copper. In the cupric ion the copper atom has lost two electrons, leaving it with only seventeen electrons in the M shell. In fact, the $3d$ electrons and the $4s$ electrons in copper are held by the atom with about the same energy—you may have noticed that the electronic structure given in Table 28-1 for copper differs from that given in the energy-level diagram, Figure 5-6, in that in the diagram copper is represented as having two $4s$ electrons and only nine $3d$ electrons.

The unipositive silver ion, Ag^+, is stable, and forms many salts. A very few compounds have also been made containing bipositive and terpositive silver. These compounds are very strong oxidizing agents. The stable oxidation state $+1$ shown by silver corresponds to the electronic structure of the element as given in Table 28-1. The Ag^+ ion is an eighteen-shell ion.

The gold(I) ion, Au^+, and the gold(III) ion, Au^{++}, are unstable in aqueous solution. The stable gold(I) compounds and gold(III) compounds contain covalent bonds, as in the complex ions $AuCl_2^-$ and $AuCl_4^-$.

The chemistry of zinc and cadmium is especially simple, in that these elements form compounds representing only the oxidation state $+2$. This oxidation state is closely correlated with the electronic structures shown in Table 28-1; it represents the loss or the sharing of the two outermost electrons. The ions Zn^{++} and Cd^{++} are eighteen-shell ions.

Mercury also forms compounds (the mercuric compounds) representing the oxidation state $+2$. The mercuric ion, Hg^{++}, is an eighteen-shell ion. In addition, mercury forms a series of compounds, the mercurous compounds, in which it has oxidation number $+1$. The electronic structure of the mercurous compounds is discussed in Section 28–10.

28–2. *The Properties of Copper, Silver, and Gold*

The metallurgy of copper, silver, and gold has been discussed in Chapter 26.

Copper is a red, tough metal with a moderately high melting point (Table 28-2). It is an excellent conductor of heat and of electricity when pure, and it finds extensive use as an electric conductor. Pure copper which has been heated is soft, and can be drawn into wire or shaped by hammering. This "cold work" (of drawing or hammering) causes the metal to become hard, because the crystal grains are broken into much smaller grains, with grain boundaries which interfere with the process of deformation and thus strengthen the metal. The hardened metal can be made soft by heating ("annealing"), which permits the grains to coalesce into larger grains.

Silver is a soft, white metal, somewhat denser than copper, and with a lower melting point. It is used in coinage, jewelry, and tableware, and as a filling for teeth.

Gold is a soft, very dense metal, which is used for jewelry, coinage, dental work, and scientific and technical apparatus. Gold is bright yellow by reflected light; very thin sheets are blue or green. Its beautiful color and fine luster, which, because of its inertness, are not affected by exposure to the atmosphere, are responsible for its use for ornamental purposes. Gold is the most malleable and most ductile of all metals; it can be hammered into sheets only $1/100,000$ cm thick, and drawn into wires $1/5,000$ cm in diameter.

Alloys of Copper, Silver, and Gold. The transition metals find their greatest use in alloys. Alloys are often far stronger, harder, and tougher than their constituent elementary metals. The alloys of copper and zinc are called *brass*, those of copper and tin are called *bronze*, and those of copper and aluminum are called *aluminum bronze*. Many of these alloys have valuable properties. Copper is a constituent also of other useful alloys, such as beryllium copper, coinage silver, and coinage gold.

TABLE 28-2   *Some Physical Properties of Copper, Silver, and Gold*

	ATOMIC NUMBER	ATOMIC WEIGHT	DENSITY	MELTING POINT	BOILING POINT	METALLIC RADIUS	COLOR
Copper	29	63.54	8.97 g/cm³	1,083° C	2,310° C	1.28 Å	Red
Silver	47	107.880	10.54	960.5°	1,950°	1.44	White
Gold	79	197.0	19.42	1,063°	2,600°	1.44	Yellow

Coinage silver in the United States contains 90% silver and 10% copper. This composition also constitutes *sterling silver* in the United States. British sterling silver is 92.5% silver and 7.5% copper.

Gold is often alloyed with copper, silver, palladium, or other metals. The amount of gold in these alloys is usually described in *carats*, the number of parts of gold in 24 parts of alloy—pure gold is 24 carat. American coinage gold is 21.6 carat and British coinage gold is 22 carat. *White gold*, used in jewelry, is usually a white alloy of gold and nickel.

28–3. The Compounds of Copper

Cupric Compounds. The hydrated **cupric ion,** $Cu(H_2O)_4{}^{++}$, is an ion with light blue color which occurs in aqueous solutions of cupric salts and in some of the hydrated crystals. The most important cupric salt is **copper sulfate,** which forms blue crystals $CuSO_4 \cdot 5H_2O$. The metal copper is not sufficiently reactive to displace hydrogen ion from dilute acids (it is below hydrogen in the electromotive-force series, Chapter 12), and copper does not dissolve in acids unless an oxidizing agent is present. However, hot concentrated sulfuric acid is itself an oxidizing agent, and can dissolve the metal, and dilute sulfuric acid also slowly dissolves it in the presence of air:

$$Cu + 2H_2SO_4 + 3H_2O \longrightarrow CuSO_4 \cdot 5H_2O + SO_2 \uparrow$$

or

$$2Cu + 2H_2SO_4 + O_2 + 8H_2O \longrightarrow 2CuSO_4 \cdot 5H_2O$$

Copper sulfate, which has the common names *blue vitriol* and *bluestone*, is used in copper plating, in printing calico, in electric cells, and in the manufacture of other compounds of copper.

Cupric chloride, $CuCl_2$, can be made as yellow crystals by direct union of the elements. The hydrated salt, $CuCl_2 \cdot 2H_2O$, is blue-green in color, and its solution in hydrochloric acid is green. The blue-green color of the salt is due to its existence as a complex,

$$\begin{array}{c} OH_2 \\ | \\ Cl-Cu-Cl \\ | \\ OH_2 \end{array}$$

in which the chlorine atoms are bonded directly to the copper atom. The green solution contains ions $CuCl_3(H_2O)^-$ and $CuCl_4^{--}$. All of these ions are planar, the copper atom being at the center of a square formed by the four attached groups. The planar configuration is shown also by other complexes of copper, including the deep-blue ammonia complex, $Cu(NH_3)_4^{++}$.

Cupric bromide, $CuBr_2$, is a black solid obtained by reaction of copper and bromine or by solution of cupric oxide, CuO, in hydrobromic acid. It is interesting that cupric iodide, CuI_2, does not exist; when a solution containing cupric ion is added to an iodide solution there occurs an oxidation-reduction reaction, with precipitation of cuprous iodide, CuI:

$$2Cu^{++} + 4I^- \longrightarrow 2CuI \downarrow + I_2$$

This reaction occurs because of the extraordinary stability of cuprous iodide, which is discussed in the following section. The reaction is used in a method of quantitative analysis for copper, the liberated iodine being determined by titration with sodium thiosulfate solution.

Cupric hydroxide, $Cu(OH)_2$, forms as a pale blue gelatinous precipitate when an alkali hydroxide or ammonium hydroxide is added to a cupric solution. It dissolves very readily in excess ammonium hydroxide, forming the deep-blue complex $Cu(NH_3)_4^{++}$ (Chapter 22). Cupric hydroxide is slightly amphoteric, and dissolves to a small extent in a very concentrated alkali, forming $Cu(OH)_4^{--}$.

The complex of cupric ion with tartrate ion, $C_4H_4O_6^{--}$, in alkaline solution is used as a test reagent (*Fehling's solution*) for organic reducing agents, such as certain sugars. This complex ion, $Cu(C_4H_4O_6)_2^{--}$, ionizes to give only a very small concentration of Cu^{++}, not enough to cause a precipitate of $Cu(OH)_2$ to form. The organic reducing agents reduce the copper to the unipositive state, and it then forms a brick-red precipitate of cuprous oxide, Cu_2O. This reagent is used in testing for sugar in the urine, in the diagnosis of diabetes.

Cuprous Compounds.   Cuprous ion, Cu^+, is so unstable in aqueous solution that it undergoes auto-oxidation-reduction into copper and cupric ion:

$$2Cu^+ \longrightarrow Cu \downarrow + Cu^{++}$$

Very few cuprous salts of oxygen acids exist. The stable cuprous compounds are either insoluble crystals containing covalent bonds or covalent complexes.

When copper is added to a solution of cupric chloride in strong hydrochloric acid a reaction occurs which results in the formation of a colorless solution containing cuprous chloride complex ions such as $CuCl_2^-$:

$$CuCl_4^{--} + Cu \longrightarrow 2CuCl_2^-$$

This complex ion involves two covalent bonds, its electronic structure being

$$\left[\ : \overset{..}{\underset{..}{Cl}}-Cu-\overset{..}{\underset{..}{Cl}} : \ \right]^-$$

Other cuprous complexes, $CuCl_3^{--}$ and $CuCl_4^{---}$, also exist.

If the solution is diluted with water a colorless precipitate of **cuprous chloride,** CuCl, forms. This precipitate also contains covalent bonds, each copper atom being bonded to four neighboring chlorine atoms and each chlorine atom to four neighboring copper atoms, with use of the outer electrons of the chloride ion. The structure is closely related to that of diamond, with alternating carbon atoms replaced by copper and chlorine (Figure 7-2).

Cuprous bromide, CuBr, and **cuprous iodide,** CuI, are also colorless insoluble substances. The covalent bonds between copper and iodine in cuprous iodide are so strong as to make cupric iodide relatively unstable, as mentioned above.

Other stable cuprous compounds are the insoluble substances cuprous oxide, Cu_2O (red), cuprous sulfide, Cu_2S (black), cuprous cyanide, CuCN (white), and cuprous thiocyanate, CuSCN (white).

28–4. The Compounds of Silver

Silver oxide, Ag_2O, is obtained as a dark-brown precipitate on the addition of sodium hydroxide to a solution of silver nitrate. It is slightly soluble, producing a weakly alkaline solution of silver hydroxide:

$$\underline{Ag_2O} + H_2O \longrightarrow 2Ag^+ + 2OH^-$$

Silver oxide is used in inorganic chemistry to convert a soluble chloride, bromide, or iodide into the hydroxide. For example, cesium chloride solution can be converted into cesium hydroxide solution in this way:

$$2Cs^+ + 2Cl^- + \underline{Ag_2O} + H_2O \longrightarrow 2AgCl \downarrow + 2Cs^+ + 2OH^-$$

This reaction proceeds to the right because silver chloride is much less soluble than silver oxide.

The **silver halogenides,** AgF, AgCl, AgBr, and AgI, can be made by adding silver oxide to solutions of the corresponding halogen acids. Silver fluoride is very soluble in water, and the other halogenides are nearly insoluble. Silver chloride, bromide, and iodide form as curdy precipitates when the ions are mixed. They are respectively white, pale yellow, and yellow in color, and on exposure to light they slowly turn black, through photochemical decomposition. Silver chloride and bromide dissolve in ammonium hydroxide solution, forming the **silver ammonia complex** $Ag(NH_3)_2^+$ (Chapter 22); silver iodide does not dissolve in ammonium hydroxide. These reactions are used as qualitative tests for silver ion and the halide ions.

Other complex ions formed by silver, such as the silver cyanide complex $Ag(CN)_2^-$ and the silver thiosulfate complex $Ag(S_2O_3)_2^{---}$, have been mentioned in Chapter 22.

Silver nitrate, $AgNO_3$, is a colorless, soluble salt made by dissolving silver in nitric acid. It is used to cauterize sores. Silver nitrate is easily reduced to metallic silver by organic matter, such as skin or cloth, and is for this reason used in making indelible ink.

Silver ion is an excellent antiseptic, and several of the compounds of silver are used in medicine because of their germicidal power.

28–5. *Photography—An Important Use of Silver*

A photographic film is a sheet of cellulose acetate coated with a thin layer of gelatin in which very fine grains of silver bromide are suspended. This layer of gelatin and silver bromide is called the *photographic emulsion.* The silver halogenides are sensitive to light, and undergo photochemical decomposition. The gelatin increases this sensitivity, apparently because of the sulfur which it contains.

When the film is briefly exposed to light some of the grains of silver bromide undergo a small amount of decomposition, perhaps forming a small particle of silver sulfide on the surface of the grain. The film can then be *developed* by treatment with an alkaline solution of an organic reducing agent, such as Metol or hydroquinone, the *developer.* This causes the silver bromide grains which have been sensitized to be reduced to metallic silver, whereas the unsensitized silver bromide grains remain unchanged. By this process the developed film reproduces the pattern of the light which exposed it. This film is called the *negative,* because it is darkest (with the greatest amount of silver) in the places which were exposed to the most light.

The undeveloped grains of silver halide are next removed, by treatment with a fixing bath, which contains thiosulfate ion, $S_2O_3^{--}$ (from sodium thiosulfate, "hypo," $Na_2S_2O_3 \cdot 5H_2O$). The soluble silver thiosulfate complex is formed:

$$\underline{AgBr} + 2S_2O_3{}^{--} \longrightarrow Ag(S_2O_3)_2{}^{---} + Br^-$$

The fixed negative is then washed. Care must be taken not to transfer the negative from a used fixing bath, containing a considerable concentration of silver complex, directly to the wash water, as insoluble silver thiosulfate might precipitate in the emulsion:

$$2Ag(S_2O_3)_2{}^{---} \longrightarrow Ag_2S_2O_3 \downarrow + 3S_2O_3{}^{--}$$

Since there are three ions on the right, and only two on the left, dilution causes the equilibrium to shift toward the right.

A positive print can be made by exposing print paper, coated with a silver halide emulsion, to light which passes through the superimposed negative, and then developing and fixing the exposed paper.

Sepia tones are obtained by converting the silver to silver sulfide, and gold and platinum tones by replacing silver by these metals.

Many other very interesting chemical processes are used in photography, especially for the reproduction of color.

The Chemistry of Color Photography. The electromagnetic waves of light of different colors have different wavelengths. In the visible spectrum these wavelengths extend from a little below 4,000 Å (violet in color) to nearly 8,000 Å (red in color). The sequence of colors in the visible region is shown in the next to the top diagram of Figure 28-1.

The visible spectrum is only a very small part of the complete spectrum of electromagnetic waves. At the top of Figure 28-1 other parts are indicated. Ordinary x-rays have wavelengths approximately 1 Å. Even shorter wavelengths, 0.1, 0.01, 0.001 Å, are possessed by the gamma rays that are produced in radioactive decompositions and through the action of cosmic rays (Chapter 32). The ultraviolet region, not visible to the eye, consists of light somewhat shorter in wavelength than violet light, and the infrared consists of wavelengths somewhat longer than red. Then there come the microwave regions, approximately 1 centimeter, and the longer radiowaves.

When gases are heated or are excited by the passage of an electric spark, the atoms and molecules in the gases emit light of definite wavelengths. The light that is emitted by an atom or molecule under these conditions is said to constitute its *emission spectrum*. The emission spectra of the alkali metals, mercury, and neon are shown in Figure 28-1. The emission spectra of elements, especially of the metals, can be used for identifying them, and *spectroscopic chemical analysis* is an important technique of analytical chemistry.

When white light (light containing all wavelengths in the visible

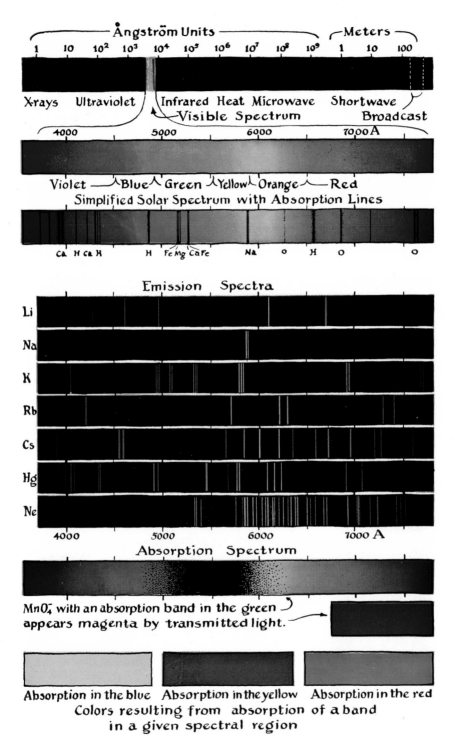

FIGURE 28-1　*Emission spectra and absorption spectra.*

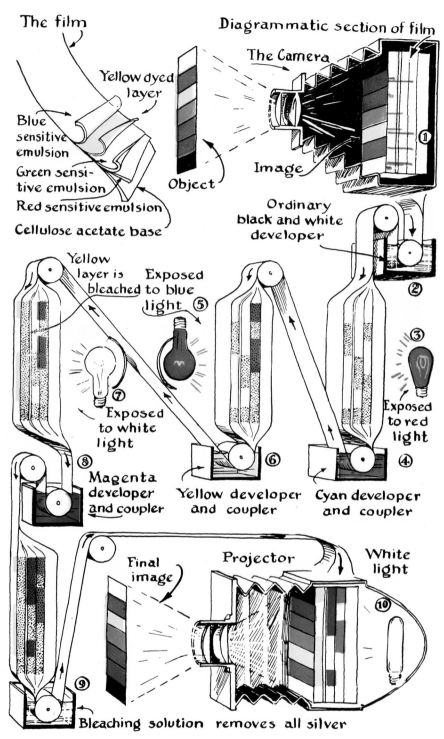

The film

Diagrammatic section of film

Yellow dyed layer

The Camera

Blue sensitive emulsion

Green sensitive emulsion

Red sensitive emulsion

Cellulose acetate base

Object

Image

①

Ordinary black and white developer

②

Yellow layer is bleached

Exposed to blue light ⑤

③

Exposed to red light

⑦

Exposed to white light

⑥

④

⑧

Magenta developer and coupler

Yellow developer and coupler

Cyan developer and coupler

Final image

Projector

White light

⑩

⑨

Bleaching solution removes all silver

FIGURE 28-2 *The Kodachrome process of color photography.*

region) is passed through a substance, light of certain wavelengths may be absorbed by the substance. The solar spectrum is shown in Figure 28-1. It consists of a background of white light, produced by the very hot gases in the sun, on which there are superimposed some dark lines, resulting from absorption of certain wavelengths by atoms in the cooler surface layers of the sun. It is seen that the yellow sodium lines, which occur as bright lines in the emission spectrum of sodium atoms, are shown as dark lines in the solar spectrum.

Molecules and complex ions in solution and in solid substances sometimes show sharp line spectra, but usually show rather broad absorption bands, as is indicated for the permanganate ion near the bottom of Figure 28-1. The permanganate ion has the power of absorbing light in the green region of the spectrum, permitting the blue violet light and red light to pass through. The combination of blue-violet and red light appears magenta in color. We accordingly say that permanganate ion has a magenta color.

The human eye does not have the power of completely differentiating between light of one wavelength and that of another wavelength in the visible spectrum. Instead, it responds to three different wavelength regions in different ways. All of the colors that can be recognized by the eye can be composed from three fundamental colors. These may be taken as red-green (seen by the eye as yellow), which is complementary to blue-violet; blue-red, or magenta, which is complementary to green; and blue-green, or cyan, which is complementary to red. Three *primary colors*, such as these, need to be used in the development of any method of color photography.

An important modern method of color photography is the *Kodachrome method*, developed by the Kodak Research Laboratories. This method is illustrated in Figure 28-2. The film consists of several layers of emulsion, superimposed on a cellulose acetate base. The uppermost layer of photographic emulsion is the ordinary photographic emulsion, which is sensitive to blue and violet light. The second layer of photographic emulsion is a green-sensitive emulsion. It consists of a photographic emulsion that has been treated with a magenta-colored dye, which absorbs green light and sensitizes the silver bromide grains, thus making the emulsion sensitive to green light as well as to blue and violet light. The third photographic emulsion, red-sensitive emulsion, has been treated with a blue dye, which absorbs red light, making the emulsion sensitive to red light as well as to blue and violet (but not to green). Between the first layer and the middle layer there is a layer of yellow filter, containing a yellow dye, which during exposure prevents blue and violet light from penetrating to the lower layers. Accordingly when such a film is exposed to light the blue-sensitive emulsion is exposed by blue light, the middle emulsion is exposed by green light, and the bottom emulsion is exposed by red light.

The exposure of the different layers of photographic emulsion in the film is illustrated diagrammatically as Process 1 in Figure 28-2.

The development of Kodachrome film involves several steps, which are represented as Processes 2 to 9 in Figure 28-2. First (Process 2) the Kodachrome film after exposure is developed with an ordinary black and white developer, which develops the silver negative in all three emulsions. Then, after simple washing in water (not shown in the figure) the film is exposed through the back to red light, which makes the previously unexposed silver bromide in the red-sensitive emulsion capable of development (Process 3). The film then passes into a special developer, called cyan developer and coupler (Process 4). This mixture of chemical substances has the power of interacting with the exposed silver bromide grains in such a way as to deposit a cyan dye in the bottom layer, at the same time that the silver bromide grains are reduced to metallic silver. The cyan dye is deposited only in the regions occupied by the sensitized silver bromide grains. The next process (Process 5) consists in exposure to blue light from the front of the negative. The blue light is absorbed by the yellow dye, and so affects only the previously unexposed grains in the first emulsion, the blue-sensitive emulsion. This emulsion is then developed in a special developer (Process 6), a yellow developer and coupler, which deposits a yellow dye in the neighborhood of these recently exposed grains. The film is then exposed to white light, to sensitize the undeveloped silver bromide grains in the middle emulsion, the yellow layer is bleached, the middle emulsion is developed with a magenta developer and coupler (Process 8), and the deposited metallic silver in all three solutions is removed by a bleaching solution (Process 9), leaving only a film containing deposited cyan, yellow, and magenta dyes in the three emulsion layers, in such a way that by transmitted light the originally incident colors are reproduced (Process 10).

The development of the Kodachrome method and other methods of color photography has been a triumph of organic chemistry. It was the organic chemists who solved the problem of the synthesis of stable dyes with the special properties required for this purpose. The photographic industry, like most industries of the modern world, is a chemical industry.

28–6. The Compounds of Gold

$KAu(CN)_2$, the potassium salt of the complex **gold(I) cyanide ion** $Au(CN)_2^-$, with electronic structure

$$[: N \equiv C - Au - C \equiv N :]^-$$

is an example of a gold(I) compound.* The **gold(I) chloride** complex

---
* The gold(I) and gold(III) compounds are often called *aurous* and *auric* compounds, respectively.

$AuCl_2^-$ has a similar structure, and the **halogenides,** AuCl, AuBr, and AuI, resemble the corresponding halogenides of silver.

Gold dissolves in a mixture of concentrated nitric and hydrochloric acids to form **hydrogen aurichloride,** $HAuCl_4$. This acid contains the aurichloride ion, $AuCl_4^-$, a square planar complex ion:

$$
\left[
\begin{array}{c}
: \overset{..}{Cl} : \\
| \\
: \overset{..}{Cl} \overset{..}{\underset{..}{—}} Au \overset{..}{\underset{..}{—}} \overset{..}{Cl} : \\
| \\
: \underset{..}{Cl} :
\end{array}
\right]
$$

Hydrogen aurichloride can be obtained as a yellow crystalline substance, which forms salts with bases. When heated it forms **gold(III) chloride,** $AuCl_3$, and then gold(I) gold(III) chloride, Au_2Cl_4, and then gold(I) chloride, AuCl. On further heating all the chlorine is lost, and pure gold remains.

28–7. *Color and Mixed Oxidation States*

The gold halogenides provide examples of an interesting phenomenon—the *deep, intense color often observed for a substance which contains an element in two different oxidation states.* Gold(I) gold(III) chloride, Au_2Cl_4, is intensely black, although both gold(I) chloride and gold(III) chloride are yellow. Cesium gold (I) gold (III) bromide, $Cs_2^+[AuBr_2]^-\,[AuBr_4]^-$, is deep black in color, and both $CsAuBr_2$ and $CsAuBr_4$ are much lighter. Black mica (biotite) and black tourmaline contain both ferrous and ferric iron. Prussian blue is ferrous ferricyanide; ferrous ferrocyanide is white, and ferric ferricyanide is light yellow. When copper is added to a light green solution of cupric chloride a deep brownish-black solution is formed, before complete conversion to the colorless cuprous chloride complex.

The theory of this phenomenon is not understood. The very strong absorption of light is presumably connected with the transfer of an electron from one atom to another of the element present in two valence states.

28–8. *The Properties and Uses of Zinc, Cadmium, and Mercury*

Zinc is a bluish-white, moderately hard metal. It is brittle at room temperature, but is malleable and ductile between 100° and 150° C, and becomes brittle again above 150°. It is an active metal, above hydrogen in the electromotive-force series, and it displaces hydrogen even from dilute acids. In moist air zinc is oxidized, and becomes coated with a tough film of basic zinc carbonate, $Zn_2CO_3(OH)_2$, which protects it from further corrosion. This behavior is responsible for its principal use, in protecting iron from rusting. Iron wire or sheet iron is *galvanized* by cleaning with sulfuric acid or a sandblast, and then dipping in molten zinc; a thin layer of zinc adheres to the iron. Galvanized iron in some shapes is made by electroplating zinc onto the iron pieces. *Sherardized iron* is iron which has been coated with a layer of iron-zinc alloy by treatment with zinc dust and baking at 800°.

Zinc is also used in making alloys, the most important of which is *brass* (the alloy with copper), and as a reacting electrode in dry cells and wet cells.

TABLE 28-3   *Some Physical Properties of Zinc, Cadmium and Mercury*

	ATOMIC NUMBER	ATOMIC WEIGHT	DENSITY	MELTING POINT	BOILING POINT	METALLIC RADIUS	COLOR
Zinc	30	65.38	7.14 g/cm³	419.4° C	907° C	1.38 Å	Bluish-white
Cadmium	48	112.41	8.64	320.9°	767°	1.54	Bluish-white
Mercury	80	200.61	13.55	−38.89°	356.9°	1.57	Silvery-white

Cadmium is a bluish-white metal of pleasing appearance. It has found increasing use as a protective coating for iron and steel. The cadmium plate is deposited electrolytically from a bath containing the cadmium cyanide complex ion, $Cd(CN)_4^{--}$. Cadmium is also used in some alloys, such as the low-melting alloys needed for automatic fire extinguishers. *Wood's metal*, which melts at 65.5° C, contains 50% Bi, 25% Pb, 12.5% Sn, and 12.5% Cd. Because of the toxicity of compounds of elements of this group, care must be taken not to use cadmium-plated vessels for cooking, and not to inhale fumes of zinc, cadmium, or mercury.

Mercury is the only metal which is liquid at room temperature (cesium melts at 28.5° C, and gallium at 29.8°). It is unreactive, being below hydrogen in the electromotive-force series. Because of its unreactivity, fluidity, high density, and high electric conductivity it finds extensive use in thermometers, barometers, and many special kinds of scientific apparatus.

The alloys of mercury are called *amalgams*. Amalgams of silver, gold, and tin are used in dentistry. Mercury does not wet iron, and it is usually shipped and stored in iron bottles, called flasks, which hold 76 lbs. of the metal.

28–9. *Compounds of Zinc and Cadmium*

The **zinc ion**, $Zn(H_2O)_4^{++}$, is a colorless ion formed by solution of zinc in acid. It is poisonous to man and to bacteria, and is used as a disinfectant. It forms tetraligated complexes readily, such as $Zn(NH_3)_4^{++}$, $Zn(CN)_4^{--}$, and $Zn(OH)_4^{--}$. The white precipitate of **zinc hydroxide,** $Zn(OH)_2$, which forms when ammonium hydroxide is added to a solution containing zinc ion, dissolves in excess ammonium hydroxide, forming the zinc ammonia complex. The zinc hydroxide complex,

$Zn(OH)_4^{--}$, which is called **zincate ion,** is similarly formed on solution of zinc hydroxide in an excess of strong base; zinc hydroxide is amphoteric.

Zinc sulfate, $ZnSO_4 \cdot 7H_2O$, is used as a disinfectant and in dyeing calico, and in making *lithopone*, which is a mixture of barium sulfate and zinc sulfide used as a white pigment in paints:

$$Ba^{++}S^{--} + Zn^{++}SO_4^{--} \longrightarrow BaSO_4 \downarrow + ZnS \downarrow$$

Zinc oxide, ZnO, is a white powder (yellow when hot) made by burning zinc vapor or by roasting zinc ores. It is used as a pigment (zinc white), as a filler in automobile tires, adhesive tape, and other articles, and as an antiseptic (zinc oxide ointment).

Zinc sulfide, ZnS, is the only white sulfide among the sulfides of the common metals. Its conditions of precipitation have been discussed in Chapter 21.

The compounds of cadmium are closely similar to those of zinc. **Cadmium ion,** Cd^{++}, is a colorless ion, which forms complexes ($Cd(NH_3)_4^{++}$, $Cd(CN)_4^{--}$) similar to those of zinc. The cadmium hydroxide ion, $Cd(OH)_4^{--}$, is not stable, and **cadmium hydroxide,** $Cd(OH)_2$, is formed as a white precipitate by addition even of concentrated sodium hydroxide to a solution containing cadmium ion. The precipitate is soluble in ammonium hydroxide or in a solution containing cyanide ion. **Cadmium oxide,** CdO, is a brown powder obtained by heating the hydroxide or burning the metal. **Cadmium sulfide,** CdS, is a bright yellow precipitate obtained by passing hydrogen sulfide through a solution containing cadmium ion; it is used as a pigment (*cadmium yellow*).

28–10. *Compounds of Mercury*

The mercuric compounds, in which mercury is bipositive, differ somewhat in their properties from the corresponding compounds of zinc and cadmium. The differences are due in part to the very strong tendency of the mercuric ion, Hg^{++}, to form covalent bonds. Thus the covalent crystal **mercuric sulfide,** HgS, is far less soluble than cadmium sulfide or zinc sulfide (Chapter 21).

Mercuric nitrate, $Hg(NO_3)_2$ or $Hg(NO_3)_2 \cdot \frac{1}{2}H_2O$, is made by dissolving mercury in hot concentrated nitric acid:

$$3Hg + 8HNO_3 \longrightarrow 3Hg(NO_3)_2 + 2NO \uparrow + 4H_2O$$

It hydrolyzes on dilution, unless a sufficient excess of acid is present, to form basic mercuric nitrates, such as $HgNO_3OH$, as a white precipitate.

Mercuric chloride, $HgCl_2$, is a white crystalline substance usually made by dissolving mercury in hot concentrated sulfuric acid, and then heating the dry mercuric sulfate with sodium chloride, subliming the volatile mercuric chloride:

$$Hg + 2H_2SO_4 \longrightarrow HgSO_4 + SO_2 \uparrow + H_2O$$

$$HgSO_4 + 2NaCl \longrightarrow Na_2SO_4 + HgCl_2 \uparrow$$

A dilute solution of mercuric chloride (about 0.1%) is used as a disinfectant. Any somewhat soluble mercuric salt would serve equally well, except for the tendency of mercuric ion to hydrolyze and to precipitate basic salts. Mercuric chloride has only a small tendency to hydrolyze because its solution contains only a small concentration of mercuric ion, the mercury being present mainly as unionized covalent molecules

$: \overset{..}{\underset{..}{Cl}}-Hg-\overset{..}{\underset{..}{Cl}}:$. The electronic structure of these molecules, which

have a linear configuration, is analogous to that of the gold(I) chloride complex, $AuCl_2^-$ (Figure 28-3). The ease of sublimation of mercuric chloride (melting point 275° C, boiling point 301°) results from the stability of these molecules.

Mercuric chloride, like other soluble salts of mercury, is very poisonous when taken internally. The mercuric ion combines strongly with proteins; in the human body it acts especially on the tissues of the kidney, destroying the ability of this organ to remove waste products from the blood. Egg white and milk are swallowed as antidotes; their proteins precipitate the mercury in the stomach.

With ammonium hydroxide mercuric chloride forms a white precipitate, $HgNH_2Cl$:

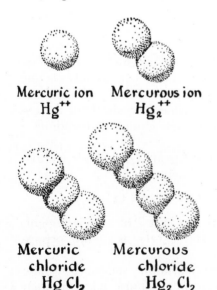

Mercuric ion
Hg^{++}

Mercurous ion
Hg_2^{++}

Mercuric chloride
$Hg\,Cl_2$

Mercurous chloride
$Hg_2\,Cl_2$

FIGURE 28-3

The structure of the mercuric ion, mercurous ion, mercuric chloride molecule, and mercurous chloride molecule. In the mercurous ion and the two molecules the atoms are held together by covalent bonds.

$$HgCl_2 + 2NH_3 \longrightarrow HgNH_2Cl \downarrow + NH_4^+ + Cl^-$$

Mercuric sulfide, HgS, is formed as a black precipitate when hydrogen sulfide is passed through a solution of a mercuric salt. It can also be made by rubbing mercury and sulfur together in a mortar. The black sulfide (which also occurs in nature as the mineral *metacinnabarite*) is converted by heat into the red form (cinnabar). Mercuric sulfide is the most insoluble of metallic sulfides. It is not dissolved even by boiling concentrated nitric acid, but it does dissolve in aqua regia, under the combined action of the nitric acid, which oxidizes the sulfide to free sulfur, and hydrochloric acid, which provides chloride ion to form the stable complex $HgCl_4^{--}$:

$$\underline{3HgS} + 12HCl + 2HNO_3 \longrightarrow 3HgCl_4^{--} + 6H^+ + \tfrac{3}{8}S_8 \downarrow$$
$$+ 2NO \uparrow + 4H_2O$$

Mercuric oxide, HgO, is formed as a yellow precipitate by adding a base to a solution of mercuric nitrate or as a red powder by heating dry mercuric nitrate or, slowly, by heating mercury in air. The yellow and red forms seem to differ only in grain size; it is a common phenomenon that red crystals (such as potassium dichromate or potassium ferricyanide) form a yellow powder when they are ground up. Mercuric oxide liberates oxygen when it is strongly heated.

Mercuric fulminate, $Hg(CNO)_2$, is made by dissolving mercury in nitric acid and adding ethyl alcohol, C_2H_5OH. It is a very unstable substance, which detonates when it is struck or heated, and it is used for making detonators and percussion caps.

Mercurous nitrate, $Hg_2(NO_3)_2$, is formed by reduction of a mercuric nitrate solution with mercury:

$$Hg^{++} + \underline{Hg} \longrightarrow Hg_2^{++}$$

The solution contains the **mercurous ion,** Hg_2^{++}, a colorless ion which has a unique structure; it consists of two mercuric ions plus two electrons, which form a covalent bond between them (Figure 28-3):

$$2Hg^{++} + 2e^- \longrightarrow [Hg:Hg]^{++} \quad \text{or} \quad [Hg-Hg]^{++}$$

Mercurous chloride, Hg_2Cl_2, is an insoluble white crystalline substance obtained by adding a solution containing chloride ion to a mercurous nitrate solution:

$$Hg_2^{++} + 2Cl^- \longrightarrow Hg_2Cl_2 \downarrow$$

It is used in medicine under the name *calomel*. The mercurous chloride molecule has the linear covalent structure $:\overset{..}{\underset{..}{Cl}}-Hg-Hg-\overset{..}{\underset{..}{Cl}}:$ (Figure 28-3).

The precipitation of mercurous chloride and its change in color from white to black on addition of ammonium hydroxide are used as the test for mercurous mercury in qualitative analysis. The effect of ammonium hydroxide is due to the formation of finely divided mercury (black) and mercuric aminochloride (white) by an auto-oxidation-reduction reaction:

$$Hg_2Cl_2 + 2NH_3 \longrightarrow Hg \downarrow + HgNH_2Cl \downarrow + NH_4^+ + Cl^-$$

Mercurous sulfide, Hg_2S, is unstable, and when formed as a brownish-black precipitate by action of sulfide ion on mercurous ion it immediately decomposes into mercury and mercuric sulfide:

$$Hg_2^{++} + S^{--} \longrightarrow Hg_2S \longrightarrow Hg + HgS$$

28–11. *Gallium, Indium, and Thallium*

The elements of group IIIb, gallium, indium, and thallium, are rare and have little practical importance. Their principal compounds represent oxidation state $+3$; thallium also forms compounds in which it has oxidation number $+1$. Gallium is liquid from $29°$ C, its melting point, to $1,700°$ C, its boiling point. It has found use as the liquid in quartz-tube thermometers, which can be used to above $1,200°$ C.

Concepts, Facts, and Terms Introduced in This Chapter

Copper, silver, and gold: their oxidation states, physical properties, and uses. Alloys: brass, bronze, aluminum bronze, sterling silver, coinage gold, white gold.

Cupric compounds: copper sulfate (blue vitriol, bluestone), cupric chloride, cupric bromide, cupric hydroxide. Test for cupric ion with Fehling's solution. Cuprous compounds: cuprous chloride, cuprous bromide, cuprous iodide, cuprous oxide. Covalent-bond structure of cuprous compounds.

Compounds of silver: silver oxide, silver chloride, silver bromide, silver iodide, silver ammonia complex, silver cyanide complex, silver thiosulfate complex, silver nitrate.

Photographic processes. Photographic emulsion, developer, negative, fixing baths, positive print.

Gold(I) chloride, gold(I) bromide, gold(I) iodide, potassium gold(I) cyanide, gold(III) chloride, hydrogen aurichloride.

Color and mixed oxidation states.

Elements of group IIb. Oxidation numbers: zinc, $+2$; cadmium, $+2$; mercury, $+1$ and $+2$. Physical properties of the metals. Uses of the metals. Galvanized iron. Sherardized iron, cadmium plate. Alloys: brass, Wood's metal, amalgams. Zinc ion, zinc hydroxide, zincate ion, zinc sulfate, lithopone, zinc oxide, zinc sulfide. Cadmium ion, cadmium hydroxide, cadmium oxide, cadmium sulfide (cadmium yellow). Mercuric ion, mercuric nitrate, mercuric chloride, mercuric iodide, mercuric sulfide, mercuric oxide, mercuric fulminate. Mercurous ion, mercurous nitrate, mercurous chloride (calomel). The electronic structure of the mercuric ion, mercurous ion, mercuric chloride, and mercurous chloride.

Exercises

28-1. What is the electronic structure of the Ag^+ ion? Of the Cu^{++} ion?

28-2. What are the constituents of brass? Of bronze?

28-3. In what form does copper exist in a cupric sulfate solution? In a strong hydrochloric acid solution? In an ammoniacal solution? Added as cupric sulfate to a solution of potassium iodide? In a solution of potassium cyanide?

28-4. Under what conditions can cuprous compounds or solutions be prepared?

28-5. Under what conditions can dilute sulfuric acid dissolve copper? Write an equation for the reaction.

28-6. Describe a simple test to show that silver iodide is less soluble than silver chloride.

28-7. What is the structure of the complexes of unipositive silver and gold?

28-8. How can you prepare a compound of terpositive gold?

28-9. What is the weight of gold in an 18-carat gold ring weighing 10 g?

28-10. What weight of copper would be deposited from a cupric sulfate solution by the passage of 3214 coulombs of electricity?

28-11. Write the equation for the formation of hydrogen aurichloride by solution of gold in a mixture of nitric and hydrochloric acids, assuming that nitric oxide, NO, is also produced.

28-12. What four products are successively formed as hydrogen aurichloride is heated?

28-13. If a solution containing cupric ion and a solution containing iodide ion are mixed, a precipitate of cuprous iodide is formed, and free iodine is liberated. Write the equation for this reaction, assuming that iodide ion is present in excess, leading to the formation of triiodide ion.

28-14. To what is the black color of biotite and black tourmaline attributed?

28-15. Compare the electronegative character of zinc, cadmium, mercury, and the alkaline-earth metals.

28-16. Suggest a possible procedure for separating an amalgam containing zinc and cadmium.

28-17. What would happen if mercury were shaken with a solution of mercuric chloride?

28-18. Compare the stabilities of zinc oxide and mercuric oxide.

28-19. A sample of mercuric oxide weighing 2.000 g is strongly heated in a test tube and the volume of oxygen evolved is measured. What would be the predicted volume of the evolved gas if the atmospheric pressure was 745 mm of mercury, the temperature was 23.5° C, and the gas was collected over water?

28-20. Describe the electronic structure of the mercurous ion, the mercuric ion, the mercurous chloride molecule, and the mercuric chloride molecule. Compare the total number of electrons surrounding each mercury atom with the number in the nearest noble gas.

28-21. Write the equation for the reaction of zinc with hydrochloric acid. Would you expect zinc to dissolve in a concentrated solution of sodium hydroxide? If so, write the equation for this reaction.

Chapter 29

Titanium, Vanadium, Chromium, and Manganese and Their Congeners

In the present chapter we shall conclude the discussion of the chemistry of the transition metals. This chapter deals with the chemistry of chromium and manganese and their congeners, of groups VIa and VIIa of the periodic table, and also the preceding elements titanium and vanadium and their congeners, of groups IVa and Va. These elements are not so well known nor so important as some other transition elements, especially iron and nickel, but their chemistry is interesting, and serves well to illustrate the general principles discussed in preceding chapters.

29–1. *Electronic Structures of Titanium, Vanadium, Chromium, and Manganese and Their Congeners*

The electronic structures of the elements of groups IIIa, IVa, Va, and VIa, as represented in the energy-level diagram (Figure 5-6), are given in Table 29-1. Each of the elements has two electrons in the s orbital of the outermost shell. In addition, there are two, three, four, or five electrons in the d orbital of the next inner shell. Reference to Figure 5-6 shows that the heaviest elements of these groups, thorium, protactinium,

TABLE 29-1 *Electronic Structures of Titanium, Vanadium, Chromium, and Manganese and their Congeners*

Z	ELEMENT	K	L		M			N				O			P
		1s	2s	2p	3s	3p	3d	4s	4p	4d	4f	5s	5p	5d	6s
22	Ti	2	2	6	2	6	2	2							
23	V	2	2	6	2	6	3	2							
24	Cr	2	2	6	2	6	4	2							
25	Mn	2	2	6	2	6	5	2							
40	Zr	2	2	6	2	6	10	2	6	2		2			
41	Nb	2	2	6	2	6	10	2	6	3		2			
42	Mo	2	2	6	2	6	10	2	6	4		2			
43	Tc	2	2	6	2	6	10	2	6	5		2			
72	Hf	2	2	6	2	6	10	2	6	10	14	2	6	2	2
73	Ta	2	2	6	2	6	10	2	6	10	14	2	6	3	2
74	W	2	2	6	2	6	10	2	6	10	14	2	6	4	2
75	Re	2	2	6	2	6	10	2	6	10	14	2	6	5	2

uranium, and neptunium, are thought to have the additional two to five electrons, respectively, in the $5f$ orbital, rather than the $6d$ orbital.

The oxidation state $+2$, corresponding to the loss of the two $4s$ electrons, is an important one for all of these elements. In particular, the elements in the first long period form the ions Ti^{++}, V^{++}, Cr^{++}, and Mn^{++}. Several other oxidation states, involving the loss or sharing of additional electrons, are also represented by compounds of these elements. The maximum oxidation state is that corresponding to the loss or sharing of all of the elements in the d orbital of the next inner shell, as well as of the two electrons in the outermost shell. Accordingly the maximum oxidation numbers of titanium, vanadium, chromium, and manganese are $+4$, $+5$, $+6$, and $+7$, respectively.

29–2. *Titanium, Zirconium, Hafnium, and Thorium*

The elements of group IVa of the periodic system are titanium, zirconium, hafnium, and thorium. Some of the properties of the elementary substances are given in Table 29-2.

Titanium occurs in the minerals *rutile*, TiO_2, and *ilmenite*, $FeTiO_3$. It forms compounds representing oxidation states $+2$, $+3$, and $+4$. Pure **titanium dioxide**, TiO_2, is a white substance. As a powder it has great power of scattering light, which makes it an important pigment. It is used in special paints and face powders. Crystals of titanium dioxide (rutile) colored with small amounts of other metal oxides have been made recently for use as gems. **Titanium tetrachloride**, $TiCl_4$, is a molecular liquid at room temperature. On being sprayed into air it hydrolyzes, forming hydrogen chloride and fine particles of titanium dioxide; for this reason it is sometimes used in making smoke screens:

TABLE 29-2   *Some Properties of Titanium, Vanadium, Chromium, and Manganese and Their Congeners*

	ATOMIC NUMBER	ATOMIC WEIGHT	DENSITY G/CM³	MELTING POINT	BOILING POINT	METALLIC RADIUS*
Titanium	22	47.90	4.44	1,800° C	3,000° C	1.47 Å
Vanadium	23	50.95	6.06	1,700°	3,000°	1.34
Chromium	24	52.01	7.22	1,920°	2,330°	1.27
Manganese	25	54.94	7.26	1,260°	2,150°	1.26
Zirconium	40	91.22	6.53	1,860°		1.60
Niobium	41	92.91	8.21	2,500°		1.46
Molybdenum	42	95.95	10.27	2,620°	4,700°	1.39
Hafnium	72	178.50	13.17	2,200°		1.36
Tantalum	73	180.95	16.76	2,850°		1.46
Tungsten	74	183.86	19.36	3,382°	6,000°	1.39
Rhenium	75	186.22	21.10	3,167°		1.37
Thorium	90	232.05	11.75	1,850°	3,500°	1.80
Uranium	92	238.07	18.97	1,690°		1.52

* For ligancy 12.

$$TiCl_4 + 2H_2O \longrightarrow TiO_2 \downarrow + 4HCl$$

Titanium metal is very strong, light (density 4.44 g/cm³), refractory (melting point 1,800° C), and resistant to corrosion. Since 1950 it has been produced in quantity, and has found many uses for which a light, strong metal with high melting point is needed; for example, it is used in airplane wings where the metal is in contact with exhaust flame.

Zirconium occurs in nature principally as the mineral *zircon*, $ZrSiO_4$. Zircon crystals are found in a variety of colors—white, blue, green and red—and because of its beauty and hardness (7.5) the mineral is used as a semi-precious stone. The principal oxidation state of zirconium is +4; the states +2 and +3 are represented by only a few compounds.

Hafnium is closely similar to zirconium, and natural zirconium minerals usually contain a few percent of hafnium. The element was not discovered until 1923, and it has found little use.

Thorium is found in nature as the mineral *thorite*, ThO_2, and in *monazite sand*, which consists of thorium phosphate mixed with the phosphates of the lanthanons (Section 26–6). The principal use of thorium is in the manufacture of gas mantles, which are made by saturating cloth fabric with thorium nitrate, $Th(NO_3)_4$, and cerium nitrate, $Ce(NO_3)_4$. When the treated cloth is burned there remains a residue of thorium dioxide and cerium dioxide, ThO_2 and CeO_2, which has the property of exhibiting a brilliant white luminescence when it is heated to a high temperature. Thorium dioxide is also used in the manufacture of laboratory crucibles, for use at temperatures as high as 2300° C. Thorium can be made to undergo nuclear fission, and it may become an important nuclear fuel (Chapter 32).

29–3. *Vanadium, Niobium, Tantalum, and Protactinium*

Vanadium is the most important element of group Va. It finds extensive use in the manufacture of special steels. Vanadium steel is tough and
strong, and is used in automobile crank shafts and for similar purposes.
The principal ores of vanadium are *vanadinite*, $Pb_5(VO_4)_3Cl$, and *carno-
lite*, $K(UO_2)VO_4 \cdot \frac{3}{2}H_2O$. The latter mineral is also important as an
ore of uranium.

The chemistry of vanadium is very complex. The element forms
compounds representing the oxidation states $+2$, $+3$, $+4$, and $+5$.
The hydroxides of bipositive and terpositive vanadium are basic, and
those of the higher oxidation states are amphoteric. The compounds of
vanadium are striking for their varied colors. The bipositive ion, V^{++},
has a deep violet color; the terpositive compounds, such as **potassium
vanadium alum**, $KV(SO_4)_2 \cdot 12H_2O$, are green; the dark-green substance **vanadium dioxide**, VO_2, dissolves in acid to form the blue
vanadyl ion, VO^{++}. **Vanadium(V) oxide**, V_2O_5, an orange substance,
is used as a catalyst in the contact process for making sulfuric acid.
Ammonium metavanadate, NH_4VO_3, which forms yellow crystals from
solution, is used for making preparations of vanadium(V) oxide for the
contact process.

Niobium (columbium) and **tantalum** usually occur together, as the
minerals *columbite*, $FeCb_2O_6$, and *tantalite*, $FeTa_2O_6$. Niobium finds some
use as a constituent of alloy steels. **Tantalum carbide**, TaC, a very
hard substance, is used in making high-speed cutting tools.

Protactinium is a radioactive element (Chapter 32) which occurs in
minute amounts in all uranium ores.

29–4. *Chromium*

The Oxidation States of Chromium. The principal oxidation states
of chromium are represented in the diagram on the following page.

The maximum oxidation number, $+6$, corresponds to the position
of the element in the periodic table.

Ores of Chromium. The most important ore of chromium is *chromite*,
$FeCr_2O_4$. The element was not known to the ancients, but was discovered in 1798 in lead chromate, $PbCrO_4$, which occurs in nature as
the mineral *crocoite*.

Metallic Chromium. The metal can be prepared by reducing chromic
oxide with metallic aluminum (Chapter 25). Metallic chromium is also
made by electrolytic reduction of compounds, usually chromic acid in
aqueous solution.

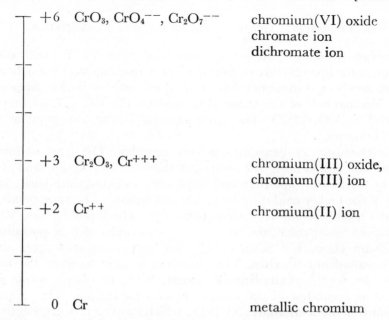

+6 CrO_3, CrO_4^{--}, $Cr_2O_7^{--}$ chromium(VI) oxide
chromate ion
dichromate ion

+3 Cr_2O_3, Cr^{+++} chromium(III) oxide,
chromium(III) ion

+2 Cr^{++} chromium(II) ion

0   Cr   metallic chromium

Chromium is a silvery white metal, with a bluish tinge. It is a very strong metal, with a high melting point, 1830° C. Because of its high melting point it resists erosion by the hot powder gases in big guns, the linings of which are accordingly sometimes plated with chromium.

Although the metal is more electropositive than iron, it easily assumes a passive (unreactive) state, by becoming coated with a thin layer of oxide, which protects it against further chemical attack. This property and its pleasing color are the reasons for its use for plating iron and brass objects, such as plumbing fixtures.

Ferrochrome, a high-chromium alloy with iron, is made by reducing chromite with carbon in the electric furnace. It is used for making alloy steels. The alloys of chromium are very important, especially the *alloy steels*. The chromium steels are very hard, tough, and strong. Their properties can be attributed to the high metallic valence (6) of chromium and to an interaction between unlike atoms that in general makes alloys harder and tougher than elementary metals. They are used for armor plate, projectiles, safes, etc. Ordinary *stainless steel* contains 14 to 18% chromium, and usually 8% nickel.

The Chromates and Dichromates. Chromium in its highest oxidation state (+6) does not form a hydroxide. The corresponding oxide, CrO_3, a red substance called **chromium(VI) oxide,** has acid properties. It dissolves in water to form a red solution of **dichromic acid,** $H_2Cr_2O_7$:

$$2CrO_3 + H_2O \longrightarrow H_2Cr_2O_7 \rightleftarrows 2H^+ + Cr_2O_7^{--}$$

The salts of dichromic acid are called **dichromates;** they contain the dichromate ion, $Cr_2O_7^{--}$. Sexivalent chromium also forms another important series of salts, the **chromates,** which contain the ion CrO_4^{--}.

The chromates and dichromates are made by a method which has general usefulness for preparing salts of an acidic oxide—the method of *fusion with an alkali hydroxide or carbonate*. The carbonate functions as a basic oxide by losing carbon dioxide when heated strongly. Potassium carbonate is preferred to sodium carbonate because potassium chromate and potassium dichromate crystallize well from aqueous solution, and can be easily purified by recrystallization, whereas the corresponding sodium salts are deliquescent and are difficult to purify.

A mixture of powdered chromite ore and potassium carbonate slowly forms **potassium chromate,** K_2CrO_4, when strongly heated in air. The oxygen of the air oxidizes chromium to the sexipositive state, and also oxidizes the iron to ferric oxide:

$$4FeCr_2O_4 + 8K_2CO_3 + 7O_2 \longrightarrow 2Fe_2O_3 + 8K_2CrO_4 + 8CO_2 \uparrow$$

Sometimes the oxidation reaction is aided by the addition of an oxidizing agent, such as potassium nitrate, KNO_3, or potassium chlorate, $KClO_3$. The potassium chromate, a yellow substance, can be dissolved in water and recrystallized.

On addition of an acid, such as sulfuric acid, to a solution containing chromate ion, CrO_4^{--}, the solution changes from yellow to orange-red in color, because of the formation of dichromate ion, $Cr_2O_7^{--}$:

$$\underset{\text{yellow}}{2CrO_4^{--}} + 2H^+ \rightleftharpoons \underset{\text{orange-red}}{Cr_2O_7^{--}} + H_2O$$

The reaction can be reversed by the addition of a base:

$$\underset{\text{orange-red}}{Cr_2O_7^{--}} + 2OH^- \rightleftharpoons \underset{\text{yellow}}{2CrO_4^{--}} + H_2O$$

At an intermediate stage* both chromate ion and dichromate ion are present in the solution, in chemical equilibrium.

The chromate ion has a tetrahedral structure. The formation of dichromate ion involves the removal of one oxygen ion O^{--} (as water), by combination with two hydrogen ions, and its replacement by an oxygen atom of another chromate ion (see Figure 29-1).

Both chromates and dichromates are strong oxidizing agents, the chromium being easily reduced from $+6$ to $+3$ in acid solution. **Potassium dichromate,** $K_2Cr_2O_7$, is a beautifully crystallizable bright-red substance used considerably in chemistry and industry. A solution of this substance or of chromium(VI) oxide, CrO_3, in concentrated sulfuric acid is a very strong oxidizing agent which serves as a cleaning solution for laboratory glassware.

---

* There is also present in the solution some hydrogen chromate ion, $HCrO_4^-$:

$$H^+ + CrO_4^{--} \rightleftharpoons HCrO_4^-$$

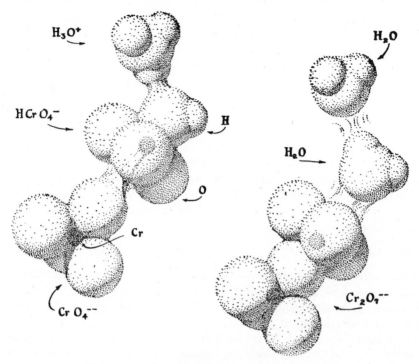

FIGURE 29-1   *The reaction of a hydrogen chromate ion, a chromate ion, and a hydronium ion to form a dichromate ion and water.*

Large amounts of **sodium dichromate**, $Na_2Cr_2O_7 \cdot 2H_2O$, are used in the tanning of hides, to produce "chrome-tanned" leather. The chromium forms an insoluble compound with the leather protein.

Lead chromate, $PbCrO_4$, is a bright yellow, practically insoluble substance which is used as a pigment (*chrome yellow*).

Compounds of Terpositive Chromium. When ammonium dichromate, $(NH_4)_2Cr_2O_7$, a red salt resembling potassium dichromate, is ignited, it decomposes to form a green powder, **chromium(III) oxide**, Cr_2O_3:

$$(NH_4)_2Cr_2O_7 \longrightarrow N_2 \uparrow + 4H_2O \uparrow + Cr_2O_3$$

This reaction involves the reduction of the dichromate ion by ammonium ion. Chromium(III) oxide is also made by heating sodium dichromate with sulfur, and leaching out the sodium sulfate with water:

$$Na_2Cr_2O_7 + S \longrightarrow Na_2SO_4 + Cr_2O_3$$

It is a very stable substance, which is resistant to acids and has a very high melting point. It is used as a pigment (*chrome green*, used in the green ink for paper money).

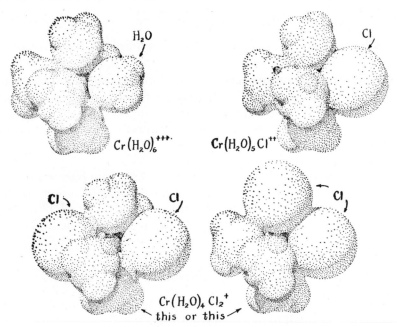

FIGURE 29-2 *Octahedral chromic complex ions.*

Reduction of a dichromate in aqueous solution produces **chromium(III) ion,** Cr^{+++} (really the hexahydrated ion, $[Cr(H_2O)_6]^{+++}$), which has a violet color. The salts of this ion are similar in formula to those of aluminum. *Chrome alum,* $KCr(SO_4)_2 \cdot 12H_2O$, forms large violet octahedra.

Chromium(III) chloride, $CrCl_3 \cdot 6H_2O$, forms several kinds of crystals, varying in color from violet to green, the solutions of which have similar colors. These different colors are due to the formation of stable complex ions (Figure 29-2):

$[Cr(H_2O)_6]^{+++}$	violet
$[Cr(H_2O)_5Cl]^{++}$	green
$[Cr(H_2O)_4Cl_2]^{+}$	green

In each of these complex ions there are six groups (water molecules and chloride ions) attached to the chromium ion. Chromium ion can be oxidized to chromate ion or dichromate ion by strong oxidizing agents, such as sodium peroxide in alkaline solution.

Chromium(III) hydroxide, $Cr(OH)_3$, is obtained as a pale grayish-green flocculent precipitate when ammonium hydroxide or sodium hydroxide is added to a chromium(III) solution. The precipitate dissolves in an excess of sodium hydroxide, forming the *chromite anion,* $Cr(OH)_4^-$:

$$Cr(OH)_3 + OH^- \longrightarrow Cr(OH)_4^-$$

Chromium(III) hydroxite is hence an amphoteric hydroxide.

Chromium(II) Compounds. Chromium(III) solutions are reduced by zinc in acid solution or by other strong reducing agents to *chromium(II) ion*, Cr^{++} or $[Cr(H_2O)_6]^{++}$, which is blue in color. This solution and solid chromium(II) salts are very strong reducing agents, and must be protected from the air.

Peroxychromic Acid. A useful test for chromium is to add some hydrogen peroxide to a sulfuric acid solution thought to contain dichromate ion, and then to shake the solution with some ether. A blue coloration of the ether shows the presence of a peroxychromic acid. The formula of this acid is still uncertain.

29–5. *The Congeners of Chromium*

The three heavier elements in group VIa, molybdenum, tungsten, and uranium, have all found important special uses.

Molybdenum. The principal ore of molybdenum is *molybdenite*, MoS_2, which occurs especially in a great deposit near Climax, Colorado. This mineral forms shiny black plates, closely similar in appearance to graphite.

Molybdenum metal is used to make filament supports in radio tubes and for other special uses. It is an important constituent of alloy steels.

The chemistry of molybdenum is complicated. It forms compounds corresponding to oxidation numbers +6, +5, +4, +3, and +2.

Molybdenum(VI) oxide, MoO_3, is a yellow-white substance made by roasting molybdenite. It dissolves in alkalis to produce molybdates, such as **ammonium molybdate,** $(NH_4)_6Mo_7O_{24} \cdot 4H_2O$. This reagent is used to precipitate orthophosphates, as the substance $(NH_4)_3PMo_{12}O_{40} \cdot 18H_2O$.

Tungsten. Tungsten (also called *wolfram*) is a strong, heavy metal, with very high melting point ($3,370°$ C). It has important uses, as filaments in electric light bulbs, for electric contact points in spark plugs, as electron targets in x-ray tubes, and, in tungsten steel (which retains its hardness even when very hot), as cutting tools for high-speed machining.

The principal ores of tungsten are *scheelite*, $CaWO_4$, and *wolframite*, $(Fe,Mn)WO_4$.[*]

Tungsten forms compounds in which it has oxidation number +6

---

[*] The formula $(Fe,Mn)WO_4$ means a solid solution of $FeWO_4$ and $MnWO_4$, in indefinite ratio.

(tungstates, including the minerals mentioned above), +5, +4, +3, and +2. **Tungsten carbide,** WC, is a very hard compound which is used for the cutting edge of high-speed tools.

Uranium. Uranium is the rarest metal of the chromium group. Its principal ores are *pitchblende*, U_3O_8, and *carnotite*, $K_2U_2V_2O_{12} \cdot 3H_2O$. Its most important oxidation state is +6 (**sodium diuranate,** $Na_2U_2O(OH)_{12}$; **uranyl nitrate,** $UO_2(NO_3)_2 \cdot 6H_2O$; etc.).

Before 1942 uranium was said to have no important uses—it was used mainly to give a greenish-yellow color to glass and glazes. In 1942, however, exactly one hundred years after the metal was first isolated, uranium became one of the most important of all elements. It was discovered in that year that uranium could be made a source of nuclear energy, liberated in tremendous quantity at the will of man.

Nuclear Fission. Ordinary uranium contains two isotopes,[*] U^{238} (99.3%) and U^{235} (0.7%). When a neutron collides with a U^{235} nucleus it combines with it, forming a U^{236} nucleus. This nucleus is unstable, and it immediately decomposes spontaneously by splitting into two large fragments, plus several neutrons. *Each of the two fragments is itself an atomic nucleus,* the sum of their atomic numbers being 92, the atomic number of uranium.

This nuclear fission is accompanied by the emission of a very large amount of energy—about 5×10^{12} calories[†] per gram-atom of uranium decomposed (235 g of uranium). This is about 2,500,000 times the amount of heat evolved by burning the same weight of coal, and about 12,000,000 times that evolved by exploding the same weight of nitroglycerine. The large numbers indicate the very great importance of uranium as a source of energy; one ton of uranium (pre-war price about $5000) could produce the same amount of energy as 2,500,000 tons of coal; and the use of uranium and other fissionable elements in place of coal may ultimately eliminate the disagreeable, but at present necessary, coal-mining industry.

The heavier uranium isotope, U^{238}, also can be made to undergo fission, but by an indirect route—through the trans-uranium elements. These elements are discussed in Chapter 32.

29–6. *Manganese*

The Oxidation States of Manganese. The principal oxidation states of manganese are represented in the following diagram:

---

[*] A minute amount, 0.006%, of a third isotope, U^{234}, is also present.

[†] This amount of energy weighs about 0.25 g, by the Einstein equation $E = mc^2$ (E = energy, m = mass, c = velocity of light). The material products of the fission are 0.25 g lighter than the gram-atom of U^{235}.

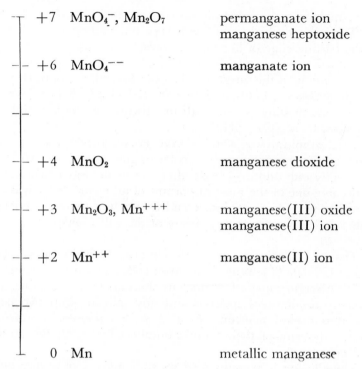

+7	MnO_4^-, Mn_2O_7	permanganate ion
		manganese heptoxide
+6	MnO_4^{--}	manganate ion
+4	MnO_2	manganese dioxide
+3	Mn_2O_3, Mn^{+++}	manganese(III) oxide
		manganese(III) ion
+2	Mn^{++}	manganese(II) ion
0	Mn	metallic manganese

The maximum oxidation number, $+7$, corresponds to the position of the element in the periodic table (group VIIa).

Ores of Manganese. The principal ore of manganese is *pyrolusite*, MnO_2. Pyrolusite occurs as a black massive mineral and also as a very fine black powder. Less important ores are *braunite*, Mn_2O_3 (containing some silicate); *manganite*, $MnO(OH)$; and *rhodochrosite*, $MnCO_3$.

Metallic Manganese. Impure manganese can be made by reducing manganese dioxide with carbon:

$$MnO_2 + 2C \longrightarrow Mn + 2CO \uparrow$$

Manganese is also made by the aluminothermic process:

$$3MnO_2 + 4Al \longrightarrow 2Al_2O_3 + 3Mn$$

Manganese alloy steels are usually made from special high-manganese alloys prepared by reducing mixed oxides of iron and manganese with coke in a blast furnace (see Chapter 27). The high-manganese alloys (70 to 80% Mn, 20 to 30% Fe) are called *ferromanganese*, and the low-manganese alloys (10 to 30% Mn) are called *spiegeleisen*.

Manganese is a silvery-gray metal, with a pinkish tinge. It is reactive, and displaces hydrogen even from cold water. Its principal use is in the manufacture of alloy steel.

Manganese Dioxide.   Manganese dioxide (pyrolusite) is the only important compound of quadripositive manganese. This substance has many uses, most of which depend upon its action as an oxidizing agent (with change from Mn^{+4} to Mn^{+2}) or as a reducing agent (with change from Mn^{+4} to Mn^{+6} or Mn^{+7}).

Manganese dioxide oxidizes hydrochloric acid to free chlorine, and is used for this purpose:

$$MnO_2 + 2Cl^- + 4H^+ \longrightarrow Cl_2 \uparrow + Mn^{++} + 2H_2O$$

Its oxidizing power also underlies its use in the ordinary dry cell (Chapter 10).

The Manganates and Permanganates.   When manganese dioxide is heated with potassium hydroxide in the presence of air it is oxidized to **potassium manganate,** K_2MnO_4:

$$2MnO_2 + 4KOH + O_2 \longrightarrow 2K_2MnO_4 + 2H_2O$$

Potassium manganate is a green salt, which can be dissolved in a small amount of water to give a green solution, containing potassium ion and the *manganate ion*, MnO_4^{--}. The manganates are the only compounds of Mn^{+6}. They are powerful oxidizing agents, and are used to a small extent as disinfectants.

The manganate ion can be oxidized to *permanganate ion*, MnO_4^-, which contains Mn^{+7}. The electron reaction for this process is

$$MnO_4^{--} \longrightarrow MnO_4^- + e^-$$

In practice this oxidation is carried out electrolytically (by anodic oxidation) or by use of chlorine:

$$2MnO_4^{--} + Cl_2 \longrightarrow 2MnO_4^- + 2Cl^-$$

The process of auto-oxidation-reduction is also used; manganate ion is stable in alkaline solution, but not in neutral or acidic solution. The addition of any acid, even carbon dioxide (carbonic acid), to a manganate solution causes the production of permanganate ion and the precipitation of manganese dioxide:

$$\underset{\text{green}}{3MnO_4^{--}} + 4H^+ \longrightarrow \underset{\text{magenta}}{2MnO_4^-} + MnO_2 \downarrow + 2H_2O$$

When hydroxide is added to the mixture of the purple solution and the brown or black precipitate a clear green solution is again formed, showing that the reaction is reversible.

This reaction serves as another example of Le Chatelier's principle: the addition of hydrogen ion, which occurs on the left side of the equation, causes the reaction to shift to the right.

Potassium permanganate, $KMnO_4$, is the most important chemical compound of manganese. It forms deep purple-red prisms, which dissolve readily in water to give a solution intensely colored with the magenta color characteristic of permanganate ion. The substance is a powerful oxidizing agent, which is used as a disinfectant. It is an important chemical reagent, especially in analytical chemistry.

On reduction in acidic solution the permanganate ion accepts five electrons, to form the manganese(II) ion:

$$MnO_4^- + 8H^+ + 5e^- \longrightarrow Mn^{++} + 4H_2O$$

In neutral or basic solution it accepts three electrons, to form a precipitate of manganese dioxide:

$$MnO_4^- + 2H_2O + 3e^- \longrightarrow MnO_2 \downarrow + 4OH^-$$

A one-electron reduction to manganate ion can be made to take place in strongly basic solution:

$$MnO_4^- + e^- \longrightarrow MnO_4^{--}$$

Permanganic acid, $HMnO_4$, is a strong acid which is very unstable. Its anhydride, **manganese(VII) oxide,** can be made by the reaction of potassium permanganate and concentrated sulfuric acid:

$$2KMnO_4 + H_2SO_4 \longrightarrow K_2SO_4 + Mn_2O_7 + H_2O$$

It is an unstable, dark-brown oily liquid.

Terpositive Manganese. The manganese(III) ion, Mn^{+++}, is a strong oxidizing agent, and its salts are unimportant. The insoluble oxide, Mn_2O_3, and its hydrate, $MnO(OH)$, are stable. When manganese(II) ion is precipitated as hydroxide, $Mn(OH)_2$, in the presence of air, the white precipitate is rapidly oxidized to the brown compound $MnO(OH)$:

$$Mn^{++} + 2OH^- \longrightarrow \underset{\text{white}}{Mn(OH)_2} \downarrow$$

$$4Mn(OH)_2 + O_2 \longrightarrow 4\underset{\text{brown}}{MnO(OH)} + 2H_2O$$

Manganese(II) Ion and Its Salts. *Manganese(II) ion,* Mn^{++} or $[Mn(H_2O)_6]^{++}$, is the stable cationic form of manganese. The hydrated ion is pale rose-pink in color. Representative salts are $Mn(NO_3)_2 \cdot 6H_2O$, $MnSO_4 \cdot 7H_2O$, and $MnCl_2 \cdot 4H_2O$. These salts and the mineral *rhodochrosite*, $MnCO_3$, are all rose-pink or rose-red. Crystals of rhodochrosite are isomorphous with calcite.

With hydrogen sulfide manganese(II) ion forms a flesh-colored precipitate of **manganese sulfide,** MnS:

$$Mn^{++} + H_2S \longrightarrow MnS \downarrow + 2H^+$$

29–7. *Acid-Forming and Base-Forming Oxides and Hydroxides*

Chromium and manganese illustrate the general rules about the acidic and basic properties of metallic oxides and hydroxides:

1. *The oxides of an element in its higher oxidation states tend to form acids.*
2. *The lower oxides of an element tend to form bases.*
3. *The intermediate oxides may be amphoteric; that is, they may serve either as acid-forming or as base-forming oxides.*

The highest oxide of chromium, chromium(VI) oxide, is acidic, and forms chromates and dichromates. The lowest oxide, CrO, is basic, forming the chromium(II) ion Cr^{++} and its salts. Chromium(III) hydroxide, $Cr(OH)_3$, representing the intermediate oxidation state, is amphoteric. With acids it forms the salts of chromium(III) ion, such as chromium(III) sulfate, $Cr_2(SO_4)_3$, and with strong base it dissolves to form the chromite ion, $Cr(OH)_4^-$.

Similarly the two highest oxidation states of manganese, $+7$ and $+6$, are represented by the anions MnO_4^-, and MnO_4^{--}, and the two lowest states are represented by the cations Mn^{++} and Mn^{+++}. The intermediate state $+4$ is unstable (except for the compound MnO_2), and is feebly amphoteric.

You may want to check the rules given above by considering the properties of oxides of other elements.

29–8. *The Congeners of Manganese*

Technetium.   No stable isotopes of element 43 exist. Minute amounts of radioactive isotopes have been made, by Segré and his collaborators, who have named the element technetium, symbol Tc.

Rhenium.   The element rhenium, atomic number 75, was discovered by the German chemists Walter Noddack and Ida Tacke in 1925. The principal compound of rhenium is potassium perrhenate, $KReO_4$, a colorless substance. In other compounds all oxidation numbers from $+7$ to -1 are represented: examples are Re_2O_7, ReO_3, $ReCl_5$, ReO_2, Re_2O_3, $Re(OH)_2$.

Neptunium.   Neptunium, element 93, was first made in 1940, by E. M. McMillan and P. H. Abelson, at the University of California, by the reaction of a neutron with U^{238}, to form U^{239}, and the subsequent emission of an electron from this nucleus, increasing the atomic number by 1:

$$_{92}U^{238} + {_0}n^1 \longrightarrow {_{92}}U^{239}$$

$$_{92}U^{239} \longrightarrow e^- + {_{93}}Np^{239}$$

Neptunium is important as an intermediate in the manufacture of plutonium (Chapter 32).

Concepts, Facts, and Terms Introduced in This Chapter

The electronic structures of titanium, vanadium, chromium, and manganese and their congeners.

Titanium metal, rutile, ilmenite, titanium dioxide, titanium tetrachloride. Zirconium, zircon. Hafnium. Thorium, thorite, monazite sand, thorium dioxide.

Vanadium, vanadium steel, vanadinite, carnotite. V^{++}, $KV(SO_4)_2 \cdot 12H_2O$, VO_2, VO^{++}, V_2O_5 (catalyst for contact process of making sulfuric acid), NH_4VO_3. Niobium, tantalum, columbite, tantalite, tantalum carbide.

Oxidation states of chromium: $+2$, $+3$, and $+6$. Ores of chromium: chromite, $FeCr_2O_4$, and crocoite, $PbCrO_4$. Chromium metal and its alloys: ferrochrome, alloy steels, stainless steel. Chromium(VI) oxide, chromic acid, dichromic acid, potassium chromate, potassium dichromate, sodium chromate, lead chromate. Equilibrium between chromate ion and dichromate ion. Chrome-tanned leather. Chromium(III) oxide (chrome green); chromium(III) ion, chrome alum, chromium(III) chloride, chromium(III) hydroxide, chromite ion. Chromium(II) compounds. Peroxychromic acid.

Molybdenum and its uses. Molybdenite, molybdenum trioxide, ammonium molybdate. Tungsten and its uses. Scheelite, $CaWO_4$, and wolframite, $(Fe, Mn)WO_4$. Tungsten carbide. Uranium and its ores: pitchblende, carnotite. Sodium diuranate, uranyl nitrate. Nuclear fission.

Oxidation states of manganese: $+2$, $+3$, $+4$, $+6$, and $+7$. Ores of manganese: pyrolusite, braunite, manganite, rhodochrosite. Manganese and its alloys: alloy steels, ferromanganese, spiegeleisen. Manganese dioxide, potassium manganate, manganate ion, potassium permanganate, permanganate ion, manganese(VII) oxide, manganese(II) ion and its salts.

Acid-forming and base-forming oxides and hydroxides, in relation to position in the periodic table. Amphoteric hydroxides.

Congeners of manganese: technetium, rhenium, and neptunium.

Exercises

29-1. Discuss the oxidation states of titanium, vanadium, chromium, and manganese in relation to their electronic structures. What electrons are removed in forming the bipositive ions. What electrons determine the highest oxidation states?

29-2. Explain why $TiCl_4$ is more effective in making smoke screens over the ocean than over dry land.

29-3. Make a diagram listing compounds representative of the various important oxidation levels of chromium and manganese.

29-4. What reduction product is formed when dichromate ion is reduced in acidic solution? When permanganate ion is reduced in acidic solution? When permanganate ion is reduced in basic solution? Write the electron reactions for these three cases.

29-5. Write equations for the reduction of dichromate ion by (a) sulfur dioxide; (b) ethyl alcohol, C_2H_5OH, which is oxidized to acetaldehyde, H_3CCHO; (c) iodide ion, which is oxidized to iodine.

29-6. Write an equation for the chemical reaction which occurs on fusion of a mixture of chromite ($FeCr_2O_4$), potassium carbonate, and potassium chlorate (which forms potassium chloride).

29-7. Write the chemical equations for the preparation of potassium manganate and potassium permanganate from manganese dioxide, using potassium hydroxide, air, and carbon dioxide.

29-8. What property of tungsten makes it suitable for use as the filament material in electric light bulbs?

29-9. Barium chromate, $BaCrO_4$, is only extremely slightly soluble and barium dichromate, $BaCr_2O_7$, is soluble in water. What effect will the addition of Ba^{++} ion have on the equilibrium

$$2H^+ + 2CrO_4^{--} \rightleftharpoons Cr_2O_7^{--} + H_2O$$

in a solution containing both CrO_4^{--} and $Cr_2O_7^{--}$?

29-10. The two most important oxidation levels of uranium are $+4$ and $+6$. Which of these levels would you expect to have the more acidic properties?

29-11. Write the equation for the reduction of chromium(III) ion by zinc in acidic solution.

29-12. Give the name and formula of one ore of each of the following metals: chromium, manganese, molybdenum, tungsten, uranium.

29-13. The only compounds of iron in which it has oxidation number $+6$ are the ferrates, such as potassium ferrate, K_2FeO_4. Does the formation of this compound and of the ferrous and ferric salts correspond or not correspond to the general rules of acidic and basic character of oxides?

29-14. Can you explain why the vanadium oxide VO dissolves readily in acids but not in alkalis, whereas V_2O_5 dissolves in alkalis?

References

J. C. Hackney, "Technetium—Element 43," *J. Chem. Ed.*, **28**, 186 (1951).

PART SIX

Organic Chemistry, Biochemistry, and Nuclear Chemistry

The concluding section of our book contains chapters on two essentially unrelated branches of chemistry.

Chapter 30 is entitled Organic Chemistry and Chapter 31 is entitled Biochemistry. Organic chemistry is defined as the chemistry of compounds of carbon, usually excluding the metal carbides, carbonates, and a few other compounds. A discussion of some of the compounds of carbon was given in Chapter 7. In addition, many organic compounds have been taken up in connection with the theoretical discussions in the book, as, for example, in Chapter 11, dealing with covalence and electronic structure. The discussion of compounds of carbon is now continued in Chapters 30 and 31, with special attention to compounds that occur in living organisms or are important in twentieth-century civilization.

The science of organic chemistry is a very extensive one, and the selection of a small number of facts to be presented in these two chapters has necessarily been arbitrary. You can, of course, learn additional facts about organic chemistry later on in life, especially if you have mastered some basic principles. Perhaps the most important one is that the molecules of organic compounds in general involve a chain or framework of carbon atoms (together with other atoms, especially hydrogen, nitrogen, and oxygen), and that organic chemists, as well as plants and animals, are able to convert molecules of one organic substance into molecules of a closely related one, by the use of certain reagents.

Some details about the chemical substances that make up the human body and other living organisms are given in Chapter 31. This chapter also contains a discussion of chemical reactions that take place in living organisms, the food requirements of man, and the structure and action of drugs.

Our book ends with a chapter on the structure and reactions of the nuclei of atoms. The subject of nuclear chemistry has developed greatly during the last twenty-five years. This development has led to the manufacture of new elements, some of which are valuable in medicine and in technology as well as in science. The possibilities of the use of nuclear reactions as a source of energy are so great that it is difficult to overestimate the importance of nuclear science.

Chapter 30

Organic Chemistry

30–1. *The Nature and Extent of Organic Chemistry*

Organic chemistry is the chemistry of the compounds of carbon. It is a very great subject—nearly half a million different organic compounds have already been reported and described in the chemical literature. Many of these substances have been isolated from living matter, and many more have been synthesized (manufactured) by chemists in the laboratory.

The occurrence in nature, methods of preparation, composition, structure, properties, and uses of some organic compounds (hydrocarbons, alcohols, chlorine derivatives of hydrocarbons, and organic acids) were discussed in Chapter 7. This discussion is continued in the following sections, with emphasis on natural products, especially the valuable substances obtained from plants, and on synthetic substances useful to man. Several large parts of organic chemistry will not be discussed at all; these include the methods of isolation and purification of naturally occurring compounds, the methods of analysis and determination of structure, and the methods of synthesis used in organic chemistry, except to the extent that they have been described in Chapter 7.

There are two principal ways in which organic chemists work. One of these ways is to begin the investigation of some natural material, such as a plant, which is known to have special properties. This plant might, for example, have been found by the natives of a tropical region to be beneficial in the treatment of malaria. The chemist then proceeds to make an extract from the plant, with use of a solvent such as alcohol or ether, and, by various methods of separation, to divide the extract into fractions. After each fractionation a study is made to see which fraction still contains the active substance. Finally this process may be carried so far that a pure crystalline active substance is obtained. The chemist then analyzes the substance, and determines its molecular weight, in order to find out what atoms are contained in the molecule of the substance. He next investigates the chemical properties of the substance, splitting its molecules into smaller molecules of known substances, in order to determine its molecular structure. When the structure has been determined, he attempts to synthesize the substance; if he is successful, the active material may be made available in large quantity and at low cost.

The other way in which organic chemists work involves the synthesis and study of a large number of organic compounds, and the continued effort to correlate the empirical facts by means of theoretical principles. Often a knowledge of the structure and properties of natural substances is valuable in indicating the general nature of the compounds that are worth investigation. The ultimate goal of this branch of organic chemistry is the complete understanding of the physical and chemical properties, and also the physiological properties, of substances in terms of their molecular structure. At the present time chemists have obtained a remarkable insight into the dependence of the physical and chemical properties of substances on the structure of their molecules. So far, however, only a small beginning has been made in attacking the great problem of the relation between structure and physiological activity. *This problem remains one of the greatest and most important problems of science, challenging the new generation of scientists.*

30–2. *Petroleum and the Hydrocarbons*

One of the most important sources of organic compounds is petroleum (crude oil). Petroleum, which is obtained from underground deposits that have been tapped by drilling oil-wells, is a dark-colored, viscous liquid that is in the main a mixture of hydrocarbons (compounds of hydrogen and carbon; see Section 7–6). A very great amount of it, approximately one billion tons, is produced and used each year. Much of it is burned, for direct use as a fuel, but much is separated or converted into other materials.

The Refining of Petroleum. Petroleum may be separated into especially useful materials by a process of distillation, called *refining*. It was mentioned in Section 7–6 that petroleum ether, obtained in this way, is an easily volatile pentane-hexane-heptane (C_5H_{12} to C_7H_{16}) mixture that is used as a solvent and in the dry cleaning of clothes, gasoline is the heptane-to-nonane (C_7H_{16} to C_9H_{20}) mixture used in internal-combustion engines, kerosene the decane-to-hexadecane ($C_{10}H_{22}$ to $C_{16}H_{34}$) mixture used as a fuel, and heavy fuel oil a mixture of still larger hydrocarbon molecules.

The residue from distillation is a black, tarry material called *petroleum asphalt*. It is used in making roads, for asphalt composition roofing materials, for stabilizing loose soil, and as a binder for coal dust in the manufacture of briquets for use as a fuel. A similar material, *bitumen* or *rock asphalt*, is found in Trinidad, Texas, Oklahoma, and other parts of the world, where it presumably has been formed as the residue from the slow distillation of pools of oil.

It is thought that petroleum, like coal, is the result of the decomposition of the remains of plants that grew on the earth long ago (estimated 250 million years ago).

Cracking and Polymerizing Processes. As the demand for gasoline became greater, methods were devised for increasing the yield of gasoline from petroleum. The simple "cracking" process consists in the use of high temperature to break the larger molecules into smaller ones; for example, a molecule of $C_{12}H_{26}$ might be broken into a molecule of C_6H_{14} (hexane) and a molecule of C_6H_{12} (hexene, containing one double bond). There are now several rather complicated cracking processes in use. Some involve heating liquid petroleum, under pressure of about 50 atm, to about 500° C, perhaps with a catalyst such as aluminum chloride, $AlCl_3$. Others involve heating petroleum vapor with a catalyst such as clay containing some zirconium dioxide.

Polymerization is also used to make gasoline from the lighter hydrocarbons containing double bonds. For example, two molecules of ethylene, C_2H_4, can react to form one molecule of butylene, C_4H_8 (structural formula $CH_3—CH=CH—CH_3$).

Some gasoline is also made by the hydrogenation (reaction with hydrogen) of petroleum and coal. Many organic chemicals are prepared in great quantities from these important raw materials.

Hydrocarbons Containing Several Double Bonds. The structure and properties of ethylene, a substance whose molecules contain a double bond, were discussed in Section 7–7. Some important natural products are hydrocarbons containing several double bonds. For example, the red coloring matter of tomatoes, called *lycopene*, is an unsaturated hydrocarbon, $C_{40}H_{56}$, with the structure shown in Figure 30-1.

The molecule of this substance contains thirteen double bonds. It is seen that eleven of these double bonds are related to one another in a special way—they alternate regularly with single bonds. A regular alteration of double bonds and single bonds in a hydrocarbon chain is called a *conjugated system of double bonds*. The existence of this structural feature in a molecule confers upon the molecule special properties, such as the power of absorbing visible light, causing the substance to be colored.

Other yellow and red substances, isomers of lycopene, with the same formula $C_{40}H_{56}$, are called **α-carotene**, **β-carotene**, and similar names. These substances occur in butter, milk, green leafy vegetables, eggs, cod liver oil, halibut liver oil, carrots, tomatoes, and other vegetables

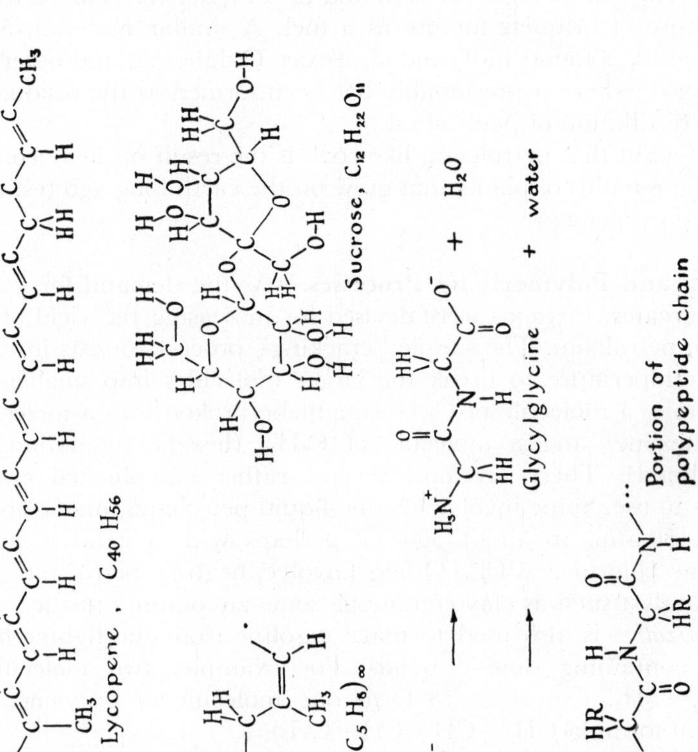

Lycopene, $C_{40}H_{56}$

Sucrose, $C_{12}H_{22}O_{11}$

Portion of rubber polymer $(C_5H_8)_\infty$

Glycine + glycine $\longrightarrow$ Glycylglycine + H_2O

Portion of polypeptide chain

FIGURE 30-1 *Structural formulas of some organic molecules.*

and fruits. They are important substances because they serve in the human body as a source of Vitamin A (see Chapter 31).

Cyclic Hydrocarbons. A hydrocarbon whose molecule contains a ring of carbon atoms is called a *cyclic hydrocarbon*. **Cyclohexane,** C_6H_{12}, with the structure

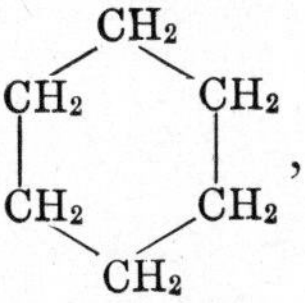

$$
\begin{array}{c}
CH_2 \\
CH_2 \qquad CH_2 \\
\\
CH_2 \qquad CH_2 \\
CH_2
\end{array}
$$

, is representative of this class of substances. It is a volatile liquid, closely similar to normal hexane (gasoline) in its properties.

Many important substances exist whose molecules contain two or more rings, fused together. One of these substances is **pinene,** $C_{10}H_{16}$, which is the principal constituent of *turpentine*. Turpentine is an oil obtained by distilling a semifluid resinous material that exudes from pine trees. The pinene molecule has the following structure:

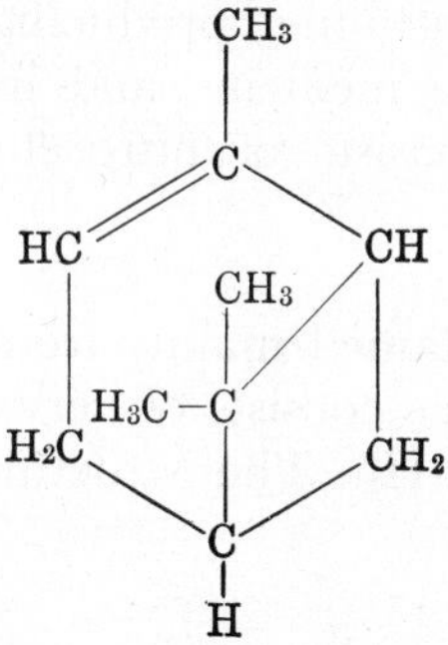

$$
\begin{array}{c}
CH_3 \\
| \\
C \\
HC \qquad\qquad CH \\
\quad CH_3 \\
\quad H_3C-C \\
H_2C \qquad\qquad CH_2 \\
C \\
| \\
H
\end{array}
$$

Another interesting polycyclic substance is **camphor,** obtained by steam distillation of the wood of the camphor tree, or, in recent years, by a synthetic process starting with pinene. The molecule of camphor is roughly spherical in shape—it is a sort of "cage" molecule. Its structure is shown in Figure 30-2.

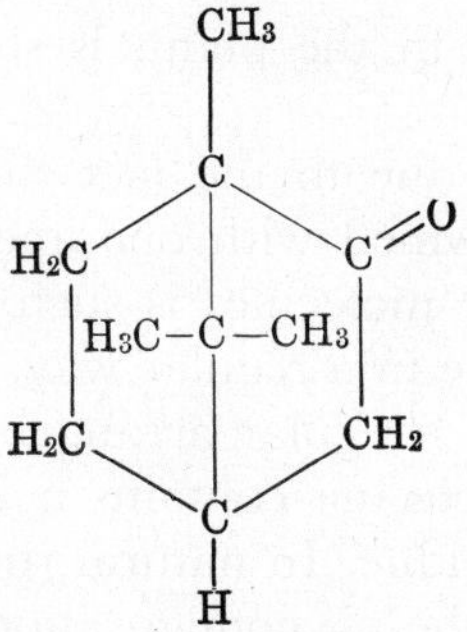

$$
\begin{array}{c}
CH_3 \\
| \\
C \\
H_2C \qquad\qquad C=0 \\
H_3C-C-CH_3 \\
H_2C \qquad\qquad CH_2 \\
C \\
| \\
H
\end{array}
$$

It is to be noted that camphor is not a hydrocarbon, but contains one

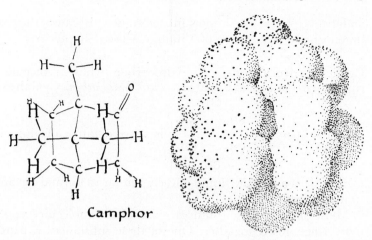

Camphor

FIGURE 30-2   *The structure of the camphor molecule.*

oxygen atom, its formula being $C_{10}H_{16}O$. A hydrocarbon is obtained by replacing the oxygen atom by two hydrogen atoms, producing the substance called *camphane*. Camphor is used in medicine and in the manufacture of plastics. Ordinary *celluloid* consists of nitrocellulose plasticized with camphor.

Rubber.   Rubber is an organic substance, obtained mainly from the sap of the rubber tree, *Hevea brasiliensis*. Rubber consists of very long molecules, which are polymers of *isoprene*, C_5H_8. The structure of isoprene is

and that of the rubber polymer, as produced in the plant, is shown in Figure 30-1.

The characteristic properties of rubber are due to the fact that it is an aggregate of very long molecules, intertwined with one another in a rather random way. The structure of the molecules is such that they do not tend to align themselves side by side in a regular way, that is, to crystallize, but instead tend to retain an irregular arrangement.

It is interesting to note that the rubber molecule contains a large number of double bonds, one for each C_5H_8 residue. In natural rubber the configuration about the double bonds is the *cis* configuration, as shown in the structural formula in Figure 30-1. **Gutta percha,** a similar product which does not have the elasticity of rubber, contains the same molecules, with, however, the *trans* configuration around the double bonds. This difference in configuration permits the molecules of gutta percha to crystallize more readily than those of rubber.

Ordinary unvulcanized rubber is sticky, as a result of a tendency for the molecules to pull away from one another, a portion of the rubber thus adhering to any material with which it comes in contact. The stickiness is eliminated by the process of *vulcanization*, which consists in heating rubber with sulfur. During this process sulfur molecules, S_8, open up and combine with the double bonds of rubber molecules, forming bridges of sulfur chains from one rubber molecule to another rubber molecule. These sulfur bridges bind the aggregate of rubber molecules together into a large molecular framework, extending through the whole sample of rubber. Vulcanization with a small amount of sulfur leads to a soft product, such as that in rubber bands or (with a filler, carbon black or zinc oxide) in automobile tires. A much harder material, called vulcanite, is obtained by using a larger amount of sulfur.

The modern materials called **"synthetic rubber"** are not really synthetic rubber, since they are not identical with the natural product. They are, rather, substitutes for rubber—materials with properties and structure similar to but not identical with those of natural rubber. For example, the substance **chloroprene,** C_4H_5Cl, with the structure

is similar to isoprene except for the replacement of a methyl group by a chlorine atom. Chloroprene polymerizes to a rubber called *chloroprene rubber*. It and other synthetic rubbers have found extensive uses, and are superior to natural rubber for some purposes.

Benzene and Other Aromatic Hydrocarbons. An important hydrocarbon is **benzene,** which has the formula C_6H_6. It is a volatile liquid (b.p. 80° C), which has an aromatic odor. Benzene and other hydrocarbons similar to it in structure are called the *aromatic hydrocarbons*. Benzene itself was first obtained by Faraday, by the distillation of coal.

For many years there was discussion about the structure of the benzene molecule. The German chemist August Kekulé suggested that the six carbon atoms form a regular planar hexagon in space, the six hydrogen atoms being bonded to the carbon atoms, and forming a larger hexagon. Kekulé suggested that, in order for a carbon atom to show its normal quadrivalence, the ring contains three single bonds and three double bonds in alternate positions, as shown below. A structure of this sort is called a Kekulé structure.

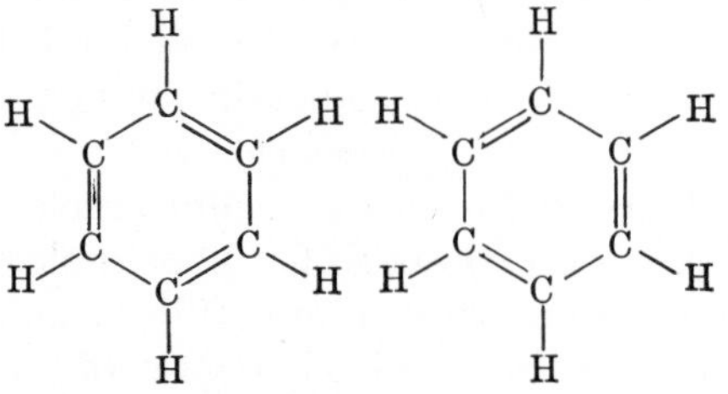

Other hydrocarbons, derivatives of benzene, can be obtained by replacing the hydrogen atoms by methyl groups or similar groups. Coal tar and petroleum contain substances of this sort, such as **toluene,** C_7H_8, and the three **xylenes,** C_8H_{10}. These formulas are usually written $C_6H_5CH_3$ and $C_6H_4(CH_3)_2$, to indicate the structural formulas, as shown below.

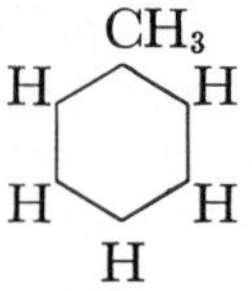

| Toluene | Ortho-xylene (o-xylene) | Meta-xylene (m-xylene) | Para-xylene (p-xylene) |

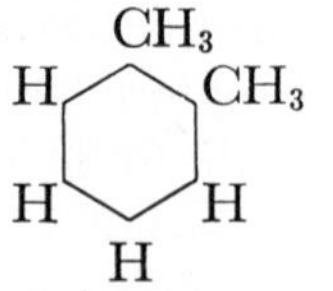

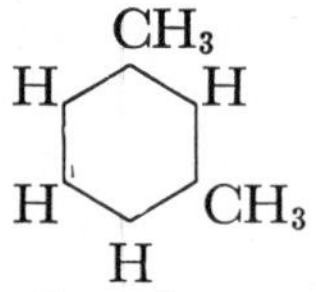

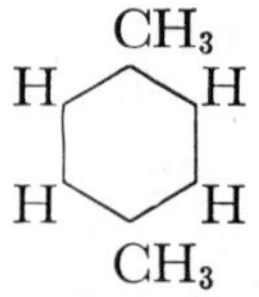

In these formulas the benzene ring of six carbon atoms is shown simply as a hexagon. This convention is used by organic chemists, who often also do not show the hydrogen atoms, but only other groups attached to the ring.

It is to be noted that we can draw two Kekulé structures for benzene and its derivatives. For example, for ortho-xylene the two Kekulé structures are

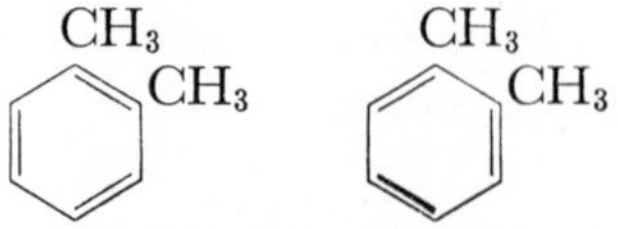

In the first structure there is a double bond between the carbon atoms to which methyl groups are attached, and in the second there is a single bond in this position. The organic chemists of eighty years ago found it impossible, however, to separate two substances, isomers, corresponding to these formulas. In order to explain this apparent impossibility of separation Kekulé suggested that the molecule does not retain one Kekulé structure, but rather slips easily from one to the other. The modern theory of molecular structure says that these two structures do not correspond to separate forms of ortho-xylene, and that neither one alone represents the molecule satisfactorily; instead, the actual structure of the ortho-xylene molecule is a hybrid of these two structures, with each bond between two carbon atoms in the ring intermediate in character between a single bond and a double bond. Even though this *resonance structure* is accepted for benzene and related compounds, it is often convenient simply to draw one of the Kekulé structures, or just a hexagon, to represent a benzene molecule.

Benzene and its derivatives are extremely important substances. They are used in the manufacture of drugs, explosives, photographic developers, plastics, synthetic dyes, and many other substances. For example, the substance **trinitrotoluene,** $C_6H_2(CH_3)(NO_2)_3$, is an important explosive (TNT). The structure of this substance is

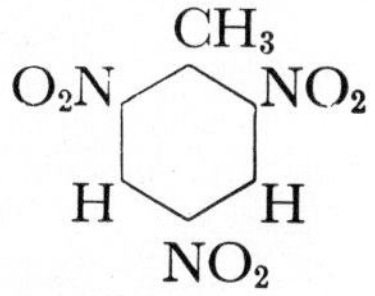

In addition to benzene and its derivatives, there exist other aromatic hydrocarbons, containing two or more rings of carbon atoms. **Naphthalene,** $C_{10}H_8$, is a solid substance with a characteristic odor; it is used as a constituent of moth balls, and in the manufacture of dyes and other organic compounds. **Anthracene,** $C_{14}H_{10}$, and **phenanthrene,** $C_{14}H_{10}$, are isomeric substances containing three rings fused together. These substances are also used in making dyes, and derivatives of them are important biological substances (cholesterol, sex hormones; see Chapter 31). The structures of naphthalene, anthracene, and phenanthrene are the following:

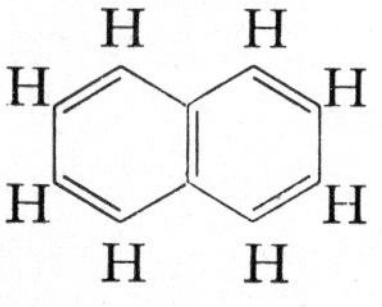

Naphthalene 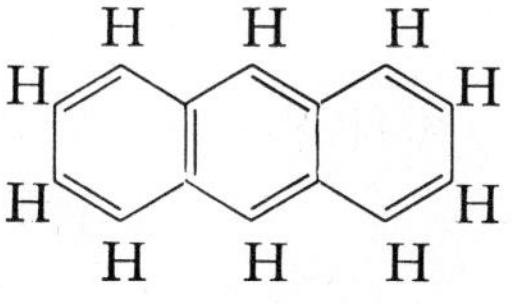   Anthracene 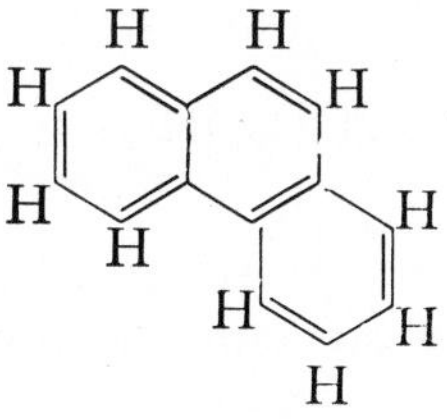   Phenanthrene

These molecules also have hybrid structures: the structures shown do not represent the molecules completely, but are analogous to one Kekulé structure for benzene.

30–3. *The Polyhydric Alchohols*

Alcohols are substances containing the hydroxyl group, —OH. The simple alcohols methanol, CH_3OH, and ethanol, C_2H_5OH, were discussed in Section 7–8.

Alcohols containing two or more hydroxyl groups attached to different carbon atoms can be made. **Diethylene glycol,** CH_2OH, is used

$$| \\ CH_2OH$$

as a solvent and as an anti-freeze material for automobile radiators. **Glycerol** (glycerine), $C_3H_5(OH)_3$, is a trihydroxypropane, with the structure

```
        H
        |
  H—C—OH
        |
  H—C—OH
        |
  H—C—OH
        |
        H
```

30–4. *Aldehydes and Ketones*

The alcohols represent the first stage of oxidation of hydrocarbons. Further oxidation leads to substances called *aldehydes* and *ketones*. The aldehydes contain the group $-C\overset{H}{\underset{O}{\diagdown}}$, and the ketones contain the carbonyl group, $\diagup\!\!\!C=O$. The simplest aldehyde is **formaldehyde,** which can be made by passing methyl alcohol vapor and air over a heated metal catalyst:

$$2CH_3OH + O_2 \longrightarrow 2HCHO + 2H_2O$$

The structural formula of formaldehyde is $\overset{H}{\underset{H}{\diagdown}}C=O$. This substance is a gas with a sharp irritating odor. It is used as a disinfectant and antiseptic, and in the manufacture of plastics and of leather and artificial silk. It forms polymers, such as paraldehyde, $(CH_2O)_3$, and metaldehyde, $(CH_2O)_4$.

Acetaldehyde, CH_3CHO, is a similar substance made from ethyl alcohol.

The ketones are closely similar in structure: whereas an aldehyde contains a carbonyl group with an alkyl group and a hydrogen atom attached (or two hydrogen atoms, in the case of formaldehyde), the ketones contain a carbonyl group with two hydrocarbon groups attached. The ketones are effective solvents for organic compounds, and are extensively used in chemical industry for this purpose. **Acetone,** $(CH_3)_2CO$, which is dimethyl ketone, is the simplest and most important of these substances. It is a good solvent for nitrocellulose.

30–5. *The Organic Acids and Their Esters*

The *organic acids* represent a still higher stage of oxidation of hydrocarbons than the aldehydes and ketones; namely, the stage of oxidation

to a molecule containing a group $-C\overset{\displaystyle O}{\underset{\displaystyle OH}{\Big/\!\!\!\!}}$. This group is called the

carboxyl group. It has the properties of a weak acid; the extent of ionization of the carboxyl group in most organic acids is such as to correspond to an equilibrium constant (acid constant) of about 1×10^{-4} or 1×10^{-5}.

The simplest organic acid is **formic acid,** $HCOOH$. It can be made by distilling ants, and its name is from the Latin word for ant.

A brief discussion of acetic acid, CH_3COOH, which is the second member of the homologous series of carboxylic acids, has been given in Section 7–8.

The next two acids in the series are **propionic acid,** CH_3CH_2COOH, and **butyric acid,** $CH_3CH_2CH_2COOH$. Butyric acid is the principal odorous substance in rancid butter.

Some of the important organic acids occurring in nature are those in which there is a carboxyl group at the end of a long hydrocarbon chain. **Palmitic acid,** $C_{15}H_{31}COOH$, and **stearic acid,** $C_{17}H_{35}COOH$, have structures of this sort. **Oleic acid,** $C_{17}H_{33}COOH$, is similar to stearic acid except that it contains a double bond between two of the carbon atoms in the chain.

Oxalic acid, $(COOH)_2$, is a poisonous substance which occurs in some plants. Its molecule consists of two carboxyl groups bonded together:

$$\underset{\displaystyle O}{\overset{\displaystyle HO}{\diagdown}}\!\!\!\diagup\overset{}{C}\!\!-\!\!\overset{}{C}\underset{\displaystyle O}{\overset{\displaystyle OH}{\diagup}}\!\!\!\diagdown$$

Lactic acid, having the structural formula $H_3C\overset{\displaystyle OH}{\underset{\displaystyle H}{\overset{|}{-}C\overset{|}{-}}}COOH$, contains

a hydroxyl group as well as a carboxyl group; it is a hydroxypropionic acid. It is formed when milk sours and when cabbage ferments, and it gives the sour taste to sour milk and sauerkraut. **Tartaric acid,** which occurs in grapes, is a dihydroxydicarboxylic acid, with the structural formula

$$
\begin{array}{c}
\text{H} \\
| \\
\text{HO—C—COOH} \\
| \\
\text{HO—C—COOH} \\
| \\
\text{H}
\end{array}
$$

Citric acid, which occurs in the citrus fruits, is a hydroxytricarboxylic acid, with the formula

$$
\begin{array}{c}
\text{H} \\
\text{HC—COOH} \\
| \\
\text{HO—C—COOH} \\
| \\
\text{HC—COOH} \\
\text{H}
\end{array}
$$

Esters are the products of reaction of acids and alcohols. For example, ethyl alcohol and acetic acid react with the elimination of water to produce **ethyl acetate:**

$$C_2H_5OH + CH_3COOH \longrightarrow H_2O + CH_3COOC_2H_5$$

Ethyl acetate is a volatile liquid with a pleasing, fruity odor. It is used as a solvent, especially in lacquers.

Many of the esters have pleasant odors, and are used in perfumes and flavorings. The esters are the principal flavorful and odorous constituents of fruits and flowers.

The natural *fats* and *oils* are also esters, principally of the trihydroxy alcohol glycerol. Animal fats consist mainly of the glyceryl esters of palmitic acid and stearic acid. **Glyceryl oleate,** the glyceryl ester of oleic acid, is found in olive oil, whale oil, and the fats of cold-blooded animals; these fats tend to remain liquid at ordinary temperatures, whereas **glyceryl palmitate** and **glyceryl stearate** form the solid fats.

Esters can be decomposed by boiling with strong alkali, such as sodium hydroxide. This treatment forms the alcohol and the sodium salt of the carboxylic acid. When fat is boiled with sodium hydroxide, glycerine and sodium salts of the fatty acids, sodium palmitate, sodium stearate, and sodium oleate, are formed. These sodium salts of the fatty acids are called *soap*.

30–6. *Amines and Other Organic Compounds*

The amines are derivatives of ammonia, NH_3, obtained by replacing one or more of the hydrogen atoms by organic radicals. The lighter amines, such as **methylamine, CH_3NH_2, dimethylamine, $(CH_3)_2NH$,** and **trimethylamine, $(CH_3)_3N$,** are gases. Trimethylamine has a pronounced fishy odor, and many other amines also have disagreeable odors.

Aniline is aminobenzene, $C_6H_5NH_2$. It is a colorless oily liquid, which on standing becomes dark in color, because of oxidation to highly colored derivatives. It is used in the manufacture of dyes and other chemicals.

Many substances which occur in plant and animal tissues are compounds of nitrogen. One of these, **urea,** is the principal nitrogenous product of metabolism in the animal body (Chapter 31). Urea has the formula $(NH_2)_2CO$, its structural formula being

$$\begin{array}{c} H_2N \\ \diagdown \\ \qquad C{=}O \\ \diagup \\ H_2N \end{array}$$

30–7. *Carbohydrates, Sugars, Polysaccharides*

The *carbohydrates* are substances with the general formula $C_x(H_2O)_y$. They occur widely in nature. The simpler carbohydrates are called *sugars*, and the complex ones, consisting of very large molecules, are called *polysaccharides* (see Chapter 31).

A common simple sugar is **D-glucose** (also called *dextrose* and *grape sugar*), $C_6H_{12}O_6$. It occurs in many fruits, and is present in the blood of animals. Its structural formula (not showing the spatial configuration of bonds around the four central carbon atoms) is

$$\begin{array}{ccccccccc} H_2C & {-\!\!-} & CH & {-\!\!-} & CH & {-\!\!-} & CH & {-\!\!-} & CH & {-\!\!-} & CH \\ | & & | & & | & & | & & | & & \| \\ OH & & OH & & OH & & OH & & OH & & O \end{array}$$

The molecule thus contains five hydroxyl groups and one aldehyde group.

Ordinary sugar, obtained from sugar cane and sugar beets, is **sucrose, $C_{12}H_{22}O_{11}$.** The molecules of sucrose have a complex structure, consisting of two rings (each containing one oxygen atom), held together by bonds to an oxygen atom as shown in Figure 30-1.

Many other simple carbohydrates occur in nature. These include *fructose* (fruit sugar), *maltose* (malt sugar), and *lactose* (milk sugar).

Important polysaccharides include *starch*, *glycogen*, and *cellulose*. Starch, $(C_6H_{10}O_5)_x$, occurs in plants, mainly in their seeds or tubers. It is an important constituent of foods. Glycogen, $(C_6H_{10}O_5)_x$, is a substance similar to starch which occurs in the blood and the internal organs, especially the liver, of animals. Glycogen serves as a reservoir of readily available food for the body; whenever the concentration of glucose in the blood becomes low, glycogen is rapidly hydrolyzed into glucose.

Cellulose, which also has the formula $(C_6H_{10}O_5)_x$, is a stable polysaccharide which serves as a structural element for plants, forming the walls of cells. Like starch and glycogen, cellulose consists of long molecules containing rings of atoms held together by oxygen atoms, in the way shown in Figure 30-1 for the two rings of sucrose.

The sugars have the properties of dissolving readily in water, and of crystallizing in rather hard crystals. These properties are attributed to the presence of a number of hydroxyl groups in these molecules, which form hydrogen bonds with water molecules and (in the crystals) with **each** other.

30–8. *Fibers and Plastics*

Silk and wool are protein fibers, consisting of long polypeptide chains (see Chapter 31). Cotton and linen are polysaccharides (carbohydrates), with composition $(C_6H_{10}O_5)_x$. These fibers consist of long chains made from carbon, hydrogen, and oxygen atoms, with no nitrogen atoms present.

In recent years synthetic fibers have been made, by synthesizing long molecules in the laboratory. One of these, which has valuable properties, is **nylon**. It is the product of condensation of adipic acid and diaminohexane. These two substances have the following structures:

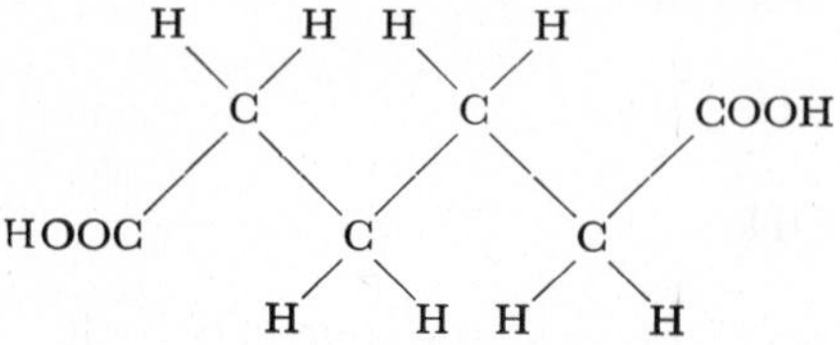

Adipic acid 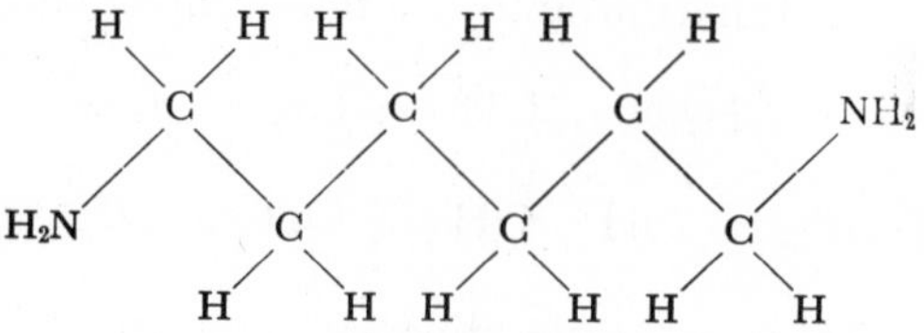   Diaminohexane

Adipic acid is a chain of four methylene groups with a carboxyl group at each end, and diaminohexane is a similar chain of six methylene groups with an amino group at each end. A molecule of adipic acid can react with a molecule of diaminohexane in the following way:

If this process is continued, a very long molecule can be made, in which the adipic acid residues alternate with the diaminohexane residues. Nylon is a fibrous material which consists of these long molecules in approximately parallel orientation.

Other artificial fibers and plastics are made by similar condensation reactions. A *thermolabile plastic* usually is an aggregate of long molecules of this sort which softens upon heating, and can be molded into shape. A *thermosetting plastic* is an aggregate of long molecules containing some reactive groups, capable of further condensation. When this material is molded and heated, these groups react in such a way as to tie the molecules together into a three-dimensional framework, producing a plastic material which cannot be further molded.

With a great number of substances available for use as his starting materials, the chemist has succeeded in making fibers and plastics which are for many purposes superior to natural materials. This field of chemistry, that of synthetic giant molecules, is still a new field, and we may look forward to further great progress in it in the coming years.

Concepts, Facts, and Terms Introduced in This Chapter

Organic chemistry—chemistry of the compounds of carbon. Two ways in which organic chemists work: isolation of substances from plants and animals, followed by synthesis of the substances; and synthesis and study of carbon compounds that do not occur in nature.

Petroleum and the hydrocarbons. The refining of petroleum. Cracking and polymerizing processes. Lycopene, conjugated systems of double bonds. Pinene, turpentine, camphor, camphane, celluloid. Rubber, isoprene, gutta percha, vulcanization, synthetic rubber, chloroprene. Aromatic hydrocarbons: benzene, toluene, xylene, naphthalene, anthracene, phenanthrene. Ortho, meta, and para isomers of xylene. Alcohols: methanol, ethanol, diethylene glycol, glycerol. Aldehydes: formaldehyde, acetaldehyde. Ketones: acetone. Organic acids: formic acid, acetic acid, propionic acid, butyric acid, palmitic acid, stearic acid, oleic acid, oxalic acid, lactic acid, tartaric acid, citric acid. The carboxyl group. Esters: ethyl acetate; fats and oils. Amines: methylamine, dimethylamine, trimethylamine, aniline. Halogen derivatives: chloroform, carbon tetrachloride, iodoform, urea. Carbohydrates, sugars, polysaccharides: D-glucose (dextrose, grape sugar), sucrose, fructose, maltose, lactose, starch, glycogen, cellulose. Fibers and plastics: silk, wool, cotton, linen, nylon. Thermolabile and thermosetting plastics. Giant molecules, three-dimensional frameworks.

Exercises

30-1. What is the difference in the structures of the saturated and the unsaturated hydrocarbons?

30-2. Describe the processes of cracking and polymerization, in relation to the manufacture of gasoline.

30-3. What do you suppose the structure of cyclopentane, C_5H_{10}, is? How many isomers of this substance can you draw?

30-4. How does a study of the properties of ortho-xylene pertain to the question of the structure of benzene?

30-5. What is the oxidation number of carbon in each of the following compounds: CH_4, CH_3OH, CH_3OCH , H_2CO, $HCOOH$, CO_2? Name these compounds. and draw their structural formulas.

30-6. Which do you think is the more soluble in water, sodium palmitate or ethyl palmitate? In benzene?

30-7. Which do you think is the more soluble in water, acetic acid or stearic acid?

30-8. In what ways does the reaction

$$C_2H_5OH + CH_3COOH \longrightarrow H_2O + CH_3COOC_2H_5$$

differ from the neutralization of acetic acid with sodium hydroxide?

30-9. Write the chemical reaction for the preparation of soap.

30-10. What relation is there between sugar, glycogen, and starch?

30-11. Why are large molecules so much more important in organic chemistry than in inorganic chemistry?

Reference Books

B. H. Shoemaker, E. L. d'Ouville, and R. F. Marschner, "Recent Advances in Petroleum Refining," *Journal of Chemical Education*, **32**, 30 (January **1955**).

See the list at the end of Chapter 7.

Chapter 31

Biochemistry

Biochemistry is the study of the chemical composition and structure of the human body and other living organisms, of the chemical reactions that take place within these organisms, and of the drugs and other substances that interact with them.

During the past century biochemistry has developed into an important branch of science. We shall not be able in the limited space of the present chapter to give a general survey of this interesting subject, but shall instead have to content ourselves with a simple introductory discussion of a few of its aspects.

31-1. The Nature of Life

All of our ideas about life involve chemical reactions. What is it that distinguishes a living organism,* such as a man or some other animal or a plant, from an inanimate object, such as a piece of granite? We recognize that the plant or animal may have several attributes that are not possessed by the rock. The plant or animal has, in general, the power of **reproduction**—the power of having progeny, which are sufficiently similar to itself to be recognized as belonging to the same species of living organisms. The process of reproduction involves chemical reactions, the reactions that take place during the growth of the progeny. The growth of the new organism may occur only during a small fraction of the total lifetime of the animal, or may continue throughout its lifetime.

A plant or animal in general has the ability of ingesting certain materials, foods, subjecting them to chemical reactions, involving the release of energy, and secreting some of the products of the reactions.

---

* The word *organism* is used to refer to anything that lives or has ever been living—we speak of dead organisms, as well as of living organisms.

617

This process, by which the organism makes use of the food which it ingests by subjecting it to chemical reaction, is called **metabolism.**

Most plants and animals have the ability to respond to their environment. A plant may grow toward the direction from which a beam of light is coming, in response to the stimulus of the beam of light, and an animal may walk or run in a direction indicated by increasing intensity of the odor of a palatable food.

In order to illustrate the difficulty of defining a living organism, let us consider the simplest kinds of matter that have been thought to be alive. These are the *plant viruses,* such as the tomato bushy stunt virus, of which an electron micrograph has been shown as Figure 2-8. These viruses have the power of reproducing themselves when in the appropriate environment. A single molecule (individual organism) of tomato bushy stunt virus, when placed on the leaf of a tomato plant, can cause the material in the cells of the leaf to be in large part converted into replicas of itself. This power of reproduction seems, however, to be the only characteristic of living organisms possessed by the virus. After the particles are formed, they do not grow. They do not ingest food nor carry on any metabolic processes. So far as can be told by use of the electron microscope and by other methods of investigation, the individual particles of the virus are identical with one another, and show no change with time—there is no phenomenon of aging, of growing old. The virus particles seem to have no means of locomotion, and seem not to respond to external stimuli in the way that large living organisms do. But they do have the power of reproducing themselves.

Considering these facts, should we say that a virus is a living organism, or that it is not? At the present time scientists do not agree about the answer to this question—indeed, the question may not be a scientific one at all, but simply a matter of the definition of words. If we were to define a living organism as a material structure with the power of reproducing itself, then we would include the plant viruses among the living organisms. If, however, we require that living organisms also have the property of carrying on some metabolic reactions, then the plant viruses would be described simply as molecules (with molecular weight of the order of magnitude of 10,000,000) which have such a molecular structure as to permit them to catalyze a chemical reaction, in a proper medium, leading to the synthesis of molecules identical with themselves.

31–2. *The Structure of Living Organisms*

Chemical investigation of the plant viruses has shown that they consist largely of the materials called **proteins,** the nature of which is discussed in the following section. The giant virus particles or molecules, with molecular weight of the order of magnitude of 10,000,000, may perhaps be described as aggregates of smaller molecules, tied together in a definite way. However, very little is known about the nature of these structures. Investigation with the electron microscope has shown that the plant virus molecules have definite size and shape, but has not given any evidence about their internal structure.

On the other hand, the animal viruses—viruses which grow on animal tissues—are seen in the electron microscope to have a definite structure. These viruses are in general considerably larger than the plant viruses, their molecular weight being of the order of 1,000,000,000. The vaccinia virus (cowpox virus, used for vaccination against smallpox) is shown by the electron microscope to have roughly the shape of a rectangular box, in the interior of which there are some round particles of material that absorb the beam of electrons more strongly than the remaining material.

Many micro-organisms, such as molds and bacteria, consist of single **cells.** These cells may be just big enough to be seen with an ordinary microscope, having diameter around 10,000 Å (10^{-4} cm), or they may be much bigger, as large as a millimeter or more in diameter. The cells have a well-organized structure, consisting of a *cell wall*, a few hundred Ångströms in thickness, within which is enclosed a semi-fluid material called *cytoplasm*, and often other structures that can be seen with the microscope. Other plants and animals consist largely of aggregates of cells, which may be of many different kinds in one organism. The muscles, blood vessel and lymph vessel walls, tendons, connective tissues, nerves, skin, and other parts of the body of a man consist of cells attached to one another to constitute a well-defined structure. In addition there are many cells that are not attached to this structure, but float around in the body fluids. Most numerous among these cells are the *red corpuscles* of the blood. The red corpuscles in man are flattened disks, about 70,000 Å in diameter and 10,000 Å thick. The number of red cells in a human adult is very large. There are about 5 million red cells per cubic millimeter of blood, and a man contains about 5 l of blood, that is, 5 million cubic millimeters of blood. Accordingly there are 25×10^{12} red cells in his body. In addition, there are many other cells, some of them small, like the red cells, and some somewhat larger—a single nerve cell may be about 10,000 Å in diameter and 100 cm long, extending from the toe to the spinal cord. The total number of cells in the human body is between 10^{13} and 10^{14}. The amount of *organization* in the human organism is accordingly very great.

The human body does not consist of cells alone. In addition there are the *bones*, which have been laid down as excretions of bone-making cells. The bones consist of inorganic constituents, calcium hydroxyphosphate, $Ca_5(PO_4)_3OH$, and calcium carbonate, and an organic constituent, *collagen*, which is a protein. The body also contains the body fluids blood and lymph, as well as fluids which are secreted by special organs, such as saliva and the digestive juices. Very many different chemical substances are present in these fluids.

The structure of cells is determined by their framework materials, which constitute the cell walls and, in some cases, reinforcing frameworks within the cells. In plants the carbohydrate cellulose, described in the preceding chapter, is the most important constituent of the cell walls. In animals the framework materials are proteins. Moreover, the cell contents consist largely of proteins. For example, a red cell is a thin membrane enclosing a medium that consists of 60% water, 5% miscellaneous materials, and 35% **hemoglobin,** an iron-containing protein, which has molecular weight 68,000, and has the power of combining reversibly with oxygen. It is this power that permits the blood to combine with a large amount of oxygen in the lungs, and to carry it to the tissues, making it available there for oxidation of foodstuffs and body constituents. It has been mentioned earlier in this section that the simplest forms of matter with the power of reproducing themselves, the viruses, consist largely of proteins, as do also the most complex living organisms.

31–3. *Amino Acids and Proteins*

Proteins may well be considered the most important of all the substances present in plants and animals. Proteins occur either as separate molecules, usually with very large molecular weight, ranging from about 10,000 to many millions, or as reticular constituents of cells,

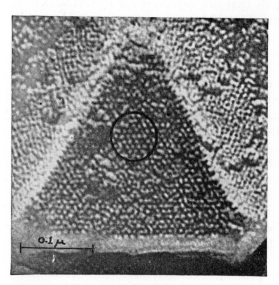

FIGURE 31-1

Electron micrograph of an edestin crystal showing individual molecules in the octahedral face (magnification 200,000 ×). Within the circumscribed area, and in other places where the surface has not been disturbed during preparation, the molecules form a hexagonal pattern. The molecules are about 80 Å in diameter and the molecular weight is 300,000. Note the molecular layers growing out over the supporting film from the edges of the crystal. Edestin is a protein found in wheat, corn, and other seeds. Reference: C. E. Hall, J. Am. Chem. Soc., **71,** *2915 (1949).*

constituting their structural framework (Figure 31-1). The human body contains many thousands of different proteins, which have special structures that permit them to carry out specific tasks.

All proteins are nitrogenous substances, containing approximately 16% of nitrogen, together with carbon, hydrogen, oxygen, and often other elements such as sulfur, phosphorus, iron (four atoms of iron are present in each molecule of hemoglobin), and copper.

Amino Acids. When proteins are heated in acidic or basic solution they undergo hydrolysis, producing substances called amino acids. Amino acids are carboxylic acids in which one hydrogen atom has been replaced by an amino group, —NH_2. The amino acids which are obtained from proteins are *alpha* amino acids, with the amino group attached to the carbon atom next to the carboxyl group (this carbon atom is called the alpha carbon atom). The simplest of these amino acids is **glycine**, $CH_2(NH_2)COOH$. The other natural amino acids contain another group, usually called R, in place of one of the hydrogen atoms on the alpha carbon atom, their general formula thus being $CHR(NH_2)COOH$.

The amino group is sufficiently basic and the carboxyl group is sufficiently acidic so that in solution in water the proton is transferred from the carboxyl group to the amino group. The carboxyl group is thus converted into a carboxyl ion, and the amino group into a substituted ammonium ion. The structure of glycine and of the other amino acids in aqueous solution is accordingly the following:

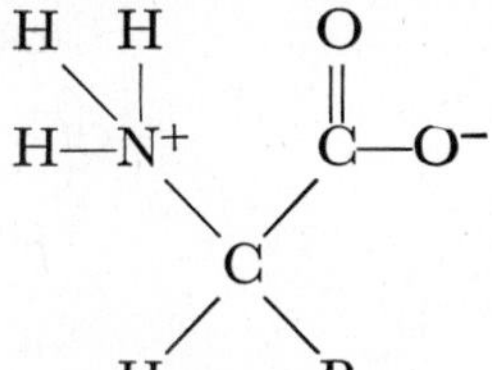

The amino groups and carboxyl groups of most substances dissolved in animal or plant liquids, which usually have *p*H about 7, are internally ionized in this way, to form an ammonium ion group and a carboxyl ion group within the same molecule.

There are twenty-four amino acids that have been recognized as important constituents of proteins. Their names are given in Table 31-1, together with the formulas of the characteristic group R. Some of the amino acids have an extra carboxyl group or an extra amino group. There is one double amino acid, *cystine*, which is closely related to a simple amino acid, *cysteine*. Four of the amino acids contain *heterocyclic rings*—rings of carbon atoms and one or more other atoms, in this case nitrogen atoms. Two of the amino acids given in the table, *asparagine*

TABLE 31-1   *The Principal Amino Acids Occurring in Proteins*

MONOAMINOMONOCARBOXYLIC ACIDS

Glycine, aminoacetic acid $-R = -H$

Alanine, α-aminopropionic acid $-CH_3$

Serine, α-amino-β-hydroxypropionic acid $-CH_2OH$

Threonine, α-amino-β-hydroxybutyric acid
$$-CH \begin{smallmatrix} CH_3 \\ \\ OH \end{smallmatrix}$$

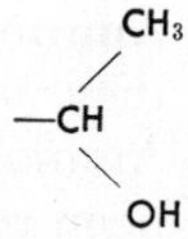

Methionine, α-amino-γ-methylmercaptobutyric acid $-CH_2-CH_2-S-CH_3$

Valine, α-amino-isovaleric acid
$$-CH \begin{smallmatrix} CH_3 \\ \\ CH_3 \end{smallmatrix}$$

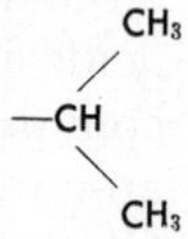

Norvaline, α-aminovaleric acid $-CH_2-CH_2-CH_3$

Leucine, α-amino-isocaproic acid
$$-CH_2-CH \begin{smallmatrix} CH_3 \\ \\ CH_3 \end{smallmatrix}$$

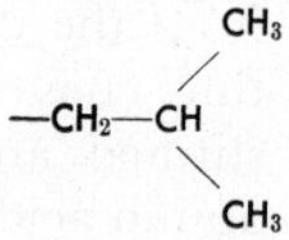

Isoleucine, α-amino-β-methylvaleric acid
$$-CH \begin{smallmatrix} CH_2-CH_3 \\ \\ CH_3 \end{smallmatrix}$$

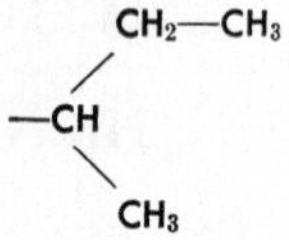

Phenylalanine, α-amino-β-phenylpropionic acid
$$-CH_2-\langle \text{C}_6\text{H}_5 \rangle$$

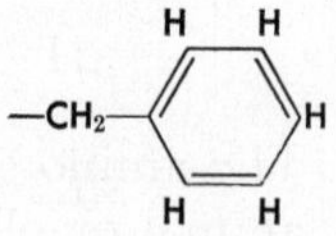

Tyrosine, α-amino-β-(para-hydroxyphenyl)propionic acid
$$-CH_2-\langle \text{C}_6\text{H}_4 \rangle-OH$$

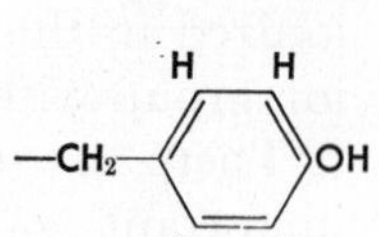

Cysteine, α-amino-β-sulfhydrylpropionic acid $-CH_2-SH$

TABLE 31-1 (*continued*)

MONOAMINODICARBOXYLIC ACIDS

Aspartic acid, aminosuccinic acid $-CH_2-COOH$

Glutamic acid, α-aminoglutaric acid $-CH_2-CH_2-COOH$

Hydroxyglutamic acid, α-amino-β-hydroxyglutaric acid

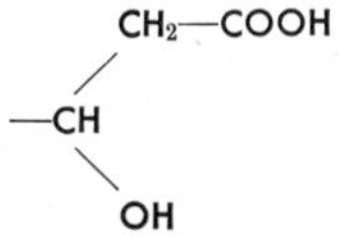

$$CH_2-COOH$$
$$-CH$$
$$OH$$

DIAMINOMONOCARBOXYLIC ACIDS

Arginine, α-amino-δ-guanidinevaleric acid

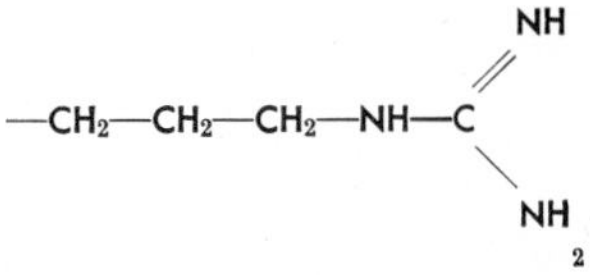

$$-CH_2-CH_2-CH_2-NH-C\begin{array}{c}NH\\\\NH_2\end{array}$$

Lysine, α,ϵ-diaminocaproic acid $-CH_2-CH_2-CH_2-CH_2-NH_2$

DIAMINODICARBOXYLIC ACIDS

Cystine, di-β-thio-α-aminopropionic acid $-CH_2-S-S-CH_2-$

AMINO ACIDS CONTAINING HETEROCYCLIC RINGS

Histidine, α-amino-β-imidazolepropionic acid

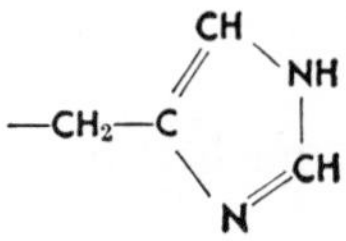

$$-CH_2-C\begin{array}{c}CH\\ \quad NH\\ CH\\N\end{array}$$

Proline, 2-pyrrolidinecarboxylic acid*

$$\begin{array}{cccc} & H & H & \\ & N^+ & H & O \\ H_2C & C-C & \\ H_2C & CH_2 & O^- \end{array}$$

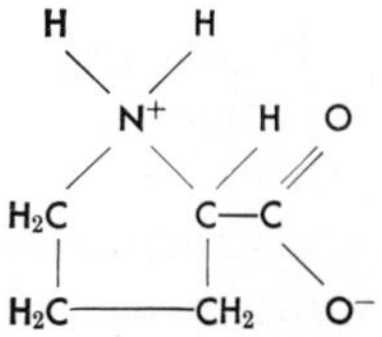

Hydroxyproline, 4-hydroxy-2-pyrrolidinecarboxylic acid*

$$\begin{array}{cccc} & H & H & \\ & N^+ & H & O \\ H_2C & C-C & \\ HC & CH_2 & O^- \\ OH & & \end{array}$$

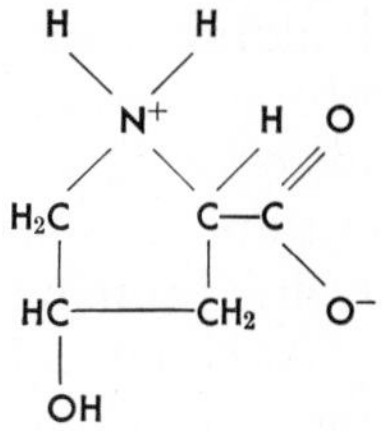

* The formulas given for proline and hydroxyproline are those of the complete molecules, and not just of the groups R.

TABLE 31-1 (*continued*)

Tryptophan, α-amino-β-indolepropionic acid *⌐

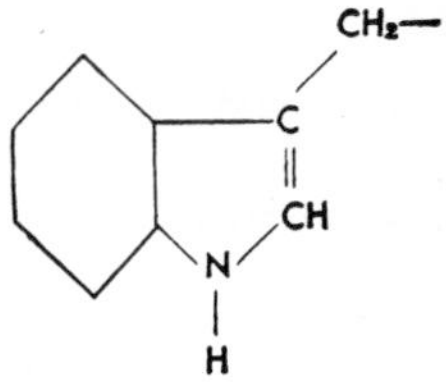

AMINO ACIDS CONTAINING AN AMIDE GROUP

Asparagine, aminosuccinic acid monoamide

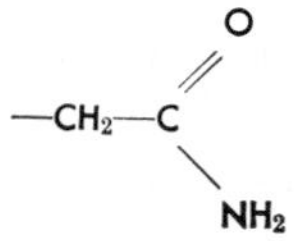

Glutamine, α-aminoglutaric acid monoamide

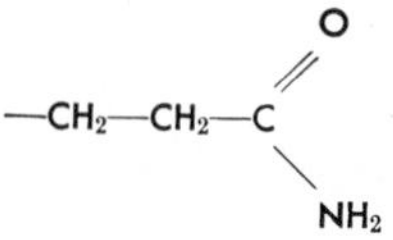

---

* The hexagon represents a benzene ring.

and *glutamine*, are closely related to two others, *aspartic acid* and *glutamic acid*, differing from them only in having the extra carboxyl group

changed into an amide group,

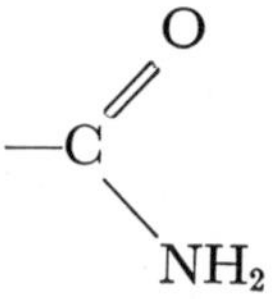

$$-C\Big\langle\!\!\begin{array}{l}\!\!^{O}\\[-2pt]\!\!_{NH_2}\end{array}$$

Proteins are important constituents of food. They are digested by the digestive juices in the stomach and intestines, being split in the process of digestion into small molecules, probably mainly the amino acids themselves. These small molecules are able to pass through the walls of the stomach and intestines into the blood stream, by which they are carried around into the tissues, where they may then serve as building stones for the manufacture of the body proteins. Sometimes people who are ill and cannot digest foods satisfactorily are fed by the injection of a solution of amino acids directly into the blood stream. A solution of amino acids for this purpose is usually obtained by hydrolyzing proteins.

Although all of the amino acids listed in Table 31-1 are present in the proteins of the human body, not all of them need to be in the food. Experiments have been carried out which show that nine of the amino acids are essential to man. These nine **essential amino acids** are *histidine, lysine, tryptophan, phenylalanine, leucine, isoleucine, threonine, methionine,* and *valine.* The human body seems to be able to manufacture the others, which are called the non-essential amino acids. Some organisms that we usually consider to be simpler than man have greater powers than the human organisms in that they are able to manufacture all of the amino acids from inorganic constituents. The red bread mold, *Neurospora*, has this power.

Protein foods for man may be classed as *good protein foods*, those that contain all of the essential amino acids, and *poor protein foods*, those that are lacking in one or more of the essential amino acids. *Casein*, the principal protein in milk, is a good protein, from this point of view, whereas *gelatin*, a protein obtained by boiling bones and tendons (partial hydrolysis of the insoluble protein collagen produces gelatin) is a poor protein. Gelatin contains no tryptophan, no valine, and little or no threonine.

Right-handed and Left-handed Molecules. Every amino acid except glycine can exist in two isomeric forms. These two forms, called L (levo) and D (dextro) forms, are identical with one another except for the arrangement in space of the four groups attached to the α-carbon atom. The two molecules are *mirror images* of one another—one can be called the left-handed molecule, and the other the right-handed molecule.* Figure 31-2 shows the two isomers of the amino acid alanine, in which R is the methyl group, CH_3.

A most extraordinary fact is that only one of the two isomers of each of the twenty-four amino acids has been found to occur in plant and animal proteins, and that this isomer has the same configuration for all of these amino acids; that is, the hydrogen atom, carboxyl ion group, and ammonium ion group occupy the same position relative to the group R around the alpha carbon atom. This configuration is called the L configuration—*proteins are built entirely of L-amino acids.*

This is a very puzzling fact. Nobody knows why it is that we are built of L-amino acid molecules, rather than of D-amino acid molecules. All the proteins that have been investigated, obtained from animals and from plants, from higher organisms and from very simple organisms—bacteria, molds, even viruses—are found to have been made of L-amino acids. Now right-handed molecules and left-handed molecules have exactly the same properties, so far as their interaction with ordinary substances is concerned—they differ in their properties only when they interact with other right-handed or left-handed molecules. The earth might just as well be populated with living organisms made of D-amino acids as with those made of L-amino acids. A man who was

* The term *optical isomers* is used to describe right-handed and left-handed molecules of this sort, because these isomers have the power of rotating the plane of polarization of polarized light. Two optical isomers rotate the plane of polarization by equal amounts in opposite directions. The isomers are also called *stereoisomers*.

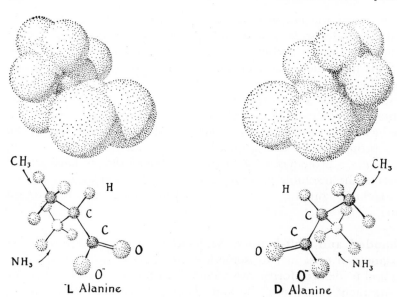

CH₃

H
C
C
O
NH₃
O⁻
L Alanine

CH₃

H
C
C
O
NH₃
O⁻
D Alanine

FIGURE 31-2   *The two stereoisomers of the amino acid alanine.*

suddenly converted into an exact mirror image of himself would not at first know that anything had changed about him, except that he would write with his left hand, instead of his right, his hair would be parted on the right side instead of the left, his heartbeat would show his heart to be on the right side, and so on; he could drink water, inhale air and use the oxygen in it for combustion, exhale carbon dioxide, and carry on other bodily functions just as well as ever—so long as he did not eat any ordinary food. If he were to eat ordinary plant or animal food he would find that he could not digest it. He could be kept alive only on a diet containing synthetic D-amino acids, made in the chemical laboratory. He could not have any children, unless he could find a wife who had been subjected to the same process of reflection into a mirror image of her original self. We see that there is the possibility that the earth might have been populated with two completely independent kinds of life—plants, animals, human beings of two kinds, who could not use one another's food, could not produce hybrid progeny.

No one knows why living organisms are constructed of L-amino acids. Perhaps the protein molecules that are made of amino acid molecules of one sort only are especially suited to the construction of a living organism—but if this is so, we do not know why.* Nor do we know why it is that living organisms have evolved in the L-system rather than in the D-system. The suggestion has been made that the first living organism

---

* A possible reason is that the alpha helix, described in the following section, can be built out of either L-amino acids or D-amino acids, but not out of a mixture of the two, because the groups R then interfere with one another.

happened by chance to make use of a few molecules with the L configuration, which were present with D molecules in equal number; and that all succeeding forms of life that have evolved have continued to use L-amino acid molecules through inheritance of the character from the original form of life. Perhaps a better explanation than this can be found—but I do not know what it is.

The Structure of Proteins.   During the past century much effort has been devoted by scientists to the problem of the structure of proteins. This is a very important problem; if it were to be solved, we should have a much better understanding than at present of the nature of physiological reactions, and the knowledge of the structure of protein molecules would probably help in the attack on important medical problems, such as the problem of the control of heart disease, cancer, and other diseases.

In the period between 1900 and 1910 strong evidence was obtained by the German chemist Emil Fischer (1852–1919) to indicate that the amino acids in proteins are combined into long chains, called *polypeptide chains*. For example, two molecules of glycine can be condensed together, with elimination of water, to form the double molecule glycylglycine, shown in Figure 30-1. The bond formed in this way is called a *peptide bond*. The process of forming these bonds can be continued, resulting in the production of a long chain containing many amino-acid residues, as shown in Figure 30-1.

Chemical methods have been developed to determine how many polypeptide chains there are in a protein molecule. These methods involve the use of a reagent (fluorodinitrobenzene) that combines with the free amino group of the amino-acid residue at the end of the polypeptide chain, to form a colored complex, which can be isolated and identified after the protein has been hydrolyzed into its constituent amino acids (and the end amino acid with the colored group attached). For example, lysozyme, a protein in tears and in egg white which has the power of destroying bacteria, has been found by use of the ultracentrifuge to have molecular weight about 14,000, and to consist of about 125 amino-acid residues. Application of the chemical method mentioned above has shown that there is only one free amino group at the chain end, and accordingly it has been concluded that the molecule consists of a single polypeptide chain. If this polypeptide chain were to be stretched out it would be about 450 Å long. However, it has been found, by use of the ultracentrifuge, x-ray diffraction, and other methods of investigation, that the lysozyme molecule is approximately spherical in shape, with diameter about 25 Å. Hence the polypeptide chain cannot be stretched out, but must be folded back and forth, to produce the globular molecule.

The order of amino-acid residues in the polypeptide chains has only recently been determined for a protein, insulin. The insulin molecule has molecular weight about 12,000. It consists of four polypeptide chains, of which two contain 21 amino-acid residues apiece, and the other two contain 30. The sequence of amino acids in the short chains and in the long chains was determined, in the years between 1945 and 1952, by the English biochemist F. Sanger and his collaborators. The four chains in the molecule are attached to one another by sulfur-sulfur bonds, between the halves of cystine residues (see Table 31-1).

Considering their structure, we see that the existence of a great number of different proteins (perhaps 50,000 different proteins in one human being) is not surprising. Protein molecules might differ from one another not only in the numbers of residues of different amino acids, but also in the order of the residues in the polypeptide chains, and the way in which the chains are folded. The number of possible structures is extremely great.

Proteins such as lysozyme, insulin, and hemoglobin have certain special properties that make them valuable to the organism. Lysozyme helps to protect the organism against infection, through its power of causing some bacteria to split open. Insulin is a hormone that assists in the process of oxidation of sugar in the body. Hemoglobin has the power of combining reversibly with oxygen, permitting it to attach oxygen molecules to itself in the lungs, and to liberate them in the tissues. These well-defined properties show that the protein molecules have very definite structures.

A protein that retains its characteristic properties is called a *native protein:* hemoglobin as it exists in the red cell or in a carefully prepared hemoglobin solution, in which it still has the power of combining reversibly with oxygen, is called native hemoglobin. Many proteins lose their characteristic properties very easily. They are then said to have been *denatured.* Hemoglobin can be denatured simply by heating its solution to 65° C. It then coagulates, to form a brick-red insoluble coagulum of denatured hemoglobin. Most other proteins are also denatured by heating to approximately this temperature. Egg white, for example, is a solution consisting mainly of the protein *ovalbumin,* with molecular weight 43,000. Ovalbumin is a soluble protein. When its solution is heated for a little while at about 65° C the ovalbumin is denatured, forming an insoluble white coagulum of denatured ovalbumin. This phenomenon is observed when an egg is cooked.

It is believed that the process of denaturation involves uncoiling the polypeptide chains from the characteristic structure of the native protein. In the coagulum of denatured hemoglobin or denatured ovalbumin the uncoiled polypeptide chains of different molecules of the protein have become tangled up with one another in such a way that they cannot be separated; hence the denatured protein is insoluble.

Some chemical agents, including strong acid, strong alkali, and alcohol, are good denaturing agents.

The principal method of folding polypeptide chains in proteins has recently been discovered, through application of the x-ray diffraction technique. The polypeptide chain is folded into a helix, as shown in Figure 31-3. There are about 3.6 amino-acid residues per turn of the helix—about 18 residues in 5 turns. Each residue is linked to residues in the preceding and following turns by hydrogen bonds between the

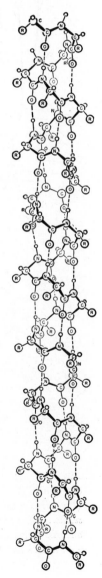

FIGURE 31-3

A drawing of the α helix, a hydrogen-bonded helical configuration of the polypeptide chain present in many proteins. The polypeptide chain is coiled into the configuration of a left-handed screw, with about 3.6 amino-acid residues per turn of the helix. The circles labeled R represent the side chains of the various amino-acid residues.

FIGURE 31-4   *A drawing representing the molecular structure of hair, fingernail, muscle, and related fibrous proteins. The protein molecules have the configuration of the α helix (Fig. 31-3); each molecule is represented in this drawing as a rod with circular cross section. These fibrous proteins contain seven-strand cables, consisting of a central α helix and six others which are twisted about it. The spaces between these cables are filled with additional α helixes.*

N—H groups and the oxygen atom of the C=O group. The side chains R of the different residues project radially from the helix; there is plenty of room for them, so that the sequence of residues can be an arbitrary one. This configuration is called the alpha helix.

Many fibrous proteins, including hair, fingernails, horn, and muscle, consist of polypeptide chains with the configuration of the alpha helix, arranged approximately parallel to one another, with the axis of the helix in the direction of the fiber. In some of these proteins the polypeptide chains, with the configuration of the alpha helix, are twisted about one another, to form cables or ropes (Figure 31-4). Hair and horn can be stretched out to over twice their normal length; this process involves breaking the hydrogen bonds of the alpha helix, and forcing the polypeptide chains into a stretched configuration. Silk fibers consist of polypeptide chains with the stretched configuration, attached to one another by hydrogen bonds that extend laterally.

It has been found that lysozyme, insulin, hemoglobin, and many other soluble proteins also have polypeptide chains folded into the configuration of the alpha helix. In these molecules an individual polypeptide chain does not form a single helix, but instead coils into a short segment, with the configuration of the alpha helix—perhaps half a dozen turns of the helix—and then bridges over to another helical segment.

31–4. *Metabolic Processes. Enzymes and Their Action*

The chemical reactions that take place in a living organism are called *metabolic processes* (Greek *metabole*, change). These reactions are of very many kinds. Let us consider what happens to food that is ingested. The food may contain complex carbohydrates, especially starch, that are split up into simple sugars in the process of digestion, and then pass through the walls of the digestive tract into the blood stream. The sugars may then be converted, in the liver, into glycogen (animal starch), which has the same formula as starch, $(C_6H_{10}O_5)_x$, where x is a large number. Glycogen and other polysaccharides constitute one of the important sources of energy for animals. They combine with oxygen to form carbon dioxide and water, with liberation of energy, part of which can be used for doing work, and part to keep the body warm.

We have mentioned before that proteins in foodstuffs are split in the stomach and intestines into amino acids or simple peptides, which pass through the walls into the blood stream, and then may be built up into the special proteins needed by the organism. A process of tearing down the proteins of the body also takes place. For example, red cells have a lifetime of a few weeks, at the end of which they are destroyed, being replaced by newly formed red cells. The nitrogen of the protein molecules that are torn down is eliminated in the urine, as urea, $CO(NH_2)_2$.

Fats that are ingested are also decomposed in the process of digestion into simpler substances, which then are used by the body for fuel
and as structural material.

Some of the chemical reactions that take place in the body can also
be made to take place in beakers or flasks in the laboratory. For example, a protein can be decomposed into amino acids in the laboratory
by adding strong acids to it and boiling for a long time. Similarly sugar
can be oxidized to carbon dioxide and water; if a little cigarette ash
or other solid material is rubbed onto a cube of sugar, the sugar can
be lighted by a match, and it will then burn in air, producing carbon
dioxide and water:

$$C_{12}H_{22}O_{11} + 12O_2 \longrightarrow 12CO_2 + 11H_2O$$

However, it has not been found possible to cause these chemical reactions to take place in the laboratory at the temperature of the human
body, except in the presence of special substances obtained from plants
or animals. These substances, which are called **enzymes,** are proteins
that have a catalytic power for certain reactions. Thus the saliva contains a special protein, an enzyme called *salivary amylase* or *ptyalin,*
which has the power of catalyzing the decomposition of starch into a
sugar, maltose, $C_{12}H_{22}O_{11}$. The reaction that is catalyzed by salivary
amylase is

$$(C_6H_{10}O_5)_x + \frac{x}{2}\,H_2O \longrightarrow \frac{x}{2}\,C_{12}H_{22}O_{11}$$

Saliva is mixed with a food, such as potato, while the food is being
chewed, and during the first few minutes that the food is in the stomach the salivary amylase causes the conversion of the starch into maltose
to take place.

Similarly there is an enzyme in the stomach, *pepsin,* which has the
power of serving as a very effective catalyst for the reaction of hydrolysis of proteins into amino acids, that is, for splitting the peptide bond
by reaction with water, to form an amino group and a carboxyl group.
Pepsin does its work most effectively in a somewhat acidic solution.
Gastric juice is in fact rather strongly acidic, its pH being about 0.8—
it is hence somewhat more strongly acidic than 0.1 F hydrochloric acid.

The stomach also contains an enzyme, *rennin,* which assists in the
digestion of milk, and another enzyme, *lipase,* which catalyzes the
decomposition of fats into simpler substances. Additional enzymes
involved in the digestion of polysaccharides, proteins, and fats take
part in the continuation of the digestion in the intestines; these enzymes are contained in the intestinal juice, pancreatic juice, and bile.

The chemical reactions that take place in the blood and in the
cells of the body are also in general catalyzed by enzymes. For example,
the process of oxidation of sugar is a complicated one, involving a

number of steps, and it is believed that a special enzyme is present to catalyze each of these steps. It has been estimated that there may be twenty thousand or thirty thousand different enzymes in the human body, each constructed in such a way as to permit it to serve as an effective catalyst for a particular chemical reaction useful to the organism.

In recent years many enzymes have been isolated and purified. Many have, indeed, been crystallized. A great deal of work has been done in an effort to discover the mechanism of the catalytic activity of enzymes. So far, however, no one has succeeded in determining the structure of any enzyme, nor in finding out how the enzyme does its job. This general problem is one of the most important of all of the problems of biochemistry.

31–5. *Vitamins*

It was mentioned above that man requires nine amino acids in his diet, in order to keep in good health. It is not enough, however, that the diet contain proteins that provide these nine amino acids, and a sufficient supply of carbohydrates and fats to provide energy. Other substances, both inorganic and organic, are also essential to health.

Among the inorganic constituents that must be present in foods in order that a human being be kept in good health we may mention sodium ion, chloride ion, potassium ion, calcium ion, magnesium ion, iodide ion, phosphorus (which may be ingested as phosphate), and several of the transition metals. Iron is necessary for the synthesis of hemoglobin and of some other protein molecules in the body which serve as enzymes; in the absence of sufficient iron in the diet anemia will develop. Copper is also required; it seems to be involved in the process of manufacture of hemoglobin and the other iron-containing compounds in the body.

The organic compounds other than the essential amino acids which are required for health are called *vitamins*. Man is known to require at least thirteen vitamins: Vitamin A, B_1 (thiamine), B_2 (riboflavin), B_6 (pyridoxin), B_{12}, C (ascorbic acid), D, K, niacin, pantothenic acid, inositol, para-aminobenzoic acid, and biotin.

Although it has been recognized for over a century that certain diseases occur when the diet is restricted, and can be prevented by additions to the diet (such as lime juice for the prevention of scurvy), the identification of the essential food factors as chemical substances was not made until a few years ago. Progress in the isolation of these substances and in the determination of their structure has been rapid in recent years, and many of the vitamins are now being made synthetically, for use as dietary supplements. It is usually possible for a diet to be obtained that provides all of the essential food substances in satisfactory amounts, but in some cases it is wise to have the diet supplemented by vitamin preparations.

Vitamin A has the formula $C_{20}H_{29}OH$, and the structure

It is a yellow, oily substance, which occurs in nature in butter fat and fish oils. Lack of Vitamin A in the diet causes a scaly condition of the eyes, and similar abnormality of the skin in general, together with a decreased resistance to infection of the eyes and skin. In addition there occurs a decreased ability to see at night, called *night-blindness*. There are two mechanisms for vision, one situated in the cones of the retina of the eye, which are especially concentrated in the neighborhood of the fovea (the center of vision), and the other situated in the rods of the retina. Color vision, which is the ordinary vision, used when the intensity of light is normal, involves the retinal cones. Night vision, which operates when the intensity of light is very small, involves the rods; it is not associated with a recognition of color. It has been found that a certain protein, *visual purple*, which occurs in the rods, takes part in the process of night vision. Vitamin A is the prosthetic group of the visual purple molecule, and a deficiency in this vitamin leads for this reason to a decrease in the ability to see at night.

A protein such as visual purple which has a characteristic chemical group other than the amino acid residues as part of its structure is called a *conjugated protein*. Such a characteristic group in a conjugated protein is called a *prosthetic group* (Greek *prosthesis*, an addition). Hemoglobin is another example of a conjugated protein. Each hemoglobin molecule consists of a simple protein called globin to which there are attached four prosthetic groups called *heme groups*. The formula of the heme group is $C_{34}H_{32}O_4N_4Fe$.

It is not essential that vitamin A itself be present in food in order to prevent the vitamin A deficiency symptoms. Certain hydrocarbons, the *carotenes*, with formula $C_{40}H_{56}$ (similar in structure to lycopene, Figure 30-1) can be converted into vitamin A in the body. These substances, which are designated by the name *provitamin A*, are red and yellow substances which are found in carrots, tomatoes, and other vegetables and fruits, as well as in butter, milk, green leafy vegetables, and eggs.

Thiamine, Vitamin B₁, has the following formula (that shown is for thiamine chloride):

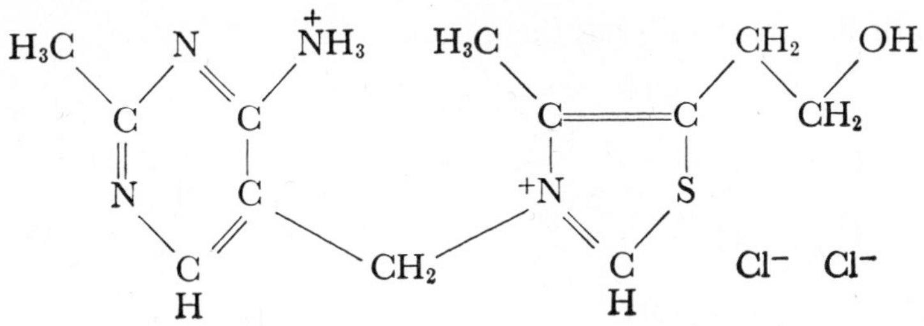

A lack of thiamine in the diet causes the disease beri-beri, a nerve disease which in past years was common in the Orient. Just before 1900 it was found by Eijkman in Java that beri-beri occurred as a consequence of a diet consisting largely of polished rice, and that it could be cured by adding the rice polishings to the diet. In 1911 Casimir Funk assumed that beri-beri and similar diseases were due to lack of a substance present in a satisfactory diet and missing from a deficient diet, and he attempted to isolate the substance the lack of which was responsible for beri-beri. He coined the name vitamin for substances of this sort (he spelled it vitamine because he thought that the substances were amines). The structure of vitamin B_1, thiamine, was determined by R. R. Williams, E. R. Buchman, and their collaborators in 1936.

Thiamine seems to be important for metabolic processes in the cells of the body, but the exact way in which it operates is not known. There is some evidence that it is the prosthetic group for an enzyme involved in the oxidation of carbohydrates. The vitamin is present in potatoes, whole cereals, milk, pork, eggs, and other vegetables and meats.

Riboflavin (Vitamin B_2) has the following structure:

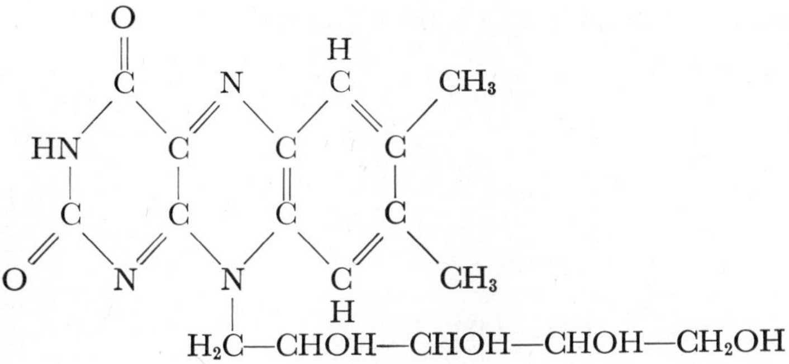

$$H_2C—CHOH—CHOH—CHOH—CH_2OH$$

It seems to be essential for growth and for a healthy condition of the skin. Riboflavin is known to be the prosthetic group of an enzyme, called *yellow enzyme*, which catalyzes the oxidation of glucose and certain other substances in the animal body.

Vitamin B₆ (pyridoxin) has the formula

$$
\begin{array}{ccccc}
\text{H} & & \text{N} & & \text{CH}_3 \\
\diagdown & & \diagup\diagdown & & \diagup \\
 & \text{C} & & \text{C} & \\
 & \| & & | & \\
 & \text{C} & & \text{C} & \\
\diagup & & \diagdown\diagup & & \diagdown \\
\text{H}_2\text{C} & & \text{C} & & \text{OH} \\
| & & & & \\
\text{OH} & & \text{H}_2\text{C} &\!\!-\!\!& \text{OH}
\end{array}
$$

It is present in yeast, liver, rice polishings, and other plant and animal foods, and is also produced synthetically. It has the power of stimulating growth, and of preventing skin eruptions (dermatitis).

Vitamin B₁₂ is involved in the manufacture of the red corpuscles of the blood. It can be used for the treatment of pernicious anemia, and it is perhaps the most potent substance known in its physiological activity: 1 microgram per day (1×10^{-6} g) of vitamin B₁₂ is effective in the control of the disease. The vitamin can be isolated from liver tissue, and is also produced by molds and other micro-organisms. The structure of the molecule of vitamin B₁₂ has not yet been determined. It is known that the molecular weight is about 1400, and that each molecule contains one cobalt atom. This is the only compound of cobalt that is known to be present in the human body.

Ascorbic acid, Vitamin C, is a water-soluble vitamin of great importance. A deficiency of vitamin C in the diet leads to scurvy, a disease characterized by loss of weight, general weakness, hemorrhagic condition of the gums and skin, loosening of the teeth, and other symptoms. Sound tooth development seems to depend upon a satisfactory supply of this vitamin, and a deficiency is thought to cause a tendency to incidence of a number of diseases.

The formula of ascorbic acid is the following:

$$
\begin{array}{ccccc}
 & & \text{O} & & \\
 & & \| & & \\
\text{HO} & & \text{C} & & \\
\diagdown & & \diagup\diagdown & & \\
 & \text{C} & & & \\
 & \| & & \text{O} & \\
 & \text{C} & & \diagup & \\
\diagup & & \diagdown & & \\
\text{HO} & & \text{C} & & \text{CH}_2\!\!-\!\!\text{OH} \\
 & \diagup & \diagdown & \diagup & \\
\text{H} & & \text{C} & & \\
 & \diagup & \diagdown & & \\
\text{H} & & \text{OH} & &
\end{array}
$$

The vitamin is present in many foods, especially fresh green peppers, turnip greens, parsnip greens, spinach, orange juice, and tomato juice. The daily requirement of vitamin C is about 60 mg.

Vitamin D is necessary in the diet for the prevention of rickets, a disease involving malformation of the bones and unsatisfactory development of the teeth. There are several substances with anti-rachitic activity. The form that occurs in oils from fish livers is called vitamin D_3; it has the following chemical structure:

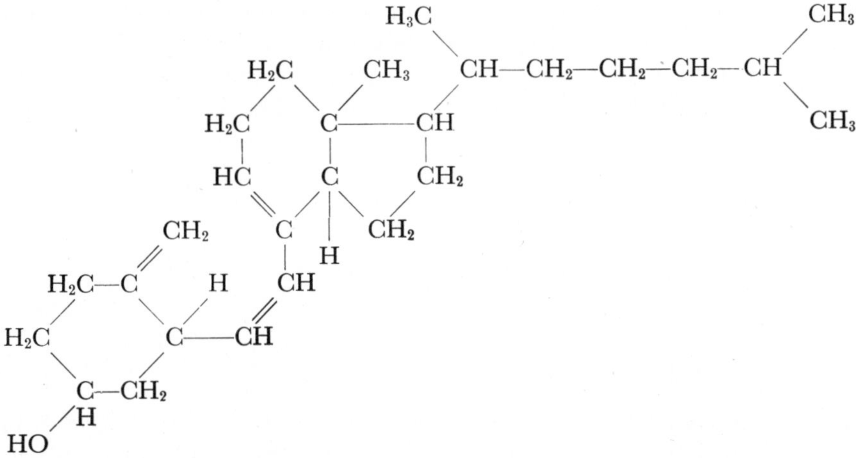

Only a very small amount of vitamin D is necessary for health— approximately 0.01 mg per day. The vitamin is a fat-soluble vitamin, occurring in cod liver oil, egg yolks, milk, and in very small amounts in other foods. Cereals, yeast, and milk acquire an added vitamin D potency when irradiated with ultraviolet light. The radiation converts a fatty substance (a *lipid*) that is present in the food, a substance called *ergosterol*, into another substance, *calciferol* (vitamin D_2), which has vitamin D activity. The structure of calciferol is closely related to that of vitamin D_3.

Whereas most vitamins are harmless even when large quantities are ingested, vitamin D is harmful when taken in large amounts.

Vitamin E, while not necessary for health, seems to be required for the reproduction and lactation of animals. Niacin, a member of the B group of vitamins, is necessary for the prevention of the deficiency disease pellagra. Pantothenic acid, inositol, *p*-aminobenzoic acid, and biotin are substances involved in the process of normal growth. Vitamin K is a vitamin that prevents bleeding, by assisting in the process of clotting of the blood.

It is interesting that many "simpler organisms" do not require so many substances for growth as does man. It was mentioned above that the red bread mold, *Neurospora*, can synthesize all of the amino acids present in proteins, whereas man is unable to synthesize nine of them, but must obtain them in his diet. The red bread mold is also able to manufacture other substances that man requires as vitamins. The only organic growth substance required by this organism is biotin. Similarly the food requirements of the rat, while greater than those of *Neurospora*, are not so great as those of man. The rat, for example, does not require ascorbic acid (vitamin C) in its diet, but is able to synthesize this substance, which is present as an important constituent in the tissues of the animal.

31–6. Hormones

Another class of substances of importance in the activity of the human body consists of the *hormones*, which are substances that serve as messengers from one part of the body to another, moving by way of the blood stream. The hormones control various physiological processes. For example, when a man is suddenly frightened, a substance called *epinephrine* (also called adrenalin) is secreted by the suprarenal glands, small glands which lie just above the kidneys. The formula of epinephrine is

$$
\begin{array}{c}
\text{OH} \\
| \\
\text{CH} \quad \text{NH} \\
\diagdown \quad \diagup \diagdown \\
\text{CH}_2 \quad \text{CH}_3
\end{array}
$$

HO⟨ring⟩OH

When epinephrine is introduced into the blood stream it speeds up the action of the heart, causes the blood vessels to contract, thus increasing the blood pressure, and causes glucose to be released from the liver, providing an immediate source of extra energy.

Thyroxin is a secretion of the thyroid gland which controls metabolism. *Insulin* is a secretion of the pancreas which controls the combustion of carbohydrates. Both of these hormones are proteins, thyroxin having a prosthetic group which contains iodine. Many other hormones are known, some of which are proteins and some simpler chemical substances.

It has been recognized that diseases (such as goiter) affecting the thyroid gland may arise from a deficient production of thyroxin, which can be remedied by the introduction of added iodide ion into the diet. The disease *diabetes mellitus*, characterized by the appearance of sugar in the urine and perhaps due to a deficient production of the hormone insulin, has in recent decades been treated by the injection of insulin, obtained from the pancreatic glands of animals. The hormones *cortisone* and *ACTH* (adrenocorticotropic hormone) have been shown recently to have strong therapeutic activity toward rheumatoid arthritis and some other diseases.

31–7. Chemistry and Medicine

From the earliest times chemicals have been used in the treatment of disease. The substances that were first used as drugs are natural products such as in the leaves, branches, and roots of plants. As the alchemists discovered or made new chemical substances, these substances were tried out to see if they had physiological activity, and many of them were introduced into early medical practice. For example, both mercuric chloride, $HgCl_2$, and mercurous chloride, Hg_2Cl_2, were used in medicine, mercuric chloride as an antiseptic, and mercurous chloride, taken internally, as a cathartic and general medicament.

The modern period of *chemotherapy*, the treatment of disease by use of chemical substances, began with the work of Paul Ehrlich (1854–1916). It was known at the beginning of the present century that certain organic compounds of arsenic would kill protozoa, parasitic micro-organisms responsible for certain diseases, and Ehrlich set himself the task of synthesizing a large number of arsenic compounds, in an effort to find one which would be at the same time toxic (poisonous) to protozoa in the human body and non-toxic to the human host of the micro-organism. After preparing many compounds he synthesized *arsphenamine*, which has the following structure:

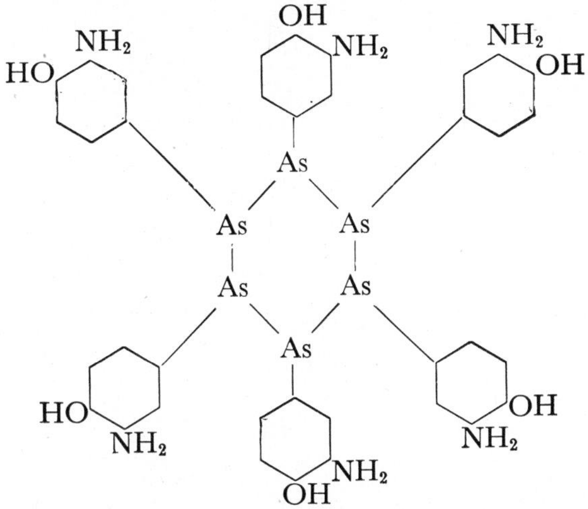

This compound used to be called 606; the name is said to have resulted from the fact that it was the 606th compound of arsenic synthesized by Ehrlich in his investigation.

Arsphenamine has been found to be extremely valuable. Its greatest use is in the treatment of syphilis; the drug attacks the micro-organism responsible for this disease, *Spirocheta pallida*. It has also been useful in the treatment of some other diseases. At the present time it seems to be in the process of being superseded by penicillin (which we shall discuss below) in the treatment of syphilis.

Ehrlich later synthesized another compound, *neoarsphenamine*, which is somewhat superior to arsphenamine for the treatment of syphilis.

It is closely related in structure, differing only in having a more complicated side chain in place of three of the amino groups of the molecule.

Since Ehrlich's time there has been continual progress in the development of new chemotherapeutic agents. Fifteen years ago the infectious diseases constituted the principal cause of death; now most of these diseases are under effective control by chemotherapeutic agents, some of which have been synthesized in the laboratory and some of which have been isolated from micro-organisms. At the present time only a few of the infectious diseases, especially certain viral diseases, such as poliomyelitis, constitute major hazards to the health of man,

TABLE 31-2   *Structural Formulas of Sulfa Drugs and Related Substances*

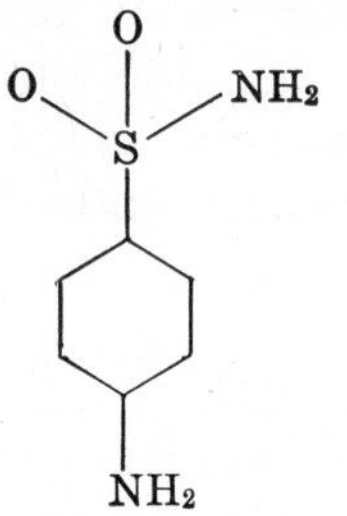

Sulfanilamide

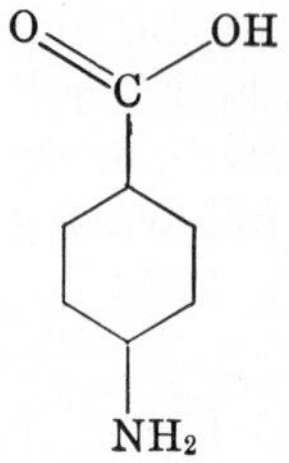

Para-aminobenzoic acid

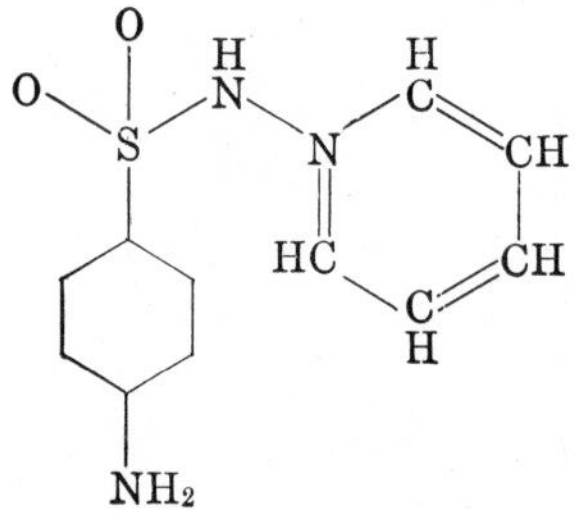

Sulfapyridine

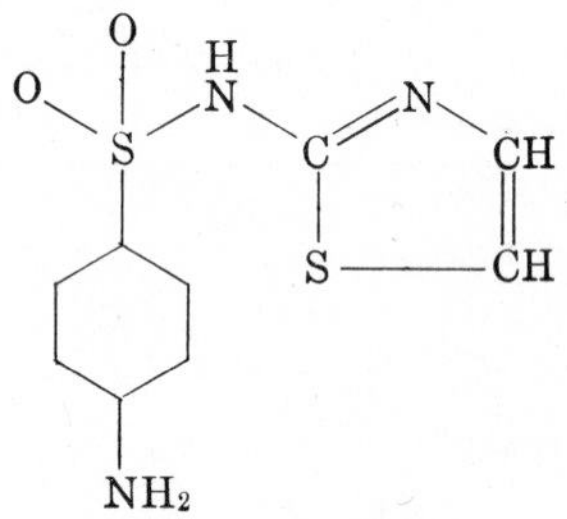

Sulfathiazole

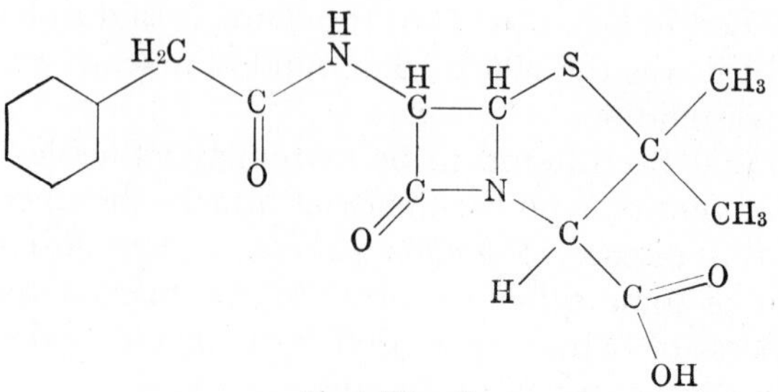

Penicillin G

and we may confidently anticipate that the control of these diseases by chemotherapeutic agents will be achieved in a few years.

The recent period of rapid progress began with the discovery of the **sulfa drugs** by G. Domagk. In 1935 Domagk discovered that the compound prontosil, a derivative of *sulfanilamide*, was effective in the control of streptococcus infections. It was soon found by other workers that sulfanilamide itself is just as effective in the treatment of these diseases, and that it could be administered by mouth. The formula of sulfanilamide is given in Table 31-2. Sulfanilamide is effective against hemolytic streptococcic infections and meningococcic infections. As soon as the value of sulfanilamide was recognized chemists synthesized hundreds of related substances, and investigations were made of their usefulness as bacteriostatic agents (agents with the power of controlling the spread of bacterial infections). It was found that many of these related substances are valuable, and their use is now an important part of medical practice. *Sulfapyridine* has been found valuable for the control of pneumococcic pneumonia (pneumonia due to the *Pneumococcus* micro-organisms), as well as of other pneumococcic infections and gonorrhea. *Sulfathiazole* is used for these infections and also for the control of staphylococcic infections, which occur especially in carbuncles and eruptions of the skin. These and other sulfa drugs are all derivatives of sulfanilamide itself, obtained by replacing one of the hydrogen atoms of the amide group (the NH_2 bonded to the sulfur atom) by some other group (Table 31-2).

The introduction of **penicillin** into medical treatment was the next great step forward. In 1929 Professor Alexander Fleming, a bacteriologist working in the University of London, noticed that bacteria that he was growing in a dish in his laboratory were not able to grow in the region immediately surrounding a bit of mold that had accidentally begun to develop. He surmised that the mold was able to produce a chemical substance that had *bacteriostatic action*, the power of preventing the bacteria from growing, and he made a preliminary investigation of the nature of this substance. Ten years later, perhaps spurred on by the successful use of the sulfa drugs in medicine, Professor Howard Florey of the University of Oxford decided to make a careful study of the antibacterial substances that had been reported in order to see whether they would be similarly useful in the treatment of disease. When he tested the bacteriostatic power of the liquid in which the mold *penicillium notatum* that had been observed by Fleming was growing, he found it to be very great, and within a few months the new antibiotic substance penicillin was being used in the treatment of patients. Through the cooperative effort of many investigators in the United States and England, rapid progress was made during the next two or three years in the determination of the structure of penicillin, the development of methods of manufacturing it in large quantities, and the investigation of the diseases that could be effectively treated by use of it. Within less than a decade this new antibiotic agent has become the most valuable of all drugs. It provides an effective therapeutic treatment of many diseases.

The structure of penicillin is shown in Table 31-2. The substance has been synthesized, but no cheap method of synthesizing it has been developed, and the large amount of penicillin that is being manufactured and used in the treatment of disease is made by growing the mold penicillium in a suitable medium and then extracting the penicillin from the medium. Important forward steps in the introduction of penicillin into medical treatment were the development of strains of the mold which produced the desired penicillin in large quantities, and the discovery of the best medium on which to grow the mold.

It is interesting that a number of slightly different penicillins are formed in nature by different strains of the mold. The formula in Table 31-2 represents benzyl penicillin (penicillin G), which is the product that is now manufactured and used. Other naturally occurring penicillins differ from benzyl penicillin only with respect to the part of the molecule that is shown on the left side of the structure. In benzyl penicillin there is indicated a benzyl group, C_6H_5—CH_2—, in this position. Penicillin K contains the normal heptyl group in this position, the hydrocarbon chain $CH_3CH_2CH_2CH_2CH_2CH_2$—. It is not so effective as penicillin G in the treatment of infections. Scores of other penicillins have been made and investigated.

The spectacular success of penicillin as a chemotherapeutic agent has led to the search for other antibiotic products of living organisms. *Streptomycin*, which is produced by the mold *Actinomyces griseus*, has been found to be valuable in the treatment of diseases that are not effectively controlled by penicillin, and some other bacteriostatic agents also have been found to have significant value.

Another very great step forward has been made during the past two years by the discovery of substances which can control the development of viral infections. Penicillin, streptomycin, and the sulfa drugs are effective against bacteria but not against viruses. It has recently been found, however, that *chloramphenicol* (Chloromycetin) and *aureomycin*, both of which are substances manufactured by molds (the molds *Streptomyces venezuele* and *Streptomyces aureofaciens* respectively), have the power of controlling certain viral infections.

The Relation between the Molecular Structure of Substances and Their Physiological Activity.   No one knows what the relation between the molecular structure of substances and their physiological activity is. We know the structural formulas of many drugs, vitamins, and hormones—some of these formulas have been given in the preceding sections. It is probable, however, that most of these substances produce their physiological action by interacting with or combining with proteins in the human body or in the bacterium or virus that they counteract; and we do not yet know the structure of any of these proteins.

Ten years ago a suggestion was made about the way in which the sulfa drugs exercise their bacteriostatic action. It seems probable that this suggestion is essentially correct. It was found that a concentration of sulfanilamide or other sulfa drug that would prevent bacterial cultures from growing under ordinary circumstances lost this power when some para-aminobenzoic acid was added. The amount of para-aminobenzoic acid required to permit the bacteria to increase in number was found to be approximately proportional to the excess of the amount of the sulfa drug over the minimum that would produce bacteriostatic action. This *competition* between the sulfa drug and para-aminobenzoic acid can be given a reasonable explanation. Let us assume that the bacteria need to have some para-aminobenzoic acid in order to grow; that is, that para-aminobenzoic acid is a vitamin for the bacteria. Probably it serves as a vitamin by combining with a protein to form an essential enzyme; presumably it serves as the prosthetic group of this enzyme. It is likely that the bacterium synthesizes a protein molecule which has a small region, a cavity, on one side of itself into which the para-aminobenzoic acid molecule just fits.

The sulfanilamide molecule is closely similar in structure to the para-aminobenzoic molecule (see Table 31-2). Each of the molecules contains a benzene ring, an amino group ($-NH_2$) attached to one of the carbon atoms of the benzene ring, and another group attached to the opposite carbon atom. It seems not unlikely that the sulfanilamide molecule can fit into the cavity on the protein, thus preventing the para-aminobenzoic molecule from getting into this place. If it is further assumed that the sulfanilamide molecule is not able to function in such a way as to make the complex with the protein able to act as an enzyme, then the explanation of the action of sulfanilamide is complete. It is thought that the protein fits tightly around the benzene ring and the amino group, but not around the other end of the molecule. The evidence for this is that derivatives of sulfanilamide in which various other groups are attached to the sulfur atom are effective as bacteriostatic agents, whereas compounds in which other groups are attached to the benzene ring or the amino group are not effective.

Nobody knows why penicillin is able to control many bacterial infections, nor why chloramphenicol and aureomycin attack viruses; but we may hope that further studies will lead to the solution of this great problem of the molecular basis of the action of drugs, and we may then expect great further progress to occur in medical research. When the mechanism of the action of drugs has been understood, it will be possible for investigators to attack the problem presented by a new disease in a logical and systematic way; new chemotherapeutic agents can then be developed by logical, scientific procedures, rather than by chance.

Concepts, Facts, and Terms Introduced in This Chapter

The nature of life. Living organism, dead organism. Ability to reproduce. Plant viruses. Structure of organisms. Cells. Cell walls, cell contents. Cytoplasm. Red corpuscles. Bone constituents. Collagen. Proteins. Hemoglobin. The twenty-four amino acids in plant and animal proteins. The nine essential amino acids. Right-handed and left-handed molecules. Polypeptide chains. The structure of proteins. Metabolic processes. Enzymes and their action. Salivary amylase, pepsin, rennin, lipase. Vitamins: Vitamin A, B_1, B_2, B_6, B_{12}, C, D. Conjugated proteins. Prosthetic group. Hormones: epinephrine, thyroxin, insulin, cortisone, ACTH. Chemotherapy. Arsphenamine, sulfanilamide and other sulfa drugs, penicillin, streptomycin, chloramphenicol, aureomycin. Bacteriostatic action of sulfa drugs through competition with a bacterial growth substance, para-aminobenzoic acid.

Reference Books

Garrett Hardin, *Biology, Its Human Implications*, W. H. Freeman and Company, San Francisco, **1949.**

Roger J. Williams and Ernest Beerstecher, Jr., *An Introduction to Biochemistry*, D. Van Nostrand Company, Inc., New York, **1948.**

W. Gortner and R. A. Gortner, Jr., *Outlines of Biochemistry*, John Wiley and Sons, Inc., New York, **1949.**

J. H. Northrop, *Crystalline Enzymes*, Columbia University Press, New York, **1949.**

M. Bodansky, *Introduction to Physiological Chemistry*, John Wiley and Sons, Inc., New York, **1938.**

H. C. Sherman, *Chemistry of Food and Nutrition*, The Macmillan Company, New York, **1941.**

F. C. McLean, "Bone," *Scientific American*, **192**, 84, February **1955.**

G. W. Gray, "Unknown Viruses," *Scientific American*, **192,** 60, March **1955.**

Chapter 32

Nuclear Chemistry

The field of science dealing with the nature and reactions of the fundamental particles and of atomic nuclei has developed more rapidly during the past twenty years than any other field. Work in this branch of science has been carried out by both physicists and chemists, and the field itself may be properly considered to be a borderline field between physics and chemistry. The discussion of nuclear science in the present chapter, under the title "Nuclear Chemistry," is designed to cover the whole subject, but with special emphasis on its chemical aspects.

Nuclear chemistry has now become a large and very important branch of science. Over four hundred radioactive nuclides (isotopes) have been made in the laboratory, whereas only about three hundred stable nuclides have been detected in nature. Three elements—technetium (43), astatine (85), and promethium (61)—as well as some transuranium elements, seem not to occur in nature, and are available only as products of artificial transmutation. The use of radioactive isotopes as "tracers" has become a valuable technique in scientific and medical research. The controlled release of nuclear energy promises to lead us into a new world, in which the achievement of man is no longer severely limited by the supply of energy available to him.

32–1. *Natural Radioactivity*

After their discovery of polonium and radium in 1896 (Chapter 3), the Curies found that radium chloride could be separated from barium chloride by fractional precipitation of the aqueous solution by addition of alcohol, and by 1902 Madame Curie had prepared 0.1 g of nearly pure radium chloride, with radioactivity about 3,000,000 times that of uranium. Within a few years it had been found that natural radioactive materials emit three kinds of rays capable of sensitizing the photographic plate (Chapter 3). These rays, alpha rays, beta rays, and gamma rays, are affected differently by a magnetic field (Figure 3-10). Alpha rays are the nuclei of helium atoms, moving at high speeds; beta rays are electrons, also moving at high speeds; and gamma rays are photons, with very short wavelengths.

It was soon discovered that the rays from radium and other radio-active elements cause regression of cancerous growths. These rays also affect normal cells, "radium burns" being caused by overexposure; but often the cancerous cells are more sensitive to radiation than normal cells, and can be killed by suitable treatment without serious injury to

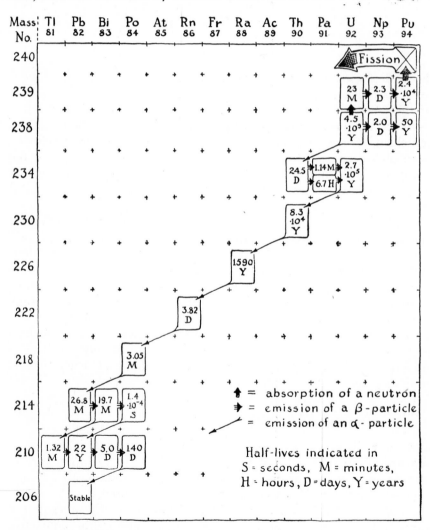

FIGURE 32-1   *The uranium-radium series.*

normal tissues. The medical use in the treatment of cancer is the main use for radium. Since about 1950 considerable use has also been made of the artificial radioactive isotope cobalt 60 as a substitute for radium (Section 32–4).

Through the efforts of many investigators the chemistry of the radioactive elements of the uranium series and the thorium series was unraveled during the first two decades of the twentieth century, and that of the neptunium series during a few years from 1939 on.

The Uranium Series of Radioactive Disintegrations.   When an alpha particle (He^{++}) is emitted by an atomic nucleus the nuclear charge decreases by two units; the element hence is transmuted into the element two columns to the left in the periodic table. Its mass number (atomic weight) decreases by 4, the mass of the alpha particle. When a beta particle (an electron) is emitted by a nucleus the nuclear charge

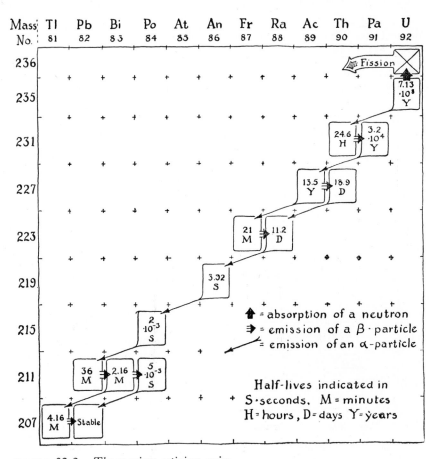

FIGURE 32-2   *The uranium-actinium series.*

is increased by one unit, with no change in mass number (only a very small decrease in atomic weight); the element is transmuted into the element one column to its right. No change in atomic number or atomic weight is caused by emission of a gamma ray.

The nuclear reactions in the **uranium-radium series** are shown in Figure 32-1. The principal isotope of uranium, U^{238}, constitutes 99.28% of the natural element. This isotope has a half-life of 4,500,000,000 years. It decomposes by emitting an alpha particle and forming Th^{234}. This isotope of thorium undergoes decomposition with β-emission,* forming Pa^{234}, which in turn forms U^{234}. Five successive α-emissions then occur, giving Pb^{214}, which ultimately changes to Pb^{206}, a stable isotope of lead.

The **uranium-actinium series,** shown in Figure 32-2, is a similar series beginning with U^{235}, which occurs to the extent of 0.71% in natural uranium. It leads, through the emission of seven alpha particles and four beta particles, to the stable isotope Pb^{207}.

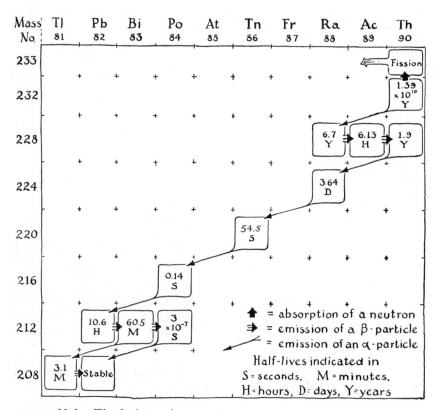

FIGURE 32-3   *The thorium series.*

* It is interesting to note that two isotopes Pa^{234} exist, with different half-lives.

The Thorium Series. The third natural radioactive series begins with the long-lived naturally occurring isotope of thorium, Th^{232}, which has half-life 1.39×10^{10} years (Figure 32-3). It leads to another stable isotope of lead, Pb^{208}.

The Neptunium Series. During the last war the fourth radioactive series was discovered.* This series (Figure 32-4) is named after its longest-lived member, which is Np^{237}. None of the members of the chain has been found in nature except the final stable product, Bi^{209}.

The nature of radioactive disintegration within each of the four series—the emission of β-particles, with mass nearly zero, or of α-particles, with mass 4—is such that all the members of a series have mass

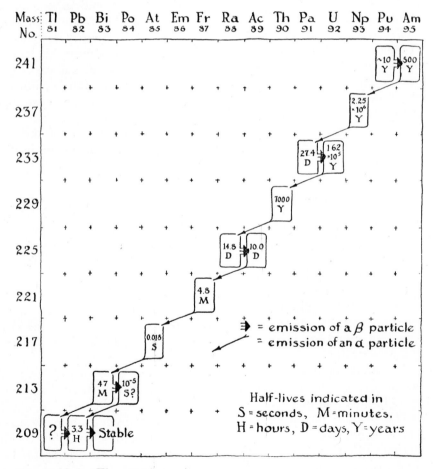

FIGURE 32-4   *The neptunium series.*

* See G. T. Seaborg, *Chem. and Eng. News,* **26,** 1902 (1948).

numbers differing by a multiple of 4. The four series can hence be classified as follows (n being integral):

The $4n$ series = the thorium series
The $4n + 1$ series = the neptunium series
The $4n + 2$ series = the uranium-radium series
The $4n + 3$ series = the uranium-actinium series

32–2. *The Age of the Earth*

Measurements made on rocks containing radioactive elements can be interpreted to provide values of the age of the rocks, and hence of the age of the earth; that is, the time that has elapsed since the oldest rocks were laid down. For example, one gram of U^{238} would in its half-life of 4.5 billion years decompose to leave 0.5000 g of U^{238} and to produce 0.0674 g of helium and 0.4326 g of Pb^{206}. (Each atom of U^{238} which decomposes forms eight atoms of helium, with total mass 32, leaving one atom of Pb^{206}.) Analyses of the amount of helium gas entrapped in uranium ores have shown somewhat smaller ratios of helium to uranium than 0.0674/0.500; the ratios found indicate, however, that the rocks are very old, up to a maximum of 2.8 billion years.

Values of about two billion years for the age of ores of thorium have also been estimated from the excess of Pb^{208} found in the lead in these ores.

32–3. *The Fundamental Particles*

All of the simple particles which exist in nature have been found to undergo reactions in which they are converted into or obtained from other particles or radiation. There are, then, no particles which are immutable and which can be said to be truly fundamental.

The twelve particles mentioned in Table 32-1 are the simplest known particles. These particles can be considered to serve as the building units for more complicated forms of matter. Thus the deuteron, the nucleus of H^2, can be considered to be built up from a proton and a neutron.*

The **electron** has been discussed throughout this book. It was the first of the simple particles to be recognized, having been discovered by J. J. Thomson in 1897.

The **proton**, the nucleus of the ordinary hydrogen atom, was observed as positively charged rays in a discharge tube in 1886, by the German physicist E. Goldstein. The nature of the rays was not at first

---

* It is not required that the deuteron be considered to be built from a proton and a neutron. For example, it might be described as built from two neutrons and a positron, or from some other combination of known particles. However, the properties of atomic nuclei are most simply explained if we assume that they are composed of protons and neutrons.

TABLE 32-1   *The Simplest Known Particles*

POSITIVE PARTICLES ELECTRIC CHARGE e	NEUTRAL PARTICLES CHARGE 0	NEGATIVE PARTICLES CHARGE −e
Proton mass 1836.6	Neutron mass 1839.0	Negative proton mass 1836.6
Positive mesons masses about 216, 285, 900	Neutral meson mass about 300	Negative mesons masses about 216, 285, 900
Positron mass 1	Neutrino mass 0 or nearly 0 (Existence surmised but not yet proved)	Electron mass 1

Masses given in units equal to the mass of the electron (atomic weight 0.0005485 on the chemists' scale).

understood. In 1898 the German physicist W. Wien determined their ratio of charge to mass, and more accurate measurements of this sort, which verified the existence of protons as independent particles in a tube containing ionized hydrogen at low pressure, were made by J. J. Thompson in 1906.

The next very simple particle to be discovered was the **positron,** found in 1932 by Professor Carl Anderson of the California Institute of Technology. The positrons were found among the particles produced by the interaction of cosmic rays with matter. They seem to be identical with electrons except that their charge is $+e$ instead of $-e$. Their span of life as free particles is very short, usually less than a microsecond (1×10^{-6} sec).

The **neutron** was discovered by the English physicist J. Chadwick, also in the year 1932. Neutrons are particles with mass only slightly larger than that of the proton, and with zero electric charge. Because they have no electric charge, neutrons interact with other forms of matter only very weakly, and it is accordingly hard to prove their existence by direct methods. On passage through solid substances they undergo deflection only when they approach extremely closely to nuclei, that is, when they undergo direct collisions with nuclei. Because neutrons and nuclei are so small, the chance of collision is very small and neutrons are accordingly able to penetrate through great thicknesses of heavy elements.

The existence of the *negative proton* has not yet been thoroughly verified, but in 1954 it was reported by Marcel Schein of the University of Chicago that a pattern of tracks of ionizing particles found in photographic emulsions exposed, with use of a balloon, for six hours at an altitude exceeding 100,000 feet could be well accounted for on the assumption that the particles were produced during the annihilation of a negative proton by a positive proton, the negative proton being in the cosmic rays coming from outside the atmosphere, and that the observed phenomenon could not be accounted for in any other way. The negative proton is presumably a stable particle, but any negative proton in contact with ordinary matter would be at once destroyed through reaction with a positive proton.

Mesons were discovered in 1936, by the American physicists Carl Anderson and Seth Neddermeyer at the California Institute of Technology. They are produced by interaction of cosmic rays with matter. They are either positive or negative in charge; neutral mesons may also exist. Mesons are known with masses about 216 and 285 times that of the electron (called μ mesons and π mesons, respectively), and there is evidence also for the existence of still heavier mesons (with mass about 900 times that of the electron). Mesons have very short lives; they probably undergo decomposition into a positron or electron and two neutrinos.

The **neutrino** is a particle with very small or zero mass and with no electric charge. Its existence was surmised about 1925, in order to account for some experimental results on the emission of beta particles by radioactive substances which seemed to contradict the law of the conservation of energy. Since then a number of further experiments have been carried out in an effort to verify the existence of the neutrino. These experiments also indicate that neutrinos exist, but have not yet provided proof of their existence. Physicists seem generally to feel that the neutrino should be accepted as one of the simple particles.

The **photon** or light quantum may also be described as one of the fundamental particles. Newton discussed both a corpuscular theory and a wave theory of light. During the nineteenth century, however, the wave character alone of light was emphasized, in connection with experiments on the diffraction of light. Then in 1905 Einstein pointed out that a number of puzzling experimental results could be interpreted in a simple way if it were assumed that light (visible light, ultraviolet light, x-rays, etc.) has some of the properties of particles. He called these "particles" of light "light quanta," and the name photons has since been introduced. The amount of light constituting a light quantum is determined by the frequency of the light, $\nu = \frac{c}{\lambda}$ (that is, frequency [in $\sec^{-1}$] = velocity of light [in cm/sec] divided by wavelength [in cm]). The amount of energy in a light quantum is $h\nu$, where h is *Planck's constant*, 6.60×10^{-27} erg sec.

The properties of light cannot be described completely by analogy with either ordinary waves or ordinary particles. In the discussion of some phenomena the description of light as wave motion is found to be the more useful, and in the discussion of other phenomena the description of light in terms of photons is to be preferred.

This *wave-particle duality* applies also to matter. Electrons, protons, neutrons, and other material particles have been found to have properties which we usually correlate with wave motion. For example, a beam of electrons can be diffracted in the same way as a beam of x-rays. The wavelength associated with an electron depends upon the speed with which it is traveling. For electrons which have been accelerated by a potential drop of 40,000 volts, the wavelength is 0.06 Å.

A main distinction between photons and material particles is that in a vacuum photons travel always at constant speed, the speed of light, whereas material particles are able to travel at various speeds relative to the observer, up to a maximum of the speed of light.

Cosmic Rays. Cosmic rays are particles of very high energy which reach the earth from interstellar space or other parts of the cosmos, or which are produced in the earth's atmosphere by the rays from outer space. The discovery that ionizing radiation on the earth's surface comes from outer space was made by the Austrian physicist Victor Hess (born 1883), who made measurements of ionization during balloon ascents to a height of 15,000 feet in 1911 and 1912. Many discoveries, in particular the discovery of most of the particles described in Table 32-1, have been made in the course of studies of cosmic rays.

At the present time it is believed that the cosmic rays that impinge on the outer part of the earth's atmosphere consist of protons and the nuclei of heavier atoms, moving with very great speeds. The cosmic rays that reach the earth's surface consist in large part of mesons, positrons, electrons, and protons, produced by reaction of the fast photons and other atomic nuclei with particles (mainly atomic nuclei) in the earth's atmosphere.

Some of the phenomena produced by cosmic rays can be explained only if it is assumed that particles are present with energy in the range from 10^{15} to 10^{17} *ev*. The great accelerators (cyclotron, synchrotron, bevatron) which have been, or are being, built (see the following section) produce or will produce particles with energies in the range from 10^6 to 10^9 *ev*. There is no way known at present to accelerate particles to energies as great as those of the fastest particles in cosmic rays, and the study of cosmic rays will probably continue to yield information about the world that cannot be obtained in any other way.

32–4. *Artificial Radioactivity*

Stable atoms can be converted into radioactive atoms by the collision of particles traveling at high speeds. In the early work the high-speed particles used were alpha particles from Bi^{83} (called radium C). The first nuclear reaction produced in the laboratory was that between alpha particles and nitrogen, carried out by Lord Rutherford and his collaborators in the Cavendish Laboratory at Cambridge in 1919. The nuclear reaction which occurs when nitrogen is bombarded with alpha particles is the following:

$$N^{14} + He^4 \longrightarrow O^{17} + H^1$$

In this reaction a nitrogen nucleus reacts with a helium nucleus, which strikes it with considerable energy, to form two new nuclei, an O^{17} nucleus and a proton.

The O^{17} nucleus is stable, so that this nuclear reaction does not lead to the production of artificial radioactivity. Many other elements, however, undergo similar reactions with the production of unstable nuclei, which then undergo radioactive decomposition.

Sources of High-Speed Particles. In recent years great progress has been made in the laboratory production of high-speed particles. The first efforts to accomplish this involved the use of transformers. Different investigators built transformers and vacuum tubes operating to voltages as high as 3 million volts, in which protons, deuterons, and helium nuclei could be accelerated. In 1931 an electrostatic generator was developed by R. J. Van de Graaff, an American physicist, involving the carrying of charge to the high potential electrode on a moving insulated belt. Several Van de Graaff generators have been built and

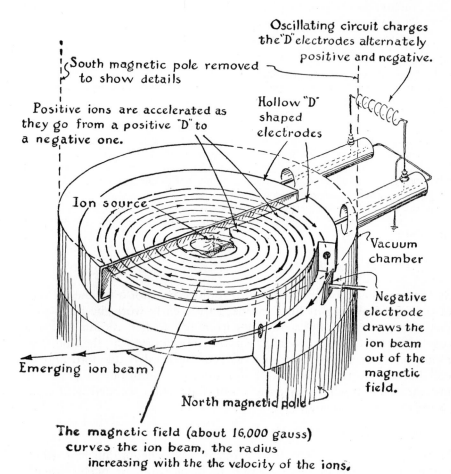

FIGURE 32-5 *Diagram showing how the cyclotron works.*

operated to produce potential differences of from 2 million to over 5 million volts.

The *cyclotron* was invented by Professor E. O. Lawrence of the University of California in 1929. In the cyclotron positive ions (usually protons or deuterons) are given successive accelerations by falling through a potential difference of a few thousand volts. The charged particles are caused to move in circular paths by a magnetic field, produced by a large magnet between whose pole pieces the apparatus is placed (Figure 32-5). The 37-inch cyclotron at Berkeley produces deuterons with as much energy as they would gain by falling through a single potential drop of 7 million volts, and the 60-inch cyclotron produces 20-million volt deuterons. The new 184-inch cyclotron at Berkeley yields 200-million volt deuterons.

A new accelerator, the *synchrotron*, proposed by Professor E. M. McMillan of the University of California and independently by V. Veksler in Russia, yields particles with speeds corresponding to a potential drop of several billion volts.

Other similar instruments, such as the linear accelerator and the betatron, are also in use.

Many nuclear reactions result from the interaction of nuclei and neutrons. The early experiments with neutrons were carried out by use of a mixture of radon, Rn^{222}, and beryllium metal. The alpha particles from radon react with the beryllium isotope Be^9 to produce neutrons in the following ways:

$$Be^9 + He^4 \longrightarrow C^{12} + n^1$$
$$Be^9 + He^4 \longrightarrow 3He^4 + n^1$$

Neutrons are also prepared by reactions in the cyclotron and in uranium piles.

The Kinds of Nuclear Reactions. Many different kinds of nuclear reactions have now been studied. Spontaneous radioactivity is a nuclear reaction in which the reactant is a single nucleus. Other known nuclear reactions involve a proton, a deuteron, an alpha particle, a neutron, or a photon (usually a gamma ray) interacting with the nucleus of an atom. The products of a nuclear reaction may be a heavy nucleus and a proton, an electron, a deuteron, an alpha particle, a neutron, two or more neutrons, or a gamma ray. In addition, there occurs the very important type of nuclear reaction in which a very heavy nucleus, made unstable by the addition of a neutron, breaks up into two parts of comparable size, plus several neutrons. This process of fission has been mentioned in Chapter 29 and is described in a later section of the present chapter.

Examples of a few of these reactions have been mentioned above.

As another example, the production of radioactive phosphorus, P^{32}, by bombardment of ordinary phosphorus, P^{31}, with 10-million volt deuterons from a cyclotron may be mentioned. The reaction is

$$P^{31} + H^2 \longrightarrow P^{32} + H^1$$

The P^{32} isotope decomposes with emission of electrons, its half-life being 14.3 days.

Manufacture of the Trans-Uranium Elements. The first trans-uranium element to be made was a neptunium isotope, Np^{239}. This isotope was made by E. M. McMillan and P. H. Abelson, in 1940, by bombarding uranium with high-speed deuterons:

$$U^{238} + H^2 \longrightarrow U^{239} + H^1$$
$$U^{239} \longrightarrow Np^{239} + e^-$$

The first isotope of plutonium to be made was Pu^{238}, by the reactions

$$U^{238} + H^2 \longrightarrow Np^{238} + 2n^1$$
$$Np^{238} \longrightarrow Pu^{238} + e^-$$

The Np^{238} decomposes spontaneously, emitting electrons. Its half-life is 2.0 days.

During and since World War II some quantity of the isotope Pu^{239} has been manufactured. This isotope is relatively stable; it has a half-life of about 24,000 years. It slowly decomposes with the emission of alpha particles. It is made by the reaction of the principal isotope of uranium, U^{238}, with a neutron, to form U^{239}, which then undergoes spontaneous radioactive decomposition with emission of an electron to form Np^{239}, which in turn emits an electron spontaneously, forming Pu^{239}:

$$U^{238} + n^1 \longrightarrow U^{239}$$
$$U^{239} \longrightarrow Np^{239} + e^-$$
$$Np^{239} \longrightarrow Pu^{239} + e^-$$

Plutonium and the next four trans-uranium elements, americium, curium, berkelium, and californium, were discovered by Professor G. T. Seaborg and his collaborators at the University of California in Berkeley. Americium has been made as the isotope Am^{241} by the following reactions:

$$U^{238} + He^4 \longrightarrow Pu^{241} + n^1$$
$$Pu^{241} \longrightarrow Am^{241} + e^-$$

This isotope slowly undergoes radioactive decomposition, with emission of alpha particles. Its half-life is 500 years. Curium is made from plutonium 239 by bombardment with helium ions accelerated in the cyclotron:

$$Pu^{239} + He^4 \longrightarrow Cm^{242} + n^1$$

The isotope Cm^{242} is an alpha-particle emitter, with half-life about 5 months. Another isotope of curium has also been made. It is Cm^{240}, made by bombarding plutonium, Pu^{239}, with high-speed helium ions:

$$Pu^{239} + He^4 \longrightarrow Cm^{240} + 3n^1$$

Using only very small quantities of the substances, Seaborg and his collaborators succeeded in obtaining a considerable amount of information about the chemical properties of the trans-uranium elements. They have found that, whereas uranium is similar to tungsten in its properties, in that it has a pronounced tendency to assume oxidation state +6, the succeeding elements are not similar to rhenium, osmium, iridium, and platinum, but show an increasing tendency to form ionic compounds in which their oxidation number is +3. This behavior is similar to that of the rare-earth metals. In the periodic table given in Chapter 5 these facts were taken into consideration and the trans-uranium metals were shown in two places, one directly to the right of uranium, and the other below the corresponding rare-earth metals. It seems very probable that the elements with atomic numbers greater than 100 will be closely similar to the rare earths, until the $5f$ shell of electrons has been completely filled.

32–5. *The Use of Radioactive Elements as Tracers*

A valuable technique for research that has been developed in recent years is the use of both radioactive and nonradioactive isotopes as tracers. By the use of these isotopes an element can be observed in the presence of large quantities of the same element. For example, one of the earliest uses of tracers was the experimental determination of the rate at which lead atoms move around through a crystalline sample of the metal lead. This phenomenon is called *self-diffusion*. If some radioactive lead is placed as a surface layer on a sheet of lead, and the sample is allowed to stand for a while, it can then be cut up into thin sections parallel to the original surface layer, and the radioactivity present in each section can be measured. The presence of radioactivity in layers other than the original surface layer shows that lead atoms from the surface layer have diffused through the metal.

In the discussion of chemical equilibrium in Chapter 19 it was pointed out that a system in chemical equilibrium is not static, but that instead chemical reactions may be proceeding in the forward direction and the reverse direction at equal rates, so that the amounts of different substances present remain constant. At first thought it would seem to be impossible to determine experimentally the rates at which different chemical reactions are proceeding at equilibrium. It was mentioned in Chapter 19 that it has now been found possible to make experiments of this sort, however, with the use of isotopes as tracers.

The arsenic isotope used in the work described in Chapter 19 was As^{76}, with half-life 26.8 hours. It is made from As^{75}, which is the only isotope of ordinary arsenic, by treatment with slow neutrons:

$$As^{75} + n^1 \longrightarrow As^{76}$$

Perhaps the greatest use for isotopes as tracers will be in the field of biology and medicine. The human body contains such large amounts of the elements carbon, hydrogen, nitrogen, oxygen, sulfur, etc., that it is difficult to determine the state of organic material in the body. An organic compound containing a radioactive isotope, however, can be traced through the body. An especially useful radioactive isotope for these purposes is carbon 14. This isotope of carbon has a half-life of about 5000 years. It undergoes slow decomposition with emission of beta rays, and the amount of the isotope present in a sample can be followed by measuring the beta activity. Large quantities of C^{14} can be readily made in a uranium pile, by the action of slow neutrons on nitrogen:

$$N^{14} + n^1 \longrightarrow C^{14} + H^1$$

The process can be carried out by running a solution of ammonium nitrate into the uranium pile, where it is exposed to neutrons. The carbon which is made in this way is in the form of the hydrogen carbonate ion, HCO_3^-, and it can be precipitated as barium carbonate by adding barium hydroxide solution. The samples of radioactive carbon are very strongly radioactive, containing as much as 5% of the radioactive isotope.

The Unit of Radioactivity, the Curie. It has been found convenient to introduce a special unit in which to measure amounts of radioactive material. The unit of radioactivity is called the *curie*. One curie of any radioactive substance is an amount of the substance such that 3.70×10^{10} atoms of the substance undergo radioactive disintegration per second.

The curie is a rather large unit. One curie of radium is approximately one gram of the element (the curie was originally defined in such a way as to make a curie of radium equal to one gram, but because of improvement in technique it has been found convenient to define it instead in the way given above).

It is interesting to point out that in a disintegration chain of radioactive elements in a steady state all of the radioactive elements are present in the same radioactive amounts. For example, let us consider one gram of the element radium, in a steady state with the first product of its decomposition, radon (Rn^{222}), and the successive products of disintegration (see Figure 32-2). The rate at which radon is being produced is proportional to the amount of radium present, one atom of radon being produced for each atom of radium which undergoes decomposition. The number of atoms of radium which undergo decomposition in unit time is proportional to the number of atoms of radium present; the decomposition of radium is a unimolecular reaction. Now when the system has reached a steady state the number of atoms of radon present remains unchanged, so that the rate at which radon is itself undergoing radioactive decomposition must be equal to the rate at which it is being formed from radium. Hence the radon present in a steady state with one gram of radium itself amounts to one curie.

The amount of radon present in a steady state with one gram of radium can be calculated by consideration of the first-order reaction-rate equations discussed in Chapter 19. The reaction-rate constant for the decompostion of radium is inversely proportional to its half-life. Hence when a steady state exists, and the number of radium atoms undergoing decomposition is equal to the number of radon atoms undergoing decomposition, the ratio of the numbers of radon atoms and radium atoms present must be equal to the ratio of their half-lives.

32–6. *Dating Objects by Use of Carbon 14*

One of the most interesting recent applications of radioactivity is the determination of the age of carbonaceous materials (materials containing carbon) by measurement of their radioactivity due to carbon 14. This technique of radiocarbon dating, which was developed by an American physical chemist, Willard F. Libby, of the Institute for Nuclear Studies of the University of Chicago, permits the dating of samples containing carbon with an accuracy of around 200 years. At the present time the method can be applied to materials that are not over about 25,000 years old.

Carbon 14 is being made at a steady rate in the upper atmosphere. Cosmic-ray neutrons transmute nitrogen into carbon 14, by the reaction given in the preceding section. The radiocarbon is oxidized to carbon dioxide, which is thoroughly mixed with the non-radioactive carbon dioxide in the atmosphere, through the action of winds. The steady-state concentration of carbon 14 built up in the atmosphere by cosmic rays is about one atom of radioactive carbon to 10^{12} atoms of ordinary carbon. The carbon dioxide, radioactive and non-radioactive alike, is absorbed by plants, which fix the carbon in their tissues. Animals that eat the plants also similarly fix the carbon, containing 1×10^{-12} part radiocarbon, in their tissues. When a plant or animal dies the amount of radioactivity of the carbon in its tissues is determined by the amount of radiocarbon present, which is the amount corresponding to the steady state in the atmosphere. After 5,568 years (the half-life of carbon 14), however, half of the carbon 14 has undergone decomposition, and the radioactivity of the material is only half as great. After 11,136 years only one quarter of the original radioactivity is left, and so on. Accordingly, by determining the radioactivity of a sample of carbon from wood, flesh, charcoal, skin, horn, or other plant or animal remains, the number of years that have gone by since the carbon was originally extracted from the atmosphere can be determined.

In applying the method of radiocarbon dating, a sample of material containing about 30 g of carbon (about 1 ounce) is burned to carbon dioxide, which is then reduced to elementary carbon, in the form of lamp black. The beta-ray activity of the elementary carbon is then determined, with the use of Geiger counters, and compared with the beta-ray activity of recent carbon. The age of the sample is then calculated by the use of the equation for a first-order reaction (Chapter 19). The method was checked by measurement of carbon from the heartwood of a giant Sequoia tree, for which the number of tree rings showed that 3,000 years had passed since the wood was laid down. This check was satisfactory.

The method of radiocarbon dating has now been applied to several hundred samples. One of the interesting conclusions that have been reached is that the last glaciation of the northern hemisphere occurred about 11,000 years ago. Specimens of wood from a buried forest in Wisconsin, in which all of the tree trunks are lying in the same direction as though pushed over by a glacier, were found to have an age of 11,400 $\pm$ 700 years. The age of specimens of organic materials laid down during the last period of glaciation in Europe was found to be 10,800 $\pm$ 1,200 years. Many samples of organic matter, charcoal, and other carbonaceous material from human camp sites in the western hemisphere have been dated as extending to, but not beyond, 10,000 years ago.

The eruption of Mt. Mazama in southern Oregon, which formed the crater now called Crater Lake, was determined to have occurred 6,453 $\pm$ 250 years ago, by the dating of charcoal from a tree killed by the eruption. Several pairs of woven rope sandals found in Fort Rock Cave, which had been covered by an earlier eruption, were found to be 9,053 $\pm$ 350 years old; these are the oldest human artefacts measured on the American continents. The Lascaux Cave near Montignac, France, contains some remarkable paintings made by prehistoric man; charcoal from camp fires in this cave was found to have the age 15,516 $\pm$ 900 years. Linen wrappings from the Dead Sea scrolls of the Book of Isaiah, recently found in a cave in Palestine and thought to be from about the first or second century B.C., were dated 1,917 $\pm$ 200 years old.

32–7. The Properties of Isotopes

The isotopes of the elements show several interesting properties. Most of the known isotopes for the first 10 elements are listed in Table 32-2. The masses given in column 3 of this table refer to the physicists' atomic weight scale, in which $O^{16} = 16.00000$.

Except for the elements which form part of the natural radioactive series, the distribution of isotopes for an element has been found to be the same for all natural occurrences. This distribution is shown in the fourth column of the table.

Some striking regularities are evident, especially for the heavier elements. The elements of odd atomic number have only one or two natural isotopes, whereas those of even atomic number are much richer in isotopes, many having eight or more. It is also found that the odd elements are much rarer in nature than the even elements. The elements with no stable isotopes (technetium, astatine) usually have odd atomic numbers.

TABLE 32-2   *Isotopes of the Lighter Elements*

ELEMENT NAME	M	MASS	PERCENT ABUNDANCE	HALF-LIFE	RADIA- TION
0 Electron...............	0	0.000548			
0 Neutron..............	1	1.00897			
1 Proton................	1	1.007582			
1 Hydrogen.............	1	1.008130	99.98		
	2	2.014722	0.02		
	3	3.01705		12.4 Y	e^-
2 Alpha................	4	4.002764			
2 Helium...............	3	3.01699	10^{-9}		
	4	4.00386	100		
	6			0.8 S	e^-
3 Lithium...............	6	6.01684	7.3		
	7	7.01818	92.7		
	8	8.0251		0.88 S	e^-
4 Beryllium.............	7	7.01908		43 D	γ
	9	9.01494	100		
	10	10.01671		$>>10^3$ Y	e^-, γ
5 Boron................	10	10.01633	18.8		
	11	11.01295	81.2		
	12	12.019		0.022 S	e^-
6 Carbon...............	10	10.01833		8.8 S	e^+
	11	11.01499		20.5 M	e^+
	12	12.00386	98.9		
	13	13.00766	1.1		
	14	14.00780		5568 Y	e^-
7 Nitrogen..............	13	13.01005		9.93 M	e^+, γ
	14	14.00756	99.62		
	15	15.00495	0.38		
	16	16.011		8.0 S	e^-
8 Oxygen..............	15	15.0078		126 S	e^+
	16	16.000	99.76		
	17	17.00449	0.04		
	18	18.00369	0.20		
	19			31 S	e^-
9 Fluorine..............	17	17.0076		70 S	e^+
	18	18.0056		112 M	e^+
	19	19.00452	100		
	20	20.0063		72 S	e^-, γ
10 Neon................	19			20.3 S	e^+
	20	19.99896	90.0		
	21	20.99968	0.27		
	22	21.99864	9.73		
	23	23.0005		40 S	e^-

The Packing Fraction. Consideration of the masses of the isotopes shows that they are not additive. Thus the mass of the ordinary hydrogen atom is 1.00813, and that of the neutron is 1.00897. If the helium atom were made from two hydrogen atoms and two neutrons without change in mass, its mass would be 4.03420, but it is in fact less, only 4.00386. The masses of the heavier atoms are also less than they would be if they were composed of hydrogen atoms and neutrons without change in mass.

The loss in mass accompanying the formation of a heavier atom from hydrogen atoms and neutrons is due to the fact that these reactions are strongly exothermic. A very large amount of energy is evolved in the formation of the heavier atoms from hydrogen atoms and neutrons, so large an amount that the mass of the energy, as given by the Einstein equation $E = mc^2$, is significant. The more stable the heavy nucleus, the larger is the decrease in mass from that of the neutrons and protons from which the nucleus may be considered to be made.

It is customary to describe the decrease in mass by means of a quantity called the "packing fraction." This is the difference in mass, per fundamental particle (proton or neutron) in the nucleus, relative to O^{16} as standard. An isotope which has atomic mass equal exactly to its mass number on the O^{16} scale is said to have zero packing fraction.

The packing fractions for the elements are shown in Figure 32-6. It is seen that the elements of the first long group of the periodic table, between chromium and zinc, lie at the minimum of the curve, and can accordingly be considered to be the most stable of all the elements. If one of these elements were to be converted into other elements,

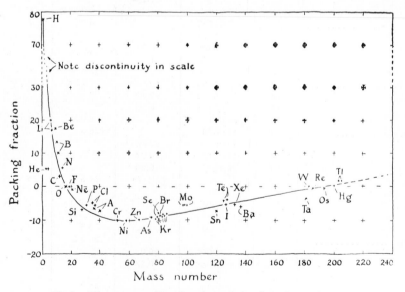

FIGURE 32-6   *The mass packing fractions of the elements.*

the total mass of the other elements would be somewhat greater than that of the reactants, and accordingly energy would have to be added in order to cause the reaction to occur. On the other hand, either the heavier or the lighter elements could undergo nuclear reactions to form the elements with mass numbers in the neighborhood of 60, and these nuclear reactions would be accompanied by the evolution of a large amount of energy.

32–8. *Nuclear Fission and Nuclear Fusion*

The instability of the heavy elements relative to those of mass number around 60, as shown by the packing fraction curve, suggests the possibility of spontaneous decomposition of the heavy elements into fragments of approximately half-size (atomic masses 70 to 160, atomic numbers 30 to 65). This fission has been accomplished.

It was reported on January 6, 1939, by the German physicists O. Hahn and F. Strassmann that barium, lanthanum, cerium, and krypton seemed to be present in substances containing uranium which had been exposed to neutrons. Within two months more than 40 papers were then published on the fission of uranium. It was verified by direct calorimetric measurement that a very large amount of energy is liberated by fission, over 5×10^{12} calories per mole. Since a pound of uranium contains about 2 gram-atoms, the complete fission of one pound of this element, or a similar heavy element, produces about 10×10^{12} calories. This may be compared with the heat of combustion of 1 pound of coal, which is approximately 4×10^6 calories. Thus uranium as a source of energy may be $2\frac{1}{2}$ million times more valuable than coal.

Uranium 235 and plutonium 239, which can be made from uranium 238, are capable of undergoing fission when exposed to slow neutrons. It was also shown by the Japanese physicist Nishina in 1939 that the thorium isotope Th^{232} undergoes fission under the influence of fast neutrons. It seemed likely that all of the elements with atomic number 90 or greater can be made to undergo this reaction.

Uranium and thorium may well become important sources of heat and energy in the world of the future. There are large amounts of these elements available—the amount of uranium in the earth's crust has been estimated as 4 parts per million and the amount of thorium as 12 parts per million. The deposits occur distributed all over the world.

The fission reactions can be chain reactions. These reactions are initiated by neutrons. A nucleus U^{235}, for example, may combine with a neutron to form U^{236}. This isotope is unstable, and undergoes spontaneous fission, into two particles of roughly equal atomic number, the sum of the atomic numbers being 92; that is, the protons in the

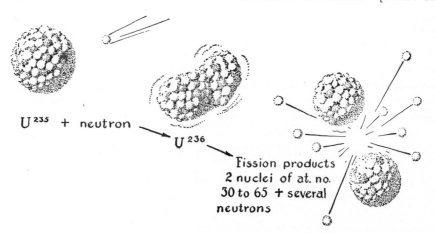

U^{235} + neutron

U^{236}

Fission products
2 nuclei of at. no.
30 to 65 + several
neutrons

FIGURE 32-7   *The process of nuclear fission (linear magnification about 10^{12}).*

the U^{236} nucleus are divided between the two daughter nuclei (Figure 32-7). These daughter nuclei also contain some of the neutrons originally present in the U^{236} nucleus. Since, however, the ratio of neutrons to protons is greater in the heavier nuclei than in those of intermediate mass, the fission is also accompanied by the liberation of several free neutrons.. The neutrons which are thus liberated may then combine with other U^{235} nuclei, forming additional U^{236} nuclei which themselves undergo fission. A reaction of this sort, the products of which cause the reaction to continue, is called a *chain reaction,* or an *auto-catalytic reaction.*

If a few pounds of U^{235} or Pu^{239} are brought together suddenly (within about one millionth of a second) into a small volume, the auto-catalytic fission of the nuclei occurs nearly completely, and an amount of energy is released equal to that accompanying the detonation of about twenty thousand tons of a high explosive such as TNT. An ordinary *atomic bomb* consists of a few pounds of U^{235} or Pu^{239} and a mechanism for suddenly compressing the metal.

The process of *nuclear fusion* also may liberate energy. From the packing-fraction diagram (Figure 32-6) we see that the fission of a very heavy nucleus converts about 0.1% of its mass into energy. Still larger fractions of the mass of very light nuclei are converted into energy by their fusion into heavier nuclei. The process 4H $\longrightarrow$ He, which is the principal source of the energy of the sun, involves a change in mass from 4×1.00813 to 4.00386, and hence a conversion of 0.7% of the mass into energy. The similar reaction of a deuteron and a triton to form a helium nucleus and a neutron is accompanied by the conversion of 0.4% of the mass into energy:

$$_1H^2 + {}_1H^3 \longrightarrow {}_2H^4 + {}_0n^1$$

It has been found by experiment that a mixture of these materials surrounding an ordinary atomic bomb undergoes reaction at the temperature of many millions of degrees produced by the detonation of the bomb. The nuclear fusion of one ton of hydrogen may produce a detonation thousands of times greater than that of an ordinary atomic bomb. The name *hydrogen bomb* is commonly used for such super-bombs, one of which could destroy any city in the world.

The *manufacture of plutonium* is carried out by a controlled chain reaction. A piece of ordinary uranium contains 0.71% of U^{235}. An occasional neutron strikes one of these atoms, causing it to undergo fission and release a number of neutrons. The auto-catalytic reaction does not build up, however, if the piece of uranium is small, because the neutrons escape, and some of them may be absorbed by impurities, such as cadmium, the nuclei of which combine very readily with neutrons.

However, if a large enough sample of uranium is taken, nearly all of the neutrons which are formed by the fission remain within the sample of uranium, and either cause other U^{235} nuclei to undergo fission, or are absorbed by U^{238}, converting it into U^{239}, which then undergoes spontaneous change to Pu^{239}. This is the process used in practice for the manufacture of plutonium. A large number of lumps of uranium are piled together, alternately with bricks of graphite, in a structure called a reactor, or pile. The first uranium pile ever constructed, built at the University of Chicago and put into operation on December 2, 1942, contained 12,400 pounds of uranium metal. Cadmium rods are held in readiness to be introduced into cavities in the pile, and to serve to arrest the reaction by absorbing neutrons, whenever there is danger of its getting out of hand.

The large reactors which were put into operation in September, 1944, at Hanford, Washington, were of such size as to permit the fission reaction to proceed at the rate corresponding to an output of energy amounting to 1,500,000 kilowatts.

The significance of the uranium reactors as a source of radioactive material can be made clear by a comparison with the supply of radium now in use. About 1000 curies (1000 grams) of radium has been separated from its ores and put into use, mainly for medical treatment. The rate of operation mentioned above for the reactors at Hanford represents the fission of about 5×10^{20} nuclei per second, forming about 10×10^{20} radioactive atoms. The concentration of these radio active atoms will build up until they are undergoing decomposition at the rate at which they are being formed. Since 1 curie corresponds to 3.70×10^{10} disintegrating atoms per second, these reactors develop a radioactivity of approximately 3×10^{10} curies; that is, about thirty million times the radioactivity of all the radium which has been so far isolated from its ores.

The foregoing calculation illustrates the great significance of the fissionable elements as a source of radioactive material. Their significance as a source of energy has also been pointed out, by the statement that 1 pound of uranium or thorium is equivalent to $2\frac{1}{2}$ million pounds of coal. When we remember that uranium and thorium are not rare elements, but are among the more common elements—the amount of uranium and thorium in the earth's crust being about the same as that of the common element lead*—we begin to understand the promise of nuclear energy for the world of the future, and the possibility of its contributions to human welfare. I believe that it will soon be recognized that the discovery of the controlled fission of atomic nuclei and controlled release of atomic energy is the greatest discovery that has been made since the controlled use of fire was discovered by primitive man.

Concepts, Facts, and Terms Introduced in This Chapter

Natural radioactivity. Use of radium and other radioactive elements in the treatment of cancer.

The series of radioactive disintegrations: the uranium-radium series, the uranium-actinium series, the thorium series, and the neptunium series. The age of the earth. The fundamental particles: electron, proton, positron, neutron, mesons, neutrino. The photon (light quantum); the energy of a photon, $h\nu$. Planck's constant. The wave-particle duality of light and of matter. The wavelengths of electrons.

Artificial radioactivity. The first artificial nuclear reaction—the reaction between alpha particles and nitrogen to form oxygen and hydrogen, carried out by Rutherford in 1919. Sources of high-speed particles: Van der Graaff generator, cyclotron, synchrotron, linear accelerator, betatron. Kinds of nuclear reactions. Manufacture of transuranium elements, neptunium, plutonium, americium, curium, berkelium, californium. The use of radioactive elements as tracers. Self diffusion. Determination of the rates of opposing chemical reactions at equilibrium. Tracers in biology and medicine. Carbon 14. The unit of radioactivity, the curie.

The properties of isotopes. Packing fraction. Structure of atomic nuclei. Nuclear fission. Nuclear chain reaction. Manufacture of plutonium. Fission of U^{235} and Pu^{239}. Uranium reactors—the uranium pile. Nuclear energy as a source of power.

References on Nuclear Chemistry

J. M. Cork, *Radioactivity and Nuclear Physics*, Ann Arbor, Michigan, **1946.**

H. D. Smyth, *Atomic Energy for Military Purposes*, Princeton University Press, **1945.**

G. Friedlander and J. W. Kennedy, *Introduction to Radiochemistry*, John Wiley and Sons, Inc., New York, **1949.**

L. N. Ridenour, "The Hydrogen Bomb," *Scientific American*, **182,** 11, March **1950.**

K. K. Darrow, *Atomic Energy*, John Wiley and Sons, Inc., New York, 1948.

* Although uranium and thorium are not rare elements, they tend to be widely distributed in very small concentrations, and not many rich deposits have been discovered.

Articles on the hydrogen bomb by Thirring, Einstein, and many others, *Bulletin of the Atomic Scientists*, early issues in 1950 (published by the University of Chicago Press, 5750 Ellis Ave., Chicago 37, Ill.).

V. J. Linnenbom, "Radioactivity and the Age of the Earth," *Journal of Chemical Education*, **32**, 58 (February **1955**).

W. F. Libby, *Radiocarbon Dating*, University of Chicago Press, Chicago, **1952**.

E. S. Deevey, Jr., "Radiocarbon Dating," *Scientific American*, **186**, 24 (1952).

J. R. Arnold and W. F. Libby, "Radiocarbon Dates," *Science*, **113**, 111 (1951).

W. F. Libby, "Radiocarbon Dates, II," *Science*, **114**, 291 (1951).

P. J. Lovewell, "The Uses of Fission Products," *Scientific American*, **186**, 19 (June 1952).

R. E. Marshak, "The Multiplicity of Particles," *Scientific American*, **186**, 22 (January 1952).

P. Morrison and E. Morrison, "The Neutron," *Scientific American*, **185**, 44 (October 1951).

M. G. Mayer, "The Structure of the Nucleus," *Scientific American*, **184**, 42 (March 1951).

J. F. Flagg and E. L. Zebroski, "Atomic Pile Chemistry," *Scientific American*, **187**, 62 (July 1952).

L. R. Hafstad, "Reactors," *Scientific American*, **184**, 43 (April 1951).

L. P. Smith, "The Bevatron," *Scientific American*, **184**, 20 (February 1951).

E. D. Courant, "A 100-Billion-Volt Accelerator," *Scientific American*, **188**, 40 (May 1953).

R. E. Marshak, "The Energy of Stars," *Scientific American*, **182**, 42 (January 1950).

I. Perlman and G. T. Seaborg, "The Synthetic Elements," *Scientific American*, **182**, 38 (April 1950).

K. Way, L. Fano, M. R. Scott, and K. Thew, Nuclear Data: *A Collection of Experimental Values of Half-lives, Radiation Energies, Relative Isotopic Abundances, Nuclear Moments and Cross Sections*, Circular of the National Bureau of Standards 499, U. S. Government Printing Office, Washington, D. C. **1950**.

A. M. Weinberg, "Power Reactors," *Scientific American*, **191**, 33 (December 1954).

Appendix I

The Metric System of Weights and Measures

It is customary in scientific work to express quantities in terms of the units of the metric system. This system is simpler than the system of weights and measures commonly used in the United States, in that only powers of ten are involved in the relation between different units for the same quantity.

The *mass* of an object is measured in terms of *grams* (g) or *kilograms* (kg), the kilogram being equal to 1,000 g. The kilogram is defined as the mass of a standard object made of a platinum-iridium alloy and kept in Paris. One pound is equal approximately to 454 g, and hence 1 kg is equal approximately to 2.2 lb. Note that it has become customary in recent years for the abbreviations of units in the metric system to be written without periods.

The metric unit of length is the *meter* (m), which is equal to 39.37 inches. The *centimeter* (cm), which is 1/100 m, is about 0.4 inch, the inch being equal to 2.54 cm. The *millimeter* (mm) is 1/1,000 m or 1/10 cm.

The *metric unit of volume* is the *liter* (l), which is approximately 1.06 U.S. quarts. The *milliliter* (ml), equal to 1/1,000 l, is usually used as the unit of volume in the measurement of liquids in chemical work. The milliliter is defined as the volume occupied by exactly 1 g of water at 3.98°C (the temperature at which its density is the greatest) and under a pressure of one atmosphere (that is, the normal pressure due to the weight of the air).

At the time that the metric system was set up, in 1799, it was intended that the milliliter be exactly equal to the cubic centimeter (cm³). However, it was later found that the relation between the gram, as given by the prototype kilogram, and the centimeter, one one-hundredth of the distance between two engraved lines on a standard platinum-iridium bar, the prototype meter kept in Paris by the International Bureau of Weights and Measures, is such that the milliliter is not exactly equal to the cubic centimeter, but is instead equal to 1.000027 cm³. It is obvious that the distinction between ml and cm³ is ordinarily unimportant.

A table of conversion factors for some units in the metric system and the corresponding units in the English system is given on the following page.

Conversion Factors

	ENGLISH TO METRIC	METRIC TO ENGLISH
Length	1 in. = 2.540 cm	1 cm = 0.3937 in.
Area	1 sq. in. = 6.4516 cm²	1 cm² = 0.1550 sq. in.
Volume and capacity	1 cu. in. = 16.386 cm³	1 ml = 1 cm³ = 0.061 cu. in. = 0.033814 U.S. fluid oz.
	1 cu. ft. = 28.317 liters	1 liter = 0.26418 U.S. gal = 0.21998 Br. gal
	1 U.S. gal (liq) = 3.7853 l	1 l = 0.035316 cu. ft.
Mass	1 lb. (avoir) = 453.59 g 1 oz. (avoir) = 28.35 g	1 g = 0.03527 oz. (avoir) 1 kg = 2.20462 lb. (avoir)

Force

$$1 \text{ dyne} = 1.01972 \text{ mg}$$
$$1 \text{ g} = 980.665 \text{ dyne}$$

Pressure		
	1 lb/sq. in. = 70.307 g/cm²	1 g/cm² = 0.01422 lb/sq. in.
	1 lb/sq.in. = 0.068046 atm	1 atm = 14.696 lb/sq. in.

$$1 \text{ atm} = 1033.2 \text{ g/cm}^2 = 760 \text{ mm of Hg}$$

Energy, Work, Heat		
	1 ft. lb. = 1.35582 joule (absolute)	1 joule (abs) = 0.73756 ft. lb.

$$1 \text{ cal} = 4.1840 \text{ joule (abs)}$$
$$1 \text{ joule} = 10^7 \text{ erg} = 0.23901 \text{ cal}$$
$$1 \text{ kilocalorie (kcal)} = 1,000 \text{ cal}$$

Appendix II

Probable Values of Some Physical and
Chemical Constants (Chemists' Scale)

Avogadro's number
$$N = (0.602283 \pm 0.00011) \times 10^{24}$$

Electronic charge
$$e = (1.602033 \pm 0.00034) \times 10^{-19} \text{ abs.-coulombs}$$
$$= (4.80251 \pm 0.0010) \times 10^{-10} \text{ abs.-e.s.u.}$$

Mass of electron
$$m = (9.10660 \pm 0.0032) \times 10^{-28} \text{ g}$$

Liter
$$1 \text{ liter} = 1000.028 \pm 0.002 \text{ cm}^3$$

Ice point on absolute scale
$$0°C = 273.16 \pm 0.01°K$$

Standard molal gas volume
$$(RT)_{0°C} = 22.4140 \pm 0.0006 \text{ l atm mole}^{-1}$$

Gas constant
$$R = 0.08205447 \pm 0.0000037 \text{ l atm deg}^{-1} \text{ mole}^{-1}$$

Faraday
$$F = 96501.2 \pm 10 \text{ international coulombs}$$
$$= 96487.7 \pm 10 \text{ abs.-coulombs}$$

Ratio of physical to chemical atomic weights
$$r = 1.000272 \pm 0.000005$$

Velocity of light
$$c = (2.99776 \pm 0.00004) \times 10^{10} \text{ cm sec}^{-1}$$

Planck's constant
$$h = (6.6242 \pm 0.0024) \times 10^{-27} \text{ erg sec}$$

Energy in ergs of one absolute-volt-electron
$$(1.602033 \pm 0.00034) \times 10^{-12} \text{ erg}$$

Energy in calories per mole for one absolute-volt-electron per molecule
$$23052.85 \pm 3.2 \text{ cal mole}^{-1}$$

Appendix III

The Vapor Pressure of Water
at Different Temperatures

TEMPERATURE (°C)	VAPOR PRESSURE (MM OF MERCURY)	TEMPERATURE (°C)	VAPOR PRESSURE (MM OF MERCURY)
−10 (ice)	1.0	31	33.7
−5 "	3.0	32	35.7
0	4.6	33	37.7
5	6.5	34	39.9
10	9.2	35	42.2
15	12.8	36	44.6
16	13.6	37	47.1
17	14.5	38	49.7
18	15.5	39	52.4
19	16.5	40	55.3
20	17.5	45	71.9
21	18.6	50	92.5
22	19.8	60	149.4
23	21.1	70	233.7
24	22.4	80	355.1
25	23.8	90	525.8
26	25.2	100	760.0
27	26.7	110	1,074.6
28	28.3	150	3,570.5
29	30.0	200	11,659.2
30	31.8	300	64,432.8

Index